GONADOTROPINS 1968

GONADOTROPINS 1968

PROCEEDINGS OF THE WORKSHOP CONFERENCE
HELD AT VISTA HERMOSA, MOR., MEXICO
JUNE 24–26, 1968

Edited by

EUGENIA ROSEMBERG, M.D.

Research Director, Medical Research Institute, Inc.
Worcester City Hospital
Worcester, Massachusetts.

GERON-X, INC.   **1968**   **LOS ALTOS, CALIFORNIA**

PREFACE

This book describes the proceedings of the Workshop Conference on Gonadotropins held at Vista Hermosa, Mor., Mexico from June 24th to June 26th, 1968.

The format of the book has been arranged according to topics discussed during the Conference. The reader will note that each chapter includes individual contributions followed by discussion. Thus, the information which appears in this volume provides a current critical evaluation of the various subjects discussed. The Editor assumes responsibility for any shortcomings and wishes to thank all the contributors for their unprecedented cooperation in making this book possible.

The Conference could not have taken place without the support of The Medical Research Institute and the Worcester City Hospital. The Editor desires to place on record her appreciation to the Members of the Staff of The Medical Research Institute: Miss B. Martin, Mr. G. Bulat, Miss M. M. Shea, Mr. L. E. Fournier, and Mr. R. O. Jette for their devoted assistance. Recognition is also due to Mrs. M. Flack, Mrs. M. Rano and Mrs. L. Corio for their secretarial assistance.

I express my thanks to our publisher Geron-X, Inc., for their fine cooperation and for ensuring the rapid publication of this volume.

EUGENIA ROSEMBERG

Worcester, Massachusetts

October, 1968

ACKNOWLEDGEMENTS

Individual participants wish to thank Editors and Publishers of journals and books for permission to reproduce previously published figures and tables.

A number of participants desire to express their gratitude to the Endocrine Study Section, National Institutes of Health, USPHS, Bethesda, Maryland, to the National Pituitary Agency, Baltimore, Maryland and to the Department of Biological Standards, National Institute for Medical Research, Mill Hill, London, for generous supplies of hormones.

Grants supporting work presented in these proceedings are acknowledged by individual participants and indicated in their respective contributions.

This Workshop could not have taken place without generous financial support from the Istituto Farmacologico Serono, Rome, Italy; the Ortho Research Foundation, Raritan, New Jersey; Cutter Laboratories, Berkeley, California and the Upjohn Company, Kalamazoo, Michigan.

FOREWORD

During the past few years, research in the gonadotropin field has achieved considerable progress. In part, this has been due to 1) the availability of human gonadotropic preparations for basic and clinical investigations, 2) the development of radioimmunologic techniques for measuring pituitary gonadotropin levels in body fluids and 3) the continued efforts to purify and define the two major pituitary gonadotropins, FSH and LH.

To place this activity in proper prospective, investigators need an opportunity to test their data and prevailing concepts with their colleagues. In this regard, a small workshop conference serves this purpose best. European investigators have dealt with this in the form of "Gonadotropin Club" meetings.

The first workshop conference, organized by investigators from the U.S.A., to discuss the gonadotropins was held in Gatlinburg, Tennessee (1959) under the chairmanship of Dr. A. Albert. In October of 1965, an informal workshop conference under the chairmanship of Dr. Eugenia Rosemberg was held at Puerto Vallarta, Jalisco, Mexico. This year, prior to the Third International Congress of Endocrinology, the third workshop conference on gonadotropins was held. It was organized and chaired by Dr. Eugenia Rosemberg. It took place at the Vista Hermosa Hotel in San Jose De Vista Hermosa, Mor., Mexico from June 24 - 26, 1968. This volume contains the proceedings of this meeting and is designed to give the interested scientist a glance at the "state of the art" in the area of gonadotropin research.

C. ALVIN PAULSEN, M. D.

October, 1968

TABLE OF CONTENTS

CHAPTER 2

BIOLOGY OF GONADOTROPINS

1. BIOLOGIC ASSAY OF PITUITARY AND URINARY
   GONADOTROPINS

2. CONTROL OF PITUITARY SECRETION OF GONADOTROPINS

3. EFFECT OF GONADOTROPINS ON THE GONADS

CHAPTER 3

IMMUNOLOGIC ASSAY OF HUMAN AND ANIMAL GONADOTROPINS

CHAPTER 4

MEASUREMENT OF GONADOTROPIC ACTIVITY BY RADIOIMMUNOASSAY

CHAPTER 5

USE OF STANDARDS IN GONADOTROPIN ASSAY

CHAPTER 6

GONADOTROPIN THERAPY. STUDIES IN FEMALE SUBJECTS

CHAPTER 7

GONADOTROPIN THERAPY.   STUDIES IN MALE SUBJECTS

LIST OF PARTICIPANTS

Dr. A. Albert, Mayo Clinic, Rochester, Minnesota.

Dr. M. S. Amoss, Baylor College of Medicine, Houston, Texas.

Dr. D. R. Bangham, Division of Biological Standards, National Institute for Medical Research, Mill Hill, London, N. W. 7, England.

Dr. E. W. Bassett, Ortho Research Foundation, Raritan, New Jersey.

Dr. E. T. Bell, Petfoods Limited, Melton Mowbray, Leicestershire, England.

Dr. G. Bettendorf, Abteilungsvorsteher, Universitats-Frauenklinik, Endokrinologische Abtlg., 2 Hamburg-Eppendorf, MartinistraBe 52, Germany.

Dr. E. M. Bogdanove, Department of Anatomy and Physiology, Indiana University, Bloomington, Indiana.

Dr. R. Borth, Associate Professor, Department of Obstetrics and Gynecology, St. Michael's Hospital, Toronto 2, Canada.

Dr. H. C. Browning, Department of Anatomy, University of Texas, Dental Branch, Houston, Texas.

Dr. M. H. Burgos, Instituto de Histologia y Embriologia, Casilla de Correo 56, Mendoza, Argentina.

Dr. C. M. Cargille, National Institutes of Health, Building 10, Bethesda, Maryland.

Dr. A. C. Crooke, The United Birmingham Hospital and Midland Hospital for Women, Department of Clinical Endocrinology, Showell Green Lane, Sparkhill, Birmingham 11, England.

Dr. P. -J. Czygan, Abteilungsvorsteher, Universitats-Frauenklinik, Endokrinologische Abtlg., 2 Hamburg-Eppendorf, MartinistraBe 52, Germany.

Dr. P. Donini, Istituto Farmacologico Serono, Sede Centrale-Via Casilina 125, Rome, Italy.

Dr. D. H. Espeland, University of Washington, School of Medicine, USPHS Hospital, 1131 14th Avenue South, Seattle, Washington.

Dr. C. Faiman, Mayo Clinic, Rochester, Minnesota.

Dr. J. Jimenez-Fonseca, Instituto Mexicano del Seguro Social, Subdireccion General Medica, Departmento de Investigacion Apartado 73-032 Postal, Mexico 73, D. F., Mexico.

Dr. H. M. Gandy, The New York Hospital-Cornell University, Medical Center, 525 East 68th Street, New York, New York.

Mr. M. M. Graff, Executive Secretary, Endocrinology Study Section, Division of Research Grants, National Institutes of Health, Bethesda, Maryland.

Dr. C. Gual, Instituto Nacional de la Nutricion, Hospital de Enfermedades de la Nutricion, Dr. Jimenez No. 261, Mexico, D. F., Mexico.

Dr. L. G. Hershberger, Head, Endocrine Section, Cutter Laboratories, Fourth and Parker Streets, Berkeley, California.

Dr. S. G. Johnsen, Hormone Department, Statens Seruminstitut, Amager Boulevard 80, Copenhagen S., Denmark.

Dr. B. Lunenfeld, Tel-Hashomer Government Hospital, Endocrinology Research and Development Unit, Tel-Hashomer, Israel.

Dr. R. E. Mancini, C. I. R., Centro de Investigaciones en Reproduccion, Facultad de Medicina, Paraguay 2155 10° Piso, Buenos Aires, Argentina.

Dr. J. R. Marshall, Building 10, Rm. 10N218, National Institutes of Health, Bethesda, Maryland.

Dr. J. W. McArthur, Vincent Memorial Hospital, Fruit Street, Boston, Massachusetts.

Dr. R. K. Meyer, Department of Zoology, University of Wisconsin, Madison, Wisconsin.

Dr. A. R. Midgley,Jr., Department of Pathology, The University of Michigan, 1335 E. Catherine Street, Ann Arbor, Michigan.

Mr. D. J. Moore, University of Washington, School of Medicine, USPHS Hospital, 1131 14th Avenue South, Seattle, Washington.

Dr. G. J. Mouratoff, Director of Clinical Investigation, Cutter, Laboratories, Fourth and Parker Streets, Berkeley, California.

Dr. F. Naftolin, Department of Human Anatomy, University of Oxford, Oxford, England

Dr. G. D. Niswender, Department of Pathology, The University of Michigan, 1335 E. Catherine Street, Ann Arbor, Michigan.

Dr. **W. D. Odell,** Chief, Endocrinology Division, Harbor General Hospital, 1000 West Carson Street, Torrance, California.

Dr. **G. Perez-Palacios,** Department of Obstetrics and Gynecology, University Hospital, The University of Michigan, Medical Center, Ann Arbor, Michigan.

Dr. **A. F. Parlow,** Department of Obstetrics and Gynecology, Harbor General Hospital, 1000 West Carson Street, Torrance, California.

Dr. **C. A. Paulsen,** University of Washington, School of Medicine, USPHS Hospital, 1131 14th Avenue South, Seattle, Washington.

Dr. **B. B. Pharriss,** Reproductive Physiology Section, Chemistry Research Division, The Upjohn Company, Kalamazoo, Michigan.

Dr. **S. S. Rao,** Officer in Charge, Reproductive Physiology Unit, (I.C.M.R.) Seth G. S. Medical College, Bombay 12, India.

Dr. **P. Rathnam,** The New York Hospital-Cornell University Medical Center, 525 East 68th Street, New York, New York.

Dr. **L. E. Reichert,** Jr., Department of Biochemistry, Division of Basic Health Sciences, Emory University, Atlanta, Georgia.

Dr. **A. M. Reiss,** Ortho Research Foundation, Raritan, New Jersey.

Dr. **C. Robyn,** Universite Libre de Bruxelles, Section de Immuno Hemotologie, Service de Bacteriologie, Faculte de Medecine, 115 Boulevard de Waterloo, Bruxelles, Belgium.

Dr. **E. Rosemberg,** Research Director, Medical Research Institute of Worcester, Inc., 26 Queen Street, Worcester, Massachusetts.

Dr. **R. J. Ryan,** Mayo Clinic, Rochester, Minnesota.

Dr. **H. A. Salhanick,** Center for Population Studies, Harvard University, 665 Huntington Avenue, Boston, Massachusetts.

Dr. **B. B. Saxena,** The New York Hospital-Cornell University, Medical Center, Department of Medicine, 525 East 68th Street, New York, New York.

Dr. **T. C. Smith,** Parke-Davis, 2800 Plymouth Road, Ann Arbor, Michigan.

Dr. **L. A. Sobrevilla,** Universidad Peruana "Cayetano Heredia" Instituto de Investigacion de la Altura, Departmento de Endocrinologia, Apartado 6083, Lima Peru.

Dr. **E. Steinberger,** Albert Einstein Medical Center, Research Laboratories, York and Tabor Roads, Philadelphia, Pennsylvania.

Dr. V. C. Stevens, Department of Obstetrics and Gynecology, Ohio State University, 410 West 10th Street, Columbus, Ohio.

Dr. R. S. Swerdloff, Harbor General Hospital, 1000 West Carson Street, Torrance, California.

Dr. M. L. Taymor, Peter Bent Brigham Hospital, 721 Huntington Avenue, Boston, Massachusetts.

Dr. R. L. Vande Wiele, College of Physicians and Surgeons, Department of Obstetrics and Gynecology, Columbia University, 630 West 168th Street, New York, New York.

Dr. J. Giner-Velazquez, Instituto Mexicano del Seguro Social, Subdireccion General Medica, Departmento de Investigacion, Apartado 73-032, Postal, Mexico, D. F. Mexico.

Dr. O. Vilar, C. I. R., Centro de Investigaciones en Reproduccion, Facultad de Medicina, Paraguay 2155 10° Piso, Buenos Aires, Argentina.

Dr. D. N. Ward, University of Texas, Anderson Hospital and Tumor Institute, Department of Biochemistry, Houston, Texas.

INTRODUCTORY REMARKS

EUGENIA ROSEMBERG, M.D.

Bienvenidos a Mejico! Welcome to Mexico and to Vista Hermosa.

This is the second time I have had the pleasure of gathering together a distinguished group of investigators interested in the gonadotropin field.

Our first Meeting took place in Mexico at Puerto Vallarta in October of 1965. Since that time, I have been urged by many of the participants at the Puerto Vallarta Meeting to organize another gathering. The opportunity did not arise until it was announced that the Third International Congress of Endocrinology was to take place in Mexico City. The recollection of the warm Mexican hospitality and the success of our previous Meeting induced me to organize this venture for the second time.

On consultation with my good friends Dr. Jorge Martinez-Manautou and Dr. Carlos Gual, the decision to conduct this conference at Vista Hermosa was made. Although I originally planned to organize a Workshop Conference, it was quite impossible to keep the membership down to Workshop size. There are many advantages of holding a true Workshop Conference. Presentation of material is kept to a minimum and the Conference itself consists almost entirely of discussion and criticism of the accumulated data. This, of course, requires that the participants be quite familiar in advance with the material to be discussed.

Our present Meeting is not in a sense a Workshop Conference. We have about fifty-six papers to be formally presented during this three-day Meeting. However, the sessions have been organized in such a manner that it is hoped that the material being presented will open the way for profitable discussion on the various subjects to be considered this week.

    The gonadotropin field has advanced considerably in the
last decade. Many of the aspects of research in this area
cannot be covered during a three-day Meeting. Hence, we will
confine ourselves to discussion of some aspects of the chemistry, biology, immunology, and measurement by biologic and
immunological procedures, and also to the clinical effect of
gonadotropins.

    Some of these topics bring back memories from previous
Meetings which I attended, one at Gatlinburg in 1959 and the
other at Copenhagen in 1960. Some of us, I am sure, feel
like long lost parents to the Second International Reference
Preparation for Human Menopausal Gonadotropins, well-known
today as the 2nd IRP. Much was said during those Meetings
about extraction and bioassay procedures, similarity or disim-
ilarity of urinary extracts and feasibility of utilizing a
urinary extract as a reference material. Looking back, it
seems amazing today that the adoption of a common reference
preparation, even of a temporary nature, was considered a real
accomplishment, and scientific gain. The new generation of
scientists who have not lived through the aches and pains of
a growing field may look at us with incredulity. And why not!
We can now talk about extraction and purification of follicle-
stimulating and luteinizing hormones from pituitary tissue and
from urinary gonadotropin extracts. We have witnessed the progress made in the bioassay field including the advent of computer programs which greatly facilitate the mathematical analyses of data. We have also witnessed the advent of various
reference preparations and we may now be facing the danger of
"overshooting the mark" as far as standards are concerned.
Moreover, the development of a new approach to the measurement
of gonadotropic activity in body fluids, mainly radioimmunoassay techniques, has opened the way to new avenues of research. Any new scientific advance poses many problems. Although the radioimmunoassay techniques have probably passed
the childhood stage and may be approaching maturity, much is
still to be learned. One point in reference which will be
discussed here is the feasibility of adopting reference preparations which could be meaningful in both biologic and immunologic terms.

    I cannot but remember the discussions held in 1959 during
the Gatlinburg Meeting in reference to the effect of human
gonadotropins of pituitary or urinary origin upon the sex
organs. It was quite evident from the start that the human

female, as expected, was more malleable than the male! However, I venture to say that in spite of a certain degree of predictability with respect to response, the human ovary maintains an aura of mystery and in some occasions still surprises the confident researcher with overwhelming reactions. I await with great interest the outcome of the discussions to be held here on this subject. Is it possible to "tame the shrew" thus consistently preventing ovarian overstimulation?

The first report, given at Gatlinburg, on the effect of human menopausal gonadotropin on the human testes made us somewhat uneasy. The testes seemed doomed to failure! However, in the ten years that have elapsed, we have learned that there is still hope for breaking the stubbornness of the "female counterpart" of the human species. The last session of our Meeting will certainly reveal to what extent we should raise our hopes.

Before turning the Meeting over to the co-chairmen, I wish to convey my sincere thanks to four people without whose help this Meeting would not have been possible: to my secretary, Miss Barbara Martin, for her tireless assistance, to Dr. C. A. Paulsen, whose keen interest in the success of this Conference goes far beyond his call of duty as a friend and to Dr. J. Martinez-Manautou and Dr. C. Gual to whom we are greatly indebted for having made possible the physical arrangements for this Meeting.

I wish to thank the working force of this Meeting: the co-chairmen of every session, Doctors L. E. Reichert, P. Donini, A. Albert, A. C. Crooke, W. D. Odell, C. Robyn, R. J. Ryan, B. B. Saxena, G. Bettendorf, C. Gual, R. E. Mancini, and C. A. Paulsen. I am especially grateful to Dr. J. Giner-Velazquez, Dr. J. Jimenez-Fonseca, Mr. M. M. Graff, Dr. F. Naftolin, Dr. A. M. Reiss, Dr. D. H. Espeland, and Dr. D. J. Moore whose efforts during the next three days will greatly contribute to the success of this Meeting.

CHAPTER 1

CHEMISTRY OF GONADOTROPINS

PURIFICATION AND PROPERTIES OF HUMAN PITUITARY FSH

B. B. SAXENA AND P. RATHNAM
DEPARTMENT OF MEDICINE
CORNELL UNIVERSITY MEDICAL COLLEGE
NEW YORK, N. Y. 10021

PURIFICATION

Extraction: One hundred grams of human pituitary acetone powder were extracted with 35% ethanol containing 10% ammonium acetate at pH 6.1 in a tissue to solvent ratio of 1:40 (w/v) (Diagram 1). Proteins in the supernatant were precipitated by two volumes of acetone. Precipitate 1 was acetone dried and designated 'crude gonadotropin'. All procedures were performed at 4°. The protein content of all fractions was determined by the biuret reaction (1).

A 1.7% solution of the crude gonadotropin in 5 mM phosphate buffer of pH 7.7 was made 48% in ethanol; the supernatant was recovered and made 85% in ethanol (v/v). The resulting Precipitate 2 was separated by centrifugation at 5000 rpm for 30 min.

Human pituitary acetone powder; 100g
 │ Extraction with 10% CH$_3$COONH$_4$ in 35% ethanol (1:40 w/v)
Supernatant
 │ Addition of two volumes of acetone
Crude gonadotropic precipitate 1
 │ Dissolved in phosphate buffer: made 48% in ethanol (v/v)
Supernatant
 │ Made 85% in ethanol (v/v)
Gonadotropic precipitate 2
 │ Recycling chromatography on Sephadex G-100
Gonadotropic fraction
 │ Chromatography on carboxymethyl SC-50
FSH fraction (pH 6.7, 0.1 M)
 │ Zone electrophoresis on cellulose
FSH fraction
 │ Preparative polyacrylamide gel electrophoresis
Purified FSH; 0.010g

Diagram 1

Purification of FSH from human pituitary glands.

Gel filtration: Precipitate 2 was dissolved in 10 mM phosphate buffer of pH 7.0 to make a clear solution, and fractionated by ascending recycling chromatography on a 10 x 100 cm column of Sephadex G-100 in the same

buffer at a flow rate of 100 ml/hr. The fraction containing gonadotropic activity was eluted at a K_d of 0.42 and a V_e/V_o ratio of 1.6.

Ion-exchange chromatography: The gonadotropic fraction from the Sephadex G-100 column was lyophilized, dialyzed against 4 mM ammonium acetate buffer of pH 5.5 and applied on a 2 x 50 cm column of carboxymethyl
Sephadex C-50 equilibrated with the same buffer. The column was eluted at
a flow rate of 20 ml/hr. The FSH fraction was eluted with 0.1 M ammonium
acetate buffer of pH 6.7 (Fig. 1). The protein containing LH and TSH activities was eluted by the same buffer at pH 9.5.

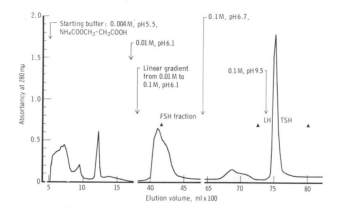

Figure 1

Ion-exchange chromatography of the gonadotropic fraction from Sephadex
G-100 column on carboxymethyl Sephadex C-50.

Zone electrophoresis: The FSH fraction from CM-Sephadex C-50 column
was lyophilized, dialyzed against 0.02 M phosphate buffer of pH 7.7 and
fractionated by zone electrophoresis (2, 3 and 4) on a 3 x 40 cm column of
cellulose, equilibrated with the same buffer (Fig. 2).

Preparative polyacrylamide gel electrophoresis: Aliquots of FSH fraction
from zone electrophoresis containing 25 mg protein were fractionated by
continuous flow electrophoresis on polyacrylamide gel (4 and 5) (Fig. 3). The
FSH fraction was lyophilized and filtered through a 2.5 x 75 cm column of
Sephadex G-25 in 1 mM phosphate buffer of pH 7.0 to remove buffer salts
and contaminating acrylamide (Fig. 4). The FSH protein was lyophilized
and stored in a dessicator in cold.

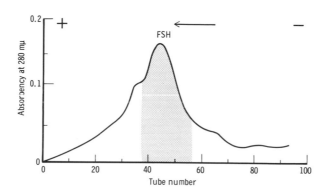

Figure 2

Zone electrophoresis of FSH fraction from carboxymethyl Sephadex C-50.

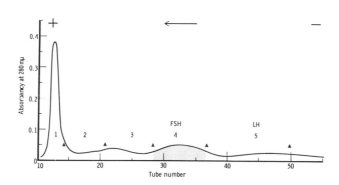

Figure 3

Preparative polyacrylamide gel electrophoresis of FSH fraction from zone electrophoresis. The electrophoresis was performed at 1000 v, 40 mA and -1°.

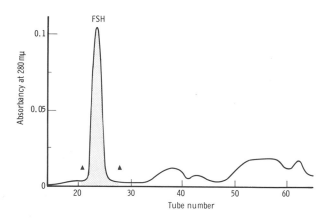

Figure 4

Gel filtration of FSH on Sephadex G-25.

Disc electrophoresis (6 and 7): The gonadotropic fraction from Sephadex G-100 column showed at least 12 protein bands (Fig. 5, b). The FSH fractions from CM-SC-50 and zone electrophoresis columns (Fig. 5, c and 5, d) showed only 5 protein bands indicating significant purification of the crude gonadotropic fraction (Fig. 5, a). The disc electrophoretic pattern of purified FSH is shown in Fig. 5, e.

Disc electrophoretic patterns of the FSH fraction from the zone electrophoresis and fractions obtained subsequently by polyacrylamide gel electrophoresis are shown in Fig. 6. The FSH fraction 4 showed a single protein band. This figure also illustrates the removal of inactive fractions 1, 2 and 3 and fraction 5 containing LH activity.

PROPERTIES

Yield and Activity (Table 1): From 100 g of acetone powder, 6.28 g of crude gonadotropin containing 1.05 units of FSH/mg were obtained. The yield of pure FSH was 10 mg representing 10,000 fold purification of the acetone powder. The results of 3 Steelman-Pohley assays (8) performed two months apart on the purified FSH showed 105 to 160 NIH-FSH-S3 units/ mg. The FSH contained LH activity unmeasurable by radioimmunoassay (9), less than 2% by OAAD method (10) and approximately 5% NIH-LH-S4 units by ventral prostate method (11). The FSH preparation was free of TSH (12), growth hormone (13), prolactin (14) and ACTH (15).

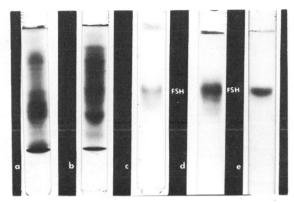

Figure 5

Disc electrophoretic patterns of (a) crude gonadotropin; (b) gonadotropic
fraction-Sephadex G-100; (c)FSH-CM-SC-50; (d) FSH-zone electrophoresis;
and (e) FSH-polyacrylamide gel electrophoresis.

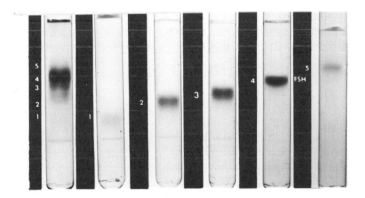

Figure 6

Disc electrophoretic patterns of FSH-zone electrophoresis and fractions 1,
2, 3 and 4 and 5 from the polyacrylamide gel electrophoresis.

Immunoelectrophoresis: The immunological purity of the FSH was demonstrated by a single precipitin band (Fig. 7, a) obtained after immunoelectrophoresis in agar using antisera prepared in rabbits (16) against a crude FSH
preparation. As shown in Fig. 7, b, 100 μg of FSH showed a single protein
band in disc electrophoresis at pH 8.6.

GONADOTROPINS 1968

Table 1

Yield and Activity of FSH

Fraction	Yield (gms)	Specific activity units[1]/mg
Crude gonadotropin	6.28 ± 1.2	1.05 ± 0.07 (10)[2]
Sephadex G-25-lyophilized FSH	0.01 ± 0.002	105-160 ((3)[3]

[1] One unit is equivalent to 1 mg of NIH-FSH S3

[2] Numbers in parentheses indicate number of experiments

[3] Assays done 2 months apart

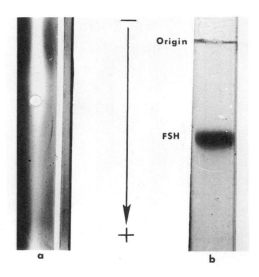

Figure 7

(a) Immunoelectrophoresis of FSH in agar at 80 v for 90 min at 4°; (b) Analytical disc electrophoretic pattern of FSH at pH 8.6.

Ultracentrifugal analysis: A 0.5% solution of the FSH in 0.01 M phosphate buffer of pH 7.0 containing 1% NaCl sedimented as a single polydispersed

boundary (Fig. 8). An $S_{20, w}$ of 2.04 was calculated. For the determination of molecular weight, 0.01, 0.03 and 0.10% solutions of FSH in 0.01 M phosphate buffer of pH 7.0 containing 1% NaCl, were studied by the method of Yphantis (17). A weight average ($\overline{M}_w$) of the sample was calculated to be 31,000±600. These preliminary studies have also suggested the possibility that a monomer of FSH may coexist with one or more of its polymers.

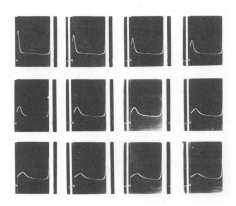

Figure 8

Sedimentation of human pituitary FSH in the ultracentrifuge at 59,780 rpm at 4°. Photographs were taken at 8 min intervals.

The isoelectric point of the FSH was determined by electrofocussing in sucrose gradient containing carrier ampholytes (18). To eliminate precipitation of protein during electrophoresis, the cathode was placed at the top of the column. The protein containing FSH activity became isoelectric at pH 4.25 (Fig. 9).

A continuous absorption spectrum of a 0.1% solution of FSH was measured between 200 to 340 mμ. A maxima at 278 mμ, with an optical density of 0.74, was obtained.

Elemental and Amino Acid analyses (19 and 20): The FSH contained 38.8% carbon, 7.3% hydrogen, 13.3% nitrogen and 31.4% oxygen.

For the amino acid analysis, 2 mg of FSH was hydrolyzed under vacuum in pyrex glass tubes with 5.7 N HCl at 110° for 24 hours. The hydrolysate was concentrated to a small volume in vacuo and lyophilized. The lyophilized material was dissolved again in a small amount of water and relyophilized to remove residual HCl. Tryptophan was determined spectrophotometrically (21). The high content of aspartic and glutamic acids is consistent with the acidic isoelectric point of the FSH (Table II).

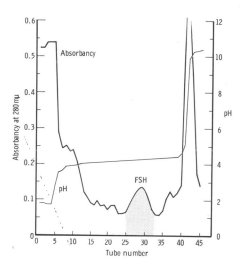

Figure 9

Isoelectric focussing of FSH

Table II

Amino Acid and Carbohydrate Composition of Human Pituitary FSH

	Lys ------------	4.5 g/100g
	His ------------	2.6
	Arg -----------	3.7
	Asp -----------	7.3
	Thr ------------	2.0
	Ser ------------	4.0
	Glu ------------	10.9
Amino acid	Pro ------------	6.2
	Gly ------------	3.4
	Ala ------------	4.7
	$^1/_2$ Cys --------	5.6
	Val ------------	5.3
	Met ------------	2.3
	Ileu ------------	2.9
	Leu -----------	5.9
	Tyr ------------	5.3
	Phe -----------	5.0
	Try ------------	0.76
	Sialic acid -----	5.0
Carbohydrate	Fucose --------	1.2
	Hexoses -------	6.1
	Hexosamines ---	5.3
Total -------------------------		99.96g

Carbohydrate analysis: The sialic acid (22), hexose (23), fucose (24) and hexosamine moieties constitute 17-18% of the FSH (Table II).

CHEMISTRY

N-terminal analysis: The N-terminal residue of human FSH was determined by 5-dimethyl amino 1-naphthalene sulphonyl chloride (DNS) (25 and 26), fluorodinitrobenzene (27) and phenyl isothiocyanate (28). N-terminal residue was also determined on FSH treated with urea, on FSH oxidized with performic acid, on FSH from which sialic acid and neutral sugars were removed sequentially and on the residual FSH protein recovered after treatment with carboxypeptidase. The results of all of these studies have so far failed to reveal a free N-terminal residue in human pituitary FSH.

C-terminal analysis: The C-terminal residue of FSH was determined on 1/2, 2 and 20 hour aliquots obtained during digestion with diisopropyl phosphorofluoridate (DFP)-treated carboxypeptidase A (29). The amino acids liberated were adsorbed on the resin AG-50W x8 (H^+ form, 200-400 mesh). The resin was then washed with water; the adsorbed amino acids were eluted with 5 N NH_4OH and identified as their DNS-derivatives. No significant amount of amino acid other than the ones liberated from the control experiment were detected in human FSH.

A further determination by selective **titration** of the C-terminal amino acid did not reveal a free C-terminal amino acid (30).

STABILITY

The FSH preparation was tested for its stability under various conditions (Table III). The activity was not lost by dialysis against water and 8 M urea, lyophilization, temperatures upto 37°, pH range of 5.5 to 9.5, iodoacetamide, mercaptoethanol, DFP and carboxypeptidase A. It would appear that the presence of disulfide bonds and of a free C-terminal amino acid may not be essential for total FSH activity of the molecule.

Table III

The Effect of Various Treatments on Biological Activity of FSH

Treatment	Effect on biological activity
Dialysis against water, 24-72 hours, 4°C ----------	retained
Dialysis against 8M urea, 24-72 hours, 4°C -------	"
Lyophilization -----------------------------------	"
Temperature (25°-37°C, 24 hours)------------------	"
pH ranges of 5.5 - 9.5 ---------------------------	"
Iodoacetamide, 0.1M, 24 hours --------------------	"
Mercaptoethanol, 0.1M, 24 hours -----------------	"
Diisopropyl phosphorofluoridate-------------------	"
Trypsin, 24 hours, 37°C --------------------------	"
Chymotrypsin, 8 hours, 25°C ----------------------	"
Carboxypeptidase A -------------------------------	"
Cyanogen bromide --------------------------------	destroyed
Removal of sialic acid and neutral sugars-----------	"

GONADOTROPINS 1968

The biological activity of the FSH was also retained after digestion with trypsin and chymotrypsin. The biological activity of the FSH was completely destroyed by cyanogen bromide and removal of sialic acid and neutral sugars.

ACKNOWLEDGEMENTS

This work was supported by grants from the National Institutes of Health (AM-11187), from the American Cancer Society (P-440) and from the Population Council of Rockefeller University (M67-27). Human pituitary glands were supplied by the National Pituitary Agency, Baltimore, Md.

REFERENCES

1. Gornall, A. G. , C. J. Bardawill, and M. M. David, J. Biol Chem 177:751,1949.
2. Flodin, P. , and D. W. Kupke, Biochim Biophys Acta 21:368, 1956.
3. Porath, J. , Biochim Biophys Acta 22:151, 1956.
4. Saxena, B. B. , and P. Rathnam, J. Biol Chem 242:3769, 1967.
5. Jovin, T. , A. Chrambach, and M. A. Naughton, Anal Biochem 9:351, 1964.
6. Davis, B. J. , Ann N. Y. Acad Sci 121:404, 1964.
7. Ornstein, L. Ann N. Y. Acad Sci 121:321, 1964.
8. Steelman, S. L. , and F. M. Pohley, Endocrinology 53:604, 1953
9. Saxena, B. B. , H Demura, H. M. Gandy, and R. E. Peterson, J Clin Endocrin 28:519, 1968.
10. Parlow, A. F. , in Albert, A. (ed) Human Pituitary Gonadotropins, Charles C. Thomas & Co. , Springfield, 1961, p. 300.
11. Greep, R. O. , H. B. vanDyke, and B. F. Chow, Proc Soc Exptl Biol Med 46:644, 1941.
12. McKenzie, J. M. , Endocrinology 63:372, 1958.
13. Greenspan, F. S. , C. H. Li , M. E. Simpson, and H. M. Evans, Endocrinology 45:455, 1949.
14. Lyons, W. R. , and E. Page, Proc Soc Exptl Biol Med 32:1049, 1935.
15. Sayers, M. A. , G. Sayers, and L. A. Woodbury, Endocrinology 42:379,1948.
16. Saxena, B. B. , and P. H. Henneman, J. Clin Endocrin 24:1271, 1964.
17. Yphantis, D. A. , Biochemistry 3:297, 1964.
18. Svennson, H. , Arch Biochem Biophys S1132, 1962.
19. Hamilton, P. B. Anal Chem 35:2055, 1963.
20. Spackman, D. H. , W. H. Stein, and S. Moore, Anal Chem 30:1190,1958.
21. Beavan, G. H. , and E. R. Holiday, Adv Prot Chem 7:319, 1952.
22. Svennerholm, L. , Biochim Biophys Acta 24:604, 1957.
23. Francois, C. , R. D. Marshall, and A. Neuberger, Biochem J 83:335,1962.
24. Dische, Z. , and L. B. Shettles, J. Biol Chem 175:595, 1948.
25. Gray, W. R. , and B. S. Hartley, Biochem J 89:50P, 1963.
26. Morse, D. , and B. L. Horecker, Anal Biochem 14:429, 1966.
27. Sanger, F. , Biochem J. 39:507,1945.
28. Edman, P. , Acta Chem Scand 4:283, 1950.
29. Fraenkel-Conrat, H. , J. J. Harris, and A. L. Levy in Glick, D. (ed), Methods of Biochemical Analysis, 2:409, 1958.
30. Holcomb, G. N. , S. A. James, and D. N. Ward, Biochemistry 7:1291, 1968.

FRACTIONATION OF HUMAN PITUITARY GONADOTROPINS
(EXTRACTION, GEL-FILTRATION AND ELECTROFOCUSING)

G. Bettendorf, M. Breckwoldt, P.-J. Czygan, A. Fock, T. Kumasaka

Abteilung Fuer Klinische Und Experimentelle Endokrinologie Der
Universitaets-Frauenklinik Hamburg-Eppendorf, Germany

INTRODUCTION

We have been interested in attempting to isolate gonadotropins
from human pituitaries in order to have a supply of material for
clinical trials and also to develop procedures for fractionation
and purification of human pituitary FSH and LH. The extraction of
pituitaries has been done by the same method since 1960. Various
protein separation procedures were used for further experiments.
I should like to describe our method of purification which is
suitable for these different purposes and to present the results
of gel filtration on Sephadex G 100 and of isoelectric focusing
in natural pH gradients. The isoelectric focusing technique was
used for separation and for characterization of FSH and LH by
their isoelectric points.

EXTRACTION

The extraction method we employed is a modification of the
procedure of Koenig and King (1, 2, 3). The pituitary glands
were collected in pathology laboratories 24 - 48 hours after
death and were stored in acetone in a refrigerator for several
months up to one year. Usually 100 pituitaries were taken for
one extraction procedure. The glands were carefully ground in a
homogenizer and washed with acetone (Fig. 1). The powder was
dried at room temperature and extracted 5 times with 40% ethanolic
acetate buffer. The extract was made 80% ethanolic and the
precipitate which formed in 2 - 3 days was dissolved in water,
dialyzed and lyophilized after centrifugation. The final product,
E_3, is the material which we mainly used for clinical studies.
The residue after extraction of the acetone dried pituitary powder with acetate buffer (R_1) was re-extracted with 0.1 m ammonium
sulfate followed by ammonium sulfate fractionation according to
Ellis (4) except using values of pH 7.1 instead of pH 4.5. The
final product, N_4, mainly contained LH.

The total gonadotropin activity was measured using the mouse-
uterus-test (5), FSH activity by the augmentation test (6), and
LH activity by the OAAD test (7). The standards used were
HMG 20 A, FSH-NIH-SI and LH-NIH-BI respectively, and in the last
years the second IRP-HMG.

GONADOTROPINS 1968

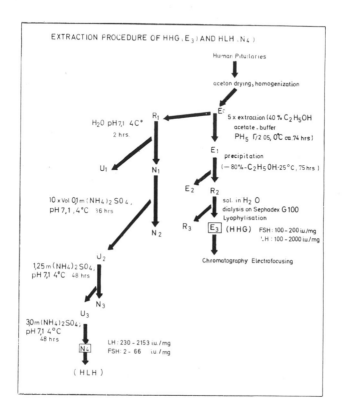

Fig. 1

Flow sheet for fractionation of human pituitaries

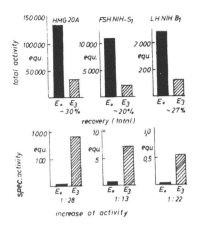

Fig. 2

Yields of total gonadotropic activity, FSH activity and LH activity. E_0: acetone dried pituitary, E_3: human hypophyseal gonadotropin.

    Comparing the specific activities of the acetone-dried glands
with the final product, we were able to calculate the recovery
and the increase of biological activity (Fig. 2). For the total
gonadotropic activity, we found a recovery of 30%, for FSH activity
20% and for LH activity 27%. The increase of specific activity
was as follows: total gonadotropic activity 1:28, FSH 1:13 and
LH 1:22 (8). In our experiments in the different batches, the
mean potency per mg of E_3 was FSH 100 - 200 I.U./mg and 100 - 1000
I.U./mg. LH. The FSH:LH ratio varied between 0.05 and 5.2.

    The re-extraction of the residue after extraction with
ethanolic acetate buffer by stepwise elution with ammonium sulfate
according to the method of Ellis (4) resulted in a preparation in
which we found only a small amount of FSH and a relatively large
amount of LH. The FSH activities were between 2 and 66 and LH
between 230 and 2150 I.U./mg. The FSH/LH ratio was between 0.01
and 0.06. These biologic activities resulted when the solutions
used had a pH of 7.1. With a pH of 4.5 only small amounts of LH
could be extracted (Fig. 3). For the FSH we found that the resulting activities were somewhat higher by using pH 4.5.

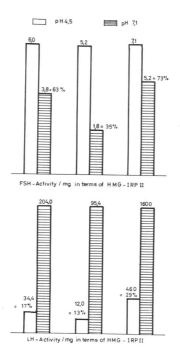

pH 4,5   pH 7,1

6,0   5,2   7,1

5,2 = 73%

3,8 = 63%

1,8 = 35%

FSH - Activity / mg in terms of H MG - IRP II

204,0   95,4   1600

460 = 29%

34,4 = 17%   12,0 = 13%

LH - Activity / mg in terms of HMG - IRP II

Fig. 3

Influence of different pH values in the extraction of LH

We have compared the extraction of E_0 (acetone-dried pituitaries) with that of R_1 (residue after extraction with ethanolic acetate buffer). The LH recovery of E_0 was 43%, that of R_1 was 59%. There was a greater increase of specific LH activity in the experiment with R_1 (table 1 and 2). Thus, it would appear that our method of pituitary extraction is adequate for obtaining a material with FSH and LH activity and in addition an LH enriched fraction.

			HMG - I RP II		
	Weight		Activity / mg	Total Activity	FSH / LH - Ratio
E_0	9,51 g	FSH	26,0	247 000	0,91
		LH	28,8	272 000	
N_4	102,3 mg	FSH	16,3	1690	0,01
		LH	1160,0	118 000	
Yield: FSH : 0,7 % LH : 43,4 %		E_0 : Aceton - dried Human Pituitaries			

Table 1

Extraction of LH (N_4); starting material E_0

			HMG - I RP II		
	Weight		Activity / mg	Total Activity	FSH / LH - Ratio
R_1	9,420g	FSH	0,56	5.200	0,15
		LH	3,79	35.600	
N_4	34,38 mg	FSH	13,1	450	0,0215
		LH	610,0	21.100	
Yield: FSH : 0,3 % LH : 59,2 %		R_1 : Human Pituitaries after Extraction of HMG			

Table 2

Extraction of LH (N_4); starting material R_1

GEL FILTRATION

The two preparations E_3 and N_4 have been filtered by gel
filtration on Sephadex G 100. The FSH activity of E_3 was 143 I.U./
mg. and the LH activity was 307 I.U./mg. (9). In this experiment,
the gonadotropic activity was tested in every single fraction.
The protein amount was calculated from the difference of the
extinction between 215 and 225 mμ. The chromatographic pattern
and biological activities are shown in Fig. 4 . Fraction 20 had
an activity equivalent to 111 I.U. FSH/mg. and 922 I.U. LH/mg.,
fraction 25:579 I.U. FSH/mg. and 692 I.U. LH/mg., fraction 33:162
I.U. FSH/mg. and 18 I.U. LH/mg. The FSH/LH ratio ranged from 0.8
in the starting material to 0.12, 0.83 and 8.1 respectively in the
different fractions, that means a splitting of FSH and LH activity.
The first fraction we obtained had particularly more LH activity,
the next both FSH and LH nearly to the same amount and the last
mainly FSH activity.

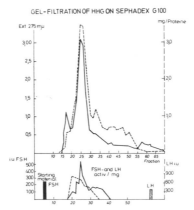

GEL-FILTRATION OF HHG ON SEPHADEX G 100

Relative Potencies of FSH and LH of the Fractions obtained by
Gel-Filtration on Sephadex G -100

Fraction	FSH i.u / mg	L H i.u / mg	FSH/LH ratio
Starting material E₃ x₆₄	243	307	0,8
x 20	111	922	0,12
x 25	579	692	0,83
x 33	162	18	8,1

Fig. 4

Gel filtration of E_3 on Sephadex G 100

In gel filtration of N_4 on Sephadex G 100 similar results
could be obtained (Fig. 5).[4] The starting material had an FSH
activity of 4.0 I.U./mg. and an LH activity of 49.0 I.U./mg.
By testing every second fraction, we found mainly LH in the first
protein peak. The FSH activity separated in the following fractions (Table 3).

CHEMISTRY

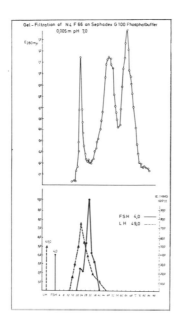

Fig. 5

Gel filtration of N_4 on Sephadex G 100

Fraction	FSH		LH	
	iu / mg	fiducial limits	iu / mg	fiducial limits
Starting material	4,0	(3,6 – 4,4)	49,0	(46,2 – 51,8)
16	< 1,2	–	17,2	(15,7 – 18,7)
18	< 1,2	–	29,8	(28,8 – 30,8)
20	< 1,2	–	50,1	(48,3 – 51,9)
22	2,55	(2,31 – 2,79)	–	
24	2,55	(2,04 – 2,44)	76,4	(72,2 – 80,6)
26	–	–	55,2	(51,0 – 59,4)
28	5,40	(2,13 – 5,67)	–	–
30	9,80	(8,60 – 11,0)	40,3	(38,1 – 42,5)
32	4,25	(3,80 – 4,70)	29,1	(27,0 – 31,2)
34	3,76	(3,42 – 4,10)	19,8	(16,2 – 23,4)
36	3,30	(3,10 – 3,50)	16,0	(12,1 – 19,9)
38	< 0,6	–	12,1	(10,0 – 14,2)

Table 3

Relative potencies of the fractions obtained by gel filtration
of N_4 on Sephadex G 100

ELECTROFOCUSING

Recently we have been using the technique of isoelectric
focusing in natural pH gradients. With this method a complete
separation of two species, requiring a difference in isoelectric
point of no more than 0.02 pH units is possible (10). In addition,
the proteins can be characterized by their isoelectric points. We
used the LKB Electrofocusing Column 8100 having a volume of about
450 ml and a cooled electrode tube. An ampholine for the pH range
3 - 10 was selected. It is a mixture containing very large numbers
of aliphatic amino carboxylic acids having an average molecular
weight of 300 - 600 and representing a large number of pH values.
Two solutions were prepared, one heavy: ampholine, sucrose and
water, and one light: ampholine and water. 35,6 mg of E_3 were
dissolved in a portion of the light solution. The gradient was
prepared and the electrode solutions added: ethanol amine in the
electrode tube (cathode) and phosphoric acid on top of the last
portion in the column (anode). For the first 48 hours, we used
200 volts and 4 mA (0.8 W). Immediately after completion of the
experiment, the column was emptied through an absorptiometer for
monitoring the effluent of 280 mμ and collected in a fraction
collector. Then the pH values of the different 5 ml fractions
were measured.

The result of the experiment is seen in Fig. 6 . Seven
fractions were pooled according to the protein peaks obtained.
The solutions were dialyzed and lyophilized. As it was very difficult to get dry material only a definite amount of each fraction
was taken for bioassays. Therefore, we cannot calculate the
recovery in this experiment. In fractions a and b, we did not
obtain a sufficient amount of material for testing and with the
fraction e, only the augmentation test could be done. The activities of the starting material and of the different fractions are
shown in Table 4 . At pH 6 - 7, we found 22 I.U./mg. LH and no
FSH using up to 90 μg in the assay. Fraction d at pH 5 showed
FSH and LH activities nearly of the same value. Fraction f at
PH 3 had an FSH activity of 998 I.U./mg. and no LH was detectable
up to 30 μg. There was an increase only in the specific activity
of FSH compared to the starting material. During the experiment,
no precipitation of proteins could be detected.

These results show that we obtained three preparations with
different FSH/LH activities, similar to those which we found in
the other experiments: One preparation with mainly FSH activity,
a second with mainly LH activity and a third with both FSH and
LH activity. A complete separation of FSH and LH could not be
achieved so far (Fig. 7).

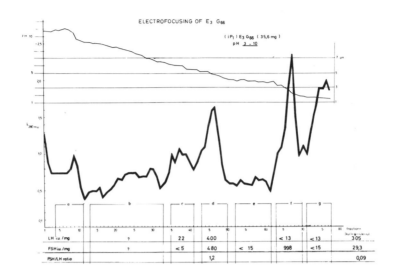

Fig. 6

Electrofocusing of E$_3$ pH 3 - 10

Fraction	pH	FSH		LH		FSH/LH ratio
		i.u/mg	Fiducial limits	i.u./mg	Fiducial limits	
Starting material E$_3$ G66		29,3	(20 - 34,8)	305	(287 - 323)	0,09
a	10	?		?	-	
b	7-8	?		?	-	
c	6-7	<5	-	22	(10,8 - 34)	
d	5	480	(372 - 558)	410	(400 - 420)	1,2
e	4	<15	-		-	
f	3	998	(374 -1488)	<13	-	
g	1,5	<15	-	<13	-	

Table 4

Relative potencies of FSH and LH of the fractions obtained by electrofocusing

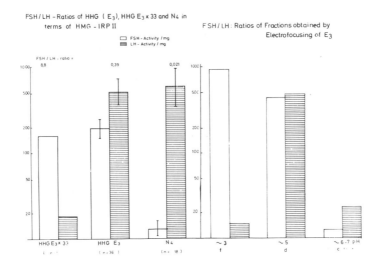

Fig. 7

FSH/LH ratios of different preparations

Our data suggest that there must be one protein with an isoelectric point of pH 5 which has both FSH and LH activity, a
second protein with an isoelectric point of pH 6 - 7 which has LH
activity and a third protein with an isoelectric point of pH 3
which has FSH activity.

Supported in part by a grant from Deutsche Forschungsgemeinschaft
and Jung-Stiftung Hamburg.

REFERENCES

1. Koenig, V.L., King, E.: Arch. Biochem. 26, 219, 1950
2. Bettendorf, G., Apostolakis, M., Voigt, K.D.: Proc. Int. Fed.
        Gyn. Obstet. III, 76, 1961
3. Bettendorf, G., Apostolakis, M., Voigt, K.D.: Acta endocrinol.
        41, 1, 1962
4. Ellis, S.: Endocrinology 69, 544, 1961
5. Heller, C.G., Lawson, H., Severinghaus, L.L.: Am.J.Physiol.
        121, 364, 1938
6. Steelman, S.L., Pohley, F.M.: Endocrinology 53, 604, 1953
7. Parlow, A.F., in Human Pituitary Gonadotropins, edit. A.
        Albert, Springfield, Ch. C. Thomas 1961, 300
8. Breckwoldt, M., Angulo, J.M., Bettendorf, G.: Arch.Gyn. 202,
        233, 1964
9. Bettendorf, G., Czygan, P.-J., Breckwoldt, M.: Geburtsh.
        Frauenheilk. 26, 640, 1966
10. Haglund, H.: Science Tools, LKB Inst.J. 14, 17, 1967

PRELIMINARY STUDIES ON THE EFFECT OF UREA AND CHYMOTRYPSIN ON THE MOLECULAR, BIOLOGICAL AND IMMUNOLOGICAL PROPERTIES OF HUMAN FOLLICLE STIMULATING HORMONE AND LUTEINIZING HORMONE

Leo E. Reichert, Jr. and A. Rees Midgley
Department of Biochemistry, Division of Basic Health Sciences
Emory University, Atlanta, Georgia
Department of Pathology, University of Michigan
Ann Arbor, Michigan

INTRODUCTION

In a program carried out in collaboration with the National Pituitary Agency, we have been concerned for some time with the development of methods for the separation, isolation and radioimmunoassay of human pituitary follicle stimulating hormone (FSH) and luteinizing hormone (LH). The availability of highly purified gonadotropins has permitted physical - chemical studies on these hormones (1)(2)(3). Recently, the reversible urea-induced dissociation of ovine LH dimer into monomer subunits was reported (4). It seemed of interest to extend such studies to human LH and to FSH as well, by comparing the effect of urea treatment on the molecular, biological and immunological properties of these gonadotropins. The effect of chymotryptic digestion on these parameters was also examined.

MATERIALS AND METHODS

Biological Assay: Luteinizing Hormone activity was assayed by the ovarian ascorbic acid depletion assay (5)(6), and expressed in terms of NIH-LH-Sl. One mg of this reference preparation was considered to have one unit of LH activity. Follicle Stimulating Hormone activity was assayed by the HCG-augmentation method (7) slightly modified (8), and expressed in terms of NIH-FSH-Sl. One mg of this reference preparation was considered to have one unit of FSH activity.

Radioimmunoassay: Radioimmunoassay of the human gonadotropins was by methods previously reported (9)(10). The standard used in these assays was LER-907, a partially purified fraction derived from acetone-dried human pituitary glands. One mg of LER-907 contained LH activity equivalent to 0.067 mg of NIH-LH-Sl and FSH activity equivalent to 5.3 mg of NIH-FSH-Sl, as determined by bioassay. The radioimmunoassay values reported in Table 3 were obtained through use of these conversion factors.

Preparation of purified Luteinizing Hormone and Follicle Stimulating Hormone: These hormones were derived from acetone-dried human pituitary glands by ammonium sulfate extraction and fractionation (11), ion-exchange chromatography (12) and gel filtration (1)(3). The LH preparation had a specific biological activity of 3.27 units/mg, and the FSH, 191 units/mg. Neither preparation gave evidence of heterogeneity when examined by polyacrylamide gel electrophoresis (3).

The Gel Filtration System: Gel filtration was carried out on a
2.5 X 91.5 column of Sephadex G-100 (Pharmacia). Only G-100 beads not
passing a U.S. Standard 200 mesh screen were utilized in these experiments. The column was equilibrated and developed with a 0.05M ammonium
bicarbonate buffer, pH 8.0. All operations were carried out in the cold
(3-5°C) at a flow rate of 3.5 ml/tube/15 minutes (14.0 ml/hr). The void
volume was determined with Blue Dextran (Pharmacia) and the column was
calibrated with proteins of known molecular weight prior to use, and
intermittently thereafter as a check on column performance. All gel
filtrations were by the ascending technique, which has the advantage of
obviating column deterioration due to bed-packing and permitting repeated
use of the same column.

        The values for the average distribution coefficients (Kav) of the
various proteins were calculated as discussed by Siegel and Monty (13)
and Laurent and Killander (14). Approximations of the stokes radii were by
the method of Ackers (15). In this, the assumption was made that the Kav
is essentially equal to the Kd (the distribution coefficient) as discussed
by Siegel and Monte (13). Good agreement was obtained between the Kav and
calculated stokes radii of the calibrating proteins and values reported in
the literature (Table I).

Table I

Calibration of the G-100[1] Column with Reference Proteins

Protein[2]	MW	Ve/Vo ratio	Kav[3]	Stokes radius "a" mμ
Bacitracin	1450	3.11	0.92	-
Cytochrome c	12400	2.59	0.69	-
Myoglobin	17800	2.32	0.58	-
Chymotrypsinogen	25000	2.20	0.52	2.10
Ovalbumin	45000	1.73	0.32	2.85
Albumin (bovine)	67000	1.43	0.19	3.83
Gamma-globulin	160000	1.12	0.052	5.93
Apoferritin	480000	1.01	-	-
Blue Dextran	2000000	Excluded	-	-

1 Column dimensions were 2.5 x 91.5 cm
2 Proteins used in this column calibration were purchased from Mann Research
   Labs, Kit #8109A, "Non-enzymic Protein Molecular Weight Markers".
3 Kav = Ve-Vo/Vt- Vo. Ve is the elution volume of the protein as determined
   from the fraction in the elution profile having maximum UV absorbancy. Vo
   is the outer volume as determined by filtration of Blue Dextran (138 ml).
   Vt is the total volume of the column, equal here to 446 ml.

EXPERIMENTAL AND RESULTS

Gel Filtration of Human LH: 3 mg of highly purified human LH was dissolved in 2 ml of 0.05 M ammonium bicarbonate, pH 8.0, and applied to the G-100 column for ascending gel filtration. A single, symmetrical peak emerged, having a Kav = 0.32, an apparent molecular weight of 41690 and a calculated stokes radius of 2.84 mμ (Table 2).

Gel Filtration of Human LH Following Urea Incubation: 3 mg of the same human LH fraction was dissolved in 2 ml of 8 M urea and allowed to incubate for 24 hours at room temperature, about 23°C. The urea-incubated LH was then subjected to gel filtration exactly as above. The protein peak which emerged showed a Kav = 0.46, an apparent molecular weight of 26300 and a calculated stokes radius of 2.10 mμ (Table 2).

Comparison of the Biological and Immunological Activities of Native and Urea-Treated Luteinizing Hormone: The potency of the purified human LH was 3.27 units/mg by bioassay and 3.0 units/mg by radioimmunoassay. Digestion with urea resulted in a 90% decrease in biological activity, to 0.31 units/mg, and a 47% decrease in immunologic activity, to 1.6 units/mg. There was some overlap in the elution profile between the native and urea-denatured hormones. The protein in the overlap area of the urea-treated preparation showed activity of 2.47 units/mg by bioassay, and 2.24 units/mg by radioimmunoassay.

Gel Filtration of Human FSH: 2 mg of highly purified human FSH was dissolved in 2 ml of ammonium bicarbonate buffer, 0.05M, pH 8.0, and applied to the G-100 column for ascending gel filtration. A single symetrical peak emerged having a Kav = 0.24, an apparent molecular weight of 52480 and a calculated stokes radius of 3.46 mμ (Table 2).

Gel Filtration of Human FSH + Urea: A like amount of FSH was dissolved in 2 ml of 8M urea and allowed to incubate for 24 hours at room temperature, about 23°C. The urea-incubated hormone was then subjected to gel filtration under identical conditions as the native FSH and human LH fractions. The FSH was resolved into two distinct components. The first showed a Kav = 0.24, an apparent molecular weight of 52480 and a calculated stokes radius of 3.46, all values identical to that obtained with the native hormone. The 2nd peak showed a Kav = 0.41, an apparent molecular weight of 30900 and a calculated stokes radius of 2.23 mμ (Table 2).

Comparison of the Biological and Immunological Activities of Native and Urea-Treated Follicle Stimulating Hormone: The potency of the purified FSH used in these studies was 191 units/mg by bioassay and 473 units/mg by immunoassay. Following digestion with urea, the potency of the protein in the Kav = 0.24 fraction had decreased 88% by bioassay (to 23 units mg) and 93% by immunoassay (to 31 units/mg). The new peak generated by urea-treatment, and which composed approximately 50% of the starting protein had less than 8 units of LH activity per mg by bioassay, a decrease of about 96%, and measured 67 units/mg by immunoassay, a decrease of 86% (Table 3).

Attempts to Regenerate Biological Activity of the Urea-Treated Preparations: a. Luteinizing Hormone: The urea-generated human LH peak having a Kav = 0.32,

GONADOTROPINS 1968

Table 2

Gel Filtration of Native and Urea-digested human FSH and LH[a]

Description	Ve/Vo Ratio	Relative MW[b]	Kav	Stokes radius(m_μ)
LH- Native	1.73	41690	0.32	2.84
LH- Urea digested	2.06	26300	0.46	2.10
FSH- Native	1.56	52480	0.24	3.46
FSH + Urea, Peak #1	1.56	52480	0.24	3.46
FSH + Urea, Peak #2	1.93	30900	0.41	2.23

a: For conditions of incubation, see text.
b: Relative to protein used for column calibration, see Table 1.

Table 3

Comparison of Biologic and Immunologic Potencies of Native and Urea-Digested Gonadotropins

Prep.	LH Activity[a] Units/mg		% Activity Remaining		FSH Activity[a] Units/mg		% Activity Remaining	
	Bio.[b]	RIA[b]	Bio.	RIA	Bio.	RIA	Bio.	RIA
LH-Native	3.27	3.00	-	-	-	2.21	-	-
LH + Urea	0.31	1.58	9.4	53	-	4.23	-	192
FSH-Native	-	0.09	-	-	191	473	-	-
FSH + Urea Peak #1[c]	-	0.041	-	46	23	31	12	7
FSH + Urea Peak #2[c]	-	0.048	-	69	7.9	67	4.0	14.2

a: Biologic and immunologic activity expressed in terms of NIH-LH-Sl or NIH-FSH-Sl.
b: Bio = biological activity as measured by OAAD or HCG-augmentation assay RIA = immunologic activity as determined by radioimmunoassay.
c: Peak #1 refers to Kav = 0.24 component, and peak #2 refers to the Kav = 0.41 component.

and a protein concentration of 25 micrograms/ml was allowed to incubate at room temperature for 16 hours after which it was bioassayed simultaneously with a "non-incubated" control which had been kept frozen. No increase in activity could be detected. This preparation was then incubated at 40°C for an additional 24 hours followed by a similar bioassay, and, again, no recovery of activity could be detected. The evaluation of the bioassays were complicated by an apparent lack of parallelism between the urea-treated human LH and the ovine LH standard.
b. Follicle-stimulating Hormone: Equal amounts of the urea-digested FSH fractions having Kav values of 0.24 and 0.41 (protein concentration = 30 micrograms/ml) were allowed to incubate first at room temperature for 16 hours and then at 40°C for 24 hours. No increase in FSH activity could be detected. The Kav = 0.24 fraction was allowed to incubate under similar conditions, again with no apparent regeneration of biological activity.

Effect of Chymotryptic Digestion on the Biologic, Immunologic and Molecular Properties of Human LH: A purified human LH fraction assaying 3.10 units/mg by bioassay and 3.29 units/mg by radioimmunoassay, was digested with bovine pancreatic chymotrypsin for 16 hours in 0.2M phosphate buffer, pH 7.0, at 40°C. The ratio of enzyme to hormone (by weight) was 1:8. Enzymic digestion virtually abolished biological activity, reducing it 98.5%, from 3.10 units/mg to 0.05 units/mg. However, immunologic activity was only reduced 63%, from 3.29 units/mg to 1.10 units/mg. In addition, gel filtration of the digested LH on Sephadex G-100 indicated that extensive hydrolysis apparently had not taken place. A single major peak emerged having a Kav = 0.45, a value almost identical to that noted for the urea-generated LH component (Table 2).

DISCUSSION

The Ve/Vo ratio (1.73) and apparent molecular weight estimate (41690) obtained in this study agree well with those previously reported by us for human LH (1)(3). The urea digestion of the human LH clearly indicated that a marked change had occured, as reflected by an increase in the Kav from 0.32 to 0.46, a decrease in the stokes radius from 2.84 to 2.10 mμ and a decrease in the apparent molecular weight from 41690 to 26300 (Table 2). The decrease in biological activity (90%) of the urea generated component having a Kav = 0.46, was almost twice the decrease in immunologic activity (47%) as determined by radioimmunoassay. This suggests that the biologic and immunologic reactive sites on the molecule are not identical. Additional evidence supporting this concept has been obtained from experiments involving digestion of human LH with chymotrypsin. When this is done, biological activity is virtually abolished, but considerable immunologic activity is retained.

De la Llosa et.al. (4) have reported native ovine LH to have a Kd of 0.30, with a component generated by urea digestion having Kd of 0.45. Our observed Kav values for the native and urea-treated human hormone agree closely with their findings. This supports the conclusion of an earlier report from this laboratory (1) indicating that the molecular dimensions of native, human, bovine, porcine and ovine LH are quite similar.

Because of the multiplicity of amino acids found in highly purified LH preparations following dinitrophenylation, digestion with carboxypeptidase A and hydrazinolysis, we suggested the possibility that LH was, in fact, composed of more than one polypeptide chain (16). De la Llosa et.al. (4) interpreted their urea-incubation experiments to indicate a reversible dissociation of ovine LH dimer to the monomer form. Ward et.al. (17) suggested that ovine LH consisted of two non-identical subunits, and Ward et.al. (17) and Papkoff and Samy (19) have reported preliminary studies on their composition and structure.

On the basis of the above studies, it is tempting to conclude that the urea generated human LH peak having a Kav = 0.46 represents either a mixture of non-identical subunit chains or the LH monomer.

It is interesting to note that Papkoff and Samy (19) report Ve/Vo ratios for the ovine LH subunits of 1.64 and 2.0 respectively, as determined by G-100 gel filtration. Such ratios may differ considerably between laboratories because of variations in a number of operational factors. By our column calibration, however, the ratio of 1.64 represents an apparent molecular weight of 46770, and the ratio of 2.0, represents an apparent molecular weight of 28180. Thus, the position that the Ve/Vo = 1.64 component represents a subunit of ovine may require reappraisal.

Gel filtration of highly purified human FSH confirmed our earlier report that this hormone has a molecular size slightly larger than that of LH, when examined at neutral pH's (3). After digestion with urea, a new component appeared, having an apparent molecular weight of 30900, a Ve/Vo ratio of 1.93, a Kav of 0.41 and a stokes radius of 2.23 mµ (Table 2). This urea-generated component showed a marked decrease in biological-activity as compared with the native FSH precursor (Table 3). A marked decrease in immunologic activity was also noted, and this marasmus was essentially identical by both measurements (Table 3). In addition to the Kav = 0.41 peak, a larger molecular weight component having characteristics identical to the native FSH was observed (Table 2). It is difficult to say at this preliminary stage whether the Kav = 0.24 component found after urea digestion (Table 2) represents a fraction refractory to urea-digestion, or whether a longer incubation period would have resulted in its conversion to the Kav = 0.46 component. Similarly, it is too early to explain the significance of the urea generated FSH-component. It may be, however, that we are observing a dissociation of the FSH similar to that noted for LH and discussed above.

The failure to recover initial activity by recombination of resolved components similar to that reported for ovine LH by De la Llosa et.al. (4) and Papkoff and Samy (19) was disappointing. However, as pointed out by De la Llosa et.al. (4) recombination in very dilute solutions is rather slow, and Papkoff and Samy (19) achieved recombination using a rather concentrated (10 mg/ml) solution of the subunits. Somewhat disturbing is an apparent lack of parallelism which we had observed between the urea-incubated human LH and the ovine LH standard when assayed in the OAAD assay. This problem is being pursued further.

SUMMARY

Incubation of human LH in 8M urea caused a marked change in the molecular dimensions of the hormone, presumably reflecting its dissociation into subunits. This "dissociation" was accompanied by a marked loss of biologic activity, although considerable immunologic activity was retained. Similar results were obtained following digestion of human LH with chymotrypsin, indicating that the biologic and immunologic reactive sites on the hormone may not be identical. Incubation of human FSH in 8M urea resulted in the generation of a new component having different molecular dimensions than the native hormone, but possessing greatly reduced biologic and immunologic activity. The results suggest that human FSH may also be dissociable into subunits.

ACKNOWLEDGEMENTS

It is a pleasure to acknowledge the able technical assistance of Mr. William Fugate, Miss Karin Westphal, Mrs. Ruth Arthur and Miss Donna Howell in various phases of this work. This is publication #885 from the Division of Basic Health Sciences, Emory University, Atlanta, Georgia. This work was supported by USPHS grants AM-3598 and HD02193.

REFERENCES

1. Reichert, L.E.Jr. and N.S. Jiang, Endocrinology 77:78, 1965
2. Kathan, R., Reichert, L.E.Jr. and R. Ryan, Endocrinology 81:45, 1967
3. Reichert, L.E. Jr., R. Kathan and R. Ryan, Endocrinology 82:109, 1968
4. De la Llosa, P., C. Courts and M. Jutisz, Biochem. Biophys. Res. Commun. 26, 411, 1967
5. Parlow, A. F. in Albert, A. (ed.) Human Pituitary Gonadotropins, Charles C. Thomas, Springfield, Tll., 1961, p. 301
6. Reichert, L. E. Jr. and A. F. Parlow, Endocrinology, 73:285, 1963
7. Steelman S. L. and Pohley, F. M., Endocrinology, 53:604, 1953
8. Parlow, A.F., and L.E. Reichert, Jr., Endocrinology 73:740, 1963
9. Midgley, A. R., J. Clin. Endo. Metab. 27:295, 1967
10. Midgley, A. R. Endocrinology, 79:10, 1966
11. Parlow, A. F., A. E. Wilhelmi, and L. E. Reichert, Jr., Endocrinology 77:1126, 1965
12. Reichert, L. E. Jr. and A. F. Parlow, Endocrinology 74:236, 1964
13. Siegel, L. M. and K. J. Monty, Biochem. Biophys. Acta. 112:346, 1966
14. Laurent, T. C. and Killander, J., J. of Chromatog. 14:317, 1964
15. Ackers, G., Biochemistry 3:723, 1964
16. Reichert, L. E. Jr., Endocrinology, 78:186, 1966
17. Ward, D. N., M. Fugjino and W. M. Lamkin, Federation Proceeding, 25:348, 1966
18. Papkoff, H. and T.S.A. Samy, Biochem., Biophys. Acta 147:175, 1967
19. Papkoff, H. and T.S.A. Samy, Federation Proceedings 27:371, 1968

SOME OBSERVATIONS ON THE MOLECULAR WEIGHT AND STRUCTURE OF HUMAN FSH

A. C. CROOKE, MD, FRCP AND C. H. GRAY, PhD.

THE UNITED BIRMINGHAM HOSPITALS, DEPARTMENT OF CLINICAL ENDOCRINOLOGY
BIRMINGHAM AND MIDLAND HOSPITAL FOR WOMEN, BIRMINGHAM, 11, ENGLAND.

It has been reported (1) that pituitary follicle stimulating hormone (FSH) appears to undergo reversible association in different ionic concentrations demonstrable on gel filtration columns. FSH dissolved in buffered 1M-NaCl and stored for several hours at 0° gave a single peak on Biogel P-30 corresponding to a molecular weight of 16,000-17,000. When the same material was made up in 0.01 M-phosphate buffer, pH 7.1, it showed peaks on Biogel P-100 and P-150 corresponding with molecular weights of about 34,000 and 68,000 respectively. When the high molecular weight material was placed in 1 M-NaCl conversion to the 17,000 molecular weight form occurred again. This association and dissociation has been demonstrated in freshly prepared material but it is difficult to demonstrate in material that has been prepared for several weeks.

These results suggest that FSH can exist in monomer, dimer and tetramer forms. Preliminary amino acid analyses on our preparations of FSH have now been carried out. Certain differences between these results and those published by other groups are evident. Light may be thrown on these differences by first comparing the results of analyses of the same preparation by different workers. Human luteinizing hormone (LH) prepared by Dr. Anne S. Hartree in Cambridge has been analysed by herself (2) and by Dr. Peter Somers (3). Their findings are shown in Table 1 and any differences must be due to analytical methods.

Table 1.

Amino acid composition of human LH[*]

Amino acid	A	B	Amino acid	A	B
Asp	16	22	Met	5	1-2
Thr	17	22	Ile	7	8
Ser	13	49	Leu	14	14
Glu	19	23	Tyr	6	6
Pro	26	28	Phe	6	8
Gly	15	35	Lys	10	10
Ala	11	26	His	7	8
Val	20-21	32	Arg	16	15
Half-Cys	20	11			

A 48-hr. hydrolysate (2); B "Corrected" (3);
[*]Adjusted to Lysine = 10.

The figures are adjusted so that lysine is constant at ten residues. The choice of lysine as reference is not important because it is clear that similar results would be obtained if certain other amino acids had been chosen. With this adjustment quite good agreement is seen with about half of the amino acids. These are proline, isoleucine, leucine, tyrosine, phenylalanine, histidine and arginine.. Amir et al (3) report higher recoveries of aspartic acid, threonine, serine, glutamic acid, glycine, alanine and valine. It must be pointed out that valine determinations are made difficult by the fact that N-acetylhexosamines are eluted from the analyser columns at the same position and may overlap. Determinations of half-cystine and methionine are complicated by the possibility of oxidation.

Amir et al repeated the analyses at different times of hydrolysis from 16 hours. They reported extensive losses in amino acid recoveries during prolonged hydrolysis and corrected for these by extrapolation. Hartree observed no such losses when hydrolyses were performed for longer periods of time.

With these comments in mind the results for human FSH may be compared. In Table 2 are results obtained by Gray (unpublished), Amir et al (3), Reichert et al (4), Roos (5). Gray's figures are based on analyses of a new preparation of FSH obtained from the cellosolve material of Butt et al (6) by several successive chromatographic passages through DEAE "Sephadex A-50". The first column shows results from a 12-hour hydrolysis and the figures in brackets refer to a 36-hour hydrolysis. Again the figures are corrected to lysine = 10. Fairly good agreement is obtained for about half of the amino acids, namely, proline, isoleucine, leucine, tyrosine, phenylalanine, lysine, histidine and arginine. These are the same amino acids for which agreement was observed in the LH analyses in Table 1. Gray's figures, in brackets, suggest that for these amino acids there is no great loss with time of hydrolysis. There is also good agreement for threonine. In this case also the 36-hour hydrolysis showed that there was little unusual loss with time. Discrepancies exist for aspartic acid, serine, glutamic acid, glycine and alanine. These are amino acids which were discrepant in the LH analyses and they are clearly also subject to considerable unusual losses on prolonged hydrolysis. Some measure of agreement may be seen for methionine and half-cystine which appear to be present in small quantities.

The differences between the various amino acid analyses reported for different preparations of human FSH are clearly very similar to the differences observed in the analyses of the same preparations of human LH. They are apparently due to losses during hydrolysis or to differences in experimental technique, or to both these factors. Gray suggests, therefore, that the different preparations of human FSH which these results represent may in fact be very similar, at least in amino acid content, and that the apparent differences may be interpreted as being due to technical problems. Gray also suggests that these technical problems arise from the fact that the analyses are of glycoproteins rather than of proteins and that the losses of amino acids may be due to reactions with sugar residues - a common reason for unsatisfactory amino acid recoveries.

The differences in potency of the preparations of FSH are interesting. One possible explanation lies in differences in carbohydrates. It has been shown previously that loss of N-acetyl neuraminic acid (NANA) is related to loss of biological activity. It is easily cleaved off in acid and by certain bacteria at room temperature. Roos (5) found 7 per cent NANA in his preparation which

Table 2.

Amino acid composition of human FSH[*]

Amino acid	Gray (unpub)	Amir et al (3)	Reichert et al (4)	Roos (5)
Asp	20 (7)	20	15	12
Thr	17 (16)	17	19	16
Ser	28 (20)	34	13	12
Glu	19 (8)	23	19	16
Gly	25 (16)	27	13	9
Ala	14 (7)	17	12	9
Val	9 (N.D.)	19	12	11
Half-Cys	5 (N.D.)	3	5	8
Met	2 (N.D.)	< 1	2	2
Pro	10 (-)	8	12	10
Ile	5 (8)	7	5	6
Leu	11 (10)	12	12	7
Tyr	5 (6)	7	3	8
Phe	7 (7)	8	7	6
Lys	10 (10)	10	10	10
His	6 (5)	5	5	5
Arg	6 (7)	6	7	7
Trp	N.D.	3	N.D.	3

[*]Adjusted to Lysine = 10; N.D. = not determined; Figures in brackets refer to 36 hr. hydrolysis.

had a potency of 14,000 IU/mg.   In this case the protein concentration was assessed by U.V. absorption.   Reichert et al (4) found 5.2 per cent in a preparation of potency 5,000 IU/mg.   Papkoff and Li (7) found 1.4 per cent with a
potency of 1,250 IU/mg.

        This work was supported by a grant made to Dr. A. C. Crooke by the
Medical Research Council of Great Britain.

                              REFERENCES

1. Gray, C. J., Nature, 216: 112, 1967.
2. Hartree, A. S., in Recent Research on Gonadotrophic Hormones.   Proc. 5th.
    Gonadotrophin Club Meeting, E. & S. Livingstone, Edinburgh, 1967, p. 131.
3. Amir, S. M., W. R. Butt, J. F. Jenkins and P. J. Somers, Biochim. biophys.
    aota, in press.
4. Reichert, L. E., Jr., R. H. Kathan and R. J. Ryan, Endocrinology 82: 109,
    1968.
5. Roos, P., Ph.D, Thesis, University of Uppsala, Almqvist and Wiksells, AB,
    1967.
6. Butt, W. R., A. C. Crooke and A. Wolf, in Gonadotrophins: Physicochemical
    and Immunological Properties, Ciba Foundation Study Group No. 22, J. & A.
    Churchill, London, 85, 1965.
7. Papkoff, H., L.-J. Mahlman and C. H. Li, Biochemistry, 6: 3976, 1967.

PURIFICATION AND PROPERTIES OF URINARY FOLLICLE- STIMULATING AND LUTEINIZING HORMONES

P. Donini, D. Puzzuoli, I. D'Alessio, G. Bergesi and S. Donini,

Research Laboratories, Instituto Farmacologico Serono, Rome (Italy)

INTRODUCTION

Highly purified preparations of follicle-stimulating hormone (FSH), luteinizing hormone (LH) and chorionic gonadotropin (HCG) were obtained. Some physical and chemical properties of these preparations are described.

MATERIALS AND METHODS

One batch of HMG (Pergonal, E134) was used as the starting material for the purification of FSH and LH. This material, prepared as described by Donini (1), was purified according to the method of Roos and Gemzell (2) to yield the precursor for further purification of FSH and LH. The immunochemical grade of HCG (12,000 IU/mg) was prepared from a commercial HCG (3400 IU/mg) by chromatography on a DEAE-C column, followed by gel filtration on Recychrom (LKB Instr., Stockholm, Sweden) packed with Sephadex G-100. The gel filtration was carried out according to the method of Donini et al (in press). The FSH activity was determined by the ovarian augmentation method of Steelman and Pohley (3). The luteinizing activity was estimated by the ovarian ascorbic acid depletion method of Parlow (4) and by radioimmunoassay, as described by Donini et al. (in press). The reference preparations used were the 2nd IRP-HMG and the 1st International Standard of HCG. The biological activities were expressed as international units (IU) of the 2nd IRP-HMG and of the 1st HCG. Statistical calculation was performed according to the method of Borth (5).

RESULTS

The flow sheet (Diagram 1) shows the purification of urinary FSH and LH.

It is of interest to point out the purity grade of the starting material (Pergonal), which had 82.7 IU of FSH and 58.3 IU of LH per mg. By each step of purification, the FSH activity was approximately doubled as compared to that of the precursor. We would like to emphasize that by using four steps of purification the FSH activity rose from 82.7 to 1,255 IU per mg. and the FSH/LH ratio rose from 1.4 to 392. The recovery of the FSH activity, obtained by the procedure described in Diagram 1, was 28.9%.

One of the most effective steps in the purification of luteinizing hormone was the chromatography on DEAE-Sephadex. This increased the LH activity from 263 to 807 IU per mg. The highly purified LH preparation obtained by the procedure described above was 20 times more active than the starting material and its FSH/LH ratio was lower than 0.0012.

Characterization of FSH and LH

Ultracentrifugation

The sedimentation pattern of the highly purified FSH showed a single symmetric peak following ultracentrifugation at 579.80 r.p.m. using a concentration of 0.6% in O.I M. phosphate buffer pH 6.5.

Electrophoretic Studies

Fig. 1 shows the disc electrophoresis of FSH and LH preparations at pH 8.3. The electrophoresis was carried out as described by Davies (6).

It is of interest to note that the FSH gives a single precipitin band, whereas with LH, which moves more slowly through the gel, at least two bands are visible.

Molecular Sieve Chromatography

The gel filtration on Sephadex G-100 was carried out as described by Andrews (7). Fig. 2 shows the elution pattern of FSH, LH and HCG preparations, as compared with the various purified proteins. The molecular weights calculated on the basis of this procedure were 61,660, 51,240 and 83,180, respectively.

Spectrophotometric Studies

The ultraviolet absorption spectra of FSH, LH and HCG dissolved in 0.01 M phosphate buffer pH 7.0 were determined in the range 240-310 mμ. The $A_{1cm}^{1\%}$ values (277 mμ) were 6.85, 9.02 and 3.75, respectively.

Carbohydrate Analysis

The sugars contained in the FSH, LH and HCG preparations were qualitatively identified by thin-layer chromatography on Alusil plates (silicagel aluminium oxide, 1:1). The chromatogram showed the presence of galactose, mannose and fucose. The carbohydrate components were quantitated and the results are illustrated in (Table 1).

It is of interest to point out that one of the main chemical differences between LH and HCG is the sialic acid content. This

finding probably explains the different electrophoretic mobility
of the two hormones.

In conclusion, it seems worthy of emphasis that, by using
the procedures reported in this study, it was possible to prepare
some of the most pure and active preparations of urinary follicle-
stimulating and luteinizing hormones.

REFERENCES

1. Donini, P., Monezemolo, R. and D. Puzzuoli, Acta. Endocr.
      45:321, 1964.
2. Roos, P. and C. A. Gemzell, Bioch. Bioph Acta. 93:217, 1964.
3. Steelman, S. L. and F. M. Pohley, Endocrinology 53:604, 1953.
4. Parlow, A. F. In A. Albert (ed.) "Human Pituitary Gonadotropins.
      A Workshop Conference" Publ. Charles Thomas, Springfield
      Ill., 1961, p. 196.
5. Borth, R., Diczfalusy, I. and H. D. Heinrichs, Arch Gynak
      188:377, 1957.
6. Davies, B. J., Ann N.Y. Acad. Sci. 121:404, 1964.
7. Andrews, P. Bioch. J. 96:595, 1965.
8. Winzler, R. J. In Glick, D. (ed.) "Methods of Bioch Analysis,
      Vol. II, Interscience Publishers, New York, 1955, p. 279.
9. Rondle, C.I.M. and W.T.G. Morgan,Biochem. J. 61:586, 1955.
10. Warren L., J. Biol. Chem. 234:1971, 1959.

Diagram 1

HMG (Pergonal, 82.7 IU of FSH and 58.3 IU of LH per mg)
5.46 g
Batchwise separation of FSH and LH on DEAE-C

FSH fraction (2.88 g; 133 IU-FSH/mg) DEAE-C column chromatography		LH fraction (1.74 g; 86 IU-LH/mg) Batchwise chromatography on CMC-70	
Eluted by borate-phosphate buffer pH 8.0 + 0.1 M NaCl (828 mg; 351 IU-FSH/mg) Gel filtration on Sephadex G-100	Other fractions with lower activity	Eluted by 0.005 M phosphate buffer pH 6 + 0.5 M NaCl (1.03 g; 102 IU-LH/mg) Gel filtration on Sephadex G-100	Impurities with lower activity
Symmetric part of the 2nd protein peak (323.7 mg; 692 IU-FSH/mg) Preparative disc electrophoresis	Other fractions with lower activity	First part of ascending limb of elution curve (240 mg; 263 IU/mg) DEAE-Sephadex chromatography	Impurities with lower activity
Part of 2nd protein peak Highly purified FSH 104.3 mg: 1255 IU-FSH/mg 3.2 IU-LH/mg	Other fractions with lower activity	Eluted by 0.002 M phosphate buffer pH 6.6 + 0.01 M NaCl (36.8 mg; 807 IU/mg) Gel filtration on Sephadex G-200	Impurities with lower activity
		Symmetric and sharp part of the first peak. Highly purified LH 20.4 mg; 1166 IU/mg	Fractions with lower activity

Purification of follicle-stimulating and luteinizing hormones from human menopausal gonadotropin. The biologic activities are expressed IU (2nd IRP-HMG).

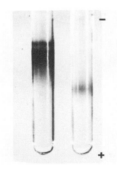

Fig. 1

Disc electrophoresis of FSH and LH preparations on 7.5% polyacrylamide gel using a 5 x 40 mm. column at 3 mamp/tube for 1 hr. Protein load was 10 μg.

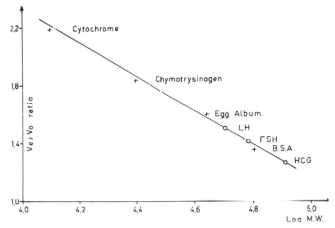

Molecular sieve chromatography on Sephadex G-100,
column 2 x 110 cm. Void volume Vo (Dextran Blue)=1170 ml
Buffer: 0.05 M Tris-HCL+ 0.1 M KCL, pH 7.5. The Ve/Vo
ratios of urinary FSH, LH, HCG and of various proteins
plotted against log of molecular weights.

Fig. 2

Gel filtration of FSH, LH and HCG preparations on a Sephadex G-100
column, according to the method of Andrews (7). 2 mg. of each
material in a 1 ml. total volume were applied to the 2 x 110 cm.
column. Flow rate 8 ml/hr., samples 2.3 ml/tube, spectrophotometric
reading at 230 mμ.

Table 1

Carbohydrate components of FSH, LH and HCG preparations.

	FSH	LH	HCG
	%*	%*	%*
Hexose [a]	10.4	8.9	9.5
Hexosamine [b]	9.6	6.5	8.9
Sialic acid [c]	3.6	1.8	9.0

a. Determined as described by Winzler (8)

b.   "   "   "   " Rondle and Morgan (9)

c.   "   "   "   " Warren (10)

* Calculated on the dry weight basis.

PURIFICATION OF RAT LH

DARRELL N. WARD, MAX AMOSS*, CAROLYN M. SWEENEY, WILEY VALE*,

JOHN W. KLEBER**, AND ROGER GUILLEMIN*

Department of Biochemistry, The University of Texas M. D. Anderson Hospital
and Tumor Institute at Houston, Houston, Texas; *Department of Physiology,
Baylor University College of Medicine, Houston, Texas; and **The Lilly
Research Laboratories, Eli Lilly Company, Indianapolis, Indiana.

INTRODUCTION

This report represents our studies on the application of the Koenig
and King (1) ethanol-acetate procedure to the fractionation of rat pituitary
glands for the isolation of rat luteinizing hormone (LH). As with our
studies on sheep, beef, and pork pituitaries (2), we have followed this with
a chromatographic separation on carboxymethyl cellulose and finally with gel
filtration on Sephadex G-100 to obtain an LH preparation with a potency
comparable to that obtained for bovine and ovine LH. The TSH potency of the
rat preparations exceeds by approximately ten-fold that found in bovine and
ovine preparations obtained by similar procedures. Attempts to remove the
TSH activity have so far been unsuccessful.

EXPERIMENTAL

Rat pituitary glands were obtained immediately after sacrifice of the
animals. Rats utilized for the collection of pituitary glands were either
discarded stock from a commercial breeder (Cheek-Jones Laboratory Animals,
Houston, Texas) or animals utilized in testing procedures not thought to
affect pituitary hormone levels (Eli Lilly Co.). Pituitaries were frozen
on dry ice and lyophilized directly in approximately 1 gm batches.

Prior to extraction the dry pituitaries were homogenized in a 50 ml
stainless steel homogenizer (Omni-mix) using three to four short 30-45
second homogenizing periods. If the charge of lyophilized glands does not
exceed 3 gm, a fine, evenly distributed particle size is obtained.

The resulting powder was extracted twice with 120 ml per 10 g dry
pituitaries for approximately 24 hr in the cold with stirring using the
pH 4.5 or pH 5.0, 40% ethanol, 0.5 μ acetate buffer of Koenig and King (1).
After each extraction the suspension was centrifuged at 14,000 rpm in a
Servall RC-2 refrigerated centrifuge. The clear supernate was decanted and
adjusted to 80% ethanol keeping the temperature below 5° C. A flocculent
precipitate, the gonadotropin fraction, was collected after 24 hrs settling
in the cold room. This was designated G-1 or G-2 according to the extraction
(first or second). The residue (R) after the second extraction was suspended
in a small volume of water and dialyzed to remove salts and ethanol, then
lyophilized.

Supernates from the G-1 and G-2 precipitates were decanted, combined,
and adjusted to 30% acetone in the cold. After standing in the cold 2 days

the precipitate was collected, dialyzed, and lyophilized and labeled fraction P. Fractions R and P were set aside for later studies. All further studies reported here were conducted on the combined G-1 and G-2 fractions.

After collection of the G fractions each was thoroughly dialyzed against distilled water to remove traces of salts. This step is important since the subsequent chromatography is begun in a very low ionic strength buffer.

Chromatography was done using 1 x 3.5 cm columns of cellulose CM-32 previously equilibrated with 0.005 M phosphate buffer, pH 6.0. Combined fractions G-1 and G-2 (200-350 mg) were dissolved in 20 ml of starting buffer. Insoluble material was removed by centrifugation, and lyophilized. The clear solution was then applied to the column at a flow rate of 20 ml/hr. The column was then developed with stepwise elution using 0.01M phosphate buffer, pH 7.0; 0.04M borate buffer, pH 8.2; and 0.04M borate buffer, pH 8.2, plus 0.2M NaCl, as described previously (3).

The LH fraction from the CM-32 chromatography was dissolved in 2.4 ml of 0.04 M borate buffer, pH 8.2, plus 0.1M NaCl. This same buffer was used to develop a Sephadex G-100 column 140 x 1.5 cm. Insoluble material, if any, was removed by centrifugation, 40 mg of sucrose then added to the sample and the sample layered under buffer on the top of the Sephadex column. The chromatogram was developed at a flow rate of 17 ml/hr. Column effluents were monitored by absorption at 275 mμ with a Gilford spectrophotometer, Model 240.

A diethylaminoethyl cellulose (DE-32) column was used in an attempt to resolve LH and thyroid stimulating hormone (TSH). This column (0.5 x 10 cm) was equilibrated with 0.005M N-2-hydroxyethylpiperazine-N'-2-ethane-sulfonic acid (HEPES). Subsequent development was with 0.1M-HEPES plus 0.1M NaCl and 0.1M HEPES plus 0.2M NaCl.

Samples for bioassay were weighed on a Cahn electrobalance. Bioassay of LH was by the Parlow ovarian ascorbic acid depletion method (4) as employed in this laboratory (5). Bioassay for TSH activity was by a modified McKenzie assay (6). Bioassay data were processed by an IBM 7094 computer with the EXBIOL program of Sakiz (7).

RESULTS

Table 1 summarizes data for four fractionations by the Koenig and King procedure. Runs I and II utilized pH 4.5 extraction reported by Koenig and King (1) to be most effective with frozen pituitaries, and Runs III and IV employed a pH 5.0 extraction, reported (1) to be most effective for acetone powder or lyophilized pituitaries of sheep. Although the weight of G-fraction in Run I and II was greater than in Runs III and IV, the LH activity was more comparable (62 units, Run I; 78 units, Run III, calculated per 10 g pituitaries).

Material from Run I and III was compared for chromatographic behavior on CM-32. A typical chromatogram is shown in Figure 1.

TABLE I

RECOVERY OF MATERIAL AFTER APPLICATION OF THE KOENIG AND KING FRACTIONATION

PROCEDURE TO RAT PITUITARY GLANDS

Description of Fraction	Run Nos.							
	I			II	III			IV
	mg	LH U/mg	TSH U/mg	mg	mg	LH U/mg	TSH U/mg	
Starting Pituitary (dry)	8,800			7,490	10,000			10,000
R	8,320			6,980	8,030			8,080
G1	409	0.12	0.21	294	199	0.38	0.34	230
G2	57	0.10	0.12		30			27
P	291			255	78			66

Runs I and II were done with the pH 4.5 ethanol-acetate extraction,
Runs III and IV were done with pH 5.0 ethanol-acetate.

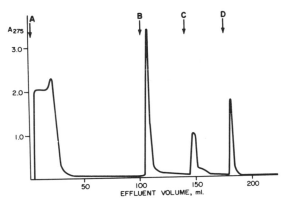

Figure 1: Chromatogram of 225 mg of fraction G on carboxymethylcellulose (CM-32). A,B,C,D, designate buffer application in sequence described in text. Column: 1 x 3.5 cm, flow rate 21 ml/hr. Peaks were labeled according to the buffer used for elution. Other data, Run III, Table 2.

GONADOTROPINS 1968

TABLE 2

WEIGHT RECOVERY AFTER CM-32 CHROMATOGRAPHY OF FRACTION G

Description	Run Nos.			
	I		III	
	mg	LH U/mg	mg	LH U/mg
Starting Weight (G1 + G2)	342.0		225.0	
Insoluble Residue	161.3		65.6	
A	88.7		70.1	
B	38.1		11.3	
C	2.9		3.3	
D	11.9	1.29 {(0.73) (2.50)	17.0	0.92 {(0.54) (1.52)

Run I, from pH 4.5 extraction, contained more material insoluble in the pH 6.0 buffer for chromatography than Run III, from a pH 5.0 extraction. Values in parentheses are the 95% confidence limits on the bioassay.

The results are summarized in Table 2. The yield of approximately 1 unit/mg LH was 37% and 21% of the theoretical based on potencies of the starting material (Table 1). The remaining activity could not be accounted for in the other fractions. These losses are far greater than we have experienced with other species of pituitary glands (2) using this general procedure. However, we usually are able to handle much larger quantities in each experiment. We have previously reported that the ratio of ion exchange material to protein load is an important factor in recovery (2) and for this reason our columns were made small, but perhaps not small enough. The yield of LH was surprisingly small compared to our experience with other species of LH. Nevertheless, the LH actually isolated at this stage of purification is approximately equipotent to sheep or beef LH at this same stage of purification.

The LH obtained from several carboxymethylcellulose chromatograms was pooled for chromatography on Sephadex G-100. In Figure 2 is shown a chromatogram of 35 mg of rat LH of approximately 1 unit per mg potency.

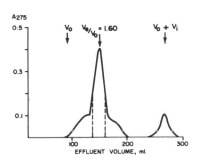

Figure 2: Chromatography of 35 mg of rat LH from carboxymethylcellulose (Fraction D, Fig. 1) on Sephadex
G-100. Column: 1.5 x 140 cm., flow rate 17 ml/hr.
Buffer: 0.04M-borate, pH 8.2, plus 0.1M-NaCl. V_0
determined with Blue Dextran, $V_0 + V_i$ with DNP-
aspartic acid.

The V_e/V_0 ratio observed for the rat LH was 1.6. Using a different column,
Dr. Kleber at Eli Lilly Laboratories has obtained a V_e/V_0 ratio of 1.63.
This value is significantly lower than the 1.71-1.75 ratios we have observed
for beef, sheep, and pork LH (2). Our V_e/V_0 values for beef, sheep and pork
LH are in agreement with those obtained by Reichert and Jiang (8) for these
same species even though they used a different buffer and temperature for
their chromatograms. Recovery of LH activity from this chromatogram
(Figure 2) was approximately 90% and in this respect is more in accord with
our experience with other species (2).

As shown in Figure 2 we took a 20 ml cut and recovered 14.1 mg of LH.
This preparation is designated DNW 8-37B. In a subsequent chromatogram
using 14.8 mg of approximately 1 unit per mg LH from carboxymethylcellulose
chromatography, a wider cut (25 ml) was employed. In this instance, 10.6
mg were recovered (designated DNW 8-39B) accounting for all the original
activity. However, the wider cut gave a preparation with a significantly
lower potency, as can be seen from Table 3.

Although the LH potency of the material after Sephadex is comparable
to that of beef and sheep LH at this same stage the TSH activity in the rat
LH preparations has assayed 6 to 11 units/mg. This is 10 to 20 times
greater than has been obtained for beef or sheep LH preparations. We have
been able to detect only one component in the rat LH preparation after
electrophoresis at pH 4.4 on Millipore Phoroslides using several concentrations of LH, but this could simply reflect inability to resolve TSH and LH
under these conditions.

In unpublished studies of D. N. Ward, W. J. Schindler, and J. D.
Mayfield it had been found that, while the conditions of Condliffe and
Bates (9) will separate small quantities of LH from TSH on DEAE-cellulose
at pH 9.5, large quantities of sheep, beef, or pork LH containing little

GONADOTROPINS 1968

TABLE 3

BIOASSAY OF RAT LH BY THE PARLOW OAAD METHOD

Preparation	Assay Design	λ	Potency Relative to NIH-LH-S11
DNW 8-37B	4-point	0.26	2.99 (1.72-5.58)
	6-point	0.15	2.22 (1.70-2.88)
			Avg. 2.60
DNW 8-39B	4-point	0.26	1.19 (0.62-2.12)
	6-point	0.15	1.45 (1.10-1.86)
			Avg. 1.32

Values in parentheses are the 95% confidence limits on the bioassay.

TSH are not separated to a significant degree. Instead of LH coming through the column unadsorbed the LH carries TSH off and in turn portions of LH are eluted with the buffers Condliffe and Bates used to remove TSH. In an attempt to circumvent this difficulty, the chromatogram shown in Figure 3 was run. Here we attempted to conduct the chromatography at pH 7.70 where LH would have essentially zero net charge and TSH a net negative charge which would allow it to be retained by the DE-32 ion exchanger.

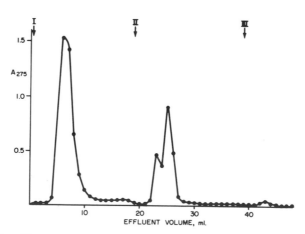

Figure 3: Chromatogram of 13.9 mg of rat LH from Sephadex G-100 chromatography (Fig. 2) on diethylaminoethyl cellulose (DE-32). Column: 0.5 x 10 cm., flow rate 6 ml/hr. Buffers applied at arrows are described in text.

Although our bioassays are as yet preliminary it is already apparent that we failed to achieve our objective. The peak eluted in the first buffer (0.005M-HEPES, pH 7.70) contained most of the LH activity as well as the TSH activity. The forward portion of the peak eluted by buffer II (0.1M-HEPES, pH 7.70, plus 0.1M-NaCl) contained LH activity, but low specific activity and the second portion of this peak was inactive. Only very low levels of TSH activity are present in the peaks eluted by buffer II. The material eluted by buffer III was insignificant and inactive.

ACKNOWLEDGEMENTS

This study was supported in part by research grants from the Institute for Arthritis and Metabolic Diseases, USPHS, (AM-09801 and AM-08290) and The Robert A. Welch Foundation (G-147).

REFERENCES

(1) Koenig, V. L., and E. King. Arch. Biochem. 26, 219, 1950.
(2) Ward, D. N., M. Adams-Mayne, N. Ray, D. E. Balke, J. Coffey, and M. Showalter. Gen. Comp. Endocrinol. 8, 44, 1967.
(3) Ward, D. N., M. Adams-Mayne, and J. Wade. Acta endocrinol. 36, 73, 1961.
(4) Parlow, A. in Human Pituitary Gonadotropins, A. Albert (ed.) p. 300, C. C. Thomas, Springfield, Ill. 1961.
(5) Sakiz, E., and R. Guillemin. Endocrinol. 72, 804, 1963.
(6) Sakiz, E., and R. Guillemin. Proc. Soc. Exp. Biol. Med. 115, 856, 1964.
(7) Sakiz, E. Proc. 2nd Internatl. Cong. Endocrinol., London. Vol. I, p. 225, Aug. 1964.
(8) Reichert, L. E., and N. S. Jiang. Endocrinol. 77, 78, 1965.
(9) Condliffe, P. C., and R. W. Bates. Arch. Biochem. Biophys. 68, 229, 1957.

DISCUSSION

STEVENS: I will make only a very brief comment about our efforts to purify LH from urinary sources. We have followed similar procedures to those discussed by Dr. Donini, using a much smaller supply of material. We obtained a preparation following preparative polyacrylamide gel electrophoresis which had approximately 50% of the potency of Dr. Donini's preparation using the OAAD assay. I would like to make one comment regarding the electrophoresis pattern which we obtained at this last step of purification. This is of interest in relation to what Dr. Donini has shown us with his disc analytical electrophoresis pattern. LH activity was distributed over a wide area of the electrophoresis pattern and, although the most potent fraction was concentrated in one area, there were other fractions of nearly the same potency in other parts of the electrophoresis pattern. I would like to hear comments from others concerning the electrophoretic mobility of LH and the experience they have had.

RAO: Dr. Donini, it was of interest to note that you have observed that urinary LH and HCG elute out from the Sephadex column at different times. Immunologically, both these gonado-tropins cross react and they also exhibit a similar biological activity by the ovarian hyperemia, ventral prostate and OAAD tests. Would your results then suggest that urinary LH and HCG are greatly different in their biochemical nature?

DONINI: I think you want to know if there is a correlation between the chemical composition of LH and HCG and their immuno-logical properties. I do not know, but I would say that some physicochemical differences exist between LH and HCG, i.e. sialic acid content and mobility in gel filtration on Sephadex columns.

RYAN: I should like to comment and ask two questions. Dr. Ann Hartree and I, independently, reported in Liege last month (Protein and Polypeptide Hormones, M. Margoulies, Ed., Excerpta Med. Fdnt., Amsterdam, 1968) on the dissociation of human LH using different techniques. Dr. Hartree used acid conditions. I dissociated LH in 2 ways: (1) with 4 M guanidine incubation and (2) by using I^{131} labelled LH at conditions approaching infinite dilution. Our data agreed quite well with that reported by Dr. Reichert. The Stokes radii of the 2 species of LH were calculated to be 28Å and 22Å. I have also studied the sedimen-tation constant of LH in acid and neutral buffers (J. Clin. Endocr. Metab. 28:886, 1968). At a neutral pH, a corrected sedimentation constant of 2.23 S was found, while under acid conditions the value was 1.57 S. From these Stokes radii and sedimentation constants, molecular weights were calculated for these two species of LH. The molecular weight for the larger species is 28,000 and for the smaller species is 14,400. Within the range of experimental error these values fit a monomer-dimer relationship. I have also studied the dissociation of human FSH. In 4 M guanidine, at room temperature for 5 hours, it dissociates into 2 species, the larger having a Stokes radii of approximately 32.5Å, the smaller being approximately 23Å. Thus far, only a single species has been found during ultracentrifugation and that had a corrected sedimentation constant of 3.1A, a value similar to that reported by Roos, (Gonadotropins, G. E. W. Wolstenholme and J. Knight, Ed., Little, Brown & Co., Boston, 1965), but greater than that found by Dr. Saxena. I am puzzled about what Dr. Bettendorf has said concerning the behavior of LH and FSH during gel filtration since I have consistently found that the FSH emerges from the column as a larger species than the LH. I understood him, perhaps incorrectly, to state that the LH was emerging as a bigger species than the FSH.

BETTENDORF: You have understood me correctly. In our experi-ments with gel filtration on Sephadex G 100 the LH emerges from the column as a larger species than the FSH. We have observed this pattern of separation with HHG (E_3) (FSH/LH ratio 0.8) and also with LH (N_4) (FSH/LH ratio 0.08).[3] We used 0.005 M phosphate buffer of pH 7.0. Using Sephadex G 25, G 50, and G 75 no separation of FSH from LH was seen.

LUNENFELD: When we started to perform amino acid analyses of gonadotropic preparations we observed that some of the discrepancies seen between laboratories might be due to the method of hydrolysis used. We now make a habit of running the analysis under various conditions, namely following various periods of hydrolysis of the native protein, after oxidation, and in the presence of phenol. By these means we have some control over what is happening, and also over some of the technical problems in amino acid analyses.

CROOKE: I am interested in what Dr. Lunenfeld has done. It is rather similar to our own work and I should like to see the results of his analyses. Our carbohydrate chemists insist that techniques which are suitable for the analysis of proteins may be unsuitable for glycoproteins because some sugars react with certain amino acids during hydrolysis giving false results. They therefore analyze hydrolysates after different times of hydrolysis and extrapolate the results. When there is disagreement between the results obtained by different workers the higher figures are more likely to be correct.

STEVENS: I would like to direct a question to Dr. Bettendorf. During his presentation in the use of LKB electrofocusing apparatus he indicated that he applied 35 milligrams of protein to a column with 200 pH intervals from pH 3 to 10. I should like to know whether his distribution of isoelectric points, finding that he had both FSH and LH together in the same fraction, could have been due to the load which he applied to the column. Could his apparatus discriminate proteins at this load or was he observing the mixing of one or more components?

BETTENDORF: We applied 35.6 mg. of E_3 to the electrofocusing column. I do not know if this amount was too high but we watched very carefully the column during this experiment and could not detect any precipitation. When the power was turned off the column was immediately emptied. We shall have to perform the same type of experiment with different amounts of HHG, recycling the three fractions in the same system, before we can form any definite conclusions. It was surprising, however, to find the same distribution pattern of FSH and LH activity using different separation techniques and various preparations.

PARLOW: I should like to call attention if I may to Dr. Donini's presentation. Let me refer back to what urinary LH actually represented in the old days of LH purification. It appeared that the best urinary preparations were about 50 to 100 times less potent than highly purified pituitary LH, leading to the conclusion that urinary LH was therefore a metabolic degradation

product of pituitary LH. If I remember Dr. Donini's data
correctly he has achieved purification of urinary LH to a point
where it is nearly one half as potent as the best preparation
of pituitary LH. Does this in any way revise our view of what
urinary LH represents? Does the difference between urinary LH
and pituitary LH merely depend on the fact that there is so
much less in the urine than in the pituitary on a concentration
basis resulting in the difficulties which we all have experienced
in purifying urine? I wonder if Dr. Donini wants to expand on
this point.

DONINI: Dr. Parlow, during our purification of urinary LH it
was possible to find one tube, corresponding to the first protein
peak obtained by gel filtration on Sephadex G-200, in which the
potency was 2,500 IU/mg. as measured by radioimmunoassay. This
preparation is not pure as shown by disc electrophoresis but I
think it is possible to prepare urinary LH with a potency similar
to that available using pituitary LH.

REICHERT: We have been able to show differences between human
pituitary and urinary LH by means of enzymic digestion. For
example, the pancreatic endopeptidase chymotrypsin markedly
inactivates human pituitary luteinizing hormone, but does not
inactivate human urinary luteinizing hormone. It is also interesting to note that chymotrypsin does not completely destroy
human pituitary LH activity, that is, some ovarian ascorbic acid
depleting activity always remains.

RYAN: Dr. Crooke, you commented earlier on the effects of various
times of hydrolysis on the amino acid composition of hFSH and
you quoted data published by Reichert, Kathan and I (Endocrinology
82, 109, 1968) concerning the amino acid composition of our hFSH
preparations. Our report presented data for 16, 24, 40, 48 and
66 hour hydrolysates. When you made your comparisons, did you
use our data from the point of view of optimum time of hydrolysis,
or did you use the averages of the 40 and 48 hour hydrolysates
that we calculated? Did it make a significant difference?

CROOKE: I am afraid I cannot answer your question without
reference to Dr. Gray who prepared our tables. The differences
in biological activity between preparations made by different
workers may be due to differences in their carbohydrate content
as much as in their amino acid content. For example, N-acetyl
neuraminic acid which is fundamental for the biological activity
of FSH is easily hydrolysed in mild acids or by certain bacteria
at room temperature. It is interesting that the neuraminic acid
content of FSH reported by different workers has varied greatly
and we have found wide variation between our own highly purified
preparations, those with high neuraminic acid having biological
activities of the order to 3,000 IU per mg. and those with low
neuraminic acid having much lower activity.

REICHERT: Dr. Donini, do LH and HCG cross react immunologically; do these preparations have similar biological activities, and why do they have different dilution profiles with Sephadex G-100?

DONINI: I would like to make clear that in the gel filtration on Sephadex G-100 performed according to the method of Andrews we used highly purified preparations of urinary LH and HCG. Under these experimental conditions HCG was eluted first and LH later. I would say that several factors such as molecular weight, electric charge and molecular structure could influence the mobility of these proteins through the Sephadex column.

FAIMAN: Dr. Donini, I should like to ask whether the assay values for LH were obtained solely by radioimmunoassay or also by bioassay? When the best pituitary preparations of LH are assayed biologically against the 2nd IRP, they have a potency of approximately 2,000 to 3,000 IU/mg. However, when they are assayed radioimmunologically, they have a potency of approximately 8,000 to 12,000 IU/mg., due to the fact that the hormone in urinary extracts is immunologically deficient, as Ryan and I pointed out a year or so ago (Proc. Soc. Exp. Biol. and Med. <u>125</u>, 1130, 1968). Therefore, your urinary preparations of 1,000 to 2,500 IU/mg. would be approximately half as potent as pure pituitary LH, if the assay values were biologically determined, but only one-tenth as potent if the assays were done radioimmunologically.

DONINI: Our LH preparation was assayed both by radioimmunoassay and by bioassay (OAAD) using the 2nd IRP as the standard in both radioimmunoassay and bioassay.

ALBERT: I would like to ask Dr. Donini about the losses encountered in preparing urinary LH and FSH with the reported activity of 1,000 IU per mg.

DONINI: The recovery of FSH activity in our first preparation was about 30%; if we refer to the activity of the starting material used for the further purification it was only 16% calculating the recovery from the biological activity of fraction A obtained from menopausal urine by the kaolin-acetone procedure.

REICHERT: I would like to comment briefly on our own experiences in the purification of rat pituitary gonadotropins. The studies to be described were carried out in collaboration with Drs. Gay, Bogdanove and Midgley. 685 mg. of acetone-dried whole rat pituitary glands were extracted with water at pH 5.5 to yield an FSH-rich extract, and the residue was re-extracted with 0.1M ammonium sulfate, pH 4.0, to give an extract rich in LH. Our studies on the purification of rat LH have not proceeded as far as those just described by Dr. Ward. Our final product had a potency of only 0.6 NIH-LH-Sl units/mg. However, this fraction did prove of sufficient purity to permit its use in the radioimmunoassay of rat LH. The pH 5.5 soluble FSH-rich extract was brought to 2.0M ammonium sulfate, pH 5.7 to remove inert protein, and the FSH was precipitated at 3.2M ammonium sulfate, pH 5.5. This precipitate was not dialyzed, but reconstituted in a minimum amount of 0.05M ammonium bicarbonate buffer, pH 8.0, and simultaneously desalted and further fractionated by gel filtration through a column of Sephadex G-100. The area of the ultraviolet elution profile having FSH activity was located by scanning bioassays, and the tubes in this area were pooled, diluted with distilled water to reduce the ionic strength, and then further purified by ion-exchange chromatography on DEAE-cellulose in 0.007M phosphate- 0.003M borate buffer at pH 8.0. The FSH was eluted from the column between 0.05M NaCl in buffer and 0.10M NaCl in buffer. The specific activity of the FSH prepared in this fashion was about 40 NIH-FSH-Sl units/mg. The LH contamination was 0.002 NIH-LH-Sl units/mg. (OAAD assay) for an FSH/LH ratio of 20,000. In further studies, 293 pituitaries, taken from castrated animals which had been treated with testosterone propionate and thyroglobulin to suppress pituitary TSH and LH content, were similarly fractionated. The final product had an FSH potency of about 70 NIH-FSH-Sl units/mg. Noteworthy, however, was the low level of LH contamination. LH activity could not be detected even by radioimmunoassay, and was estimated to be less than 0.00043 NIH-LH-Sl units/mg, for an FSH/LH ratio of greater than 160,000. This preparation is apparently heterogeneous as determined by polyacrylamide gel electrophoresis, but has proved useful in the development of a radioimmunoassay for this hormone.

WARD: Why was the TSH so high in the present study, and why were we able to obtain considerably lower levels in the collaborative study with Dr. Parlow (which unfortunately has not been published yet)? We believe that the considerable losses of LH activity that we have found in the CM 32 and DE 32 chromatography employed in the present studies result from a very high capacity for protein and therefore, apparently, a much higher density of charge groups on the microgranular ion exchangers. Accordingly, we speculate that the LH from rat pituitaries dissociates somewhat more easily into its different subunits — more readily than in the case of the other species we have tried. In so doing it partially separates into subunits and is thereby inactivated during the chromatography on these particular ion exchangers. The chromatography which we ran earlier with Dr. Parlow was with a much lower capacity (or rather charge density) ion exchangers. In that case, apparently, it did not cause this type of inactivation. Along with this we postulate that TSH does not dissociate and, therefore, stays with the remaining LH fraction. TSH thus is obtained in better relative yield in this fraction with the conditions we have described in our present report.

RYAN: I would like to make a comment concerning a point that Dr. Ward raised. There might very well be differences between species as to the ease with which protein hormones associate and dissociate. De la Llosa and Jutisz (Proteins and Polypeptide

Hormones, M. Margoulies, Ed., Excerpta Med. Fdnt., Amsterdam, 1968) reported that ovine LH could be dissociated with 2 M guanidine and a 2 hour incubation at room temperature, to the extent that 90% appeared as the smaller species. I tried these conditions with human LH and found that only about 10% appeared as the smaller species. However, if 4 M guanidine and 5 hours incubation were used, 90% of the human LH dissociated to the smaller species. Dr. Hartree has pointed out that the acid dissociation of the human LH requires a lower pH than the acid dissociation of the ovine hormone.

STEVENS; I would like to direct a question to Dr. Ward and ask for clarification of his comment regarding the losses of LH on the CMC column. I interpret his comments to mean that he has lost LH activity and I would like to extend that question to ask if he has lost solids or whether he has recovered most of the solids that lost activity?

WARD: The weight recovery was of the order of 80% or better. The LH activity losses were considerably greater than the weight losses.

CHAPTER 2

BIOLOGY OF GONADOTROPINS

1. BIOLOGIC ASSAY OF PITUITARY AND URINARY
   GONADOTROPINS

COMPARATIVE BIOASSAY OF LUTEINIZING HORMONES BY THREE METHODS

ALBERT F. PARLOW, DEPARTMENT OF OBSTETRICS AND GYNECOLOGY
UCLA SCHOOL OF MEDICINE, HARBOR GENERAL HOSPITAL CAMPUS
TORRANCE, CALIFORNIA

INTRODUCTION

In previous reports we have observed that (1) the slope of the dose-response curve for LH in the hypophysectomized rat prostate assay may differ
depending on the species source of the LH, (2) the circulatory half-time
(T $_{1/2}$) of exogenously administered LH in the rat may differ according to the
species source of the LH, (3) these previous two observations may be causally
related. The present study is an attempt to examine in detail the influence
of species differences on the estimation of biological potency of LH by three
methods of assay, the ventral prostate method (VP), the quantitative ovarian
hyperemia method of Ellis (OH), and the ovarian ascorbic acid depletion method
(OAAD). A brief description of each of these methods is listed in Table No. 1.
The reference preparations used were NIH-LH-S1 (sheep LH) and Pergonal-24, obtained from human post-menopausal urine. Pergonal-24 was used in lieu of the
International Reference Preparation for Human Menopausal Gonadotrophins (IRP-
HMG), because of the toxicity the latter preparation exhibited on intravenous
injection into rats. This toxicity influenced both the slope and the potency
of LH in the OAAD bioassay. Each of the potency estimates listed in this report represents the mean of a minimum of two replicate determinations. In all
assays, partially purified preparations of LH from various sources were tested,
except where otherwise noted.

Table No. 1

Bioassay Methods

Ventral Prostate (VP)
    48 hours post-hypophysectomy, LH, injected BID x 4 days,
    sacrifice 5th day.

Ovarian Hyperemia (OH)
    LH injected I.V. followed, 2 hours later, by R.I.S.A.*
    After 15 minutes, ovaries excised.
        *Radio-iodinated serum albumin.
Ovarian Ascorbic Acid Depletion (OAAD)
    LH injected I.V., ovaries excised four hours later.
    Rats used on 6-9 days of "Pseudopregnancy".

Reference Preparations
    NIH-LH-S1 (sheep pituitary)
    Pergonal-24 (human post-menopausal urine)

RESULTS

Table No. 2 presents the results of testing a HCG preparation in terms of five reference preparations, from five different sources. The relative potencies of two HCG preparations, obtained by the VP and the OAAD methods, were in excellent agreement. The index of discrimination (I. of D.) for the VP/OAAD comparison was 1.0. The relative potencies of HCG and LH from four different sources were always higher in the VP assay than in the OAAD assay. The index of discrimination (I. of D.) for the VP/OAAD comparisons ranged from 2.2 to 46.6. The I. of D. for the one VP/OH comparison (Table No. 2) also was considerably greater than unity.

Table No. 2

Potency of 1st International Standard for HCG (HCG-I.S.-1) in terms of (ito) a commercial HCG prep., sheep LH (NIH-LH-S1), simian LH (S-LH-1), equine LH (E-LH-1) and human pituitary LH (H-LH-1).

	NO. OF ASSAYS	MEAN POTENCY		I. OF D. VP/OA	VP/OH	OH/OA
(HCG-1 ito HCG-I.S.-1)						
VP	1	2905	I.U./mg	1.0		
OAAD	2	2966				
(HCG-I.S.-1 ito NIH-LH-S1)						
VP	4	42.40	µg/I.U.	46.6	9.8	4.7
OH	6	4.31	µg/I.U.			
OAAD	31	0.91	µg/I.U.			
(HCG-I.S.-1 ito S-LH-1)						
VP	3	66.4	µg/I.U.	7.9		
OAAD	3	8.4	µg/I.U.			
(HCG-I.S.-1 ito E-LH-1)						
VP	5	47.8	µg/I.U.	5.0		
OAAD	4	9.5	µg/I.U.			
(HCG-I.S.-1 ito H-LH-1)						
VP	6	30.2	µg/I.U.	2.2		
OAAD	7	13.8	µg/I.U.			

The relative potency of two equine LH preparations (E-LH-1 and E-LH-2) in the VP, the OH, and the OAAD bioassays were in excellent agreement (Table No. 3), even despite the fact that preparation E-LH-2 had a ten times higher concentration of FSH than E-LH-1. However the relative potencies of equine LH and either sheep LH or simian LH or HCG were significantly different when measured by the VP and the OAAD methods, the I. of D. ranging from 0.2 to 9.1. Similarly the index of discrimination for the OH/OAAD comparison was significantly greater than unity for the relative potency of equine LH and sheep LH

(Table No. 3). However the I. of D. for the VP/OH comparison of the relative potency of equine and sheep LH did not depart significantly from unity.

Table No. 3 also lists the approximate values for the circulatory half-time ($T_{1/2}$) of various LH preparations, in the rat, following a single intravenous administration. Comparison of the values for the $T_{1/2}$ with the I. of D. for the VP/OAAD comparison suggests that there may be a degree of correlation between these two parameters.

Table No. 3

Potency of equine LH (E-LH-1) in terms of (ito) equine LH (E-LH-2), sheep LH (NIH-LH-S1), simian LH (S-LH-1) and HCG (HCG-I.S.-1).

	NO. OF ASSAYS	MEAN POTENCY	I. OF D. VP/OA	VP/OH	OH/OA	$T_{1/2}$, min.
(E-LH-1 ito E-LH-2)						270 equine
VP	2	1.0	0.9	0.8	1.2	
OH	3	1.3				
OAAD	3	1.1				
(E-LH-1 ito NIH-LH-S1)						15 ovine
VP	4	0.82	9.1	1.3	6.9	
OH	3	0.62				
OAAD	12	0.09				
(E-LH-2 ito NIH-LH-S1)						15 ovine
VP	2	0.64	6.7	1.4	5.0	
OH	3	0.47				
OAAD	4	0.095				
(E-LH-1 ito S-LH-S1)						50 simian
VP	4	1.5	1.7			
OAAD	5	0.9				
(E-LH-1 ito HCG-I.S.-1)						294 HCG
VP	5	21 I.U./mg.	0.2			
OAAD	4	105				

Comparative studies of the relative potency of LH's, similar to those performed for HCG (Table No. 2) and equine LH (Table No. 3), have been extended to LH's from 7 different sources. A summary of the mean index of discrimination for all VP/OAAD comparisons is presented in Table No. 4. Note that the I. of D. fails to depart from unity only in three instances: 1) where two LH preparations from the same source are compared; 2) where rat and human LH's are compared; 3) where human pituitary LH and human urinary LH are compared. In all other comparisons, the I. of D. was significantly different from unity.

Comparison of the magnitude of departure from unity of the I. of D. for a particular comparison and the value for the T 1/2 for the LH's compared suggests a degree of correlation between these two parameters.

Table No. 4

Comparison of the relative potencies of luteinizing hormones from seven different sources, as determined by the VP and OAAD assays, with the circulatory half-time for these LH's.

$T_{1/2}$, min.		OVINE	RAT	SIMIAN	EQUINE	HUMAN PITUITARY	HUMAN URINARY	HCG
				VP/OAAD				
15	OVINE	1.0	0.05	0.16	0.11	0.05	0.05	0.02
17–30	RAT	21.0	1.0			0.6	0.8	
50	SIMIAN	6.3			0.6	0.22	0.25	0.13
270	EQUINE	8.9		1.7	1.1	0.4	0.5	0.20
65	HUMAN PITUITARY	19.7	1.6	4.0	2.0	1.0	0.9	0.31
65	HUMAN URINARY	22.0		4.0	2.0	1.1		0.5
294	HCG	47.0		7.9	5.0	2.9	2.0	1.0

The fact that the I. of D. departed from unity for those VP/OAAD comparisons which involved LH from different species sources, which have differing T 1/2 values in the rat (Tables 3 and 4), was utilized to differentiate among LH's from still other species sources for which only limited numbers of pituitaries were available. In these latter cases, extraction of sufficient LH to permit determination of the T 1/2 value was not possible. Therefore, bioassay of such unextracted pituitaries (saline homogenates) by the VP and OAAD methods, in terms of both sheep LH (NIH-LH-S1), which has a rapid T 1/2 and human LH (Pergonal-24), which has a slow T 1/2, was undertaken. The results are listed in Table No. 5.

Three apparently distinct families of species were discerned. In the case of mouse, rabbit and dog pituitaries, the I. of D. for VP/OAAD comparisons in terms of NIH-LH-S1 departed widely from unity, whereas in terms of Pergonal-24, the I. of D. was not significantly different from 1.0. On the other hand the VP/OAAD comparison in terms of Pergonal-24 was significantly different from 1.0 for cat, whale, elephant, and goat pituitaries, whereas the I. of D. in terms of NIH-LH-S1 was close to (but not identical with) 1.0. Kangaroo pituitary homogenate appeared to constitute a special class in that the I. of D. for the VP/OAAD comparison was different from unity in terms of both NIH-LH-S1 and Pergonal-24.

Table No. 5

The index of discrimination (VP/OAAD) for pituitary homogenates from seven different species, tested in terms of NIH-LH-S1 and Pergonal-24.

Unextracted Pituitaries

Species	I. of D. VP/OAAD ito NIH-LH-S1 (Ovine) (Rapid T 1/2)	I. of D. VP/OAAD ito Pergonal-24 (Slow T 1/2)
Mouse	21.6	0.8
Rabbit	15.0	0.5
Dog	22.0	1.1
Cat	2.6	0.10
Whale	2.4	0.10
Elephant	2.5	0.08
Goat	2.0	0.04
Kangaroo	5.4	0.34

As viewed in Table No. 6, the I. of D. for VP/OAAD comparisons, in terms of both NIH-LH-S1 and Pergonal-24, in the case of homogenates of cat, whale, elephant, and goat pituitaries are very similar to the corresponding I. of D. for partially purified ovine LH. From these data it is possible to conclude that the T $_{1/2}$ values for cat, whale, elephant, and goat LH, like the T $_{1/2}$ of ovine LH, are probably "rapid".

As viewed in Table No. 6 the I. of D. for VP/OAAD comparisons, in terms of NIH-LH-S1 and Pergonal-24, in the case of homogenates of mouse, rabbit, and dog pituitaries, are similar to the corresponding I. of D. for partially puri- fied preparations of human LH and HCG. From these data it is possible to con- clude that the T $_{1/2}$ values for mouse, rabbit, and dog LH, like those for human LH and HCG, are "slow".

Similarities among the I. of D. for kangaroo pituitary homogenates and those for partially purified equine and simian LH are also evident. It may be concluded that the T $_{1/2}$ for LH from these three sources are similar.

Table No. 6

Comparison of the I. of D., VP/OAAD, for certain partially purified LH's and certain pituitary homogenates.

VP/OAAD

	ito NIH-LH-S1 (Rapid T 1/2)	ito Pergonal-24 (Slow T 1/2)	T 1/2
Ovine LH	1.0	0.05	Rapid
Cat pit.	2.6	0.10	
Whale	2.4	0.10	
Elephant	2.5	0.08	
Goat	2.0	0.04	
Human LH	20.0	0.9	Slow
HCG	47.0	2.0	
Mouse pit.	21.6	0.8	
Rabbit	15.0	0.5	
Dog	22.0	1.1	
Equine LH	9.0	0.5	Slow
Simian	6.0	0.25	
Kangaroo pit.	5.4	0.34	

For all those cases in which the I. of D. for VP/OAAD comparisons, in terms of NIH-LH-S1, is significantly greater than 1.0, the I. of D. is greater than 1.0 also for OH/OAAD comparisons, with one notable exception:- RAT L.H. (Table 7). Thus, the I. of D. for VP/OAAD comparison (rat LH in terms of NIH-LH-S1) is 21.0. However, the I. of D. for the Ovarian Hyperemia/OAAD comparison (rat LH in terms of NIH-LH-S1) is 1.4. We have concluded, from these data, that the T 1/2 of rat LH in the rat is neither "slow" nor "rapid", but, instead, "intermediate". Thus the biologic nature and duration of the ventral prostate assay permits expression of the slight difference in T 1/2 between rat and sheep LH, whereas the nature and duration of the ovarian hyperemia assay does not permit expression of the difference in T 1/2 between rat LH and sheep LH.

Table No. 7

Comparison of the Index of Discrimination VP/OAAD and OH/OAAD, in terms of NIH-LH-S1, for LH from seven different sources.

INDEX OF DISCRIMINATION

| | VP/OA | | OH/OA | |
	ito (NIH-LH-S-1)	ito (PERGONAL-24)	ito (NIH-LH-S-1)	T 1/2
Ovine	1	0.05	1.0	Rapid
Rat	21	0.8	1.4	Intermediate
Human Pituitary	20	0.9	3.4	Slow
Human Urinary	22	1.0	4.2	
HCG	47	2.0	10.0	
Equine	9	0.5	7.0	
Simian	6	0.25	3.3	

It is concluded that the apparent circulatory half time of luteinizing hormones may influence:

1. "Potency" in three bio-assay systems.

It is suggested that the apparent circulatory half time of luteinizing hormones may influence:

2. The efficacy of L.H. as an "augmenter" of FSH-stimulated ovarian weight increment.

3. The efficacy of L.H. as a stimulator of estrogen secretion in intact rats.

4. The efficacy of L.H. as a stimulator of ovulation.

Acknowledgement

This study was supported by N.I.H. Grant No. AM 11214.

DISCUSSION

ROSEMBERG: When dealing with the problems of gonadotropin standards, we shall refer to the index of discrimination, as it relates to the use of various human pituitary or urinary standards compared with the use of gonadotropin standards prepared from other species. I was glad to learn that Dr. Parlow has confirmed our data regarding the numerical value of the index of discrimination when urinary extracts, or when human pituitary LH are tested against an ovine standard such as NIH-LH-Sl using two assay methods, that is the VPW and the OAAD. I was also glad to learn that Dr. Parlow acknowledges the fact that the various assay methods may have different physiological connotations. In the case of the VPW assay we agree that this assay represents a chronic growth response. Dr. Parlow mentioned that the ovarian hyperemia is a rapid, 2-hour assay. It is worth remembering that the OAAD assay is also an acute biochemical response. This may explain some of the discrepancies.

PARLOW: The OAAD is an acute biochemical response and should perhaps be distinguished from the ovarian hyperemia assay. If I did imply that the OAAD is free from influence of circulatory half-life this is not so. We now have data indicating that the OAAD is susceptible to the influence of the circulatory half-life of LH. For example, if one tests the potency of HLH against ovine LH in the OAAD assay using the 2 hour intravenous injection and the 4 hour intravenous injection, different potency estimations are obtained. The HLH has a slow half-life and ovine LH standard has a rapid half-life. The same is true for PMS i.e. all three of these LH's which have slow half-lifes when tested against ovine LH yield the highest potency estimates 4 hours after the intravenous injection. Therefore, we cannot any longer say that the OAAD, being an acute biochemical response, is free from the influence of the circulatory half-life of the LH injected into the test rat. We would rather say that the OAAD assay is less susceptible to the influence of circulatory half-life than is the ovine hyperemia assay and the prostate assay.

JOHNSEN: In our department, Peter Christiansen (Acta Endocrinol. 56, 608-618, 1967) has shown that in the ventral prostate assay method it is not possible to compare human gonadotropins (such as the 2nd IRP) with ovine material (such as NIH-LH-Sl). He analyzed the complete dose-response curves and showed that the slopes are entirely different for these two materials. Dr. Parlow, if you perform a 2 by 2 assay and if the assay shows large variations, it may be that some blind statistics will show no significant deviation from parallelism. But still the assay is completely meaningless. Therefore, how could you possibly apply statistics to these data?

PARLOW: The assays were bad enough in the case of ovine LH in the VPW assay. There is statistically no apparent significant departure from parallelism between the two substances utilizing a 2 x 2 design. But I could not agree more with Dr. Johnsen in stating that the slopes for human and ovine LH are indeed different. We published this in 1963 and wholeheartedly agree with these views that ovine LH cannot be used as a reference preparation for the bioassays of human LH in the ventral prostate assay.

ODELL: I would like to raise a speculative question on the data that Dr. Parlow has presented. Firstly, one tissue presumably responds to a hormone and another tissue does not because the former has specific receptors binding the hormone which allow the tissue to react. Secondly, reliable data are available for some steroid hormones showing that the duration of action of the hormones has little relation to the half-life of the steroid in the circulation. About 10 years ago, Dr. Hyde showed that after a single intravenous injection of cortisol the metabolic effects of the hormone were present 8 hours later, the cortisol having long since disappeared. More recently, Dr. Jensen has shown that after an intravenous injection of labeled estradiol, the uterus, a responsive tissue, is still concentrating the hormone long after it has almost disappeared from the blood. Therefore, while circulation times in Dr. Parlow's data are correlated with the index of discrimination, I wonder if the final deciding factor might not be one of three things: the relative affinity between two different species for the receptor of the responsive organ; the duration of survival of that hormone on the receptor, or the duration of the effect of the hormone on the tissue after it is bound to the receptor. These three factors could be completely unrelated to survival of the compound in the blood.

PARLOW: I agree with Dr. Odell. I thank him for raising these other possibilities which may in fact function in addition to the circulatory half-life as factors in determining the biological potency of LH.

LUNENFELD: Actually I would like to stress what Dr. Johnsen has said. I challenge the validity of all the nice work that Dr. Parlow has presented because I think we cannot assay one preparation against the other, and on the basis of kinetics it is practically invalid to come to conclusions about potency ratios.

PARLOW: Dr. Lunenfeld, I agree with you, it is biologically invalid. However, assays being as inprecise as they are, it is nevertheless statistically valid and one can therefore extrapolate some numbers with which one can then work.

JOHNSEN: No.

REICHERT: Dr. Parlow, were the data you presented obtained using the quantitative hyperemia assay of Ellis?

PARLOW: It was.

REICHERT: How many microcuries of radio-iodinated serum albumin did you inject per rat?

PARLOW: I do not recall. The experiments were done about 5 years ago.

REICHERT: How did you treat the ovaries before counting them?

PARLOW: They were dipped in NaOH.

REICHERT: We have measured the activity of pituitary LH from a number of sources in terms of NIH-LH-S1, using the hyperemia and ovarian ascorbic acid depletion assays. Ovine, bovine and porcine LH gave the same potency estimate in each assay. Equine LH gave a potency estimate in the hyperemia assay which was 2.4 times higher than that obtained in the OAAD assay. Human pituitary and urinary LH gave potency estimates in the hyperemia assay which were from 4 to 6 times higher than those obtained using the OAAD assay. Human LH has a considerably longer half-life than ovine LH (NIH-LH-S1). The end point of the OAAD assay as we use it is 4 hours, and the end point of the hyperemia assay is 2 hours. If differences in biological half-life played a signigicant part in our results, we should have seen, if anything, a higher potency estimate in the OAAD assays (4 hour end-point) than in the hyperemia assay (2 hour end-point). I think these results cast doubt on differences in biological half-life being the sole explanation for the variations in potency estimates obtained when, for example, one assays human LH in terms of the ovine NIH-LH-S1 standard in the OAAD and ventral prostate assays.

PARLOW: I agree with Dr. Reichert, however, I disagree with his conclusions. It is true that when testing HLH in terms of ovine LH by the hyperemia or OAAD assays an index of discrimination of 4 to 6 is obtained. The reason for this is that there are factors other than simply the circulatory half-life; it is the circulatory half time in relation to the dynamics of the response metameter.

REICHERT: Nevertheless, the results show that a significantly greater potency estimate was obtained when human LH was assayed in terms of the ovine NIH-LH-S1 standard using the 2 hour hyperemia assay than with the 4 hour OAAD assay. Also, the results you described are amazingly similar to those we obtained during the course of unpublished collaborative studies some time ago. Were the hyperemia assays conducted in your own laboratory?

PARLOW: With respect to the relationship between a half-life and the response in assays systems: LH has short half time. All of the LH's listed from rat to simian show an index of discrimination which is quite large, departing significantly from unity; of course NIH-LH-S1 in terms of itself shows an index of discrimination of unity. The circulatory half-life of

human pituitary LH, HCG, equine and simian LH are all in the
order of 50 minutes or longer; the circulatory half-life of rat
LH is significantly shorter, 17 to 30 minutes for exogenously
administered rat LH. Note that in the case of the prostate
assay, a 4-day assay, the rat LH circulatory half-life is long
enough to produce an index of discrimination greater than unity.
However, in the case of ovarian hyperemia assay the index of
discrimination OH/OAAD, for rat LH is 1.4. It does not depart
significantly from unity unlike that for human pituitary LH,
urinary LH, HCG and simian LH. In other words, the interplay
between half-lives and the nature of the response metameters is
a very subtle one indeed and the dynamics of the response
metameters are in fact quite important for the full expression
of the circulatory half-time of the LH in question.

ALBERT: When you say kangaroo LH, do you mean that or do you
mean a pituitary homogenate?

PARLOW: It was a pituitary homogenate. In the case of the LH's
which were available in large quantities we can in fact determine
the circulatory half-life as well as the index of discrimination.
We are interested in extending this on many species. We cannot
obtain the pituitaries of many other species in large quantities
and therefore resort to using the index of discrimination in
terms of LH-S1 which has a rapid half-life, the index of
discrimination in terms of Pergonal 24 which has a slow half-
life and noting a difference between them in relation to the
other known LH's for an assessment of the question whether they
have a long, rapid or slow half-time. So in the case of kangaroo pituitary we did in fact use a pituitary homogenate although
I may add that we now have sufficient kangaroo pituitary to
verify these following extraction of the pituitary by determining
the circulatory half-life of the exogenously administered kangaroo LH. They are quite interesting in that they suggest that
there are differences among LH's of various species and maybe a
whole family of LH's and that those differences may in fact
reflect a basic difference in the structure of LH from species
to species.

STUDIES CONCERNING THE STABILITY OF HUMAN PITUITARY AND PLACENTAL GONADOTROPINS

Janet W. McArthur, M.D., Department of Obstetrics and
Gynecology, Harvard Medical School

That the gonadotropic hormones tend to be relatively heat-stable in the dry form and heat-labile in solution has long been known (1-4). However, the practical utility of this generalization has diminished as species differences in the susceptibility of gonadotropins to inactivation by heat and other agents have come to light (5-9). In the course of measuring the residual gonadotropic activity of human plasma fractions which had been pasteurized by the method officially prescribed for the destruction of hepatitis virus in human serum albumin (10) (11), we became aware of the paucity of information concerning the stability of human gonadotropic hormone preparations. We have therefore examined the effects of heating and of mechanical agitation upon various gonadotropic hormones, together with the influence exerted by albumin, a substance thought to increase the stability of gonadotropins.

METHODS AND MATERIALS

The different human gonadotropic preparations which were studied are listed below, together with their respective biologic potencies:

TABLE I

GONADOTROPIC PREPARATIONS EMPLOYED IN STABILITY STUDIES

(a) Human chorionic gonadotropin

HCG-SC-1   3000 IU/mgm.

(b) Human pituitary gonadotropins

	FSH potency IU/mgm.	LH potency IU/mgm.
LH-H$_{55}$ Ab	75	200
HS-168 A	150	150
HS-155 B	160	160

(c) Human menopausal urinary gonadotropin

Pergonal 28 E54C	56	48

The biologic potency expressed in international units per milligram of five gonadotropic preparations of placental, pituitary and urinary origin.

The gonadotropins were placed in a Dubnoff metabolic shaking incubator and subjected to: (a) heating and shaking in a 0.15 M NaHCO$_3$ buffer solution at a pH of 8.3 and temperature of 60 $\pm$ 1° C. for 10 hours, (b) mechanical agitation in the same solution for 10 hours at room temperature, or (c) identical treatments in the buffer solution, to which had been added human serum albumin in quantities sufficient to yield concentrations of 1,3 or 7%.

The treated preparations were assayed against untreated gonado-tropins for FSH by the HCG-augmented rat ovarian weight method of Steelman and Pohley (12) and for LH and HCG by the hypophysectomized rat ventral prostate weight method of Greep (13), according to modifications which have been previously described (14). Four-point designs were employed except in those instances where all but the highest of a series of doses of a preparation exhibited complete inactivation, when a 1 + 2 design was substituted. Standard statistical methods were employed to determine assay validity, to calculate the relative potency and 95 % fiducial limits, and to obtain weighted mean potency estimates. Only assays conforming to the recognized validity criteria have been incorporated in the results.

RESULTS

The effects of heating and shaking gonadotropins dissolved in various solutions are shown below:

TABLE II

EFFECT OF HEATING PLUS MECHANICAL AGITATION UPON GONADOTROPINS DISSOLVED IN VARIOUS SOLUTIONS

0.15 M NaHCO$_3$ buffer	Buffer + 1% human serum albumin	Buffer + 3% human serum albumin	Buffer + 7% human serum albumin
I. Chorionic gonadotropin			
0.12 (0.10-0.15)	0.28 (0.21-0.37)	0.30 (0.23-0.39)	0.44 (0.35-0.54)
II. Pituitary gonadotropin			
(a) FSH activity			
0.62 (0.46-0.84)	0.93 (0.70-1.31)	1.22 (0.90-1.77)	1.02 (0.76-1.15)
(b) LH activity			
0.12 (0.08-0.17)	0.15 (0.10-0.20)	0.14 (0.09-0.19)	0.38 (0.27-0.53)
III. Urinary gonadotropin			
(a) FSH activity			
0.77 (0.57-1.035)	0.76 (0.61-0.98)	0.67 (0.53-0.85)	0.59 (0.47-0.75)
(b) LH activity			
*	*	*	*

*Complete destruction

The potency of gonadotropins dissolved in various solutions and subjected to heating plus shaking, relative to that of untreated preparations.

It can be seen that heating plus mechanical agitation resulted in a marked loss of HCG and LH activity, but in relatively good preservation of FSH activity. Heating in solutions which contained increasing concentrations of albumin appeared to preserve the FSH activity of pituitary gonadotropin, but to exert no effect upon the FSH activity of urinary gonadotropin. The LH and HCG activities of solutions containing albumin were appreciably greater than those of solutions consisting only of buffer except in the case of urinary LH, the activity of which was completely destroyed in all of the solutions tested.

The effects of mechanical agitation at room temperature are summarized below:

TABLE III

EFFECT OF MECHANICAL AGITATION AT ROOM TEMPERATURE UPON GONADOTROPINS DISSOLVED IN VARIOUS SOLUTIONS

0.15 M NaHCO$_3$ buffer	Buffer + 1% human serum albumin	Buffer + 3% human serum albumin	Buffer + 7% human serum albumin
		I. Chorionic gonadotropin	
0.55 (0.44-0.70)	2.34 (1.62-3.46)	2.74 (1.94-4.03)	2.53 (1.79-3.68)
		II. Pituitary gonadotropin	
		(a) FSH activity	
1.05 (0.82-1.35)	- - -	- - -	- - -
		(b) LH activity	
0.94 (0.76-1.16)	- - -	- - -	- - -
		III. Urinary gonadotropin	
		(a) FSH activity	
1.15 (0.96-1.38)	- - -	- - -	- - -
		(b) LH activity	
0.86 (0.60-1.23)	- - -	- - -	- - -

The potency of gonadotropins dissolved in various solutions and subjected to mechanical agitation at room temperature, relative to that of untreated preparations.

- - -

It will be noted that the gonadotropic activity of HCG was materially reduced, whereas that of the pituitary and urinary gonadotropins was unaffected. The addition of albumin, even in low concentration, to solutions of chorionic gonadotropin appeared not only to preserve, but to enhance, its gonadotropic activity.

To distinguish the protection against in vitro inactivation of gonadotropins afforded by the addition of albumin from augmentation of residual
activity, a number of control experiments were performed. The potency of
untreated chorionic and menopausal urinary gonadotropins dissolved in various
concentrations of albumin relative to their potency in buffer was first
determined. The results were then compared with the potencies of gonadotropin
solutions to which albumin had been added either before or after: (a)
mechanical agitation alone, or (b) heating plus shaking. The outcome of these
experiments is set out for each gonadotropin separately.

Below are shown the results obtained with chorionic gonadotropin:

TABLE IV

EFFECT ON GONADOTROPIC POTENCY OF ADDING SERUM ALBUMIN TO: (A) UNTREATED HCG SOLUTIONS AND (B) HCG SOLUTIONS
BEFORE OR AFTER VARIOUS TREATMENTS

Treatment	Potency in buffer	Time of addition of albumin	Concentration of human serum albumin 1%	3%	7%
None	1.00	- - - -	2.61 (1.85-3.82)	4.38 (3.09-6.30)	3.83 (2.64-5.50)
Shaking at room temperature	1.00 0.55 (0.44-0.70)	Before shaking After shaking	2.34 (1.62-3.46) 0.65 (0.39-1.09)	2.74 (1.94-4.03) 1.46 (0.89-2.48)	2.53 (1.79-3.68) 1.14 (0.69-1.89)
Heating and shaking	1.00 0.12 (0.10-0.15)	Before h. and s. After h. and s.	0.28 (0.21-0.37) 0.10 (0.07-0.15)	0.30 (0.23-0.39) 0.10 (0.07-0.15)	0.44 (0.35-0.54) 0.09 (0.06-0.13)

The potency of: (a) untreated HCG solutions to which albumin has
been added, and (b) HCG solutions to which albumin has been added either
before or after various treatments, relative to that of HCG dissolved in
buffer.

It can be seen that the addition of albumin to buffered solutions of HCG
appreciably augmented its gonadotropic activity. This augmentative action
was only slightly diminished if the albumin was added before mechanical
agitation. If the addition of albumin was delayed until after shaking,
the residual activity was augmented to, but not beyond, pre-treatment
levels. In the case of heating, albumin appeared to exert a protective
rather than an augmentative action. The addition of albumin after HCG
activity had been reduced by heating and shaking did not enhance the
activity remaining in the treated solutions.

The influence of added albumin upon solutions of urinary gonadotropins is shown in the last table:

TABLE V

EFFECT UPON GONADOTROPIN POTENCY OF ADDING HUMAN SERUM ALBUMIN TO: (A) UNTREATED URINARY GONADOTROPIN SOLUTIONS
AND (B) URINARY GONADOTROPIN SOLUTIONS BEFORE OR AFTER VARIOUS TREATMENTS

Treatment	Potency in buffer	Time of addition of albumin	Concentration of human serum albumin		
			1%	3%	7%
(a) FSH potency					
None	1.00	- - - -	1.45 (1.08-2.00)	1.26 (0.90-1.68)	1.31 (0.95-1.77)
Shaking at room temperature	1.15 (0.90-1.38)	Before shaking	- - - -	- - - -	- - - -
		After shaking	- - - -	- - - -	- - - -
Heating and shaking	1.00 0.62 (0.49-0.79)	Before h. and s.	0.76 (0.61-0.98)	0.67 (0.53-0.85)	0.59 (0.47-0.74)
		After h. and s.	1.03 (0.67-1.60)	1.35 (0.78-2.29)	1.48 (0.87-2.56)
(b) LH potency					
None	1.00	- - - -	0.89 (0.61-1.26)	1.05 (0.74-1.52)	0.85 (0.57-1.19)
Shaking at room temperature	0.86 (0.60-1.23)	Before shaking	- - - -	- - - -	- - - -
		After shaking	- - - -	- - - -	- - - -
Heating and shaking	1.00 *	Before h. and s.	_____*	_____*	_____*
		After h. and s.	- - - -	- - - -	- - - -

*Complete destruction

The potency of: (a) untreated urinary gonadotropin solutions to which albumin has been added, and (b) urinary gonadotropin solutions to which albumin has been added either before or after various treatments, relative to that of urinary gonadotropin dissolved in buffer.

- - -

It will be noted that albumin exerted a barely appreciable augmentative action upon the FSH activity of untreated hormones in buffer solution and no effect upon their LH activity. If added before heating and shaking, albumin exerted no protective effect upon FSH activity. However, if added subsequently, it produced an apparent restoration of pre-treatment levels. No protective nor augmentative effects upon urinary LH could be demonstrated under the experimental conditions employed.

DISCUSSION

The observations concerning the vulnerability of solutions of chorionic gonadotropin to heat are in accord with the findings of Zondek and Aschheim (1) and of Parkes and Agnew (2) that HCG is injured by temperatures of 60° C. and destroyed by boiling. No data concerning the effects of heating at 60° upon human FSH and LH are available. Schmidt-Elmendorff et al (15) found that only 41% of the LH activity of Pergonal remained after incubation in water at 40° C. In the same laboratory, Visutakul et al (16) observed an inexplicable potentiation of the LH, but not of the FSH, activity of human menopausal gonadotropin incubated in phosphate buffer at 40° C. Borth et al (17) achieved complete inactivation of the LH activity of HMG by heating in borate buffer at 80° C., as measured by the ovarian hyperemia method; half of the original potency remained in an extract assayed by the mouse uterine weight method and may, in part, have reflected residual FSH activity.

The partial inactivation of human chorionic, but not of urinary gonadotropins of pituitary origin, by mechanical agitation for 12 hours is at variance with Maddock and Heller's finding (5) that neither is affected by shaking for 2.5 hours, a treatment which completely destroyed rat and sheep pituitary extracts. Inactivation by shaking involves the occurrence of surface denaturation, the function of shaking being to increase the formation of new surface. It is therefore not unlikely that protracted shaking might result in destruction not evident after brief agitation. Visutakul et al (16) observed marked inactivation of HCG by a phosphate buffer at 0° C., room temperature and at 40° C., another finding which indicates that the hormone is unstable in solution.

The augmentation of chorionic gonadotropin by human serum albumin contrasts with the minimal effect noted from the addition of albumin to solutions of urinary gonadotropin. Numerous studies attest the capacity of plasma proteins, egg albumin and casein to produce a barely detectable to a two-fold increase in the potency of rat, beef and sheep pituitary gonadotropins. Although these studies antedate the introduction of quantitative techniques for bio-assay, they enabled these weak augmentors to be distinguished from such strong augmentors as metallic compounds.

Because of interest in the determination of plasma HCG levels, considerable attention has been devoted to the influence of serum proteins upon the assay of HCG in different systems. Diczfalusy and Loraine (19), using a modification of the Greep assay, found no difference in the potency of HCG dissolved in saline, serum or plasma. There is no ready explanation for the discrepancy between the results of the present study and those of Diczfalusy and Loraine. Whether it is attributable to differences in the strains of animals employed or in the injection schedule cannot be detemined at present. Maddock et al (20), measuring the increase in uterine and ovarian weight of immature female rats, observed a 5-10 fold increase in the potency of HCG by the admixture of the hormone with human plasma.

The protective as well as augmentative action exerted by albumin upon heated solutions of HCG appears to be an instance of an in vitro gonadotropin-enhancing mechanism first delineated by Maddock and Heller (5). These workers distinguished "protectors" from: (a) synergists, themselves gonadotropic substances which exert their modifying influence at the end-organ, the gonad, and (b) augmentors, which exert their modifying influence by delaying the absorption of gonadotropin from the site of injection. Serum albumin was not among the materials tested in their study. However, whole blood and egg white were shown to act both as augmentors and protectors against inactivation from shaking at 37° C. and from storage at 3° C. It is likely that serum albumin exerts similar effects.

ACKNOWLEDGMENTS

Grateful acknowledgment is made of the skilled technical assistance of Miss Ruth F. Perley and Mrs. Susan Cargill. Thanks are also due to Dr. A.E. Wilhelmi for his gift of the pituitary gonadotropins studied, and to Dr. E.C. Reifenstein, Jr. for generous supplies of Follutein.

This study was supported, in part, by grants from the Barbara C. Willcox Fund, the Sprague Fund and USPHS Research Grant 04378-07 from the National Institute of Arthritis and Metabolic Diseases.

REFERENCES

(1) Zondek, B. and Aschheim, S. Klin. Wschr. 7: 831, 1928.
(2) Askew, F.A. and Parkes, A.S. Biochem. J. 27: 1495, 1933.
(3) Wallen-Lawrence, Z. and van Dyke, H.B. J. Pharm. Exp. Therap. 43: 93, 1931.
(4) Hill, R.T. J. Physiol. 83: 137, 1934.
(5) Maddock, W.O. and Heller, C.G. Endocrinol. 41: 177, 1947.
(6) McCann, S.M. Am. J. Physiol. 202: 395, 1962.
(7) Guillemin, R., Colonge, A., Jutisz, M. and Sakiz, E. C.R. Acad. de Sci. 254: 3258, 1962.
(8) Ramirez, V.D. and McCann, S.M. Am. J. Physiol. 207: 441, 1964.
(9) Adams-Mayne, M. and Ward, D.N. Endocrinol. 75: 333, 1964.
(10) Gellis, S.S., Neefe, J.R., Stokes, J. Jr., Strong, L.E., Janeway, C.A. and Scatchard, G. J. Clin. Investig. 27: 239, 1948.
(11) Minimum Requirements: Normal Serum Albumin (Human), National Institutes of Health, Bethesda, Md.
(12) Steelman, S.L. and Pohley, F.M. Endocrinol. 53: 604, 1953.
(13) Greep, R.O., van Dyke, H.B. and Chow, B.F. Proc. Soc. Exp. Biol. and Med. 46: 644, 1941.
(14) McArthur, J.W., Antoniades, H.N., Larsen, L.H., Pennell, R.B., Ingersoll, F.M. and Ulfelder, H. J.C.E.M. 24: 425, 1964.
(15) Schmidt-Elmendorff, H., Loraine, J.A. and Bell, E.T. J. Endocrinol. 24: 153, 1962.
(16) Visutakul, P., Bell, E.T., Loraine, J.A. and Fisher, R.B. J. Endocrinol. 36: 23, 1966.
(17) Borth, R., Linder, A. and Lunenfeld, B. Acta endocrinol. 31: 192, 1959.
(18) Ling, S.M. and Wu, H. Chinese J. Physiol. 1: 407, 1927.
(19) Diczfalusy, E. and Loraine, J.A. J.C.E. 15: 424, 1955.
(20) Maddock, W.O., Tokuyama, I. and Leach, R.B. Proc. Soc. Exp. Biol. and Med. 84: 352, 1953.

DISCUSSION

BORTH: I have some data which may complement the presentation of Dr. McArthur, and which were obtained in collaboration with Mrs. Annette Menzi when I was still in Geneva. In a factorial experiment comprising 120 bioassays, we have investigated the potency of the Second International Standard Preparation of HCG after freezing under four different conditions in five different diluents, using three methods of bioassay, and repeating each assay once. Samples were frozen at either -15°C or -72°C, and then either stored immediately at -15°C until assayed, or thawed and refrozen three times at intervals of two days before being stored. None of these four treatments affected the relative potency in terms of the 0.9% NaCl solution (frozen once) employed as the standard, irrespective of the diluent and end-point used. When the standard solution was assayed several months later against a fresh solution which had

never been frozen, the relative potency and its fiducial range
(P= 0.05) were 0.8 (0.5-1.2) in the OAAD test, 0.9 (0.7-1.2) in
the uterine weight test in mice, and 1.0 (0.6-1.6) in the ovarian
hyperemia test in rats. Strong **joint** effects (interactions)
were noted regarding the two factors "end-points" and "diluents"
(0.9% NaCl, distilled water, 0.1 M borate buffer, 1% bovine serum
albumin, and 0.5% gelatin). In the OAAD test, the potency was
increased 4-5 fold by the presence of gelatin, and 2-3 fold by
the presence of albumin. In the ovarian hyperemia test, the
borate buffer augmented the potency 2-3 fold. No effect of
diluent was observed in the uterine weight assay, and whenever
the factorial design called for an assay of the standard (0.9%
NaCl, frozen once) against itself, the relative potencies were
close to unity for all end-points. I think these findings, and
similar ones reported by others, result from the interplay of
two factors, one being the time changes in concentration of
hormone at the target site, the other the dependence of the
response on the dynamics of hormone supply. Little seems to be
known on either factor, although they are both clearly of some
significance with respect to the practice of bioassay, mechanisms
of action, and hormone administration for therapeutic purposes.
A more complete report of this investigation is being published
elsewhere.

MIDGLEY: I should like to ask Dr. McArthur what was the purity
of the albumin that she used? I raise this question because
recently in our laboratory we have found that Pentex fraction V
bovine albumin can contain a large amount of bovine LH as
estimated by radioimmunoassay. The amount of contamination
varies greatly from batch to batch and is also present, although
usually to a lesser degree, in crystalline bovine albumin. To
avoid this problem, we are now using a 1:10 dilution of filtered
egg white as a protein supplement in our diluents for radioimmunoassay. We have found that with the OO rat LH radioimmunoassay, tubes containing this dilution of egg white in phosphate
buffered saline contain the same amount of antibody bound radioactivity as protein-coated tubes containing only phosphate
buffered saline. All batches of bovine albumin tested to date
at a concentration of 1% have shown significant inhibition of
the OO rat LH radioimmunoassay.

MCARTHUR: The results of our plasma fractionation studies (J.
Clin. Endocr. 24: 425, 1964) alerted us to the possibility that
endogenous gonadotropins, especially FSH, might be attached to
human serum albumin. However, no contamination was detectable
by bioassay in the lot which we employed.

MIDGLEY: I would like to return to the last comment by Dr. Borth
to the effect that freezing and thawing did not appear to alter
the biological activity. This may be true, however, I would like
to raise a note of caution. Chilson et. al (Federation Proceedings 24: S55, 1965) have clearly shown that slow freezing and
slow thawing in the presence of phosphate and sodium ions can

lead to striking changes in physical-chemical properties.

BORTH: I would not dream of generalizing from our findings to other proteins and other diluents. I may add that the freezing at -15°C took 15 minutes, and the freezing at -72°C took about 20 seconds.

STUDIES ON UTERINE GROWTH IN IMMATURE MICE

E. TREVOR BELL, DEPARTMENT OF PHYSIOLOGY, UNIVERSITY OF MANCHESTER, MANCHESTER 13, ENGLAND *

INTRODUCTION

Many investigators have shown that the administration of gonadotrophic hormones to intact immature mice results in an increase in uterine weight. This procedure measures both follicle stimulating hormone (FSH) and luteinizing hormone (LH) and forms the basis of an assay method for "total gonadotrophic activity" (1). It is generally agreed that the action of gonadotrophins is to stimulate the secretion of ovarian steroids. This in turn results in an increase uterine weight. However, it has been demonstrated that the administration of purified FSH or LH does not evoke a uterine response at dose levels which could readily be measured in a specific assay system (2), (3).

The action of steroid hormones on the uterus has also been studied by many workers and it is well known that oestrogens are capable of stimulating uterine growth (4). However, little work has been conducted in which the effects of gonadotrophins and steroids have been compared under similar experimental conditions. The present study was undertaken in an attempt to mimic the action of gonadotrophins on the uterus by the administration of oestrogens either alone or in combination with progesterone or androgens. In addition, dose response curves for uterine weight were prepared using mouse and rat pituitary gonadotrophins in order to establish that the response to a human gonadotrophin (human chorionic gonadotrophin, HCG) was qualitatively similar. This paper presents the results obtained, a preliminary account of which has previously been given (5, 6).

MATERIALS AND METHODS

Immature female mice weighing 9 - 11 g at age 21 days, and produced in a Caeserean derived colony were obtained from Messrs. Schofield, Oldham. Dose response curves for uterine weight were prepared using a two-fold dose interval. The animals were injected s.c. once per day for three days; the total volume administered being 0.6 ml. On the fourth day the mice were killed and the uteri were cleaned and weighed. In the experiments involving HCG and oestradiol, the dry weight of the uterus was determined using the procedure described by Bell and Lunn (7). Five mice were employed at each dose level.

* Present address: Petfoods Limited, Melton Mowbray, Leicestershire.

HCG (Pregnyl; Organon) was administered in 0.9% sodium chloride. Oestradiol -17β (Sigma) was dissolved in 96% ethyl alcohol and the solution was diluted prior to injection to give a final concentration of 5% ethyl alcohol in 0.9% sodium chloride.   Progesterone, testosterone,   Δ⁴-androstenedione and androsterone (Sigma) were dissolved in propylene glycol, the resultant solution was diluted 1:1 with 0.9% sodium chloride before administration.   Mouse gonadotrophins were obtained from animals of the same age and weight as those employed in the preparation of the dose response curves.   Three groups each of 300 mice were killed by ether inhalation and the whole pituitary gland removed and placed in acetone.   The gonadotrophins were extracted from the dry acetone powder by suspending this in 0.9% sodium chloride for 72 hours at 5° C. prior to the assay.   No further purification was undertaken and the test preparation was administered in 0.9% sodium chloride.   Gonadotrophins were extracted from 190 adult rat pituitaries in a similar manner.

RESULTS

DOSE RESPONSE CURVES WITH HCG

The combined results of three identical experiments with HCG are presented in Fig. 1.   Each point represents data on 15 mice.   The maximum mean uterine weight of 60.1 mg was obtained with 4 iu HCG; with higher dose levels uterine weight fell, the values for 8, 16 and 32 iu being significantly lower than that for 4 iu (p < 0.05).   The slope (b) of the ascending portion of the total weight curve was 45.9 while the coefficient of variation of the whole curve was 32%.   The dry weight curve showed a pattern similar to that for the total weight of the uterus.

DOSE RESPONSE CURVES WITH MURINE GONADOTROPHINS

Two experiments were conducted using mouse pituitary acetone powder. The data obtained were combined and the results are shown in Fig. 2.   The slope of the dose response curve was 34.9 and the curve was parallel to that for HCG (8).   With the highest dose level tested (30 pituitaries) the uterine weight appeared to have reached a plateau.   The coefficient of variation of the results was 23%.   Fig. 3 shows results of three dose response curves prepared using rat pituitary gonadotrophins.   As in previous experiments the data have been combined.   The slope of the curve between 0.125 and 0.5 pituitaries was 39.9 and this was parallel to the slope of the HCG and mouse pituitary gonadotrophin curves.   It should be noted that the maximum uterine weight was obtained with 1.0 pituitaries, and in contradistinction to the results with HCG increasing dosage did not result in a decrease in uterine weight.   The coefficient of variation of the data was 25%.   However, it will be noted that the S.D. for 0.125 pituitaries was very large while at higher dose levels greater uniformity was observed.

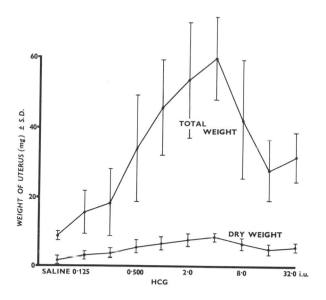

Figure 1

Dose response curve with HCG.   Mean total and dry mouse uterine
weight ± S.D.

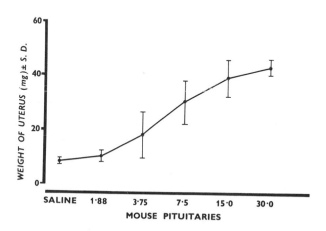

Figure 2

Dose response curve with mouse pituitary acetone powder.
Mean mouse uterine weight ± S.D.

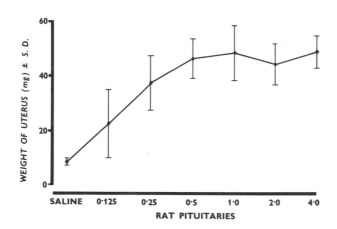

Figure 3

Dose response curve with rat pituitary acetone powder.
Mean uterine weight ± S.D.

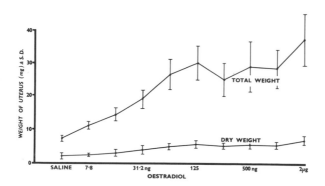

Figure 4

Dose response curve with oestradiol-17β.   Mean total and dry
mouse uterine weight ± S.D.

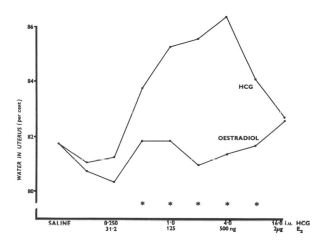

Figure 5

The effect of HCG and oestradiol on the water content of the
mouse uterus. * = significant difference between mean figures
(p< 0.05)

DOSE RESPONSE CURVES WITH STEROID HORMONES

Oestradiol was administered in dosages ranging from 7.8 ng to 2 μg
in three experiments, the results of which are shown in Fig. 4.   It will be
seen that between 7.8 and 125 ng there was a steady increase in the total
weight of the uterus.   Above this dose level the uterine weight fluctuated
but showed no decrease as was the case with HCG.   The coefficient of
variation of the total weight curve was 18% while the slope between 7.8 and
125 ug was 17.9.   The ascending portion of the oestradiol curve was not
parallel to that for HCG or the murine gonadotrophins.   Furthermore, the
maximum uterine weight obtained with oestradiol was some 20 mg less than that
for HCG.

It appeared possible that two hypotheses could account for the
disparity in the mean uterine weights obtained with oestradiol and HCG.
One was that gonadotrophin administration could have resulted in greater
imbibition of water than oestradiol.   The second depended on the fact that the
ovary secretes a variety of steroid hormones in addition to oestrogens.   For
this reason experiments were conducted in which progesterone or androgens
were added to oestradiol.

A comparison of the water content of the HCG and oestradiol treated
uteri presented in Figs. 1 and 4 is shown in Fig. 5.   It will be seen that
the water content of the HCG treated uteri was higher than with oestradiol.

However, the mean figures were significantly different only between 0.5
and 8.0 iu HCG (p< 0.05).   Over this dose range the gonadotrophin treated
uteri contained an average of 3% more water than did the uteri from the
oestrogen treated animals.   This difference can account for only 10% of the
disparity in the total weight curve at these dose levels.

Figs. 6 and 7 illustrate experiments undertaken to investigate the
effects of the administration of oestradiol together with progesterone or
androgens.   The androgens employed were testosterone, Δ^4-androstenedione
and androsterone.   The progesterone and androgens were given either alone
or in combination with two constant dosages of oestradiol and were administered each day for three days.   Fig. 6 shows that progesterone alone at
dose levels ranging from 0.33 to 333 μg had no effect on uterine weight,
while oestradiol at dosages of 25 and 250 ng produced the expected response.
Addition of progesterone to the low dose of oestradiol resulted in a
significant effect only with 333 μg when a decrease in uterine weight was
noted.   With 250 ng oestradiol, progesterone administration caused a
significant decrease in uterine weight at all dose levels.

The results obtained when Δ^4-androstenedione was added to oestradiol
are shown in Fig. 7.   It will be seen that when administered either alone or
together with oestradiol, Δ^4-androstenedione in dosages ranging from 0.33 to
333 μg produced no significant effect on uterine weight.   Similar results
were obtained with testosterone and androsterone.

DISCUSSION

The results obtained in the present study indicate that differing
patterns of uterine growth occur following the administration of HCG and
oestradiol to intact immature mice.   The data reported for HCG are very
similar to those of Bell and Easson (9) using animals of the same strain prior
to the establishment of a pathogen free colony.   Furthermore, the shape of
the gonadotrophin dose response curves compares favourably with results
obtained in the same mouse colony using pregnant mare's serum gonadotrophin
(PMSG) and human urinary gonadotrophins (10).   Lamond and Emmens (11) have
shown that following hypophysectomy the mouse uterine response to HCG and
PMSG is decreased.   They interpreted this as indicating the necessity for
the co-operation of endogenous hormones in the production of ovarian steroids.
Because of this observation the steroid hormones employed in the present study
were administered to intact rather than to ovariectomised animals.   Theoretically, this should ensure that the actions of endogenous hormones are similar
both in gonadotrophin and steroid treated mice.   However, with oestradiol the
effects of endogenous gonadotrophins and steroids appear to be of little
importance since dose response curves for uterine weight prepared both in
ovariectomised and intact mice were identical.

The results of the assays with rat and mouse pituitary gonadotrophins
confirm that the uterine response obtained with HCG is not an artefact
associated with the administration of a human gonadotrophin to a mouse.
Although the ascending portion of all the dose response curves was similar it
will be seen that high dose levels of the rat pituitary powder did not result
in a decrease in uterine weight.   Presumably this indicates that at such dose

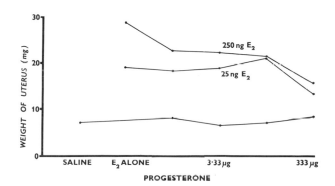

Figure 6

The effect of Progesterone alone (lowest line) or in combination
with oestradiol on mouse uterine weight.

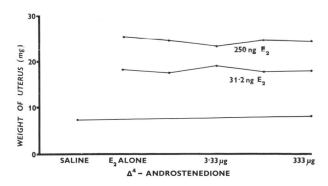

Figure 7

The effect of Δ^4-androstenedione alone (lowest line) or
in combination with oestradiol on mouse uterine weight.

levels the steroids secreted by the ovary following the administration of HCG and rat pituitary gonadotrophin are qualitatively different.

The data presented in Fig.5 indicate that the disparity between the dose response curves for HCG and oestradiol cannot be accounted for on the basis of variations in the water content of the uterus. Gross examination of the uteri reveals that following HCG and oestradiol administration more intraluminal fluid is present with the former. Such fluid is however expressed prior to weighing and therefore does not influence the weight of the uterus. In the experiments in which oestradiol was administered together with progesterone or androgens no _increase_ in uterine weight was observed. Progesterone generally caused a decrease in weight and this finding is in agreement with that of other investigators (4). It should be emphasised that the effect of progesterone cannot be attributed to the toxicity of the propylene glycol; since in control experiments propylene glycol did not influence uterine or body weight. The absence of an anabolic action of the androgenic hormones may be a reflection of the schedule of administration. It could be argued that the oestradiol should initially be given alone prior to the addition of the androgen. In this respect it is of interest that following the administration of testosterone to ovariecto-mised rats Korenchevsky et al. (12) were able to stimulate uterine growth. However, the weight of the uterus did not exceed that found in untreated intact animals.

The main conclusion which can be drawn from the results presented is that the mouse uterine response to HCG cannot readily be mimiced by the administration of oestradiol either alone or in combination with progesterone or androgens. The coefficient of variation of the steroid results was in general lower than that obtained following gonadotrophin administration. This is presumably associated with the direct action of steroids on the uterus as compared to the indirect effect of HCG acting via endogenous ovarian steroid production. Furthermore the possibility must be considered that the mouse ovary secretes a variety of oestrogenic hormones with varying degrees of biological activity. If this is so, an experiment in which only one oestrogen is used to stimulate uterine growth is relatively unlikely to mimic the combined effects of a variety of oestrogens secreted as the result of gonadotrophic stimulation of the ovary.

SUMMARY

Dose response curves for uterine weight in intact immature mice have been prepared following the administration of HCG, rat and mouse pituitary gonadotrophins, and oestradiol either alone or in combination with progester-one and androgens.

The slope of the HCG and oestradiol curves has been shown to be dissimilar. This disparity cannot be accounted for on the basis of the water content of the uterus or by the administration of combinations of oestradiol with progesterone or androgens.

It is concluded that the uterine response to gonadotrophins cannot readily be mimiced by the administration of steroid hormones.

ACKNOWLEDGMENTS

The skilled technical assistance of Miss Lena Teare was much appreciated.

REFERENCES

1.   Loraine, J.A., and E.T. Bell, Hormone Assays and their Clinical Application, E. & S. Livingstone Co., Edinburgh, 1966.

2.   Donini, P. In Bell, E.T., and J.A. Loraine, (eds.), Recent Research on Gonadotrophic Hormones, E. & S. Livingstone Co., Edinburgh, 1967. p.25.

3.   Brown, P.S., and W.Z. Billewicz, J. Endocrinol. 24 : 65, 1962.

4.   Parkes, A.S., and R. Deanesly, in Parkes, A.S., (ed.), Physiology of Reproduction. Longmans, London. 1966, vol.3, p.570.

5.   Bell, E.T., J. Physiol. (London). In press.

6.   Bell, E.T., J. Endocrinol. In press.

7.   Bell, E.T., and S.F. Lunn, J. Reprod. Fertil. 12 : 453, 1966.

8.   Gaddum, J.H., J. Pharm. Pharmacol. 6 : 345, 1953.

9.   Bell, E.T., and D.W. Easson, J. Endocrinol. 37 : xxxviii, 1967.

10. Bell, E.T., Unpublished observations, 1968.

11. Lamond, D.R., and C.W. Emmens, J. Endocrinol. 18 : 251, 1959.

12. Korenchevsky, V., M. Dennison and M. Eldridge, Biochem. J. 31 : 475, 1937.

DISCUSSION

LUNENFELD: Although Dr. Bell has already referred to it, I think we should realize that because of the constantly changing pattern of steroid biosynthesis following stimulation with HCG, we will need an unlimited amount of mice and experimental designs in order to mimic the biogenetic pattern obtained in vivo with either HCG or other pituitary gonadotropins.

BELL: I should like to emphasize that the non-monotonic dose-response curve reported for HCG has also been noted with PMSG and various urinary gonadotropin preparations.

STEINBERGER: Do the uterine weights include the intraluminal fluid, or are these "dry" uterine weights?

BELL: No, the uteri were opened and blotted before being weighed.

ALBERT: Dr. Bell, in the rat, estriol has a much steeper dose response line for its uterotropic action. I wonder if you have tried E3 or mixtures of E1, E2 and E3 or phenolic extract as to their effect on the stimulated mouse ovary.

BELL: I have not used mixtures of estrogens nor have I employed phenolic extracts. I have, however, assayed estriol, estrone and estradiol separately and find that the dose response curves for estrone and estradiol have a similar slope.

ROSEMBERG: Many aspects of our data were not discussed during our presentation. Considering the dose-response curves obtained with human urinary FSH and LH and the dose response curves obtained with estriol and estrone, we have observed that the dose-response curve for estriol is very similar to that of human urinary FSH including the two portions of the curve as shown previously. The dose-response curve for estrone is very similar to that of human urinary LH. I should point out that neither FSH or LH were tested simultaneously with estrone and estriol. However, the pattern for the estrone and estriol dose-response curves is very constant. Hence, it is justifiable to make the comparison.

BELL: I should like to ask Dr. Rosemberg if she has found that high dose levels of estrone or estradiol cause a decrease in uterine weight.

ROSEMBERG: We did not test a complete dose-response curve with either estrone or estriol. I cannot therefore tell you when the curves became asymptotic.

EFFECT OF HUMAN FOLLICLE-STIMULATING AND LUTEINIZING HORMONES ON UTERINE GROWTH OF INTACT IMMATURE MICE

Eugenia Rosemberg and Sewa R. Joshi

Medical Research Institute of Worcester, Inc.,
Worcester City Hospital, Worcester, Massachusetts

The uterine weight increase of immature female mice has been extensively used to assay urinary gonadotropin extracts obtained from normal subjects and from patients with a variety of endocrine disorders. The specificity of this assay method remains to be established. For this reason, it was decided to undertake a study of the effect of purified human urinary follicle-stimulating (FSH) and luteinizing (LH) hormones on the uterine growth of immature mice.

MATERIALS AND METHODS

GONADOTROPIN HORMONES

The urinary gonadotropin preparations FSH (P-35-E 155-3) and LH (P-31 E 113 ter-3) hormones used in this study were generously supplied by Dr. P. Donini, Istituto Farmacologico Serono, Rome, Italy. These preparations were obtained from the urine of post-menopausal women according to methods described by Dr. Donini (1 and 2). The FSH preparation contained 298 IU* of FSH activity and less than 0.6 IU of LH activity per mg. (FSH:LH ratio >497). The LH preparation contained 244 IU of LH activity and less than 2.3 IU of FSH activity per mg.(FSH:LH ratio <0.009). The hormones were kept in a vacuum dessicator at -10°C until used for the preparation of assays.

CONDITIONS FOR ASSAY

20 - 21-day-old female mice (weighing 8-10 gm.) of the Swiss albino strain, obtained from Buckberg, were employed in these studies. Batches of mice were divided randomly into treatment groups. The assay material, FSH and LH, either alone or in

---

* The biologic activity of these preparations was determined by Dr. P. Donini utilizing the augmentation reaction and ovarian ascorbic acid depletion assays to determine FSH and LH activity, respectively. The 2nd International Reference Preparation (2nd IRP) was utilized as the standard in both assays. Results were expressed as International Units (IU) 2nd IRP per milligram of hormone.

various combinations, was dissolved in distilled water. Regardless of the material being administered, the total dose given to
each animal was contained in 2.5 cc; each of 0.5 cc were given
subcutaneously, the first 72-hrs. and the last 24 hrs. before the
animals were autopsied. Each experiment included one group of
animals receiving the injecting vehicle alone. This group served
as controls. At autopsy, the uteri were separated from the vagina
by cutting through the cervix, the surrounding tissue was stripped
off and the uteral-tubal junctions were severed. The uteri were
then weighed fresh on a Roller-Smith torsion balance after pressing
out the uterine fluid on blotting paper. At autopsy, body weights
were determined to the nearest gram and the results expressed as
the ratio of milligrams of uterus per gram body weight. Statistical
evaluation of the data was performed according to the computer program described by Thorslund and Paulsen (3).

EXPERIMENTAL DESIGN AND RESULTS

In all experiments, the dosages of hormones used were separated
by a log interval of 0.301.

A.   STUDY OF THE EFFECT OF FSH AND LH GIVEN SEPARATELY.

1.   Dose levels of FSH, ranging from 2 to 256 mcg., were given to
eight groups of mice with five animals per group. Another group
of five animals served as controls. Three experiments were performed. The complete FSH dose-range was tested twice; dose levels
ranging from 2 to 64 mcg. were tested once.

2.   Dose levels of LH ranging from 1 to 64 mcg. were given to seven
groups with five animals per group. Another group of five animals
served as controls. The experiment was carried out four times. The
combined results of these experiments are presented in Figure 1.

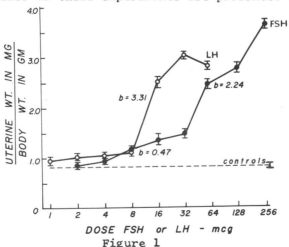

Figure 1
Dose-response curves for FSH (P-35-E 155-3) and LH (P-31 E 113 ter-
3). Vertical bars represent standard error (SE) of the mean.

The FSH dose-response showed two distinct portions. The slope
(b) calculated from doses ranging from 8 to 32 mcg. was 0.47
with confidence limits (CL) of 0.04 to 0.97; the standard error
of the slope [SE (b)] was 0.25 and the index of precision (λ) was
0.86. From 32 to 256 mcg., the value of the slope was 2.24 (CL
1.4 to 3.1); the SE (b) was 0.42 and λ value was 0.42.

The LH dose-response curve was flat from 1 to 8 mcg.; from 8 to
32 mcg. the slope was 3.31 (CL: 1.9 to 4.8); the SE (b) was 0.78
and the λ value was 0.38. The minimal effective dose (MED) was
about 8 mcg. for both hormones. The relative potency (RP) of
LH in terms of FSH was 4.1 (CL: 2.6 to 6.3).

B. STUDY OF THE EFFECT OF MIXTURES OF FSH AND LH YIELDING
   VARYING FSH:LH RATIOS.

1. Dose levels of FSH, ranging from 0.125 to 8 mcg. to which
4 mcg. of LH was added (in vitro), were given to seven groups
of mice utilizing five animals per group. Hence, each dose
level tested yielded mixtures of FSH and LH containing FSH:LH
ratios of 0.03 to 2 by mass (mcg.) or from 0.038 to 2.44 by
biologic activity that is, IU 2nd IRP (1 mg. FSH being equivalent to 298 IU FSH activity, and 1 mg. LH being equivalent to
244 IU LH activity). Another group of five animals served as
controls. The experiment was carried out three times concomitantly with the various dose levels of FSH given alone.

2. Dose levels of LH, ranging from 0.125 to 8 mcg. to which
16 mcg. of FSH was added (in vitro), were given to seven groups
of mice with five animals per group. Hence, each dose tested
yielded mixtures of FSH and LH containing FSH:LH ratios ranging
from 128 to 2 by mass (mcg.) or from 2.44 to 156.3 by biologic
activity (IU 2nd IRP). Another group of five animals served as
controls. The experiment was carried out three times concomitantly with various dose levels of LH given alone.

C. STUDY OF THE EFFECT OF MIXTURES OF FSH AND LH YIELDING
   CONSTANT FSH:LH RATIOS.

1. Dose levels of FSH, ranging from 0.125 to 8 mcg., were mixed
(in vitro) with appropriate amounts of LH so as to yield constant
FSH:LH ratio of 0.5 by mass (mcg.) at each dose level. Five
groups of animals with five animals per group were used; another
group of five animals served as controls.

2. Dose levels of FSH, ranging from 1 to 64 mcg., were mixed
(in vitro) with appropriate amounts of LH so as to yield constant
FSH:LH ratio of 8.0 by mass (mcg.) at each dose level. Seven
groups of mice with five animals in each group were used; another
group of five animals served as controls. The various dose
levels of mixtures of FSH and LH containing constant FSH:LH
ratios of 0.5 and 8.0, respectively, were assayed simultaneously.

The experiment was carried out twice. Figure 2 depicts the results of these experiments.

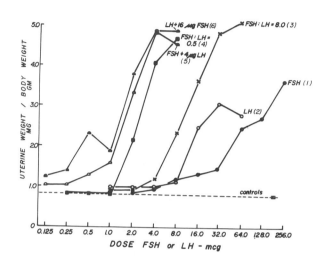

Figure 2

Dose-response curves for FSH alone (1); LH alone (2); mixtures of FSH and LH yielding constant FSH:LH ratios of 8 (3) and 0.5 (4); FSH plus 4 mcg. of LH at each dose level (5); and LH plus 16 mcg. of FSH at each dose level (6).

The dose-response curves corresponding to the various mixtures of hormones (curves 3, 4, 5 and 6) were parallel to each other. They were not parallel to the dose-response curves of either hormone FSH or LH given alone (curves 1 and 2) except for curve 6 (LH plus 16 mcg. of FSH at each dose level) which was parallel to that of LH alone (curve 2). The use of varying as well as constant FSH:LH ratios greatly increased the sensitivity of the assay of either hormone given alone.

The FSH:LH ratio (expressed in IU 2nd IRP) of mixtures of FSH and LH yielding varying ratios at each dose level (experiment B) were plotted against response (ratio uterine weight/body weight). Results are shown in Figure 3.

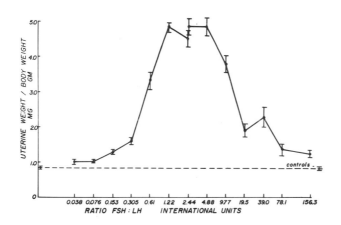

Figure 3

Effect of mixtures of FSH and LH yielding varying FSH:LH ratios.

The FSH:LH ratios tested ranged from 0.038 to 156.3 (IU 2nd IRP). Ratios ranging from 0.076 to 1.22 elicited a gradual increase in response. Ratios ranging from 1.22 to 4.88 elicited maximum responses. With ratios ranging from 4.88 to 156.3 the uterine weight/body ratios gradually decreased.

D. STUDY OF THE EFFECT OF MIXTURES OF FSH AND LH AT SINGLE DOSE LEVELS OF EACH HORMONE.

Mice were divided into five groups of ten each. Each group received mixtures of FSH and LH (prepared in vitro) of 1 mcg. of FSH and 1 mcg. of LH; 2 mcg. of FSH and 2 mcg. of LH; 4 mcg. of FSH and 4 mcg. of LH; 8 mcg. of FSH and 8 mcg. of LH, and 16 mcg. of FSH and 16 mcg. of LH, respectively. Another group of ten animals served as controls. Results of this experiment are shown in Figure 4.

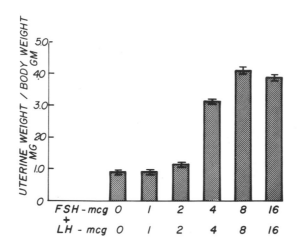

Figure 4

Effect of mixtures of FSH and LH at single dose levels of each hormone.

The addition of dose levels of each hormone which were ineffective when given alone (Figure 1) elicited a potentiation effect. These results indicated that the mouse uterus assay does not represent the summation of FSH and LH activities.

Further investigations were carried out in order to study the effect of mixtures of FSH and LH at various levels of <u>total dose</u>.

E.   STUDY OF THE EFFECT OF MIXTURES OF FSH AND LH AT VARIOUS LEVELS OF TOTAL DOSE.

1.   Total dose 4.25 mcg.   a) Dose levels of FSH, ranging from 0.25 to 2 mcg., were mixed (in vitro) with appropriate amounts of LH so as to yield a total dose of 4.25 mcg. Four groups of mice with six animals per group were used. Hence, each level tested yielded mixtures containing 5.88, 11.76, 23.53 and 47.06 percent of FSH or FSH:LH ratios by biologic activity (IU 2nd IRP) of 0.0763; 0.163; 0.376 and 1.086, respectively. b) Dose levels of LH ranging from 0.25 to 2.0 mcg. of LH were mixed with appropriate amounts of FSH so as to yield a total dose of 4.25 mcg. Four groups of mice with six animals per group were

used. Hence, each level tested yielded mixtures containing
5.88; 11.76; 23.53 and 47.06 percent of LH or, FSH:LH ratios
(IU 2nd IRP) of 19.54; 9.16; 3.97 and 1.37, respectively.

2. <u>Total dose: 8.5 mcg</u>. a) Dose levels of FSH ranging from 0.5
to 4 mcg. were mixed with appropriate amounts of LH so as to
yield a total dose of 8.5 mcg. Four groups of mice with six
animals per group were used. Hence, each level tested yielded
mixtures containing 5.88; 11.76; 23.53 and 47.06 percent of FSH
or FSH:LH ratios (IU 2nd IRP) of 0.0763; 0.163; 0.376; 1.086,
respectively. b) Dose levels of LH ranging from 0.215 to 2.0
mcg. were mixed with appropriate amounts of FSH so as to yield
a total dose of 8.5 mcg. Five groups of mice were used. Hence,
each level tested yielded mixtures containing 1.47; 2.94; 5.88;
11.76 and 23.53 percent of LH or FSH:LH ratios (IU 2nd IRP) of
81.84; 40.30; 19.54; 9.16 and 3.97, respectively.

3. <u>Total dose 17 mcg</u>. a) Dose levels of FSH ranging from 1 to
8 mcg. were mixed with appropriate amounts of LH so as to yield
a total dose of 17 mcg. Four groups of mice with six animals
per group were used. Hence, each level tested yielded mixtures
containing 5.88; 11.76; 23.53 and 47.06 percent of FSH or FSH:LH
ratios (IU 2nd IRP) of 0.0763; 0.163; 0.376 and 1.086, respectively.
b) Dose levels of LH ranging from 1 to 8 mcg. were mixed with
appropriate amounts of FSH so as to yield a total dose of 17 mcg.
Four groups of mice with six animals each were used. Hence, each
level tested yielded mixtures containing 5.88; 11.76; 23.53 and
47.06 percent of LH or FSH:LH ratios (IU 2nd IRP) of 19.54;
9.16; 3.97 and 1.37, respectively.

4. <u>Total dose 34 mcg</u>. Dose levels of LH ranging from 1 to 34
mcg. Six groups of mice with six animals each were used. Hence,
each level tested yielded mixtures containing 2.94; 5.88; 11.76;
23.53; 47.06 and 94.12 percent of LH or FSH:LH ratios (IU 2nd
IRP) of 40.30; 19.54; 9.16; 3.97; 1.37 and 0.0763 respectively.

5. <u>Total dose 68 mcg</u>. Dose levels of LH ranging from 1 to 64
mcg. were mixed with appropriate doses of FSH so as to yield a
total dose of 68 mcg. each. Seven groups of mice with six
animals each were used. Hence, each level tested yielded
mixtures containing 1.47; 2.94; 5.88; 11.76; 23.53; 47.06 and
94.12 percent of LH or FSH:LH ratios (IU) of 81.83; 40.30; 19.54;
9.16; 3.97; 1.37 and 0.0763, respectively.

In all experiments, a separate group of six mice receiving the
injection vehicle, was used as control. Figures 5 and 6
depict the results of these experiments.

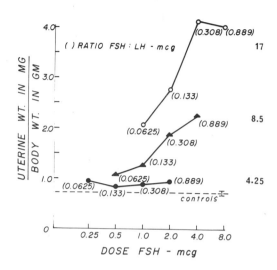

Figure 5

Effect of mixtures of FSH and LH at various levels of total dose.

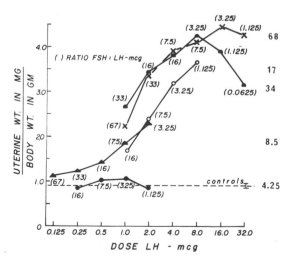

Figure 6

Effect of mixtures of FSH and LH at various levels of total dose.

Total dosages of 4.25 mcg. were ineffective. When the total
dose used was 8.5 mcg. (Figures 5 and 6), the value of the slopes
was 1.3 and 1.5; and the λ values were 0.30 and 0.42, respectively.
When the total dose used was 17 mcg. (Figures 5 and 6), the value
of the slopes was 3.4 and 2.3; and the λ values were 0.26 and
0.20, respectively. Total dosages of 34 and 68 mcg. elicited
responses in the asymptotic portion of the dose-response curve.
The FSH:LH ratios (by weight, mcg.) tested ranged from 0.625 to
67.

Figure 7 shows the plot of the data presented in Figures 5 and 6
expressing the FSH:LH ratios, not by weight, but in terms of
IU 2nd IRP. The FSH:LH ratios ranged from 0.076 to 81.8.

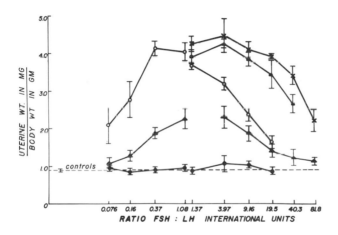

Figure 7

Effect of mixtures of FSH and LH at various levels of total dose.

The pattern is the same as the preceding experiment (experiment
B, Figure 3). It illustrates the striking interaction between
FSH and LH by showing that the uterine response depends greatly
on the proportion of the two hormones as well as the total dose.

The individual LH and FSH activities in the quantities eliciting
a response (ratio uterine weight/body weight) of 1.5 were
plotted against their ratios (FSH:LH) (Figure 8).

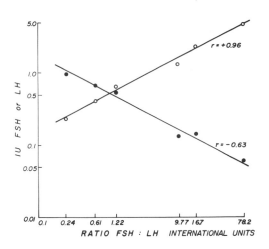

Figure 8

Relationship between FSH (o) and LH (•) activities, and the
ratio of the hormones required to elicit a response (ratio
uterine weight/body weight) of 1.5.

From these data, regression coefficients were calculated. The
regression coefficients (r) were 0.96 for FSH and -0.63 for LH.
Theoretically, with the strain of animals used, determining the
mouse uterine response of the given gonadotropin preparation,
and knowing either its FSH or LH activity, it would be possible
to calculate its FSH:LH ratio. Similar data has been reported
by Lunenfeld (4).

GENERAL CONSIDERATIONS

There has been no agreement in the literature regarding the
type of gonadotropic activity estimated by the mouse uterus
assay. Some workers (5) stated that the test only measured FSH
activity, while others (6) have suggested that the method
predominantly measures LH. The lack of specificity of this
method of assay has been emphasized (7 and 8). Brown and
Billewicz (9) and Diczfalusy et al (10) have indicated that
gonadotropin preparations with differing FSH:LH ratios,
administered at varying dose levels, may produce the same
uterine response.

Direct evidence relating to the effect of purified human FSH and LH preparations on this assay system has been meager. Butt et al (11) tested the effect of mixtures of highly purified human pituitary FSH and LH preparations. Three mixtures of the hormones were prepared by the formulae described by Lamond and Claringbold (12) and compared with FSH and LH alone in the same total dosage. Increased responses were elicited by the mixtures of hormones and analysis of variance indicated that the increases were highly significant.

Our data*, using highly purified FSH and LH preparations obtained from human urine, indicate that this system of assay responds to a variety of mixtures of FSH and LH in a variety of different doses of these two hormones. It also indicates that the uterine response depends on the proportion of the two hormones as well as on the total dose tested. Gonadotropin mixtures containing FSH:LH ratios varying from 0.076 to 156.3 (IU 2nd IRP) elicited measurable dose-response curves. Mixtures of FSH and LH, with varying FSH:LH ratios at each dose level tested, produced dose-response curves which were parallel to those obtained with mixtures of FSH and LH containing constant FSH:LH ratios at each dose level. Gonadotropin extracts obtained from human urine contain both FSH and LH activities. It would be reasonable to expect that these extracts would give valid assays when tested in the mouse uterine weight assay against a standard prepared from the same source i.e.: human urine. This implies that the unknown extract and the standard would give parallel dose-response lines.

The main conclusion which can be drawn from the results is that the mouse uterus assay would measure a wide range of FSH:LH ratios. Hence, it is justified to describe this technique as a measure of "general gonadotropin" activity.

This work was supported, in part, by Grant AM-07564, USPHS, NIH, Bethesda, Maryland, and in part by a Grant from the Ortho Research Foundation, Raritan, New Jersey.

---

* Complete statistical evaluation of the data and response surface analysis will appear elsewhere.

REFERENCES

1. Donini, P., D. Puzzuoli, I. D'Alessio, B. Lunenfeld, A. Eshkol, and A. F. Parlow. Acta Endocrinol. 52, 169, 1966

2. Donini, P. In Recent Research on Gonadotrophic Hormones. Proc. Fifth Gonadotrophin Club Meeting. Bell, E. T., and Loraine, J. A., Editors E & S Livingstone, Ltd., Edinburgh and London p.153, 1967.

3. Thorslund, T., and C. A. Paulsen. Endocrinology 72: 663, 1963.

4. Lunenfeld, B. In Recent Research on Gonadotrophic Hormones. Proc. Fifth Gonadotrophin Club Meeting. Bell, E. T., and Loraine, J. A., Editors. E & S Livingstone, Ltd., Edinburgh and London p. 48, 1967.

5. Klinefelter, H. F., Jr., Albright, F., and Griswold, G. C. J. Clin. Endocrinol., 3: 529, 1943.

6. Buchholz, R. Z. Ges. Exp. Med., 128: 219, 1957.

7. Schimdt-Elmendorff, H., J. A. Loraine, and E. T. Bell. J. Endocrinol., 24: 349, 1962.

8. Loraine, J. A., and E. T. Bell. Hormone Assays and Their Clinical Application 2nd Ed. Edinburgh: Livingstone, 1966.

9. Brown, P. S., and W. Z. Billewicz. J. Endocrinol. 24: 65, 1962.

10. Diczfalusy, E., E. Johannisson, K.-G. Tillinger, and G. Bettendorf. Acta Endocrinol. Suppl., 90: 35, 1964.

11. Butt, W. R., F. J. Cunningham , and A. S. Hartree. Proc. R. Soc. Med., 57: 107, 1964.

12. Lamond, D. R., and P. G. Claringbold. J. Endocrinol., 16: 298, 1958.

DISCUSSION

CROOKE: Dr. Rosemberg, I wonder whether you could tell us something about the preparations that you have used. The reason I ask this question is that we did very similar experiments some time ago using very highly purified preparations and we obtained a slope difference with both FSH and LH separately. These slopes were different from the mixtures of the two.

ROSEMBERG: Dr. Crooke, this is absolutely true. These preparations were provided by Dr. Donini. The FSH preparation contained 298 IU FSH activity per mg. The LH contamination of the preparation was less than 0.6 IU per mg. The FSH:LH ratio was greater than 497. The LH preparation contained 244 IU LH activity per mg. The FSH contamination was less than 2.3 IU per mg. The FSH:LH ratio was less than 0.009. As for the characteristics of the preparations these were as follows: The FSH dose response curve had two distinct portions: one from 8 to 32 micrograms; the value for the **slope** was 0.47. From 32 to 256 micrograms the slope was 2.24. For LH alone, from 8 to 32 micrograms the slope was 3.31. The mixtures of FSH and LH containing varying FSH:LH ratios produced different slopes depending on the dose levels tested. At a very low dose of FSH, from 0.25 to 1 microgram (each dose being mixed with 4 micrograms of LH), the slope was 0.92, a very flat slope. Increasing the dose of FSH from 1 to 4 micrograms (each dose being mixed with 4 micrograms of LH), the slope increased considerably. The value for this slope was 5.35. When low doses of LH were used, that is from 0.125 to 1 microgram (each dose being mixed with 16 micrograms FSH), the slope was also flat, 0.71. When the dose of LH was increased from 1 to 4 micrograms (each dose being mixed with 16 micrograms FSH) the slope was again steeper. The value for this slope was 5.0. Testing mixtures of LH and FSH containing constant ratios of 0.5 and 8 at each dose level, the slopes were 3.9 and 4.1 respectively. With respect to the relative potency of these preparations given alone or as mixtures, the calculation of the potency of LH in terms of FSH given alone was 4.1. For calculations, the portion of the dose-response curve of the standard FSH corresponding to doses ranging from 32 to 256 micrograms and for the unknown a portion corresponding to 8 to 32 micrograms were taken. However, I must point out that when mixtures of FSH and LH at varying or constant ratios at each dose level were tested against FSH or LH alone there was significant departure from parallelism for the respective slope. It is also necessary to point out that the use of mixtures increased the sensitivity of the assay of FSH and LH alone considerably. Testing mixtures of FSH and LH at various levels of total dose against FSH or LH alone again showed a significant departure from parallelism of the respective dose-response curves and also increased the sensitivity of the assay of FSH and LH when given alone. So I think, Dr. Crooke, that this data compares very well with your observations. The data suggest that the mouse

uterine weight assay would measure mixtures of gonadotropin
with FSH:LH ratios varying from less than 0.01 to 80. When
mixtures of FSH and LH are tested, the slopes are parallel
regardless of the FSH:LH ratio contained in the preparation.
The mouse uterine weight assay is widely used to measure urinary
gonadotropin extracts obtained from normal individuals or patients
with a variety of endocrine disorders. These extracts contain
mixtures of FSH and LH activity. These gonadotropin extracts
are usually assayed against a standard preparation of urinary
origin containing a mixture of FSH and LH. Regardless of the
difference in FSH:LH ratios between the standard and the unknown
extract parallel dose response curves will be obtained. A
standard containing mixtures of FSH and LH is suitable for this
assay and it is justifiable to call this assay a "general
gonadotropin" assay.

LUNENFELD: I notice that your lambda values are sometimes high.
Is it justifiable to use these assays?

ROSEMBERG: Yes, in some cases the lambda values are quite high,
and the variation is high. I think we should have to increase
the number of animals in order to reduce the lambda values.

PARLOW: I wish to congratulate Dr. Rosemberg on this monumental
work. Have you had an opportunity to test purified urinary LH
and HCG in the mouse uterine weight assay and if so are the
slopes parallel?

ROSEMBERG: No, we did not assay these two preparations simultaneously.

BORTH: I think we should realize that, in the combined action
of FSH and LH in the uterine and ovarian weight assays, we have
three-dimensional situations since the response depends on two
factors. I suggest that most of these tremendously interesting
but not easily digestible data could be summarized by constructing
one three-dimensional response surface rather than many two-
dimensional dose-response curves. Some time ago, this approach
was used by Lamond and Emmens (J. Endocr. 18 (1959) 251).

ROSEMBERG: Yes, Dr. Borth. I think it will be very useful.

CROOKE: The procedure to which Dr. Borth referred was actually
described by Lamond & Claringbold in 1958 working in Emmens'
laboratory. We used this procedure for demonstrating the joint
action of highly purified FSH and LH (Butt et al, J. Endocr. 25:
541, 1963; Proc. R. Soc. Med. 57: 107, 1964). It is a beautiful
example of the economy in time, effort and materials which can
be achieved by the proper use of sophisticated statistical
designs and deserves wider recognition.

ALBERT: Dr. Rosemberg, when speaking about the mouse uterine
weight assay as a general gonadotropin assay, you referred to

the fluctuations in FSH or LH of individual urinary specimens.
Actually what were the fluctuations in FSH and LH content of
gonadotropin extracts obtained from the urine of normal individuals or from patients with various types of endocrine disorders?

ROSEMBERG: Data which have appeared in the recent literature
relating to urinary excretion of gonadotropins, expressing
results in terms of IU of the 2nd IRP, indicate that the FSH:LH
ratio found in urinary extracts may vary from 0.5 in the urine
of children to 8 in other situations.

ALBERT: Where does this fit in the curve you showed for
artificial mixtures?

ROSEMBERG: The curve shown was constructed using artificial
ratios varying from 0.038 to 156.3. With ratios which will
approximate from unity up to a ratio of 4 the asymptotic part
of the curve is reached. Suppose one wishes to test urinary extracts
of a castrate or postmenopausal individual, then the extract
will contain a reasonable amount of activity per 24 hour period.
The FSH:LH ratio in this type of urinary extract is usually 1.
Hence, one must also consider the effect of total dose. When
the amount of FSH plus LH given to the test animal is greater
than 17 micrograms the asymptotic part of dose response curve
is reached. It now becomes understandable why only low doses
of such urinary extracts should be tested.

THE RELATIVE TOXICITY AND GONADOTROPIC POTENCY OF MONKEY URINE EXTRACTS AT SUCCESSIVE STAGES OF PURIFICATION BY THE ALBERT METHODS

Janet W. McArthur, M.D., Department of Obstetrics and Gynecology,
Harvard Medical School

The distortion which toxicity may introduce into the biological estimation of the gonadotropic potency of urinary extracts has been considered in an earlier paper (1). There it was shown that the gonadotropic activity even of post-menopausal urine, the high intrinsic potency of which obviated any need to administer large dose-equivalents, might be underestimated as the result of toxicity manifested only by impaired weight gain in the assay animals. Body weight changes were utilized to estimate the relative toxicity of extracts prepared by the tannic acid elution method of Johnsen and by the kaolin-acetone precipitation method of Albert.

The minimal toxicity of the ammonium acetate extracts of post-menopausal urine employed in the previous study precluded estimation of any further detoxification effected by treatment with DEAE-cellulose, as employed to yield Albert's Fraction C. In the present study, pools of urine collected from a cycling female stump-tail monkey (M. speciosa) have been utilized to examine this question.

METHODS AND MATERIALS

The urine of a healthy cycling female monkey maintained in a metabolic cage was collected at 24-hour intervals and deep-frozen. Subsequently, the specimens were pooled and divided into aliquots which were processed by the methods of Albert (2) to yield Fractions A, B and C. Biological assays for gonadotropic activity were performed by the HCG-augmented uterine weight method of Igarashi and McCann (3). The animals were inspected daily for such evidences of toxicity as physical inactivity and loss of glossiness of the coat, and records were kept of the initial and final body weights.

RESULTS

In a representative experiment, dose equivalents of 412 cc. of urine, corresponding to a 20-hour collection period, were administered to each mouse. None of the animals evinced any gross indication of toxicity. However, weight gain was impaired in all groups receiving the urinary extracts. The toxicity of Fractions B and C relative to that of Fraction A was determined by a modification of the method previously described. After log transformation of the body weight increments, an analysis of variance was performed. This revealed a highly significant difference between the various fractions ($p < 0.001$). The standard errors of the differences were then employed to define 95% fiducial limits according to the method of Finney (4).

The extent of the detoxification accomplished by each step in purification is shown in Table 1.

Table 1

Toxicity of ammonium acetate extracts and DEAE-C eluates relative to crude
kaolin-acetone precipitates from the same pool of toxic monkey urine
treated as the standard

Treatment	No. of animals	Mean body weight gain (Gm.)	Toxicity relative to Fraction A
Fraction A	8	0.44	- - - - - - - - -
Fraction B	8	1.06	0.339 (1.308-0.372)
Fraction C	8	2.56	0.156 (0.142-0.172)
(Controls)	8	3.16	- - - - - - - - -

The toxicity relative to Fraction A of Fractions B and C prepared
from pooled monkey urine.

- - -

The gonadotropic potency of the same extracts was determined by assay
against Pergonal 28E54C employed as a laboratory standard. All validity
criteria were fulfilled and a lambda value of 0.212 was obtained. Because
the Igarashi-McCann assay is not specific for either FSH or LH the results
(Table 2) are expressed in mcg-equivalents rather than in international units
of the 2nd International Reference Preparation for Human Menopausal Gonadotropin.

Table 2

The gonadotropin content of a kaolin-acetone precipitate, ammonium acetate
extract and DEAE-C eluate from the same pool of toxic monkey urine, assayed
by the HCG-augmented mouse uterine weight method

Treatment	Uterine weight mgm. Mean	S.E.	Gonadotropin content mcg. equiv. 2nd IRP-HMG per 100 ml
Fraction A	9.6	1.5	(not measurable)
Fraction B	18.1	3.6	1.16 (0.52-1.89)
Fraction C	29.6	4.6	1.94 (1.08-3.01)
Untreated controls	10.4	0.8	- - - - - - - -
HCG-treated controls	14.1	1.2	- - - - - - - -

The gonadotropin content of Fractions A, B, and C prepared from
pooled monkey urine, as assayed in the Igarashi-McCann system.

DISCUSSION

As is evident from Table 1, the application of additional purification steps did not completely detoxify a kaolin-acetone precipitate of the urine of a cycling female monkey. Moreover, the introduction of supplementary steps in processing necessarily entails losses of gonadotropin. Therefore, the value shown in Table 2 for the purest fraction (C) must underestimate the true potency to an unknown extent. Definitive comparisons of biologic and immunologic potency, particularly of low-titer urines, require the development of still more refined techniques of purification.

ACKNOWLEDGMENTS

Grateful acknowledgment is made of the assistance of Drs. Bernard F. Trum and Felix Garcia in procuring supplies of monkey urine.

This investigation was supported, in part, by grants from the Barbara C. Willcox Fund, the Sprague Fund and U.S.P.H.S. Research Grant 04378-07 from the National Institute of Arthritis and Metabolic Diseases.

REFERENCES

(1) McArthur, J.W., Howard, A., Somerville, A., Perley, R. and Keyes, C. J.C.E. 27: 534, 1967.

(2) Albert, A., Stellmacher, V. and Leiferman, J. J.C.E. 21: 856, 1951.

(3) Igarashi, M. and McCann, S.M. Endocrinol. 74: 440, 1964.

(4) Finney, D.J. Statistical Method in Biological Assay, ed. 2, Hafner, N.Y., 1964.

DISCUSSION

ALBERT: Dr. McArthur, have you any idea of the nature of this toxic material? Do you have any comments on the inhibitor that has been demonstrated in the bonnet monkey's urine?

McARTHUR: We have made no effort to characterize this material. I suspect that the toxin may prove to be something akin to, say kallikrein and have been interested in the application by Drs. Sairam and Moudgal of classical fractionation methods to the "gonadotropin inhibitor" in the urine of the bonnet monkey. (Endocrinol. 78: 923, 1966; J. Endocrinol. 40: 165, 1968). This seems to me to be the correct approach to this problem. Once the toxic compound or compounds have been identified, methods can probably be devised to remove them from urine extracts.

BIOASSAY OF LUTEOTROPIC ACTIVITY

Henry C. Browning, Department of Anatomy, The University of Texas at Houston, Dental Branch, Houston, Texas 77025

INTRODUCTION

Intraocular ovarian isografts in ovariectomized female mice show normal cyclicity. The newly-formed corpora lutea of each cycle exhibit a mild and ephemeral hyperemia, lasting for about one day (1). If a pituitary isograft is present, or if luteotropic hormone (LTH, prolactin) is given, the corpora show a marked hyperemia, lasting for about one week. This hyperemia denotes luteal function, for a decidual response can only be obtained when such hyperemic corpora are present in the animals (2, 3). It is not produced in response to follicle stimulating hormone or luteinizing hormone (LH) in these, or hypophysectomized females (3, 4). The duration of hyperemia is related to LTH dose level but does not exceed the period found in animals with a pituitary graft; however, it can be prolonged to over two weeks by concomitant administration of LH with the LTH, or by multiple pituitary isografts (3, 5).

Grafted female mice are not convenient for detection or bioassay of luteotropic activity by the luteal hyperemic response because the grafts are cyclic. Responsiveness only occurs if LTH administration commences as luteinization occurs; it is lost when corpora are fully formed. On the other hand, ovarian isografts in intact male mice are static; they form mature follicles that only rarely luteinize spontaneously. However, such follicles form corpora lutea readily upon LH administration and these show only the ephemeral hyperemia seen in untreated females (6). If a source of LTH is present (as from a pituitary isograft), the corpora then exhibit a well-defined hyperemia for a similar length of time to that seen in females treated with this gonadotropin (7). This report concerns the luteal hyperemic response to exogenous LTH in such males and some factors modifying it.

MATERIAL AND METHODS

Various series of groups of 6 to 12 male BALB/c or Strong A mice, two to four months of age, received bilateral intraocular ovarian isografts from females of similar age, by a technique previously described (8). After two to four weeks, during which establishment of the grafts and development of mature follicles occurred, all animals in the groups of any one series received the same luteinizing dose of LH (unless otherwise stated). This dose was usually 5 or 10 ug, given on one or three successive days, intraperitoneally in buffered sterile saline. Administration of LTH (unless otherwise stated) commenced on the second day after the initial LH dosage (i.e., as corpora lutea were forming) and was either continued daily for an indefinite period (i.e., for as long as any animal in a group still exhibited hyperemic corpora), or for a specific number of days. Individual doses ranged from 5 to 200 ug and were always given subcutaneously;

and usually in a 16% gelatin vehicle[1]/. Daily records were made of the presence of hyperemic corpora in each graft from observations of each animal under a binocular dissecting microscope (at X 20) until no such corpora remained.

Standard solutions of LH and LTH containing 1 mg and 5 mg per ml, respectively, in buffered sterile saline, were made from the lyophilized preparations[2]/. Requisite dilutions of these were made in the vehicle concerned so that the desired dose was contained in 0.1 ml. Such dilutions were occasionally made from freshly prepared solutions but usually from solutions stored at -40° C in sealed ampoules. Any excess of such thawed solutions was discarded.

The individual treatment of the groups in all series is summarized in Table 1. The following variables, that might affect duration of the luteal hyperemic response, were investigated by different treatments of groups within a specific series:

a.   Interval between successive LTH administrations and type of vehicle.
     i. Doses of 8, 40, or 200 ug of LTH were given indefinitely as single doses every 24 hours, or as half doses every 12 hours, using either buffered sterile saline or 16% gelatin as the vehicle.
     ii. A dose of 10 ug of LTH was given on three successive days in 8%, 16%, 16% Armour, 24%, or 32% gelatin, or as dry lyophilized LTH dispersed in a 5% solution of beeswax in sesame oil.

b.   Number of LTH administrations. A dose of 10 ug of LTH was given on one, two, three, or six successive days.

c.   Time of initial LTH administration. A dose of 10 ug of LTH was given on three successive days commencing three days before (A), one day before (B), on the day of (C), one day after (D), two days after (E), or three days after (F), the luteinizing dose of LH.

d.   Concomitant administration of a constant or varied dose of LTH with or without a constant or varied dose of LH.
     i. Doses of 5, 10, 20 or 40 ug of LTH were given indefinitely with or without a dose of 20 ug of LH in addition to the luteinizing dose.
     ii. A dose of 40 ug of LTH was given indefinitely, with or without a dose of 2.5 or 100 ug of LH, in addition to the luteinizing dose.

e.   "Priming" by LTH. A constant "priming" dose of 40 ug of LTH was given for 5 days ending on the day of (A), or on the day after (B), the initial luteinizing dose of LH. This was followed by "test" doses of 10 ug of LTH on three successive days, commencing on the second day after the initial

---

[1]/   Generously supplied by Armour Pharmaceutical Co., through the courtesy of Dr. P. L. Brule, in 5 ml. sterile vials and containing 0.5% phenol.

[2]/   NIH-LH-B2-4 and NIH-P-S5-8 (LTH), generously supplied by the Endocrinology Study Section, U.S.P.H.S.

Table 1.

Summary of variables, mouse strains, number of mice per group, LH dosage, and LTH dosage and vehicle for the series a. to g. of investigations of the luteal hyperemic response to LTH in intraocular ovarian isografts in male mice.

Series	Variable	Strain of mouse	Number of mice per group	Doses of LH (ug)	Doses of LTH (ug)	Vehicle for LTH
a.i.	Interval between administration & type of vehicle	BALB/c	6	10 x 1	8 indef.	saline
			"	"	40 "	"
			"	"	200 "	"
			"	"	8* "	"
			"	"	40* "	"
			"	"	200* "	"
			"	"	8 "	16% gelatin
			"	"	40 "	"
			"	"	200 "	"
			"	"	8* "	"
			"	"	40* "	"
			"	"	200* "	"
a.ii.		Strong A	8	5 x 3	10 x 3	8% gelatin**
			"	"	"	16% gelatin**
			"	"	"	16% "
			"	"	"	24% " **
			"	"	"	32% " **
			"	"		beeswax-oil
b.	Number of administrations	Strong A	10	5 x 1	10 x 1	16% gelatin
			"	"	10 x 2	"
			"	"	10 x 3	"
			"	"	10 x 6	"
c.	Time of initial administration	Strong A	10	5 x 1	10 x 3 A	16% gelatin
			"	"	" B	"
			"	"	" C	"
			"	"	" D	"
			"	"	" E	"
			"	"	" F	"
d.i.	Concomittant administration of LH and LTH	BALB/c	8	20 x 1	5 indef.	16% gelatin
			"	"	10 "	"
			"	"	20 "	"
			"	"	40 "	"
			"	20 indef.	5 "	"
			"	"	10 "	"
			"	"	20 "	"
			"	"	40 "	"
d.ii.		BALB/c	10	2.5 x 1	40 indef. A	16% gelatin
			"	2.5 indef.	" B r	"
			"	100 x 1	" C r	"
			"	100 indef.	" D r	"
e.	"Priming" with LTH	Strong A	10	5 x 3	10 x 3 A	16% gelatin
			"	"	" B	"
			"	"	" C	"
			"	"	" D	
f.	Strain of mouse	Strong A	10	5 x 3	10 x 3 r	16% gelatin
			"	"	10 indef. r	"
		BALB/c	10	5 x 3	10 x 3 r	"
			"	"	10 indef. r	"
g.	Repetition of LH and LTH dosage (also see d.ii. and f. above)	BALB/c	12	5 x 1	40 indef. Arr.	16% gelatin
			"	"	" Brr	"
			"	"	" Crr	"

* - half of the total dose every 12 hours; ** - not Armour-prepared gelatin; r - repetition of treatment of group one month later; rr - repetition of treatment of group one and two months later.

LH administration as usual. Similar groups received no "priming" but the same "test" doses (C) or the "priming" doses ending on the day after the initial LH administration but no "test" doses of LTH (D).

f.   Mouse strain. A dose of 10 ug of LTH was given on three successive days, or indefinitely, to groups of both Strong A and BALB/c mice.

g.   Repetition of LH and LTH dosage. A dose of 40 ug of LTH was given indefinitely to three groups. An identical administration (including the luteinizing dose of LH) was repeated to the same animals one and two months after the beginning of the original treatment. Group A received LTH dilutions from freshly prepared solutions at the first and second treatment but from frozen-stored solutions at the third. Group B received freshly prepared LTH at the first but frozen-stored at the second and third treatments. Group C received frozen-stored LTH at all treatments. In series d.ii. above, groups B, C, and D also received a repetition of the original LH and LTH dosage after an interval of one month; in series f. above, all groups similarly received repeated dosage after an interval of one month.

RESULTS

a.   Interval between successive LTH administrations and type of vehicle. (Figure 1: BALB/c mice).

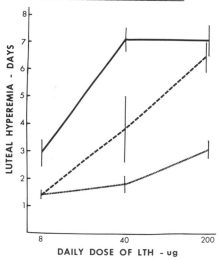

Fig. 1. Mean duration of luteal hyperemic response (DHR), with s.e., to different doses of LTH, given indefinitely in saline 12 (broken line) and 24 (dotted line) hourly or in 16% gelatin 12 or 24 hourly (solid line)

a.i. With saline as the vehicle for LTH, mean duration of the luteal hyperemic response (DHR) did not differ with a dosage of 8 ug every 24 hours or 4 ug every 12 hours (1.4 ± 0.18 days) and was similar to that in animals receiving LH only. DHR did not increase significantly with 40 ug every 24 hours (1.8 ± 0.31 days) but did with 200 ug every 24 hours (3.1 ± 0.31 days; $p < 0.01$). With half of these doses every 12 hours, no statistically significant difference in DHR occurred between each dose level; but, at 200 ug, it was highly significantly longer than with 24-hour administration of the same dosage (6.5 ± 0.58 days; $p < 0.001$).

With gelatin as the vehicle, no statistically significant differences in DHR occurred at the same dose level when given 24 or 12 hourly. Duration, however, was significantly greater at both of the lower dose levels than when given in saline every 12 hours (8 ug - 2.9 ± 0.49 days, $p < 0.01$; 40 ug - 7.1 ± 0.43 days, $p < 0.05$). There was no change in duration between

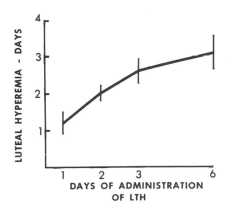

Fig. 2.   DHR, with s.e., to one, two, three, or six doses of 10 ug of LTH.

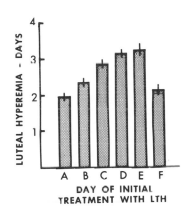

Fig. 3.   DHR, with s.e., to three doses of 10 ug of LTH commencing before, at, or after the initial luteinizing dose of LH.

the 40 and 200 ug dose levels (to 7.1 + 0.58 days), nor did it differ statistically at either of these dose levels **or** at 200 ug given in saline every 12 hours.

a.ii.   With three doses of 10 ug of LTH in different concentrations or type of gelatin vehicle, DHR in Strong A mice ranged from 5.4 to 6.2 days and did not differ statistically between any two groups. However, with bees-wax-sesame oil as the vehicle, DHR was highly significantly less (3.3 + 0.19 days; p<0.001) than with any gelatin vehicle).

b.   Number of LTH administrations. (Figure 2:   Strong A mice).

A single dose of 10 ug of LTH pro-duced a DHR of 1.2 + 0.30 days, **a value which** did not differ from that found in animals receiving LH only. Duration was significantly longer with two daily doses (2.0 + 0.20 days; p<0.05), three doses (2.6 + 0.34 days; p<0.01), and six doses (3.1 + 0.46 days; p<0.01).

c.   Day of initial administration of LTH.   (Figure 3:   Strong A mice).

With three successive daily doses of 10 ug of LTH, DHR was significantly increased when administration commenced **on** one, rather than three days before the luteinizing dose of LH (B - 2.3 + 0.11 days to A - 1.9 + 0.11 days; p<0.01). It was again increased with adminis-tration commencing on the day of LH dosage (C - 2.8 + 0.13 days; p<0.01 relative to B) and with administration commencing one day after LH dosage (D - 3.1 + 0.08 days; p<0.05 relative to C). It was not further increased statistically with administration commencing two days after LH dosage (E - 3.2 + 0.18 days) but dropped to a highly significant degree with adminis-tration commencing three days after LH dosage (F - 2.1 + 0.14 days; p<0.001 relative to E).

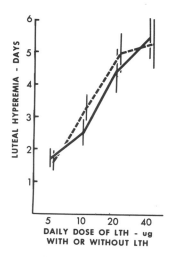

Fig. 4. DHR, with s.e., to 5, 10, 20, or 40 ug of LTH, given indefinitely without (solid line) or with 20 ug of LH (broken line).

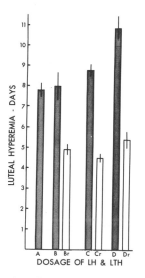

Fig. 5. DHR, with s.e., to 40 ug of LTH given indefinitely without (A, C) or with 2.5 or 100 ug of LH (B, D); and repetition of the dosage one month later (Br, Cr, Dr).

d.   Concomitant administration of a constant or varied dose of LTH with or without a constant or varied dose of LH.

d.i. (Figure 4: BALB/c mice). With a single luteinizing dose of LH, DHR did not change statistically when followed by indefinite dosage of 5 or 10 ug of LTH (1.7 ± 0.29 to 2.5 ± 0.40 days, respectively). It did increase significantly with 20 ug of LTH (4.4 ± 0.69 days; $p < 0.05$) but showed no further statistical increase with 40 ug of LTH (5.5 ± 0.65 days).

When 20 ug of LTH was given concomitantly, with LTH (in addition to the luteinizing dose of 20 ug), DHR increased significantly between a dosage of 5 ug and 10 ug of LTH (1.6 ± 0.31 to 3.3 ± 0.40 days; $p < 0.01$) and again between 10 and 20 ug of LTH (5.0 ± 0.61 days; $p < 0.05$). It did not change statistically with 40 ug of LTH (5.3 ± 0.76 days). However, no significant differences occurred in DHR at any dose level of LTH with or without concomitant administration of LH.

d.ii. (Figure 5: BALB/c mice). When a dose of 40 ug of LTH was given indefinitely, DHR did not differ statistically if preceded by a single luteinizing dose of 2.5 ug of LH, or if this dose was repeated with each LTH administration, or if the single luteinizing dose of LH was 100 ug (A - 7.8 ± 0.52; B - 8.0 ± 0.68; C - 8.8 ± 0.29 days). However, when the 100 ug dose was repeated with each LTH administration, DHR (10.9 ± 0.58 days) was significantly longer than with a single dose of 100 ug (C: $p < 0.01$) and highly significantly longer than with a single or repeated dose of 2.5 ug (A and B: $p < 0.001$).

e.   "Priming" by LTH (Strong A mice).

When three daily "test" doses of 10 ug of LTH were given from the sec-

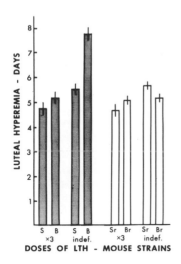

Fig. 6. DHR, with s.e., to three doses or indefinite dosage of 10 ug of LTH in Strong A (S) and BALB/c (B) mice; and to repetition of dosage one month later (Sr, Br).

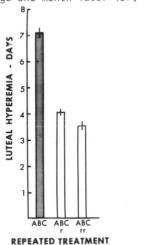

Fig. 7. DHR, with s.e., to indef-inite dosage of 40 ug of LTH (ABC); and to repetition of dosage one (ABCr) and two months (ABCrr) later.

ond day after the initial luteinizing dose of LH, as usual, DHR was unaffec-ted by the lack of a preceding "prim-ing" with LTH, or by five daily "priming" doses of 40 ug of LTH ending on the day after, or on the day of the initial LH administration (A - 3.4 ± 0.15, B - 3.7 ± 0.28, C - 3.5 ± 0.21 days, respectively). DHR was highly significantly less than all of the above values when "priming" doses of LTH were not followed by "test" doses (D - 2.2 ± 0.18 days; p<0.001).

f. Mouse strains (Figure 6: Strong A and BALB/c mice).

DHR, in response to three daily doses of 10 ug of LTH, did not differ statistically between Strong A (4.7 ± 0.26 days) and BALB/c (5.2 ± 0.23 days) mice. However, response to in-definite dosage of 10 ug of LTH was highly significantly less in Strong A than in BALB/c mice (5.5 ± 0.22 and 7.8 ± 0.26 days, respectively; p<0.001). At the same time, response to inde--finite rather than three days' dosage was significantly greater in Strong A (p<0.05) and highly significantly greater in BALB/c mice (p<0.001).

g. Repetition of LH and LTH dosage. (Figure 7: BALB/c mice).

No statistical differences occurred in relation to the use of freshly prepared or frozen-stored LTH (A, B, C; BALB/c mice) in DHR to indefinite dosage with 40 ug of LTH in the first, second and third course of treatment. Consequently, data for all three groups are pooled in Fig. 7. DHR was 7.1 ± 0.21 for the initial treatment and 4.1 ± 0.11 for the second; a highly significant decrease (p<0.001). It again decreased significantly at the third treatment to 3.5 ± 0.17 days (p<0.01).

In series d.ii (Fig. 5: BALB/c mice) above, with varying LH but con-

stant and indefinite LTH dosage, groups B, C and D also received a repetition of the original treatment one month later. DHR was approximately half
of that found in the initial treatment (B - from 8.0 $\pm$ 0.68 to 4.9 $\pm$ 0.27
days; C - from 8.8 $\pm$ 0.29 to 4.5 $\pm$ 0.21 days; D - from 10.9 $\pm$ 0.58 to
5.4 $\pm$ 0.40 days). These decreases were all highly significant (p<0.001).
No statistical differences occurred between values for the second treatment
itself.

In series f. above (Fig. 6: Strong A and BALB/c mice), the initial
treatment with LH and LTH was also repeated one month later. With a dosage of 10 ug of LTH, Strong A mice showed no statistical differences
between DHR for the original and repeated treatments with either three
doses (from 4.7 $\pm$ 0.26 to 4.7 $\pm$ 0.25 days), or indefinite dosage (from
5.5 $\pm$ 0.22 to 5.7 $\pm$ 0.18 days). With three doses of 10 ug of LTH, BALB/c
mice also showed no significant change between the values for the original
and repeated dosage (from 5.2 $\pm$ 0.23 to 5.1 $\pm$ 0.18 days). However, with
indefinite dosage, DHR in this mouse strain decreased to a highly significant degree (from 7.8 $\pm$ 0.26 to 5.2 $\pm$ 0.17 days; p<0.001).

Incidentally, the percentage of grafts that luteinized in any groups
of the entire series was unaffected by single, or three successive doses
of LH at the levels used (82 $\pm$ 1.6% and 84 $\pm$ 2.2%, respectively). It was
increased by indefinite dosage of LH (92 $\pm$ 1.3%) significantly (p<0.01)
compared to three doses and highly significantly (p<0.001) compared to a
single dose. In those series with repeated treatment with LH (d.ii., f.,
and g.), there was no statistical difference between the percentage of
graft luteinization for this and the initial LH administration (81 $\pm$ 2.2%
and 83 $\pm$ 2.4%, respectively). With LTH treatment in all groups of the
entire series, from 90 to 100% of luteinized grafts showed luteal hyperemia; repeated treatment decreased duration of this hyperemia but did not
affect its occurrence.

DISCUSSION

It appears that a useful measure of luteotropic activity, in terms of
DHR, is obtained when LTH is administered to male mice, bearing intraocular
ovarian isografts, on the second day after a luteinizing dose of LH (series
c., above), subcutaneously in a gelatin vehicle (series a.i. and ii.),
every 24 hours for three successive days (series a.i. and b.). Little
advantage is gained by the use of longer dosage (series b. and f.) or by
the concomitant administration of LH (series d.i. and ii.). Under these
conditions, either BALB/c or Strong A mice give a similar response (series
f.) and the same animals could be used for at least one further bioassay
series g.).

The limits of sensitivity of the assay lie between 15 and 60 ug, or
0.375 and 1.5 I.U., given over three days. These compare favorably with
the limits in luteotropic assays based on decidual response to LTH in hypophysectomized mice (9) of 1.5 to 3 I.U., or on prolongation of diestrus
in intact mice (10) of 0.75 to 3 I.U., but unfavorably with that based on
increased luteal cell size in hypophysectomized HCG- PMS-treated immature
female rats (11) where the lower limit was 0.1 I.U. However, the DHR assay
only approaches the upper of the limits of sensitivity (0.0037 to 0.3 I.U.)

of a pigeon-crop stimulation assay based on response to local injection (12).

The mechanism of action of LH and LTH evidently differ. LH is most effective, in terms of minimal dose requirement for luteinization of follicles, when given in a manner that promotes rapid rather than slow absorption (6). This suggests a "trigger‑like" action and, as the dose of 5 or 10 ug usually used here were more than maximal, may account for the absence of any evidence of an immune response and, therefore, of refractoriness to a second series of doses in the same animals. On the other hand, the functional hyperemic or luteotropic response seems to require a maintained, rather than a peak, level of LTH. Its action, like that of parathormone (13, 14) is prolonged when given a vehicle such as gelatin, due to a slower release from the injection site. However, such release can be too slow for, when a beeswax-oil suspension of LTH was used, DHR was reduced. This contrasts with the enhanced potency of relaxin when given in this same medium (15). The need for a maintained level of LTH for luteotropic response may account for the considerably decreased DHR with repetition of indefinite dosage in BALB/c mice, presumably due to antibody inactivation of the gonadotropin. However, in this respect, strain differences are significant, for Strong A mice did not show such a diminished response to repeated LTH administration.

SUMMARY

1.   Intraocular ovarian isografts in male mice develop mature follicles only. Such follicles luteinize upon administration of luteinizing hormone (LH) but the corpora lutea only show hyperemia of function if luteotropic hormone is then given. Duration of this hyperemia is dose-dependent.

2.   Maximal duration of luteal hyperemia, in response to a specific dosage of LTH, is obtained when LTH is given subcutaneously in 16% gelatin every 24 hours. Response to 3 daily doses approaches that to indefinitely continued dosage. Maximal responsiveness occurs when LTH administration commences one or two days after the luteinizing dose of LH.

3.   Concomitant administration of LH with LTH does not lengthen duration of response with doses of 2.5 or 20 ug but does so with doses of 100 ug of LH. Pre-treatment with LTH before test dosage does not influence response.

4.   Strong A and BALB/c mice show the same response to 3 daily doses of LTH but the latter strain gives a longer response than the former to continuous dosage. Repetition of the same treatment with LH and LTH to the same animals gives a reduced response to continuous (but not with 3 daily doses only) dosage of LTH in BALB/c but not in Strong A mice.

Supported by U.S.P.H.S. Research Grant CA-02880 and Population Council Grant M 67-26.

GONADOTROPINS 1968

REFERENCES

1. White, W. D., and H. C. Browning, Texas Rep Biol Med 20:484, 1962.
2. Browning, H. C., and W. D. White, Texas Rep Biol Med 20:570, 1962.
3. Browning, H. C., G. A. Larke and W. D. White, Proc Soc Exp Biol Med 111:686, 1962.
4. Browning, H. C., A. L. Brown, T. E. Crisp and W. E. Gibbs, Texas Rep Biol Med 23:715, 1965.
5. Browning, H. C., and W. D. White, Texas Rep Biol Med 21:176, 1963.
6. Browning, H. C., and G. A. Larke, Proc Soc Exp Biol Med 118:913, 1965.
7. Browning, H. C., and W. D. White, Proc Soc Exp Biol Med 119:1224, 1965.
8. Browning, H. C., and R. Guzman, Endocrinology 81:1311, 1967.
9. Kovacic, N., J. Endocr 28:45, 1963.
10. Kovacic, N., J. Endocr 24:227, 1962.
11. Wolthuis, O. L., Acta Endocr (Kobenhavn) 42:364, 1963.
12. Nicoll, C. S., Endocrinology 80:641, 1967.
13. Aurbach, G. D., Endocrinology 64:296, 1959.
14. Rasmussen, H., Endocrinology 64:367, 1959.
15. Kliman, B., and R. O. Greep, Endocrinology 63:586, 1958.

BIOLOGICAL INTERACTIONS BETWEEN PROSTAGLANDINS AND LUTEOTROPINS IN THE RAT

B. B. PHARRISS, L. J. WYNGARDEN & G. D. GUTKNECHT
FERTILITY RESEARCH
THE UPJOHN COMPANY
KALAMAZOO, MICHIGAN

INTRODUCTION

The prostaglandins are a biologically active class of lipids derived from prostanoic acid. Although originally described in 1933, (1,2) their diverse activities have not received widespread attention until quite recently. Prostaglandins are ubiquitous in their distribution and the male and female reproductive tracts are especially well endowed with these lipids. Although many hypotheses have been proposed to explain their function in these areas, no generally accepted theories have as yet arisen. One of the areas that has received little or no attention is the role of prostaglandins in the ovary. In 1937 (3) their presence in the ovary was reported, but no investigation was made as to their action here. While investigating one of the prostaglandins for its role in reproduction in the female rat it was necessary to test its effect on progesterone synthesis in vitro. At that time we discovered its luteotropic effect which we will report here along with several related effects in female rats.

EXPERIMENTAL SECTION

Prostaglandins occur in four basic families which are designated as A, B, E or F and are assigned by virtue of the configuration of the cyclic portion of the molecule. The F series is characterized by two hydroxyls at positions 9 and 11, and we will discuss a particular member of this family, prostaglandin $F_{2\alpha}$ ($PGF_{2\alpha}$) which has two points of unsaturation at positions 5 and 13 in the side chains (Fig 1). Our supply of $PGF_{2\alpha}$ was synthesized at The Upjohn Company by bioconversion of arachidonic acid using sheep vesicular glands (4).

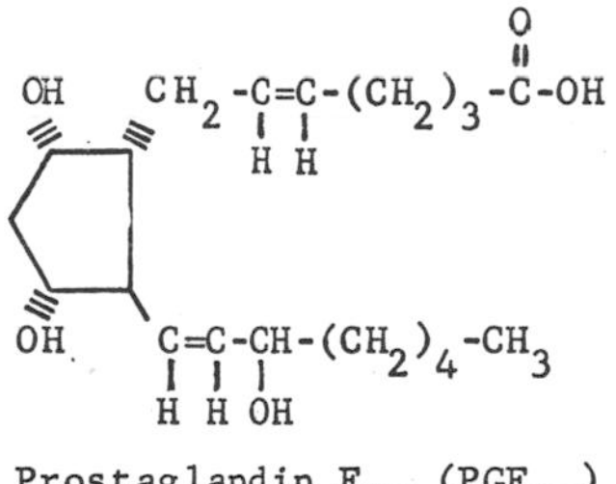

Fig 1. Prostaglandin $F_{2\alpha}$ ($PGF_{2\alpha}$)

$PGF_{2\alpha}$ was made up in incubation media in the correct concentrations for each experiment. Progesterone-7α-^{3}H and sodium acetate-1-^{14}C were obtained from New England Nuclear Corp.; 4-pregnene-20α-ol-3-one-7α^3H (20α-OH-progesterone) was synthesized by Dr. Richard C. Thomas of The Upjohn Company. Other chemicals used were standard reagent grade products from commercial sources.

Mature female rats (Upjohn Sprague-Dawley) of 200-300 gm were checked by vaginal smears for regular estrous cycles prior to use.

Pseudopregnancy was induced by vaginal stimulation with an electric probe (50 volts, 1.5 ma for 8-10 seconds), and the ovaries were collected on day 6. These were immediately minced and incubated for 2 to 4 hours at 37°C in 4 ml Krebs-Ringer bicarbonate buffer containing glucose at 1 mg/ml, and acetate-1-^{14}C, PGF$_{2\alpha}$ and LH in the appropriate vials. These were incubated in a Dubnoff shaker and gassed with 95% O_2 and 5% CO_2 (5). At the end of the incubation period all reactions were inhibited by addition of 5 ml of 2.5% NaOH and freezing.

In the initial experiments the ovaries in NaOH were homogenized in all glass homogenizers, and then known amounts of progesterone-7-^{3}H and 4-pregnene-20α-ol-3-one-7α-^{3}H were added to each homogenate for later determination of percent recovery. The homogenates were extracted with diethyl ether, and the non-saponifiable lipids were then spotted on thin layer plates for two dimensional separation. The solvent systems were 1:1 cyclohexane, ethyl acetate and then 2:5 ether, methylene chloride. After extraction from thin layer spots, progestogens were dissolved in HCCl$_3$ for vapor phase chromatographic analyses. The HCCl$_3$ contained a known amount of cholestane as an internal standard for VPC standardization. Portions of each sample were dissolved in Diatol solution, and ^{3}H (and ^{14}C when appropriate) levels were determined in a Packard Tri-Carb scintillation counter.

In later experiments the cortico-binding globulin assay for steroids (6,7) was used; male dog serum was the source of binding globulin for the progesterone determinations. In these experiments progesterone-4-^{14}C was added to determine percent recovery. Extraction of the steroids was identical to the above procedure, but only one dimensional thin layer separation was necessary for the small aliquots used in these assays.

Two similar experiments were carried out in the first study using 0, 0.1, 1.0 and 10.0 µg PGF$_{2\alpha}$/ml (Table 1). The results from Experiments 1 and 2 are quite compatible, and the only difference seems to be a higher degree of sensitivity of the ovarian tissue to the PGF$_{2\alpha}$ in Experiment 2. That our in vitro system was adequate to support luteal metabolism is evident from the de novo synthesis column where there was at least a 100% increase in progesterone concentration over the zero time values. The concentration of reduced steroid was also increased in the incubated samples but never to the extent of the progesterone levels. In both experiments there is an increasing mean concentration with an increasing dose of PGF$_{2\alpha}$ to the extent that at 10 µg/ml there is a 50% and 150% increase in Experiments 1 and 2 respectively. The levels of the 20α-reduced steroid generally parallel those of progesterone in direction but not in quantity.

The rate at which acetate was utilized as a steroid precursor was depressed as shown by the decrease not only in specific activity but also by the decrease in the absolute amount of ^{14}C that was incorporated into the two progestational steroids. Evidence that this is not indicative of some rate-limiting inhibition which would result in a decrease in progesterone synthesis with time can be seen in Table 2. The amount of cholesterol synthesized and the specific activity derived from acetate-1-^{14}C incorporation are

Table 1.

Effect of PGF$_{2\alpha}$ in vitro on Progesterone and 20α-OH-Progesterone Synthesis
and Specific Activity after Four-Hour Incubations of Pseudopregnant Ovaries with Acetate-1-^{14}C †

Sample ‡ Treatment	Average Tissue Weights (mg)	Progesterone			20α-OH-Progesterone			P/OHP Ratio
		Concentration*	de novo Synthesis*	Specific Activity**	Concentration*	de novo Synthesis*	Specific Activity**	
Experiment 1								
1 Zero time controls	496	4.43	-	-	5.77	-	-	
2 No Treatment	288	9.58	5.15	388	9.26	3.49	393	1.47
3 0.1 µg PGF$_{2\alpha}$/ml	291	9.32	4.89	239	9.61	3.84	322	1.27
4 1.0 µg PGF$_{2\alpha}$/ml	289	11.43	7.00	119	10.31	4.54	158	1.54
5 10.0 µg PGF$_{2\alpha}$/ml	292	12.04	7.61	113	10.04	4.27	129	1.78
Experiment 2								
1 Zero time controls	490	5.30	-	-	9.43	-	-	
2 No Treatment	302	12.57	7.27	173	10.66	1.23	227	5.91
3 0.1 µg PGF$_{2\alpha}$/ml	304	13.12	7.82	212	10.27	0.84	155	9.30
4 1.0 µg PGF$_{2\alpha}$/ml	304	14.67	9.37	120	11.37	1.94	120	4.83
5 10.0 µg PGF$_{2\alpha}$/ml	303	23.58	18.28	49	12.37	2.94	59	5.87

† = Each vial (4.0 ml) contained 2.5 µc

‡ = Each sample result is an average of 2 or 3 incubation trials

* = µg steroid/gm tissue

** = dpm/µg steroid

GONADOTROPINS 1968

Table 2.

Effect of PGF$_{2\alpha}$ in vitro on Cholesterol Concentration
and Specific Activity after Incubation with Acetate-1-14C ‡

Sample	Treatment	Concentration μg/gm tissue	Cholesterol de novo Synthesis	Specific Activity
Experiment 1				
1	Zero time controls	1879	-	-
2	No Treatment	2221	342	48
3	0.1 μg PGF$_{2\alpha}$/ml	1938	59	47
4	1.0 μg PGF$_{2\alpha}$/ml	2049	170	37
5	10.0 μg PGF$_{2\alpha}$/ml	1919	40	45
Experiment 2				
1	Zero time controls	2185	-	-
2	No Treatment	2145	-40	29
3	0.1 μg PGF$_{2\alpha}$	2261	76	29
4	1.0 μg PGF$_{2\alpha}$	2212	27	29
5	10.0 μg PGF$_{2\alpha}$	2301	116	26

‡ The data for this table were
obtained from the same experiments
represented in Table 1 and therefore
all conditions remain the same.

listed in this table. Although the massive amounts of cholesterol that are present prevent adequate assessment of small changes in concentration, the specific activities are sufficiently reliable for comment. As is seen, there is no decrease in radioisotope incorporation with increasing doses of $PGF_{2\alpha}$. The variability in the de novo synthesis prevents speculation about changes in cholesterol concentration, but at least the rate of incorporation of acetate into cholesterol seems unaltered by the presence of prostaglandin.

In a similar experiment designed to measure the effect of LH on mature pseudopregnant ovaries, the results in Fig 2 were obtained. LH was tested at 0, 2, 10, 25 and 100 μg/ml. There seemed to be a dose response up to the 10 μg/ml level after which the stimulation either levelled off or was slightly depressed. Acetate-1-^{14}C was not used in this experiment so rate of precursor incorporation was not measured.

In an attempt to investigate the possibility that $PGF_{2\alpha}$ and LH are working through the same mechanism these two substances were tested together. Fig 3 shows the percent increase in progesterone synthesis when pseudopregnant ovaries were exposed to 10 μg of $PGF_{2\alpha}$ and to both $PGF_{2\alpha}$ and LH at 10 μg/ml each. As was seen in Fig 2, LH at 10 μg/ml gave a maximal response. Hence if the rate of progesterone synthesis were greater in the presence of both agents, a separate mechanism of stimulation could exist. As can be seen however, the combination treatment of $PGF_{2\alpha}$ and LH resulted in a stimulation (53% increase) similar to that of the $PGF_{2\alpha}$ alone (59% increase). This information is quite preliminary however and is presented here only as our initial observation. Even if this limited data is accepted, identical mechanism of action need not be the correct answer as progesterone synthesis may be regulated by an unassociated rate limiting process.

It has been reported however (8) that LH probably works through intracellular cyclic AMP in luteal tissue, and it has been reported by Butcher and Baird (9) that PGE_1 stimulates cyclic AMP formation in adipose tissue.

As another test for similarities of action of prostaglandins and LH, the standard ovarian ascorbic acid depletion (OAAD) assay was carried out for various doses of $PGF_{2\alpha}$. The results of that assay are in Fig 4. Even at the lowest dose tested (10 μg), $PGF_{2\alpha}$ caused an 18% depletion which increased up to a dose of 250 μg where the depletion reached 32.5%. Further increases in dose (up to 1.0 mg) did not affect this percent depletion. If one wants to argue that $PGF_{2\alpha}$ and LH are working by the same mechanism, the possibility that $PGF_{2\alpha}$ might be an intracellular hormone, quite like 3'5'AMP, would render attempts to exhibit its properties by intravenous administration quite difficult.

We have also measured the effects of $PGF_{2\alpha}$ on pituitary LH and FSH content. Ovariectomized mature rats were treated b.i.d. with $PGF_{2\alpha}$ at 4 mg/day for 5 days. At the end of this time the pituitaries were removed and assayed for LH activity by the OAAD assay and for FSH by the Steelman-Pohley assay.

It is obvious that no difference exists between treated and control pituitaries insofar as the LH content is concerned (Fig 5). However when the FSH content was measured (Table 3) a difference was seen. Although there

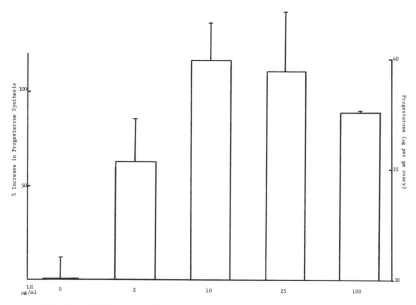

Fig 2. Effect of LH _in_ _vitro_ on progesterone synthesis
in ovaries from mature pseudopregnant rats

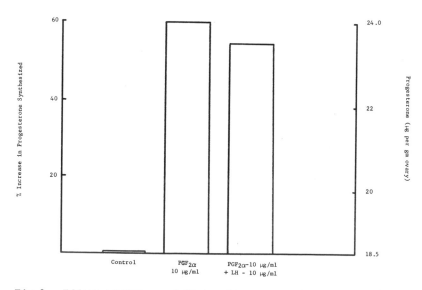

Fig 3. Effect of $PGF_{2\alpha}$ and LH _in_ _vitro_ on progesterone synthesis
in ovaries from mature pseudopregnant rats

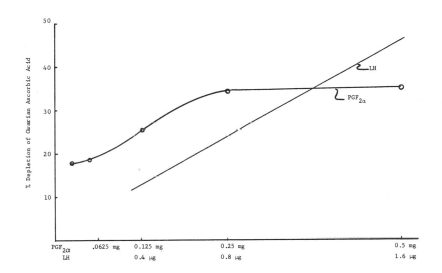

Fig 4. Effect of PGF$_{2\alpha}$ given intravenously on
ovarian ascorbic acid levels in immature rats

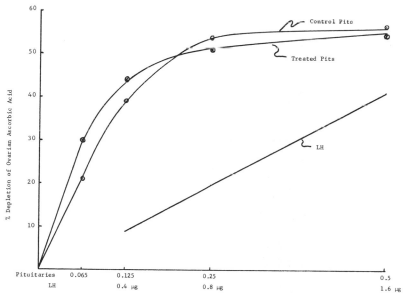

Fig 5. LH content of pituitaries from saline and PGF$_{2\alpha}$
(4 mg/day) treated ovariectomized rats

Table 3.

FSH Content of Pituitaries of $PGF_{2\alpha}$ Treated Ovariectomized Rats

Treatment	Ovarian weight (mg)	Uterine weight (mg)
Saline Control	15.6	31.1
HCG (50 IU)	46.9 ± 2.34	127.5
HCG (50 IU)+:		
FSH - 70 μg	61.4	120.0
FSH - 140 μg	94.7	115.4
FSH - 280 μg	110.8	134.5
HCG (50 IU)+:		
1.0 Control pit	72.9 ± 5.61*	122.7
0.5 Control pit	45.8 ± 3.66	110.7
0.1 Control pit	42.2 ± 2.99	133.0
	$\bar{x}$ = 53.6 **	
HCG (50 IU)+:		
1.0 $PGF_{2\alpha}$ pit	94.0 ± 11.76*	130.0
0.5 $PGF_{2\alpha}$ pit	57.3 ± 5.71	128.3
0.1 $PGF_{2\alpha}$ pit	48.9 ± 1.58	126.6
	$\bar{x}$ = 66.8 **	

 * Significantly different ($P<.01$) from HCG control.
** Significantly different ($P<.01$) between overall means.

---

was no difference in response to any specific dose of control or treated pituitaries, a definite increase of 24% ($P<.01$) was seen when the combined responses to all doses of treated pituitaries were compared to the combined responses to all doses of control tissues. We have no explanation for the meaning or significance of this information.

In summary, we have definite evidence that _in vitro_ $PGF_{2\alpha}$ behaves as a luteo-tropic substance in the rat. Whether this effect is meaningful in the animal or whether it plays a role in LH activity is not known and as yet not suggested. We do however offer this effect as one possible role of prosta-glandins in the ovary.

REFERENCES

(1) Goldblatt, W. W., <u>Chem</u> <u>Ind</u> <u>Lond</u> <u>52</u>:1056, 1933; <u>J</u> <u>Physiol</u> <u>Lond</u> <u>84</u>:208, 1935.

(2) Euler, U. S. von, <u>Arch</u> <u>Exptl</u> <u>Pathol</u> <u>Pharm</u> <u>175</u>:78, 1934.

(3) Euler, U. S. von and S. Hammarstrom, <u>Skand</u> <u>Arch</u> <u>Physiol</u> <u>77</u>:69, 1937.

(4) Daniels, E. and J. E. Pike, Worcester Symposium on Prostaglandins (1967) In Press.

(5) Armstrong, D. T., J. O'Brien and R. O. Greep, <u>Endocrin</u> <u>75</u>:488, 1964.

(6) Murphy, B. E., <u>J</u> <u>Clin</u> <u>Endocrin</u> <u>Metab</u> <u>27</u>:973, 1967.

(7) Neill, J. D., E. D. B. Johansson, J. K. Datta and E. Knobil, <u>J</u> <u>Clin</u> <u>Endocrin</u> <u>Metab</u> <u>27</u>:1167, 1967.

(8) Marsh, J. M. and K. Savard, <u>Steroids</u> <u>8</u>:133, 1966.

(9) Butcher, R. W. and C. E. Baird, <u>J</u> <u>Biol</u> <u>Chem</u> <u>243</u>:1713, 1968.

DISCUSSION

STEINBERGER: This question is directed to Dr. Pharriss. Do rats or mice produce prostaglandin?

PHARRISS: Prostaglandins have been identified in rats but not to my knowledge in mice. Both the E and F series of prostaglandins have been identified in such tissues in the rat as muscle, nerve, and adipose tissue. No report of ovarian prostaglandin has been presented.

USE OF BIOASSAYS TO STUDY LH AND FSH SECRETORY KINETICS IN THE RAT[1]

E. M. BOGDANOVE AND V. L. GAY[2], DEPARTMENT OF ANATOMY AND PHYSIOLOGY,
INDIANA UNIVERSITY, BLOOMINGTON, INDIANA 47401

INTRODUCTION

The group of studies we are considering could probably have been done better—
and could certainly have been done more economically — if radioimmunoassay
(RIA) methods for rat LH and FSH had been at our disposal. Because we had to
do them with bioassay (BA) methodology, it follows that (despite the high order
of BA sensitivity and precision we strove for and achieved) the picture we
obtained cannot be sharply drawn. It will be interesting to see, eventually,
how well or poorly this picture will compare with the better-defined one which
is sure to emerge when similar studies can be done with RIA methods, or other
more suitable tools.

Since bioassays are not well-suited to the task of obtaining the sort of
precise measurements needed for the analysis of pituitary secretory kinetics,
why did we use them at all? Why did we not wait upon methodological advancement before undertaking our studies? We can suggest four partial explanations
for our precocity.

1. The time was ripe. Methods for the mathematical analysis of steroid
secretory kinetics had been developed (1,2) and honed (3) to a gratifying
degree of usefulness. Although groping steps toward comparable elucidation
of the LH-FSH secretory systems have been taken (4,5), attempts to subject
these conceptualizations to mathematical test have been stymied by the dearth
of reliable quantitative information about the rate processes involved.

2. A simple but invaluable technical achievement, construction of a "hypophysectomy machine" (6), had made it feasible - if not easy - for us to
rapidly hypophysectomize the large numbers of big rats needed to do "stop-
entry" studies of endogenous LH and FSH disappearance by bioassay.

3. Since RIA methods do not necessarily measure biologically active hormone,
we believe that critical RIA findings must, wherever possible, be confirmed
with BA before they can be fully interpreted. Since a need exists for <u>both</u>
RIA and BA information, precedence is of little consequence.

4. Last but not least, we viewed this project as a challenge. Having been
to considerable pains to develop a high degree of LH (7) and FSH (8,9) BA
capability[3], we naturally wished to achieve with it something which could not

---

[1] The studies discussed here were supported largely by grant NB 03371, USPHS
and by emergency grants-in-aid from Eli Lilly Research Laboratories, G. D.
Searle and Co., Ayerst Laboratories, Inc. and the Upjohn Co.

[2] USPHS postdoctoral fellow, 1966-67. Present address: Department of
Pathology, University of Michigan, Ann Arbor, Michigan 48104.

[3] Details of the pains we take to extract maximum precision from our OAAD (7)
and Steelman-Pohley assays (14,8,9) have been set forth elsewhere. Suffice it
to say here that BA, like J. W. Riley's bogey-man, 'will get you eff'n you
don't watch out'.

have been achieved without it. Although it remains to be seen how well, if
at all, we succeeded in our effort, we do not think our overall success or
failure should be judged on the accuracy of our estimates. Rather, we feel
that the very existence of these (currently unique) estimates must challenge
others to verify or refute them and, in the process, to gain far more precise
information than we did. Thus, it is not of primary importance whether our
broadly sketched picture will prove, in the long run, to be of any real value.
It is sure to be of heuristic value. This is why, despite its obvious shortcomings, we are not reticent to present it.

RATIONALE AND METHODS

Figure 1 represents the major set of relationships among the processes which
govern the amounts of LH (or FSH) present in the blood and pituitary at any
moment. These processes are simply the rates of entry into and exit from the
two compartments of the diagram. Mechanisms which influence or control secretion must do so by affecting one or more of these rate processes. Ultimately,
to understand such control, ways must be devised to measure these rates under
varying conditions. We began with a smaller goal.

First, we assumed (paragraph 2 of the legend) that in the long-term castrated
rat, the LH and FSH secretory processes are in a virtually steady state. This
assumption cannot be strictly true since, contrary to what has been reported
(12), we have found that plasma and pituitary levels of LH and FSH do not
"plateau" during the second to fourth post-castration months in the rat.
Therefore, a true "steady state" cannot exist. However, the rates at which
these levels (BI and BII) change during this period are relatively slow.
Within the hourly to daily time domain we are considering, the changes can be
considered infinitesimal. This suggests that the equalities set forth in paragraph 2 of the legend are, for the practical purpose of obtaining the first
approximations we sought, sufficiently true to be useful. If so, measurement
of one rate means measurement of all. (It should be emphasized that CI = AII
by definition. AII is defined as the rate of entry from the hypophysis. It
is obvious that hormone might enter the blood from other, extrahypophysial,
compartments. In the diagram, this is allowed for by making each arrow a
symbol of net, bidirectional, flux. In the rat, entry of hormone from all
sources into compartment II will eventually have to be accounted for. Our
present calculations ignore it.)

The one rate which was accessible to direct investigation in our studies of
endogenous LH and FSH was the disappearance or decay rate (CII_X). We obtained
this rate from the fall in plasma LH or FSH activity which resulted when entry
of hormone into the plasma (AII) was suddenly halted by hypophysectomy ("stop-
entry" experiment). The patterns of fall seemed sufficiently compatible with
the classical exponential decay curve, $[H]_t = [H]_0\, e^{-kt}$, to make calculation of
a "half-life" ($t\frac{1}{2}$) and decay constant ($K = .693/t\frac{1}{2}$) for each hormone seem
permissible.

We should emphasize that these constants ($t\frac{1}{2}$ and K) are for endogenous LH and
FSH, in the form in which they are secreted by the rat. It is not wise to
assume that they are also valid for either heterologous LH or FSH preparations,
or murine LH or FSH which has had an opportunity to undergo extracorporeal
denaturation. Although we were unable to resolve any difference between the
rates at which equivalent concentrations of native LH and NIH-ovine LH (S11)

disappear from the plasma of the rat (10), this may merely reflect the inability of LH bioassay to resolve differences among a group of relatively short half-lives. We did find (13) a marked (about 5-fold) difference between the half-lives of native FSH and injected ovine FSH (NIH-FSH-S4). The exogenous hormone disappeared much more rapidly.

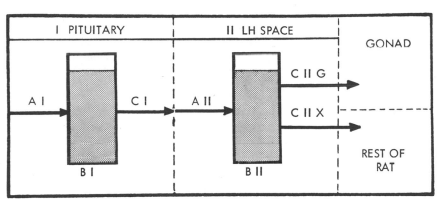

Simplified, 2-compartment model (adapted from 14, Fig. 1) illustrating LH secretory dynamics but convertible to any endocrine subsystem. Arrows labeled A (I or II) represent rates of entry into'each of the 2 adjacent compartments. Arrows labeled C (I, II_G or II_X) represent total or fractional rates of exit In compartment I, the pituitary (in the case of LH) AI is the *net rate of LH synthesis* and CI is the rate of LH *release*. Compartment II, the LH "space" (which seems to approximate the plasma volume, but see text) corresponds to the "inner pool" of Tait and Burstein (13). The rate of LH entry from the hypophysis into the LH space (AII) must, at all times, be commensurate with CI, the LH release rate. Rates CII_G and CII_X, especially the latter, might better be drawn as ⇄ to indicate that they represent *net* flux between the LH space and (CII_G) the gonad and (CII_X) all other extrahypophysial spaces, respectively. If entry of LH into the plasma from these extrahypophysial spaces (Tait and Burstein's "outer pool") were substantial, the apparent rate of exit (CII_X in our studies) would be slower than the true rate and the decay curve would not be described by the simple formula we have used.

If, in one of the compartments, a transient disequilibrium between A and C occurs, a change in B (stores or content) must result, according to the relationship $A - C = \Delta B$, where ΔB is the change in stores during the unit of time selected to express rate. BI can be measured (as concentration ×weight =content) and BII can be calculated from the concentration of the hormone in the plasma, if the distribution volume is known (concentration ×distribution volume = total circulating hormone). None of the rates (AI, CI, AII, CII_X, or CII_G) has ever been measured. However, in a relatively steady state, as in a rat castrated 4 or more weeks previously (where $CII_G = 0$), $\Delta BI \cong \Delta BII \cong 0$ and therefore $AI \cong CI = AII \cong CII_X$.

In the "stop-entry" experiment (acute removal of compartment I by hypophysectomy), AII instantaneously becomes zero but CII_X, the rate of exit from the plasma, slows gradually. Although CII_X immediately starts to decrease, seemingly as an exponential function of BII, its instantaneous initial (zero time) value, which must about equal the steady state (pre-hypophysectomy) values of AI, CI and AII, can easily be calculated, as explained in the text.

Fig. 1 Simplified, 2-compartment model for LH secretory dynamics. (From: Vernon L. Gay and E. M. Bogdanove, Endocrinology 82: 359, 1968.) The two references in the legend are included in the bibliography of this paper, but under different numbers: for 14, see 11; for 13, see 1.

The essential formula for calculating the "resting" or "steady state" rate of hormone disappearance — in a form in which it can be equated with the rates of entry into the blood and/or pituitary — must measure the change/unit time in the amount of hormone in the circulation (or hormone space), rather than concentration (amount/unit volume) which is what one actually estimates with assays. Thus, the standard rate formula $d[H]/dt = -K[H]$ must be converted to $dQ_H/dt = -KQ_H$ (10, formula II) by multiplying both sides by V_H. ($Q_H = [H] \times V_H$.)

Unfortunately the distribution volumes for endogenous LH and FSH in the rat are simply unknown. We have estimated the distribution volumes of the NIH reference materials, LH-S11 (10) and FSH-S3 and S4 (13) in the rat, and used them in calculating dQ_{LH}/dt and dQ_{FSH}/dt. However, since an exogenous hormone can have a different half-life from its endogenous counterpart (13), it may also have a different distribution volume. Until data on the distribution volumes of native murine LH and FSH become available, our estimates of V_{LH} and and V_{FSH} - about 3% of body weight (10,13) - will have to be used. We hope they will be used with reservations.

The decay rate formula, $dQ_H/dt = -KQ_H$, describes the momentary rate at which Q_H is decreasing at any time (t) after a "stop-entry" event, such as hypophysectomy. Since this rate is a constant product of Q_H, and since Q_H itself decreases as a function of t, it is obvious that KQ_H declines continuously as t increases. However, calculation of KQ_H when $t = 0$ (that is, at the instant of hypophysectomy — before Q_H has had a chance to fall) provides an expression of a decay rate which has not yet been affected by the "stop-entry" event and is, therefore, the same as the corresponding rate in a non-hypophysectomized animal (i.e. — CII_X in the castrate).

FINDINGS AND CALCULATIONS

The half-life of endogenous LH in the castrated rat is about 30 minutes[4] (19-38 minutes, with a mean of 31.6), from which K_{LH} is about 0.0219 (for a dQ/dt expressed as amount/minute). Endogenous FSH has a considerably longer half-life (96-238, with mean of 149, minutes) and, therefore, a smaller K (.0046).

Despite this difference, the product $K_{FSH} Q_{FSH}$ is much (25 to 40 times) larger than $K_{LH} Q_{LH}$. This is because FSH concentrations reach much higher levels in the castrated rat than LH concentrations do - at least when these concentrations are expressed in terms of the activity, in rats, of the ovine hormones used as reference standards. This is true if we correct for the markedly disparate degrees of impurity[5] of these reference materials. (Such a correction is meaningless because rats do not secrete ovine gonadotrophins, but it is interesting to run through the arithmetic. It turns out that the activities of the LH and FSH secreted each day by a 350 g castrated rat are about equal to the activities of 8 μg of "pure" sheep LH and FSH.) In terms of the

---

[4] One of us (V.L.G.) has recently obtained similar (30-35 minute) estimates for $t\frac{1}{2}_{LH}$ in individual non-castrated (proestrus female) rats by the "stop-entry" method using RIA.

[5] According to a statement made by Wilhelmi at the 1967 Laurentian Hormone Conference, NIH ovine LH is at least 25 times as pure as NIH ovine FSH.

impure ovine hormones used as BA reference materials, the FSH secretion and
disappearance rate for a 350 g castrated rat is about 809 μg equivalents/day
(13) while the comparable rate for LH is only about 26 μg equivalents/day (10).

SOME APPLICATIONS

Since, at the present time, these rate estimates cannot be directly compared
with each other (or even with analogous rate estimates in non-castrates, since
these have not yet been obtained), it is reasonable to ask 'What good are
they?''. In reply to a similar question, Einstein is supposed to have replied
''What good is a baby?''. Although Einstein probably had a better baby, we are
tempted to offer the same answer.

Actually, we think they may be of some use even now. If we make one more
assumption[6] we can use them to calculate pituitary "turnover time" (TT_p) for
each hormone. If we divide these rates (expressed as activity units of NIH
hormone/unit time) into the amounts of hormone (expressed in the same activity units) present in the rat's own pituitary, we obtain, for each hormone,
an index of secretory rate which has only one dimension - time. This estimate (TT_p), expressed in words, is the length of time it takes the rat to
make, release or destroy a "pit-full" of the hormone being considered. Although we realize that the rat probably does not usually "turn over" its
intrahypophysial stores of a hormone (15), we think TT_p describes the
essential quantitative relationship between rate processes (e.g. - AI and
CI) and stores (BI), and can be useful in at least some circumstances in
which there is a change (ΔBI) in the latter.

Since TT_p for LH has the same dimension as TT_p for FSH, it also provides a
way in which our LH and FSH secretory rate estimates can be compared with
each other. For LH, TT_p is about 5 (4 to 7) days (roughly 120 hours). By
contrast, TT_p for FSH is about 8 hours (roughly $\frac{1}{3}$ day).

This <u>does</u> <u>not</u> mean that the castrated rat secretes FSH 15 times faster than
it secretes LH. It <u>does</u> mean that comparable transient disparities between
the synthesis and release rates of these 2 hormones would have about a 15-
fold greater effect on FSH stores than on LH stores. Such transient per-
turbations occur in various time domains. We will discuss two.

<u>1-3 day time domain</u>. We have used our TT_p indices to show that a decrement
in FSH release, too small to effect a change in the plasma FSH titer, could
rapidly (i.e. in < 24 hours) produce a dramatic increase in intrapituitary
FSH stores, if FSH synthesis were not synchronously and commensurately reduced (8). The longer TT_p for LH indicates why considerably greater
asynchrony or disparity between comparable changes in the rates of LH release and synthesis could simply fail to disturb the intrapituitary LH level
appreciably. The marked dichotomy in pituitary LH and FSH storage (8,9)
which actually occurs acutely in response to androgen administration in the
rat (provided its initial endogenous androgen levels are low) might, therefore, merely reflect - at least in part - the basic differences between the
initial LH and FSH "turnover times".

---

[6] Calculation of TT_p implies the assumption that equal quantities of intrahypophysial and extrahypophysial hormone have equal activity in the assay
system used. This assumption needs to be tested.

An interesting corollary of this is the contrasting effect of E + P (estrogen plus progesterone, 16) treatment on the plasma and pituitary levels of FSH. Although this steroid treatment reduces plasma FSH levels more rapidly than testosterone propionate treatment does (8), it fails to elevate pituitary FSH stores detectably, if at all. This has to mean that it suppresses FSH synthesis and release synchronously and commensurately (or at least at times and to extents which are very nearly the same). Since the FSH release and synthesis processes are not inherently tightly linked (see above), there are grounds here to speculate that this may reflect a dual site of E + P action.

20-40 minute time domain. In the FSH "depletion" assays for FSH - "releasing factor" (FSH-RF,17,18) it seems safe to assume that the rate of net FSH synthesis and release in the test animal (or explanted pituitary) does not exceed the rate in the control castrate (about 809 μg equivalents/day or 34 μg equivalents/hr.). From this, we can see that in the 20-40 minutes used for the test, complete cessation of FSH synthesis could reduce pituitary FSH content by no more than 11-22 μg equivalents, unless the FSH release rate were, at the same time, to be increased above the pre-test rate (presumably 34 μg equivalents/hr., or less). Since several hundred μg equivalents must leave these glands for the depletion to be detectable by bioassay, it is kinetically impossible to account for more than a tiny fraction of the depletion on the basis of the most drastic assumption about synthesis (complete stoppage). Depletion must signify increased release.

In this situation, our findings may enable us to make a readily testable prediction. We have never done an FSH-RF assay. To our knowledge, the relative sensitivites of FSH-RF assays based on depletion of FSH activity in the test pituitaries (17,18) have not been compared directly with those of FSH-RF assays in which increased FSH activity in the blood (16) or culture medium was used as the response parameter. Most investigators who use depletion assays apparently do so in the belief that, since FSH is more concentrated in the pituitary than in the blood, changes in intrahypophysial FSH stores can be detected more readily than changes in extrahypophysial FSH levels. However, if we consider that, during the brief span of a depletion assay (usually 20 to 40 minutes), the test gland may release over 100 μg equivalents of FSH, it becomes obvious that the FSH release rate must exceed 150 to 300 μg equivalents/hour - at least for a brief period. According to our calculations, this is 5 to 10 times the rate in the normal castrate. In vivo, the effect of such a high release rate on blood FSH levels would have to be detectable by Steelman-Pohley assay. If 100 μg equivalents of ovine FSH were to be given by i.v. injection to a 300 g rat (V_{FSH} 9 ml), plasma FSH activity would be increased by more than 10 μg equivalents/ml. Since the half-life of native murine FSH is about 150 minutes, 3 times as long as that of NIH ovine FSH (13), the elevated activity would remain measurable for a convenient period. If the total amount of FSH released in such an in vivo test were to exceed 100 μg equivalents (which is a very conservative estimate, on several counts), plasma FSH levels would have to exceed those in the normal castrate, which would make them extremely easy to measure by bioassay. In vitro, the situation should be similar. In other words, if our calculations are anywhere near correct, an FSH-RF assay based on bioassay measurement of an increment in plasma FSH activity could not be less sensitive, and might well be more sensitive, than an assay based on depletion. It would obviously be safer, since "depletion" (ΔB) could be masked com-

pletely if synthesis and release increased apace. Since K_{FSH} is not likely
to be labile (13), particularly in this time domain, increased FSH activity
in the plasma or culture medium would be much easier to interpret in quantitative dynamic terms.

SUMMARY

We have not tried here to explore fully the significance of the rate estimates we have presented. We have only tried to indicate some of the oppor-
tunities our experiments appear to have created. We hope this presentation
will stimulate others to extend our explorations of LH and FSH secretion as
phenomena amenable to quantitative kinetic analysis.

REFERENCES

1. Tait, J. F. and S. Burstein, in The Hormones (eds. Pincus, Thimann and
    Astwood) vol. 5, Acad. Press, N.Y., 1964, p. 441.
2. Nugent, C. A., K. Eik-Nes and F. H. Tyler, J. Clin. Endocrinol. 21: 1106,
    1961.
3. Yates, F. E. and R. D. Brennan - IBM Tech. Rep. No. 320-3228, Dec. 1967.
4. Bogdanove, E. M. - Vit. and Horm. 22: 205, 1964.
5. Schwartz, N. B. and J. C. Hoffman, Proc. 2nd Int. Cong. Horm. Steroids,
    Milan, 1960 (Int. Cong. Series No. 132, p. 997).
6. Gay, V. L., Endocrinology 81: 1177, 1967.
7. Bogdanove, E. M. and V. L. Gay, Endocrinology 81: 1104, 1967.
8. Gay, V. L. and E. M. Bogdanove - LH and FSH in plasma and pituitary of
    the castrated rat following short-term steroid treatment. (Submitted to
    Endocrinology, June 1968)
9. Bogdanove, E. M., Anat. Rec. 157: 117, 1967.
10. Gay, V. L. and E. M. Bogdanove, Endocrinology 82: 359, 1968.
11. Bogdanove, E. M., A. F. Parlow, J. N. Bogdanove, I. Bhargava and E. V.
    Crabill, Endocrinology 74: 114, 1964.
12. Taleisnik, S. and S. M. McCann, Endocrinology 68: 263, 1961.
13. Bogdanove, E. M. and V. L. Gay - Studies on the disappearance of LH and
    FSH in the rat; a quantitative approach to the analysis of adenohypophy-
    sial secretory kinetics. (Submitted to Endocrinology, June 1968)
14. Steelman, S. L. and F. M. Pohley, Endocrinology 53: 604, 1953.
15. Bogdanove, E. M. and V. L. Gay, Endocrinology 81: 930, 1967.
16. Igarashi, M. and S. M. McCann, Endocrinology 74: 446, 1964.
17. Corbin, A. and J. C. Story, Experientia 22: 694, 1966.
18. Saito, T., A. Arimura, E. E. Müller, C. Y. Bowers and A. V. Schally,
    Endocrinology 80: 313, 1967.

DISCUSSION

LUNENFELD: Dr. Bogdanove when you spoke about the administration
of exogenous gonadotropins did you inject these materials intravenously or subcutaneously?

BOGDANOVE: Intravenously.

RECOVERY OF EXOGENOUSLY ADMINISTERED GONADOTROPINS

Eugenia Rosemberg, Sewa R. Joshi, and Than T. Nwe

Medical Research Institute of Worcester, Inc.,
Worcester City Hospital, Worcester, Massachusetts

The availability of human urinary menopausal gonadotropin (HMG)
has made possible the study of the effect of this material
upon ovarian function in the human. The administration of HMG
combined with human chorionic gonadotropin (HCG) for the purpose
of inducing ovarian stimulation leading to ovulation has proved
to be of value in the treatment of specific cases of female
infertility (1-6). In the design of treatment, many dosage
schedules have been proposed in attempts to prevent the hyperstimulation syndrome, decrease the multiple birth rate and the
incidence of abortions. Many aspects of research in this area
need further investigation. One relates to the metabolism
and excretion rate of administered gonadotropins which may play
a role in ovarian responsiveness to exogenous gonadotropins.
It was therefore decided to undertake a study related to the
rate of excretion of exogenously administered HMG preparations
in patients receiving this medication for the purpose of
induction of ovulation.

MATERIAL AND METHODS

Eighteen patients with secondary and primary amenorrhea, oligomenorrhea
and anovulatory cycles were selected to conduct this investigation. The
characteristics of the administered gonadotropins is presented in Table 1.
The patients received the gonadotropin preparations intramuscularly, in
uniform daily doses, given for periods ranging from three to seven days,
or as a single injection of a large dose. In all, 48 courses of medication
were given. Serial determinations of urinary gonadotropins (under no
medication) were performed on each patient at various intervals prior to
initiation of treatment. This investigation was carried out in order to
determine their individual variation in endogenous gonadotropin excretion.
During medication courses, 24-hour urine collections were obtained four
days preceding commencement of treatment, during the entire treatment
period, and for twenty consecutive days after withdrawal of medication.
Urinary gonadotropin levels were estimated on control days, treatment and
immediate post-treatment days, and six to eight days after withdrawal of
medication.

Table 1

CHARACTERISTICS OF ADMINISTERED GONADOTROPINS

Preparation	Contents per Ampoule mg.	Gonadotropic Activity per ampoule			
		"Total" †	FSH ††	LH ††	FSH:LH Ratio
HMG* 1942	4.96	12.35	71.0	34.8	2.0
HMG 2010	4.91	8.15	64.3	20.2	3.2
HMG 2127	3.4	2.82	66.0	6.0	11.0
HMG 2138	3.0	2.49	74.0	2.7	27.4
HMG 2167	1.4	1.98	73.0	1.4	52.0
HMG 2225	2.34	3.88	80.8	22.6	3.6
HMG 2282	3.0	9.84	81.9	27.5	2.98
P**-25-EX-1990	2.5	11.41	84.5	93.8	0.9
P -25-EX-2040	1.45	7.22	74.3	130.6	0.57
P -25-EX-2074	1.0	12.45	72.8	103.2	0.71
P -25-EX-2089	0.938	9.73	64.5	49.4	1.31

† mg. equivalent 2nd IRP; †† IU equivalent 2nd IRP.
* HMG, supplied by the Ortho Research Foundation, Raritan, New Jersey.
** Pergonal, supplied by Cutter Laboratories, Berkeley, California.

Urine collections were processed immediately upon arrival or kept frozen until processing. Creatinine determinations were performed on individual 24-hour urine specimens as a check against gross errors of collections. Urine samples were individually extracted by the kaolin-acetone procedure of Albert (7). The extracts were kept in a dessicator at room temperature until the bioassays were performed. The mouse uterine weight assay in immature female mice was used to measure "general" or "total" gonadotropic activity. The details for performing the assay have been described previously (8). The individual 24-hour urinary extracts were tested using 2 x 3 or 3 x 3 assay design simultaneously with the Second International Reference Preparation for Human Menopausal Gonadotropin (2nd IRP) which was used as the reference material. Thus, serial control as well as pre-treatment values of endogenous gonadotropin excretion were obtained. During medication days, the total amount of exogenously administered gonadotropin* which appeared in urine was determined. The excretion of administered gonadotropin was calculated as the percentage of the total daily amount given.

RESULTS

Twelve courses of medication were administered to ten patients in single daily injections for periods ranging from 3 to 7 days. Table 2 shows the gonadotropin excretion pattern.

Table 2

EXCRETION OF ADMINISTERED GONADOTROPINS
(DAILY ADMINISTRATION)

Patient	Endogenous UG mcg†/24 hr		Medication Daily Dose mg †	UG Excretion per 24 hour							
	Serial Tests Mean ± SE (No. of Tests)	Pre-Medication		Medication Days Percent ††							Post-Medication mcg †
				1	2	3	4	5	6	7	
BR	373 ± 94 (5)	735	37.35	0.7	1.9	1.0					-
JH	205 ± 139 (2)	311	37.35	3.0	1.1	3.1					-
NS	462 ± 167 (9)	112	37.35	6.1	0.8	2.0					672
NM	-	2328	37.35	4.1	17.6	15.1	12.5	11.1	6.3	-	-
CR	<217 ± 82 (12)	1013	37.10	3.1	3.7	1.8	4.6	2.4	2.8		-
		<23	37.10	2.3	3.3	1.1	2.8	3.9	3.3	4.8	690
JG	<167 ± 61 (8)	162	12.35	4.7	8.4	3.6	3.3	8.1	7.4	7.0	732
JJ	<497 ± 172 (7)	329	37.10	2.1	2.1	2.4	2.3	4.7	4.0	3.3	45
		249	37.10	4.3	2.2	4.0	2.8	2.6	4.3		286
EK	324 (1)	3818	24.40	19.8	27.1	21.0	16.4	14.4	16.2		1577
DS	<334 ± 134 (8)	355	4.98	4.3	6.2	3.5	3.3	<0.5	8.4		249
NL	104 (1)	216	14.75	<0.2	<0.2	3.2	0.8	4.4	0.8	3.0	410

UG: Urinary Gonadotropins; † Equivalent of 2nd IRP; †† Percent of Administered amount.

Eight patients responded to therapy as judged by indirect indices of ovulation i.e.: increase in basal body temperature, increase in excretion of urinary estrogens and pregnanediol, and changes in vaginal cytology and cervical mucus, or by

* Indicated in Table 1 in terms of 2nd IRP. UG excretion values in normally menstruating women as determined in our laboratory range from 120 to 1,300 mcg. equiv./2nd IRP/24-hr.

pregnancy (patient CR, second treatment course). Two patients
(NM and EK) who showed elevated endogenous gonadotropins did not
respond to medication.

In patients responding to medication, the excretion values of
administered gonadotropin varied between 0.7 and 8.4 percent of the
total amount given. The highest excretion values i.e.: 4.1 and
27.1 percent were observed in the two patients who did not respond
to medication. Despite the variation in dose given to these
patients, there was no relation between dose and amount recovered.
Furthermore, the amount excreted showed no consistent pattern in
relation to medication days.

Twenty-two courses of medication were administered to nine patients
in single daily injections. In each case, the excretion value was
determined in pooled urine samples obtained during three to five
consecutive days of medication; these values were then calculated
on 24-hr. basis and as the percent of the total daily dose
administered.

Table 3

EXCRETION OF ADMINISTERED GONADOTROPINS
DAILY ADMINISTRATION (POOLED SAMPLES)

Patient	Endogenous UG mcg†/24 hr Mean ± SE (No. of Tests)	Medication Daily Dose mg†	UG Excretion mcg† per 24-hour	
			Medication Days (% ††)	Post-Medication
JL	≤289 ± 65 (12)	5.64 5.64 4.98	108 (1.9) 216 (3.8) 195 (3.9)	261 - 456
PB	≤353 ± 82 (13)	4.98 2.49 4.98 3.95	133 (2.7) 137 (5.5) 257 (5.2) 205 (5.2)	224 739 743 645
PS	≤139 ± 49 (6)	16.30 4.98	66 (0.4) 456 (9.2)	353 ≤23
JS	≤257 ± 4 (2)	3.95	126 (3.2)	-
AG	573 ± 260 (5)	4.98 2.49	282 (5.7) 257 (10.3)	1286 1120
NM	454 ± 233 (4)	2.49 4.98 24.90	290 (11.6) 353 (7.1) 232 (0.9)	1079 440 1232
SW	744 ± 260 (5)	2.49 9.73	606 (24.3) 581 (6.0)	133 923
MF	452 ± 245 (3)	3.88 7.77 2.49	324 (8.3) 320 (4.1) 320 (12.8)	539 943 552
JH	290 ± 17 (4)	1.94 3.88	415 (21.4) 470 (12.1)	830 287

UG: Urinary Gonadotropin; † Equivalent 2nd IRP; †† Percent of administered amount.

All patients responded to therapy as judged by indirect indices of ovulation or by pregnancy (patient NM, third treatment course). Gonadotropin excretion in twenty treatment courses varied between 0.4 and 12.8 percent. Only two patients (SW and JH) showed, during one treatment course, a high excretion of gonadotropin material (24.3 and 21.4 percent, respectively).

The last group of seven patients were given the total dose of gonadotropin as single injection. Fourteen courses of medication were studied. In each case, the excretion value was determined on the day of administration of gonadotropin and for four to seven consecutive days after withdrawal of medication.

Table 4

EXCRETION OF ADMINISTERED GONADOTROPIN
TOTAL DOSE ADMINISTERED AS A SINGLE INJECTION

Patient	Endogenous UG mcg†/24 hr Serial Tests Mean ± SE (No. of Tests)	Pre-Medication	Medication Dose mg†	Medication Day (% ††)	UG Excretion mcg† per 24 hours — Days Following Medication							Post-Medication
					1	2	3	4	5	6	7	
JJ	≤497 ± 172 (7)	138	32.54	767 (2.4)	319	*	239					-
		-	32.54	548 (1.7)	239	*	956					-
		-	32.54	521 (1.6)	558	558	*					481
AM	501 ± 147 (11)	212	13.83	*	849	213	≤23	341	138	*	433	158
		415	34.96	971 (2.8)	925	842	974	347	≤23	2121	≤23	179
CR	≤217 ± 82 (12)	369	108.32	573 (0.5)	1688	622	926	727	533	478	637	70
		92	196.71	1384 (0.7)	≤23	433	370	≤23	≤23	≤23	≤23	482
DS	≤334 ± 134 (8)	≤23	205.43	2643 (1.3)	13156	621	2470	2305	689	781		164
		105	85.46	1559 (1.8)	734	3603	990	149	361	298		382
SW	744 ± 260 (5)	456	38.84	5355 (13.8)	4147	2048	2955	2065				486
		634	116.78	6951 (6.0)	7740	1867	2635	≤23				1006
JH	290 ± 17 (4)	387	98.36	1534 (1.6)	≤23	466	≤23	≤23				403
		395	97.32	≤23 (0.02)	≤23	1255	436	861				*
MF	452 ± 245 (3)	338	98.36	≤23 (≤0.02)	≤23	1610	718	705				533

UG: Urinary Gonadotropin ; †Equivalent 2nd IRP; †† Percent of administered amount; * Sample lost.

It should be noted that on the day when gonadotropin was given, the excretion of administered material varied from <0.02 to 2.8, except in one case (patient SW) who excreted 13.8 percent on the first medication course and 6.0 percent on the second course of medication. The excretion of gonadotropin did not follow any consistent pattern on days immediately after withdrawal of medication. There were no noticeable differences between patients who responded to medication with ovulation (five courses, patients AM, SW and JH) or pregnancy (two courses, patients AM and MF) and those who did not respond to therapy (patients JJ, CR and DS).

CONCLUSIONS

Because of the known variability in the daily excretion of endogenous gonadotropins, (9) studies of this nature should be interpreted with caution. The present studies showed quite conclusively that endogenous gonadotropin was measurable in all patients, either when serial determinations were performed prior to medication, or when the determinations were carried out immediately before treatment. It is reasonable to assume that endogenous gonadotropin contributed to the amount measured during medication days. Hence, because the amount of endogenous gonadotropin cannot possibly be distinguished by this method of assay from that corresponding to the exogenous material, only a very small percentage of the latter was actually excreted. Studies in hypophysectomized subjects may clarify this problem.

The data suggest that there was no relation between the dose of gonadotropin given and the amount recovered. Higher recovery was seen in patients with high endogenous gonadotropin excretion who did not respond to medication. No correlation was found between the amount of estrogen excreted during medication days and the amount of gonadotropin measured in the urine.

Finally, it should be remembered that the amount of exogenously administered gonadotropin which appears in urine reflects the various events occurring during the sojourn of the hormone in the body i.e.: metabolism and utilization by the end organ as well as renal clearance of hormonal material.

This work was supported in part by Grant AM-07564 from the National Institutes of Health, USPHS, Bethesda, Maryland, and in part by a Grant from the Ortho Research Foundation, Raritan, New Jersey, and by a Grant from Cutter Laboratories, Berkeley, California.

REFERENCES

1. Rosemberg, E., J. Coleman, M. Demany, and C. R. Garcia. J. Clin. Endocrinol. 23: 181, 1963.

2. Rosemberg, E., R. E. Maher, A. Stern, and M. Demany. J. Clin. Endocrinol. 24: 105, 1964.

3. Rosemberg, E. In: Induccion E Inhibicion de la Ovulacion. Excerpta Med. Found. Int'l. Congress Series # 104. C. Gual (Ed.) p. 39, 1966.

4.   Rosemberg, E. In: Ovulation: Stimulation, Suppression,
     Detection. J. B. Lippincott, Comp., Philadelphia,
     Pennsylvania, p. 118, 1966.

5.   Rosemberg, E. Rev. Argent. Endocrinol. Metab., <u>12</u>: 131,
     1966.

6.   Rosemberg, E., and T. T. Nwe. Fertil. Steril., <u>19</u>: 197,
     1968.

7.   Albert, A., Proc. Staff Meet. Mayo Clinic. <u>30</u>: 552,
     1955.

8.   Rosemberg, E., F. Smith, and R. I. Dorfman. Endocrinology
     <u>61</u>: 337, 1957.

9.   Rosemberg, E. J. Clin. Endocrinol. <u>20</u>: 306, 1960.

THE RECOVERY OF EXOGENOUS FOLLICLE STIMULATING HORMONE FROM URINE

A. C. CROOKE, MD, FRCP, M. MORELL, MD[*], W. R. BUTT, PhD, FRIC.

THE UNITED BIRMINGHAM HOSPITALS, DEPARTMENT OF CLINICAL ENDO-
CRINOLOGY, BIRMINGHAM AND MIDLAND HOSPITAL FOR WOMEN, BIRMING-
HAM, 11, ENGLAND.

INTRODUCTION

Infertile patients with secondary amenorrhoea have been shown to respond to a single injection of follicle stimulating hormone (FSH) by a progressive increase in the excretion of oestriol reaching a peak value up to ten to twelve days later. When this is followed by chorionic gonadotrophin (HCG) nine days after the initial injection, ovulation may occur as proved by subsequent pregnancy in a number of cases. This train of events suggested either that FSH must remain in effective concentration in the ovary for this duration of time or that if it was rapidly excreted the follicle once stimulated would continue to grow spontaneously. In order to investigate these alternatives an experiment was designed to measure the rate of excretion of exogenous gonadotrophins (1).

MATERIAL AND METHODS

Thirteen women were treated with either human pituitary FSH (fraction CP 1) (2) or human menopausal gonadotrophin (HMG - Pergonal) which was given as a single injection or in three equally divided doses at 12 or 24-hourly intervals. The total dose varied between 500 IU and 4,290 IU, depending on the individual patient's sensitivity to the hormone. Urine was collected in 24-hour lots commencing the day before starting treatment for up to ten consecutive days afterwards, and extracted by the kaolin method. FSH was measured by the augmentation method in mice (3). One hundred and nine full scale assays were carried out and the patterns of excretion were plotted. Control levels of gonadotrophin were based on the mean of 24-hour samples of urine collected immediately before treatment and on the last one or two samples collected at the end of the investigation. The recoveries were based on the total amount excreted minus the control values.

RESULTS

The excretion of FSH was calculated as the daily percentage of the total amount recovered for each patient. This allowed the excretion values for all patients to be plotted on the same scale. The mean values for the three groups of patients given single injections or triple injections at 12 or 24-hourly intervals respectively are shown in Figure 1. The mean recoveries for the three groups were of the same order, being 6.8, 10.2 and 8.0 per cent respectively. With single injections, however, most of the hormone was excreted on days 2 and 3 whereas with triple injections it was excreted on days 3 to 5.

Despite the great variation in total dose given to the different patients there was no relation between the dose and the amount recovered. This is shown in Figure 2. Furthermore the recoveries were similar whether the

*Present address: University of Granada, Department of Physiology and Biochemistry, Granada, Spain.

injected FSH was of urinary or pituitary origin (Figure 3). There was, however, a higher recovery in six patients who failed to respond to treatment than in the seven who responded, as judged by an increase in excretion of oestriol or preg- nanediol (Figure 4). The mean for the former was 10.7 per cent and for the latter 5.6 per cent. There was also a relationship between the control level of excretion of FSH and the amount recovered. This is shown in Figure 5. The recovery was greater in patients with higher control values ($r = 0.58$, $P < 0.05$).

DISCUSSION

The results suggest that less FSH is used up by patients with inactive ovaries as judged by their higher basal excretion of FSH or failure to respond to treatment than by those with active ovaries. Those with inactive ovaries, however, were not necessarily unresponsive to higher dosages but we have not yet compared the recoveries of FSH at dosages that were effective with those that were ineffective in the same patients.

The results also indicate that exogenous hormone is excreted rapidly and control levels may be reached again at a time when the excretion of oestro- gen is still rising. Furthermore, the follicle is still ripening, as judged by the fact that ovulation can be induced by HCG six or seven days after the excre- tion of FSH has returned to control levels.

The mode of action of FSH is still speculative. We are investigating it at the cellular level by in vitro studies using the ovaries of immature mice (4). The results suggest that FSH is required for the development of each successive generation of follicle cells. In the human, however, the conditions are very different. It is possible that after a certain stage of development has been reached further growth of the follicle is autonomous. Alternatively the patient may be able to produce enough endogenous gonadotrophins to permit later maturation of the follicle.

The work was supported by grants made to Dr. A. C. Crooke by Ford Foundation and the Medical Research Council and a Junior Research Training Grant to M.M. by World Health Organization. We thank Dr. J. K. Butler of G. D. Searle & Co. Ltd., for supplies of Pergonal.

REFERENCES

1. Morell, M., A. C. Crooke and W. R. Butt, J. Endocr. 41: 1968, in press[*].
2. Butt, W. R., A. C. Crooke and F. J. Cunningham, Biochem. J. 81: 596, 1961.
3. Brown, P. S., J. Endocr. 13: 59 1955.
4. Ryle, M., 1968, in press.

[*]p. 571.

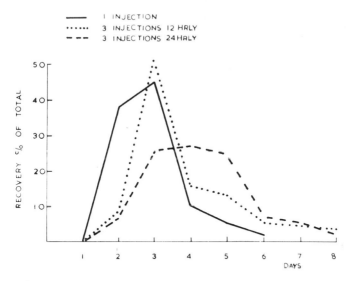

Figure 1. The mean percentage of FSH recovered daily
following single or triple injections of FSH.

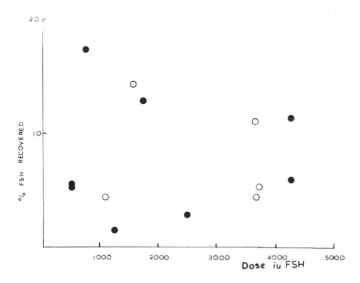

Figure 2. Variation in recovery of FSH with dose injected.

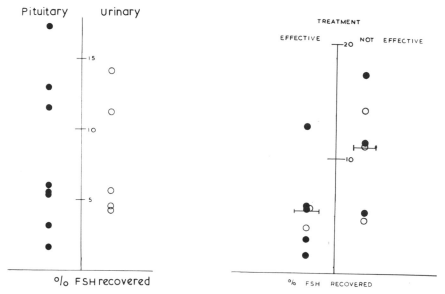

Figure 3.   Comparison of the recoveries of injected pituitary and urinary FSH.

Figure 4.   Variation in recovery of FSH with response.

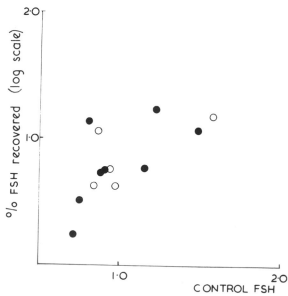

Figure 5.   Relation between the control excretion of FSH and the amount recovered.

DISCUSSION

JOHNSEN: This question is addressed to Dr. Rosemberg and also to
Dr. Crooke. I may have missed the point but how could you
possibly perform such studies in persons in whom you measure endogenous gonadotropins? We have performed similar studies in two
men. These two men had no endogenous gonadotropin. We obtained
a higher figure for recovery of about 15 or 20%.

ROSEMBERG: Yes Dr. Johnsen you are absolutely right. That is
why I indicated that in all the patients studied endogenous
gonadotropins were measurable in the urine. I pointed out that
we have to be very cautious in interpreting these results. I
also indicated that each subject had a large variation in
endogenous gonadotropin excretion. Hence, when calculating the
recovery of administered gonadotropins, the calculated percent
recovery may be misleading as we do not have any way of knowing
how much of the endogenous gonadotropin excreted is to be
subtracted from the actual value. This is interesting data.
However, until we can calculate the amount of endogenous
gonadotropin, we will not know how much of the exogenous material
is actually being excreted. Perhaps someone in the audience has
studied hypophysectomized individuals and could give us a more
precise answer.

BETTENDORF: In collaboration with Dr. Apostolakis we have
measured the clearance rate of HMG in hypogonadotropic subjects.
This was found to be 0.4 - 1.7 ml./min. The recovery in the
urine was 5 - 25% of the amount of gonadotropin administered.

VANDE WIELE: Dr. Rizkallah in our laboratory has recently
completed a study of the rate of disappearance of HCG from
plasma following the i.v. administration of 10,000 IU. In both
males and females the disappearance curve was bi-exponential
with a fast component having a mean half-life of 5.1 hours and
a slow component with a mean half-life of 23 hours. Following
the i.m. administration of the same dose a peak of HCG in plasma
was reached after approximately 6 hours, but later on the
disappearance was very similar to that following i.v. injection.
The metabolic clearance rate was 3.5 and 3.8 liters per 24 hours
in males and females respectively.

PARLOW: You measured HCG by radioimmunoassay? Is that correct?

VANDE WIELE: Yes.

TAYMOR: I would very briefly like to confirm one of the points
that Dr. Parlow made about the persistence of FSH activity after
a single injection of HMG. Subjects were given from 800 to
1600 IU of HMG in a single injection, and the levels of FSH
determined by radioimmunoassay. Assays were carried out at
daily intervals (two subjects), and every 8 hours (two subjects).
In general, there was a persistence of FSH activity in the serum

for 72 to 96 hours following a single injection. There was a
very sharp rise occurring within the first 8 hours after injection. This information is important with regard to therapy with
HMG.

ROSEMBERG: Dr. Taymor, this is very interesting data. Was the
material administered intramuscularly?

TAYMOR: Yes.

ROSEMBERG: Can you please correlate the excretion of estrogen
during the days following administration of a single injection
with serum levels of FSH?

TAYMOR; We do have additional data on estrogen excretion. In
general estrogen excretion begins to rise about the second or
third day after the single injection and in most cases falls
again within 2 or 3 days. We have not been able to duplicate
the findings of Crooke namely that estrogen levels will continue
to rise for up to 8 days after a single injection. Of course
this may be dose related.

ROSEMBERG: We have studied patients in whom the total dose was
administered as a single injection and we have confirmed Dr.
Crooke's findings. After the single dose administration the
estrogen excretion begins to rise and continues to rise for 8
days. HCG is administered on day 9. The elevation of urinary
estrogens correlates well with the cornification seen in the
vaginal smears.

FAIMAN: I should like to make two comments. The first concerns
Dr. Vande Wiele's observation on the disappearance of HCG from
serum. Dr. Ryan and I (Clin. Res. 15: 412, 1967) reported two
components in the postpartum disappearance of HCG. This was
measured by radioimmunoassay. The initial half-life was about
6 hours. This was probably an overestimation since we did not
obtain many values in the first 24 hours. The second component
had a much longer half-life but the value was not calculated.
Many years ago Dr. Albert reported (J. Clin. Endocr. 10, 371,
1950) a half-life for HCG of about 3½ hours using bioassay
methods. My second comment concerns the recovery in urine of
administered FSH. Drs. Ryan, Albert and I have studied the
excretion of FSH in the urine of a 30-year-old anovulatory
woman. After two control 24-hour urine specimens were collected,
500 IU of postmenopausal gonadotropin were injected intramuscularly and 5 daily urine specimens were subsequently collected.
Daily venous blood samples were also obtained. Each urine specimen was assayed radioimmunologically and biologically (augmentation assay) for FSH and each serum was assayed for FSH by
radioimmunoassay. Serum concentrations and daily urinary excretion of FSH paralleled each other and were maximal on the third
day after administration. The amount of FSH recovered from
urine, during the 5 days following injection, was between 5 and
6% of the administered dose whether the recovery was based on
bioassay or radioimmunoassay data.

CHAPTER 2

BIOLOGY OF GONADOTROPINS

2. CONTROL OF PITUITARY SECRETION OF GONADOTROPINS

SOME ASPECTS OF THE CONTROL OF SECRETION IN LH AND FSH IN HUMANS

R. S. Swerdloff and W. D. Odell, UCLA School of Medicine, Harbor General Hospital Campus, Department of Medicine, Torrance, California

INTRODUCTION

Development of the radioimmunoassay for LH and FSH has allowed the measurement of the small quantities of these hormones in the serum or plasma of human subjects. We have previously reported on the methodology used in our laboratory for the measurement of these hormones [1-3]. IRP-HMG#2 was used as the standard for both hormones; purified HLH and HFSH* were iodinated with I^{-131} by the method of Greenwood, et al. [4]. The rabbit anti-HCG and anti-FSH used as antisera for LH and FSH respectively have been shown to be specific for LH, HCG, and FSH [1-3]. Separation of the bound from free labeled hormone was accomplished using a double antibody technique. Normal values have been previously reported for men, children, postmenopausal women, and eugonadal women during the menstrual cycle. We are reporting now the effects of various physiologic and pharmacologic effectors of LH and FSH release.

EFFECT OF PITUITARY SUPPRESSION WITH ESTROGEN IN MALES

Fourteen male subjects were given ethinyl estradiol, 0.1 mg twice a day for four days. Serum samples obtained just before and daily after treatment (Figure 1) demonstrate the significant decrease of both LH and FSH by day four of treatment. It is of note, however, that the majority of subjects still had detectable hormone levels at that time.

EFFECT OF PITUITARY SUPPRESSION WITH ANDROGEN IN MALES

Fluoxymesterone in doses of either 10 mg or 25 mg twice a day was administered to normal male subjects. Figure 2 demonstrates the effect of this androgen on serum LH and FSH. A slight reduction in plasma LH concentrations resulted from administration of 20 mg per day ($p \leq 0.05$, paired t test) with marked suppression being attained with 50 mg per day. The larger dose resulted in undetectable levels in 6 of 9 subjects at four days. In contrast, no suppression of FSH was seen with either dose. This suggests that androgens act in the physiologic feedback inhibition of LH but not of FSH. Franchimont [5] has recently reported a similar finding.

*Obtained through the generosity of the National Pituitary Agency and prepared by Dr. L. E. Reichert, Emory University, Atlanta, Georgia.

GONADOTROPINS 1968

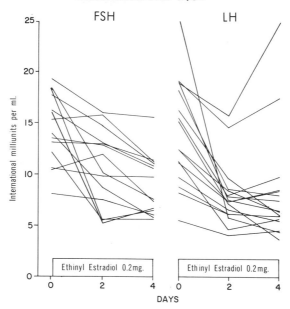

FIGURE 1: Serum FSH and LH measured before and on days 2 and
4 during ethinyl estradiol administration

DIURNAL VARIATION IN MALES

Figure 3 depicts the serum LH and FSH concentrations of 10 subjects in whom blood samples were obtained every two hours for 24
hours. No significant diurnal variation was noted for either
hormone. Six of the 10 subjects were at bed rest during the
whole period of study. Four subjects were ambulatory during the
daytime hours. No consistant difference was noted between the
groups.

Figure 4 represents serum LH and FSH levels obtained at 6 a.m.
and 6 p.m. for five consecutive days in four ambulatory subjects
plus the 6 am. and 6 p.m. samples in the above 10 subjects. FSH
shows no tendency for diurnal variation. The morning LH values
were higher than the p.m. in 19 of the 30 paired samples but for
the group paired samples at two times were not significantly
different.

Our FSH data is not in agreement with those of Faiman and
Ryan [6] and Saxena [7] who found that am. FSH was significantly
higher than p.m. values. The lack of diurnal variation in LH in
our study confirms the earlier report of Odell, et al. [1] and
is consistant with the data of other investigators [6, 7, 8].
The reason for the discrepancy in the FSH data is unclear at
the present time.

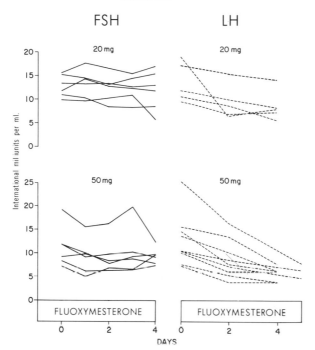

FIGURE 2:   Serum FSH (measured daily) and serum LH (measured
every other day) in male subjects treated with the synthetic
androgen, fluoxymesterone.   LH concentrations were not detectable at 4 or 5 days in 6 of 9 subjects (lowest 6 on figure).

EFFECT OF AGENTS KNOWN TO ALTER RELEASE OF OTHER PITUITARY HORMONES

No change in serum LH or FSH was noted in any subject during
glucose tolerance, arginine monochloride, or pitressin stimulation tests;   each test being performed on 5 to 8 subjects.
Figures 5 and 6 illustrate the results of the glucose and
arginine tests.

The effect of the stressful stimulus of surgery on various
pituitary hormones was recently examined in our laboratory [9].
Serum LH and FSH was measured on five eugonadal females, five
postmenopausal females and three eugonadal males before, during
and after elective surgery.   No change was noted during surgery.
However, in the first two postoperative days both LH and FSH
fell in 7 of 8 eugonadal, and all of the postmenopausal subjects.
Concentrations returned toward control levels during convales-
cence.   The effect of exercise on serum levels of the hormones
has also been examined.   No change was noted in 3 of 4 males

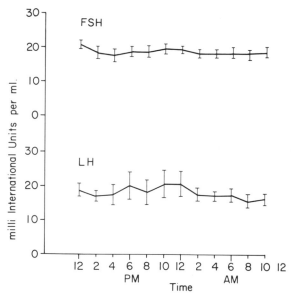

FIGURE 3: Serum LH and FSH concentrations obtained from ten patients every two hours.

subjected to very stressful exercise. A two-fold increase of LH was noted in one subject 5 minutes after exercise. This increase was not apparent 10 minutes later.

EFFECT OF SEQUENTIAL AND NON-SEQUENTIAL CONTRACEPTIVES IN EUGONADAL WOMEN

Serum LH and FSH concentrations were measured daily in fourteen eugonadal women treated with oral contraceptive agents. The results were compared to those in a larger number of untreated eugonadal women. Figure 7 is a schematic representation of a normal cycle. This is based upon our previously published findings in a large population of normal women [1,2,3 10]. Six women received a non-sequential contraceptive containing the combination of norethynodrel, 2.5 mg and mestranol 0.1 mg. No LH and FSH midcycle peaks were observed in any of these subjects and serum concentrations of both hormones remained low throughout the treatment period (Figure 8). This confirms earlier studies [2, 10, 11]. Eight women received a sequential contraceptive containing 80 mcg of mestranol alone for 15 days, followed by 5 days in which 2 mg of chlormadinone acetate was administered. One or more LH peaks occurred during the estrogen phase in 6 of the 8 subjects. In 4 of the 8 subjects LH peaks also occurred immediately after the addition of progestogen to the estrogen in the sequential regimen. No FSH peak was noted

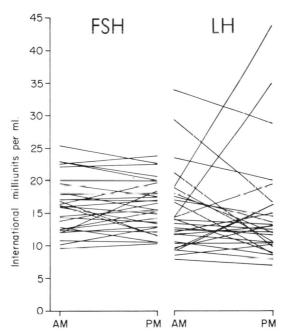

FIGURE 4:   Serum FSH and LH concentrations measured at 6:00 a.m.
            and 6:00 p.m. in eugonadal men.

at any time during treatment (Figure 6). The non-sequential
administration inhibited both LH and FSH midcycle peaks while
sequential administration stimulated LH peaks without associated FSH increases. It is suggested that inhibition of FSH is
responsible for the contraceptive action of the sequential
agent. In addition, estrogen is shown to be a potent stimulus
for LH release.

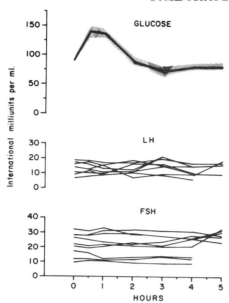

FIGURE 5

Serum LH, FSH, and
glucose concentrations
after a 100 gram oral
glucose load.   Glucose
concentration is in mg
percent.

FIGURE 6

Serum LH, FSH, and
growth hormone before
and following a 30
minute infusion of
25 grams of l-
arginine monhydrachlor-
ide.   Growth hormone
concentrations are
expressed in milli-
micrograms per ml.

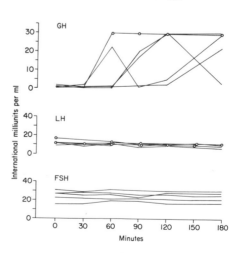

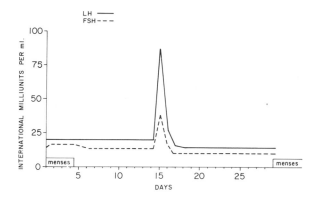

<u>FIGURE 7</u>: Schematic diagram of LH and FSH fluctuations
throughout a normal menstrual cycle, based upon data previously published from our laboratory (1-3).

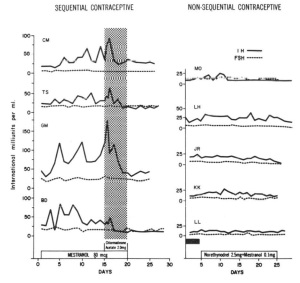

<u>FIGURE 8</u>: Daily FSH and LH determinations on serum from four
women receiving a sequential estrogen-progestogen contraceptive and from five women receiving a non-sequential estrogen-
progestogen contraceptive. These examples were selected from
a total of six that we have studied and who received the
latter and eight who received the former type of contraceptive.

GONADOTROPINS 1968
REFERENCES

These studies were supported by U. S. P. H. S. Grant #HD-02701-01. Dr. Swerdloff is a Special Fellow, U. S. P. H. S. #HD-35, 807-01, National Institute of Child Health and Human Development.

1. Odell, W. D., G. T. Ross and P. L. Rayford: J. Clin. Inv., 46:248, 1967.

2. Odell, W. D. and R. S. Swerdloff: Proceedings of the Program of Radioisotopes in Medicine: In Vitro Studies. R. L. Hayes, F. A. Goswitz and B. E. P. Murphy (eds.), AEC Symposium Series No. 13 (CONF-671111), Oak Ridge, Tennessee, 1968, pp. 185-206.

3. Odell, W. D., A. F. Parlow, C. G. Cargille and G. T. Ross; J. Clin. Inv., (to be published December, 1968).

4. Greenwood, F. C., W. M. Hunter and J. S. Glover: Biochem. J., 89:114, 1963.

5. Franchimont, P.: Protein and Polypeptide Hormones, Part I, page 99, 1968, M. Margoulies, (ed.), Excerpta Medica Foundation, Amsterdam, 1968.

6. **Faiman**, C. and R. Ryan: Nature; 215:857, 1966.

7. Saxena, B. B., H. Demura, H. M. Gandy and R. E. Peterson: J. Clin. Endocr. and Metab., 28:519, 1968.

8. Burger, H. G., J. B. Brown, K. J. Catt, B. Hudson and J. R. Stockigt. Protein and Polypeptide Hormones, Part II, page 412, M. Margoulies (ed.), Excerpta Medical Foundation, Amsterdam, 1968.

9. Charters, C., W. D. Odell and J. Thompson: Submitted for publication.

10. Ross, G. T., W. D. Odell and P. L. Rayford: Science, 155:1679, 1967.

11. Cargille, C. M., G. T. Ross, L. A. Howland and P. L. Rayford: Clin. Res., 16:263, 1968.

DISCUSSION

BOGDANOVE: Dr. Swerdloff stated that treatment with an androgen (fluoroxymesterone) did not inhibit the release of FSH in the human male. This was, I think, short-term treatment. In the rat, too, androgens do not inhibit the release of FSH immediately but there is a delayed effect (Bogdanove, E. M., Anat. Rec., 157: 117-136, 1967). I think that we should be careful always to consider the time-domain of a particular response before drawing conclusions which the reader may easily overinterpret.

SWERDLOFF: We have not looked at the effect of androgens in eugonadal males for any period longer than six days. During that time interval, no evidence of feedback inhibition of FSH was noted.

PAULSEN: One of the issues raised by Dr. Swerdloff concerns the specific role played by gonadotropins in the testis, i.e. FSH regulating spermatogenesis and LH (ICSH) regulating steroidogenesis. We have had an opportunity to examine the differential excretion of FSH and LH in a number of situations, but one in particular emphasizes the selective nature of gonadotropin action. If the normal testis is exposed to acute x-ray irradiation the germinal epithelium is affected while Leydig cell formation remains unchanged. For example, at radiation doses ranging from 30 to 400 r azoospermia develops but plasma testosterone levels remain unaltered. Urinary FSH titers (as measured by the Steelman Pohley assay) increase while urinary LH excretion does not appear to change. Since androgen production is not depressed these studies emphasize the fact that pituitary FSH secretion is controlled in some manner by the germinal cell epithelium and not by testosterone production. I wish to call to your attention another interesting aspect of our radiation study. We find that urinary FSH titers increase prior to the decrease in seminal fluid sperm concentration and does return to normal levels before the sperm count or the germinal epithelium fully recovers. These observations imply that the control of FSH secretion is not related to the actual number of germ cells nor the production "rate" of mature sperm. The exact identity of the testicular site for control of FSH secretion unfortunately remains obscure.

LUNENFELD: During the last few days we have seen a number of different excretion patterns during the normal cycle. Here we see another extreme. We see that the curve both for LH and FSH is completely flat, both in the follicular and luteal stage, and that there is only a peak at midcycle. The values of these peaks are rather lower than those shown in the other presentations during the past few days. I wonder if there is any difference in the pathology which could explain these findings. Could someone tell us why we see such large variations between different centers concerning the FSH and LH excretion patterns during the normal menstrual cycle.

SWERDLOFF: With regard to the levels of LH and FSH seen during the mid-cycle peak, I think that most workers using radioimmuno-assay have values very similar to ours. We find LH values in the mid-cycle peak between 40 and 160 mIU and FSH values between 15 and 35 mIU. With regard to the early follicular phase levels of FSH, we have shown a statistically significant increase in the first half as compared to the second half of the follicular phase. The first half follicular phase values are about 10% higher than the second half values. This difference is quantitatively less than that Dr. Cargille has found with his method but quantitatively similar to the findings of most investigators.

MIDGLEY: I commented yesterday that our LH and FSH values during the menstrual cycle were very similar to those which Dr. Cargille presented. In view of the preceding discussion I would like to refer to our results (J. Clin. Endocr., In press). The results were plotted in two ways, according to the day of the cycle and days from the LH peak at mid-cycle. In our hands the FSH peak coincided with the LH peak in all cycles in which both were observed. The two peaks preceded the rise in basal body temperature. There was a striking increase in concentration of FSH on the first day of the cycle with an associated increase in LH. Just prior to the peak at mid-cycle, the FSH level fell while LH began to rise. After the mid-cycle peak, LH often showed finer daily peaks which were not associated with changes in FSH concentrations. Both hormones then fell to the lowest concentrations of the entire menstrual cycle on the one or two days prior to the next menstruation.

ALBERT: Although I did not come prepared to discuss this Dr. Rosemberg has just asked me to summarize the urinary excretion of FSH and LH during the menstrual cycle as measured by bioassay methods. There seems to be no problem with respect to LH. The pattern of LH excretion during the menstrual cycle has been known for years using bioassay technics and the radioimmunoassay method confirms this. Dr. Rocca and I have recently published a study on FSH excretion (Mayo Clinic Proc. 42: 536, 1967). We carried out daily FSH excretions in 28 young women. These were novitiates and lived under fairly standard conditions. The general pattern showed an increase on FSH excretion during the first 5 days and then a gradual drop towards mid-cycle. I will omit the mid-cycle pattern for a moment. During the luteal phase a further drop was noted and then just before the next menses an increase occurred. Coming back to the mid-cycle, some but not all of these subjects showed a mid-cycle increase in FSH just as was found by radio-immunoassay in serum. I think that bioassay and radioimmunoassay agree very well except for the mid-cycle FSH peak. I wonder if by radioimmunoassay of serum, this peak would be found in every normal cycle and also in the same patient over several consecutive cycles.

ROSEMBERG: It is worth noting that the bioassay of FSH and LH in the urine of normally menstruating women is difficult due to the low levels excreted during a 24-hour period and the low sensitivity of the bioassays used. The main problem has been the necessity of pooling the urine horizontally or vertically, or both, in order to obtain sufficient material for satisfactory assays. Horizontal pooling of urine imposes some errors in that it may mask significant daily fluctuations of gonadotropin excretion; vertical pooling is unsatisfactory because considerable variation in individual titers may occur between different subjects. One of our studies included horizontal (48-hour) and vertical (7 subjects) pooling of urine (Rosemberg, E. and Keller, P. J., J. Clin. Endocr. 25: 1262, 1965) and showed that FSH excretion values during the proliferative phase of the cycle were higher than those recorded during the luteal phase, with a significant increase on days 15 and 16. We re-studied the problem of FSH excretion by assaying individual daily samples of urine (Rosemberg, E., Joshi, S. R. and Nwe T. T., J. Clin. Endocr. and Metab. In press) using the "one point" bioassay design described by Dr. Albert (Mayo Clin. Proc. 42: 288, 1967). The individual FSH assays corresponding to 7 subjects with cycles of 25 to 29 days indicated that FSH excretion was increased on the first few days of the proliferative phase of the cycle and then decreased until about mid-cycle when another increase was observed. From the early part of the luteal phase, FSH excretion decreased gradually until the end of the cycle. In general, FSH excretion was higher during the proliferative phase than during the luteal phase. This study, as well as that of Rocca and Albert, did not confirm a consistent decrease of FSH to undetectable levels during the mid-cycle as observed by Fukushima et al (J. Clin. Endocr. 24: 205, 1964), who studied 28-day cycles. However, all published reports, including a later publication by Stevens et al (Metabolism 14: 327, 1965) indicate that occasional cycles may show a decrease near mid-cycle. As pointed out by Dr. Albert, daily measurement of FSH by radioimmunoassay may help in defining what could be considered typical or as representing an average pattern of urinary FSH excretion or serum FSH levels during the normal menstrual cycle.

MIDGLEY: Although an LH peak was seen in all 37 subjects examined, an FSH peak was not seen in 6 of these subjects. In our experience, the peak in FSH at mid-cycle was considerably smaller in duration and magnitude than the peak of LH. Although it would be very difficult to miss the LH peak by obtaining samples once a day, it would be quite easy to miss the FSH peak with this frequency of sampling.

GANDY: Do you want me to comment on the FSH-LH values in the cycle? I would like to ask Dr. Swerdloff about the age of his male subjects and whether they were at bed rest for 24 hours or ambulatory. We have obtained blood samples every 4 hours for 24 hours in a total of 7 ambulatory male subjects. The highest values for FSH and LH occurred in the 4 or 8 a.m. samples for each subject; p.m. values were significantly lower than a.m. values.

SWERDLOFF: Unfortunately, Dr. Gandy, I am not able to explain
the differences in diurnal LH and FSH response obtained in different laboratories. I can only present our experience using our
antisera which failed to demonstrate any consistent diurnal change
in these hormones. We do not feel that ambulation is an important
factor influencing serum LH and FSH values. No consistent difference was noted between the ambulatory and non-ambulatory subjects
in whom serum LH and FSH was measured every two hours. Furthermore,
even severe exercise has failed to consistently influence the
concentration of these hormones.

STUDIES ON THE MECHANISMS CONTROLLING THE RELEASE OF FSH

FROM THE PITUITARY GLAND

E. STEINBERGER and G.E. DUCKETT

Division of Endocrinology and Reproduction
Research Laboratories
Albert Einstein Medical Center
Philadelphia, Pa. 19141

INTRODUCTION

It has been suggested that Leydig cell secretions control FSH release, while the germinal epithelium may be involved in regulating the production of this hormone (1). A possibility that testosterone is the agent involved in controlling FSH release was tested in experiments in which blood and pituitary levels of FSH were measured simultaneously in a properly prepared experimental animal (2). Extirpation of Leydig cells by orchiectomy resulted in a drop of pituitary FSH levels and a concomitant rise of blood FSH. These results were considered to be positive evidence that the release of FSH from the pituitary gland is augmented in response to orchiectomy. Administration of testosterone propionate to orchiectomized rats produced either normal or elevated levels of FSH in the pituitary gland, depending on the testosterone dose, and undetectable quantities of FSH in blood. From these experiments, it was concluded that a steroid produced by the Leydig cells, most likely testosterone, is the agent exerting a negative feedback on the FSH releasing mechanism from the pituitary gland.

We have examined a number of factors in order to define this mechanism more precisely. First, if testosterone regulates FSH release, this action should be relatively rapid, so that pituitary FSH levels should drop well before seven days after orchiectomy. Second, one should be able to obtain a testosterone dose-response curve. Present studies were designed to answer these two questions and to investigate the effect of estrogen on pituitary FSH levels in orchiectomized and orchiectomized testosterone-treated rats.

MATERIALS AND METHODS

In all experiments adult hooded rats of the Long-Evans strain bred in our laboratories were used. Subcutaneous injections of testosterone propionate or estradiol benzoate in 0.1 ml of sesame oil were administered daily. Orchiectomies were performed via the scrotal route.

FSH was determined by the augmentation method of Steelman and Pohley (3). A parallel line 2 x 2 assay design was employed and statistical calculations were performed, utilizing the Exbiol computer program written by Dr. Edvart Sakiz*.

RESULTS

Pituitary FSH levels following orchiectomy

One hundred and ten rats were orchiectomized and groups of animals were sacrificed 24, 48, 72 hours or seven days after the operation. The changes in pituitary FSH levels found at these time intervals are illustrated in Fig. 1. A significant drop was noted in pituitaries of rats sacrificed forty-eight hours after orchiectomy, and a further drop at seventy-two hours. Indications of a return to normal levels were observed seven days after orchiectomy.

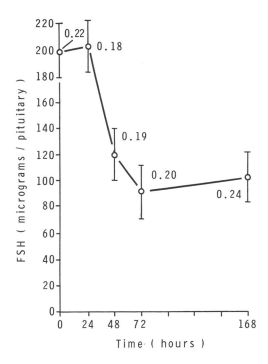

Fig. No. 1 - Pituitary FSH levels following orchiectomy. Each point represents the mean and the indicated 95% confidence limits. The numbers at each point are the lambda values.

*This program was kindly supplied by Dr. Roger Guillemin.

Pituitary FSH levels in orchiectomized rats treated with testosterone
propionate

One hundred and four rats were orchiectomized and divided into six
groups. Testosterone propionate in doses ranging from 0.02 mg. to 10 mg.
were administered daily and the animals were sacrificed seven days after
orchiectomy. The pituitary FSH levels are illustrated in Fig. 2.
Testosteronepropionate at the dose level of 0.02 mg. had only a slight
effect, but 0.1 mg. significantly increased pituitary FSH levels; maximum
increase was observed with 0.5 mg. of testosterone propionate. Further
increase in the dose caused a diminution of FSH levels; at the 10 mg.
dose, FSH levels were only slightly above that of intact controls; however,
significantly above that of the orchiectomized controls.

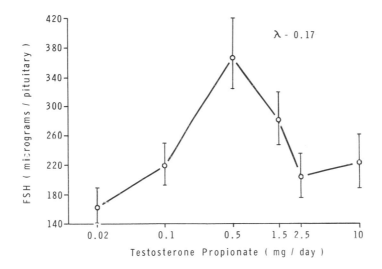

Fig. No. 2 - Pituitary FSH levels in orchiectomized and testosterone-
treated animals. Each point represents the mean and 95% confidence
limits as indicated.

Effects of estrogen on pituitary FSH levels

To examine the effect of estrogen, the duration of treatment with
estrogen necessary to suppress pituitary FSH levels in unoperated adult
male rats was first determined. Groups of animals were treated daily with
50 γ estradiol benzoate, sacrificed at daily intervals and pituitary FSH
levels measured. Pituitary FSH levels dropped significantly forty-eight
hours after initiation of estrogen treatment. There was a further drop
after seventy-two hours, but no additional change through the seventh day
of treatment (Fig. 3).

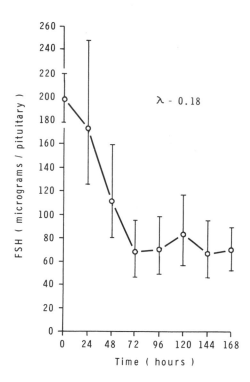

Fig. No. 3 - Pituitary FSH levels in animals treated with estrogen.
Each point represents the mean and the 95% confidence limits as
indicated.

In subsequent experiments, animals were treated with estradiol benzoate
for seven days, then - a) given estrogen for another seven days, b) orchiectomized and given estrogen for another seven days, c) given estrogen and
testosterone for another seven days, or d) orchiectomized and given estrogen
plus testosterone for another seven days. At the end of the experiment, the
animals were sacrificed and pituitary FSH levels measured (Fig. 4). Treatment with estrogen for additional seven days did not change the FSH levels
from those observed after the first seven days of treatment. Similarly,
orchiectomy did not change the levels significantly. Administration of
testosterone to estrogen-treated not-operated animals produced slight increase in FSH levels. Administration of testosterone to estrogen-treated
orchiectomized animals produced a significant rise in the FSH levels.

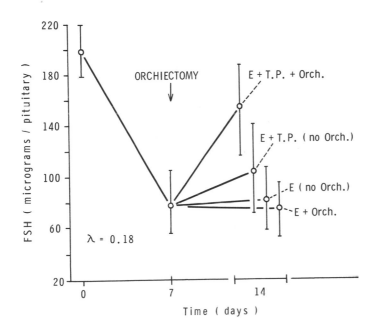

Fig. No. 4 - Explanation of this figure is given in the text. Each
point represents the mean of the pituitary FSH levels and the 95%
confidence limits as indicated.

DISCUSSION

In conjunction with the previously observed rise in plasma FSH levels
following orchiectomy (2), the marked drop in pituitary FSH levels forty-
eight hours after orchiectomy suggests that the fall in pituitary levels of
FSH was due to a rapid release of this hormone in response to the orchiectomy. These data support past suggestions that there is a rapid release of
FSH from the pituitary gland following orchiectomy (1,4).

The response of pituitary FSH levels in orchiectomized rats to treatment with testosterone propionate varied with the dose of testosterone
administered. Injection of 0.02 mg. testosterone increased the levels
slightly over those of orchiectomized rats. Administration of 0.1 mg.
testosterone elevated FSH levels to significantly above those of non-
orchiectomized untreated rats. A further increase in the dose of testosterone
(0.5 mg.) induced a further rise in pituitary FSH levels. However, when the

dose exceeded 0.5 mg. per day, the levels dropped back to those observed in non-orchiectomized untreated adult male rats. These data show a differential dose-related response. The drop observed with high doses is open to interpretation. Possibly at such high doses testosterone blocks FSH production. On the other hand, one may postulate the presence of a "short" negative feedback loop from the pituitary to the hypothalamus with respect to high levels of FSH in the pituitary gland, as proposed for ACTH (5) and for the luteinizing hormone (6).

It has been generally accepted that estrogens block the production of FSH in the male pituitary, although no direct experiments using specific methods for FSH assay have been performed (7). Consequently, the effect of 50 µg. of estradiol on the FSH content of normal adult males was investigated prior to the study of the effect of estradiol on pituitary FSH in orchiectomized and testosterone-treated animals. A progressive diminution of pituitary FSH levels was observed commencing within twenty-four hours after the first injection of estradiol. Lowest levels were reached seventy-two hours after initiation of treatment, and these low levels were maintained for the entire experimental period.

Since the pituitary FSH levels were stabilized after seven days of estrogen treatment, subsequent experiments were conducted on animals pretreated with estrogen for seven days. Continuation of estrogen treatment in such animals for additional seven days produced no significant changes in pituitary FSH levels. Likewise, orchiectomy on day seven of the experiment produced no effect. Administration of testosterone induced a slight rise in pituitary FSH, but when the estrogen-treated animals were orchiectomized and given testosterone, a marked rise was observed. These results could be explained in a number of ways - we favor the following interpretation: (a) Seven days after initiation of treatment with estrogen, pituitary FSH levels are very low, due primarily to diminished production. Orchiectomy performed at this time induces increased FSH release, but the estrogen-induced block of production is counteracted by absence of germinal epithelium, with the resulting lack of net changes in pituitary FSH levels. (b) Administration of testosterone, commencing on the seventh day of treatment with estrogen, blocks release of whatever small amount of FSH is produced in the face of estrogen blockade, causing a slight rise in pituitary FSH levels. (c) When animals treated for seven days with estrogen are orchiectomized, the lack of germinal epithelium as mentioned above counteracts the estrogen blockade, causing increased FSH production. Concomitant treatment with testosterone blocks the release, resulting in significantly increased levels of FSH in the pituitary gland.

Experiments utilizing more sensitive techniques for FSH determination and techniques which enable direct measurement of the rate of FSH synthesis in the pituitary should provide the necessary evidence for definitive conclusions with regard to the mechanisms controlling FSH synthesis and release.

ACKNOWLEDGMENT

This work was supported in part by U.S. Public Health Service
Grant No. AM 05449.

REFERENCES

1. Steinberger, E. and G.E. Duckett, Endocrinology 79:912, 1966.

2. Steinberger, E. and G.E. Duckett, Acta Endocrinologica 57:289,
    Feb. 1968.

3. Steelman, S. and F.M. Pohley, Endocrinology 53:604, 1953.

4. Yasuda, M. and D. Johnson, Endocrinology 76:1033, 1965.

5. Christian, J.J., Endocrinology 75:653, 1964.

6. David, M.A., F. Fraschini, and L. Martini, Endocrinology,
    78:55, 1966.

7. Greep, R.O., In Young, W.C. (ed.), Sex and Internal Secretions,
    Vol. 1, The Williams & Wilkins Co., Baltimore, 1961, p. 240.

DISCUSSION

JOHNSEN: Dr. Steinberger, I am a little concerned about the
doses of testosterone given. As far as I recall you administered
0.5 or 1 mg. of testosterone in order to see the effects on FSH.
These doses are about 10 times greater than the endogenous
production of testosterone. This study therefore is not a
physiological study.

STEINBERGER: You are absolutely correct, Dr. Johnsen. The dose
of testosterone we used was probably not physiologic. However,
the response of the pituitary gonadotropins was not physiologic
either. We have used this dose and the entire experimental
design to create a model rather than to study the physiological
effect of testosterone.

RYAN: Does the same apply to the 50 μg of estradiol benzoate?

STEINBERGER: No, the dose of estrogen was completely unphysiologic.
We were interested only in depleting the pituitary of FSH as
rapidly and as completely as possible. This is why we used this
rather high dose of estrogen.

CHAPTER 2

BIOLOGY OF GONADOTROPINS

3. EFFECT OF GONADOTROPINS ON THE GONADS

METABOLISM OF LABELLED ^{125}I-HCG BY THE RAT OVARY

D.H. Espeland[+], F. Naftolin[*] and C.A. Paulsen[+]

[+]Department of Medicine
University of Washington
Seattle, Washington

[*]Department of Obstetrics
and Gynecology
U.S.P.H.S. Hospital
Seattle, Washington

INTRODUCTION

Reproductive endocrinologists have long considered that the gonadotrophic hormones might be "utilized" or "consumed" by the gonads while exerting their stimulatory effect. When testing this hypothesis, investigators have arrived at opposing conclusions (1-7).

Now that gonadotrophic hormones can be labelled with radioactive compounds such as iodine, it has been possible to study this problem more directly. Certain experiments have demonstrated that the ovary concentrates radioactive gonadotrophin (8,9) while other studies have failed to show this phenomenon (10,11). In our laboratory the metabolism of ^{125}I-HCG has been studied in the pseudopregnant rat. This report will deal with our preliminary results.

MATERIAL AND METHODS

Human chorionic gonadotrophin (APL, Ayerst Laboratories, Inc., New York, New York) was purified by sephadex and DEAE cellulose chromatography as described by others (12-14). The biologic activity of the final product was 6600 I.U./mg and formed a single band with anti-HCG sera by immunoelectrophoresis. This purified HCG was labelled with ^{125}I by the method of Hunter and Greenwood (15). For our studies the concentration of ^{125}I was reduced to 200 microcuries per microgram of protein. All metabolic studies were performed on the same day of iodination.

Mature Holtzman-Sprague Dawley, 250 gram, cycling female rats were used. In order to increase ovarian function each rat was pretreated with subcutaneous injections of estradiol (benzoate), 5.0 gamma on day one, and pregnant mare serum (Equinex, Ayerst Laboratories, Inc., New York, New York) 50 I.U. on days 3, 6 and 9. On day 10, each rat received approx-

imately 0.35 I.U. of ^{125}I-HCG via tail vein injection. Two
rats were sacrificed with lethal amounts of ether at 10, 20,
30, 45, 60 and 120 minutes following ^{125}I-HCG administration
and appropriate organs obtained. The ovaries, liver, thyroid,
and renal cortex were weighed immediately, placed in counting
tubes, covered with 1 cc of 0.5 molar phosphate buffered
saline and submitted to gamma spectometry (Picker Nuclear
Autowell, Twin Model 600-175). Following gamma spectroanalysis, the counts per minute (CPM) per mg of tissue were
divided by the CPM per microliter of blood from the same
animal so that a working ratio could be obtained. We defined active concentration as being present whenever this
ratio was greater than 1.0. For radioautography, organs were
frozen and sectioned on a cryostat at a thickness of 4 microns
They were then dipped in photographic emulsion (K.5 Nuclear
Emulsion, Lot 25009, Ilford Limited, Ilford, Essex, England).
Exposure time was three weeks at 4° centigrade. Specimens
were developed in the usual manner and stained for study.

Fig. 1

EXPERIMENTAL   DESIGN

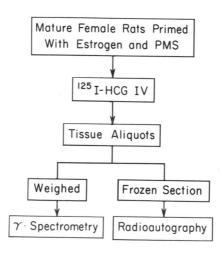

RESULTS

Within twenty minutes following ^{125}I-HCG administration
the radioactivity in the ovary increased to an ovarian/blood
ratio of 3.0 (Table 1, Fig. 2). Further concentration of
radioactivity was observed at later periods with peak values

of 7.0 and 8.03 noted at the 45 and 120 minute intervals, respectively. The renal cortex maintained a fairly consistent concentration ranging from ratios of 1.08 to 2.9 during the various time intervals In the liver radioactivity remained low throughout the study i.e. ratios of 0.23 to 0.43, which probably represented sequestered blood. Thyroid radioactivity became equal to that encountered in blood samples at 30 minutes, rose gradually for the next 30 minutes and finally increased markedly to a ratio of 12.27 at 120 minutes. This sharp rise in radioactivity most likely represents thyroidal trapping of freed iodine.

Analysis of the radioautographs from ovarian tissue obtained at 120 minutes demonstrated that the granules were primarily confined to the corpora lutea (Figs. 3, 4, and 5). The surrounding follicles, stroma and limiting membranes showed little or no evidence of radioactivity.

When the number of granules were compared between the ovarian radioautographs obtained at 10 and 120 minutes, the greater concentration at 120 minutes was obvious. This observation agrees favorably with data obtained by gamma spectroanalysis.

Fig. 2

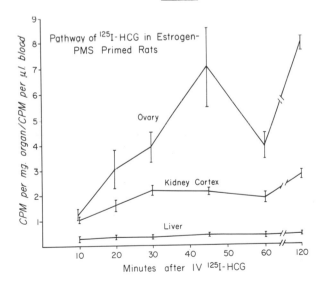

CPM per mg of tissue expressed as a ratio of organs to blood. Each point represents the mean value from two rats, the vertical bars indicate the range.

TABLE 1

GAMMA SPECTROMETRY*
AT VARIOUS TIME INTERVALS (MINUTES)
FOLLOWING ^{125}I-HCG ADMINISTRATION

Tissue	10 CPM	CPM per mg	O/B** Ratio	20 CPM	CPM per mg	O/B Ratio	30 CPM	CPM per mg	O/B Ratio
Blood	416,000	416		415,000	415		359,000	359	
	455,000	455		423,500	425		301,000	301	
Ovary	73,253	419	1.26	303,060	953	3.0	499,867	1492	3.88
	236,563	678		474,485	1625		330,190	1072	
Kidney Cortex	52,803	400	1.08	61,985	574	1.58	82,823	720	2.17
	60,117	552		78,961	759		76,460	715	
Liver	6,535	107	0.25	10,877	109	0.29	18,051	117	0.31
	13,599	113		9,699	139		11,108	94	
Thyroid	3,010	158	0.28	3,777	236	0.49	5,919	370	1.10
	2,078	90		3,050	153		6,827	359	

Tissue	45 CPM	CPM per mg	O/B Ratio	60 CPM	CPM per mg	O/B Ratio	120 CPM	CPM per mg	O/B Ratio
Blood	279,000	279		473,000	473		208,000	208	
	276,000	276		334,000	334		242,000	242	
Ovary	450,169	1521	7.0	406,543	1546	3.84	367,421	1685	8.03
	366,908	2367		457,428	1561		532,744	1937	
Kidney Cortex	155,650	552	2.68	98,307	774	1.78	50,026	562	2.9
	133,374	606		71,804	665		57,460	746	
Liver	35,574	119	0.43	37,599	143	0.23	4,759	70	0.32
	27,005	121		14,672	92		5,330	73	
Thyroid	8,176	629	2.17	12,096	526	1.78	52,646	2289	12.27
	11,532	577		9,044	904		55,161	3244	

*Two rats were analyzed for each time interval.
**O/B Ratio = CPM per mg of each tissue over CPM per µl blood.

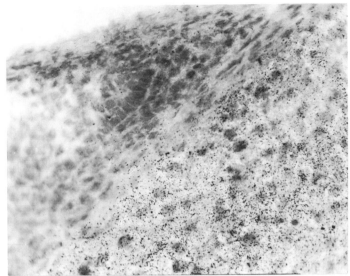

Figure 3 - 2 hours post injection - Photomicrograph of a
corpus luteum (lower right-hand corner) and
adjoining developing follicle (upper left-hand
corner). Note, granules primarily restricted
to the cells in the corpus luteum. (X 400)

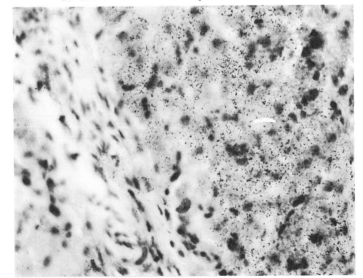

Figure 4 - 2 hours post injection - Photomicrograph of corpus
luteum on the right, stromal tissue on the left.
Note that the radioactivity is located in the
corpus luteum. (X 400)

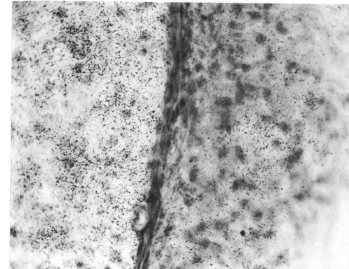

Figure 5 -   2 hours post injection - Photomicrograph of two
adjacent corpora lutea separated by their respective membranes. Note the absence of granules
over the surrounding membranes. (X 400)

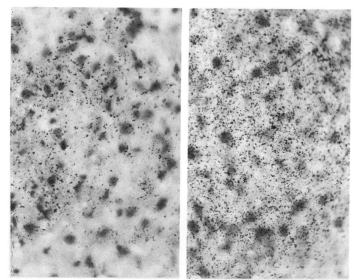

Figure 6 - Left, 10 minutes post injection. Right, 2 hours
post injection - Photomicrographs from center of
two corpora lutea obtained at different time intervals post injection. Note that the grain count
per Cm^2 at 10 minutes is much less than the grain
count at 2 hours post injection. (X 400)

DISCUSSION

These data demonstrate that ^{125}I-HCG is actively concentrated by the ovary of the pseudopregnant rat. Inspection of the various organs/blood ratios obtained indicate that increased blood flow through the ovary would not by itself explain our data. For even if ovarian blood content increased many fold, the resultant ovarian/blood ratio would not exceed unity as was observed in our analyses. Furthermore, the radioautographs showed selective concentration by the corpora lutea. Also in this regard, Eshkol et al. (2) have demonstrated a discriminate uptake pattern by the mouse ovary following the administration of radioactive labelled HCG as opposed to labelled albumin or free radioactive iodine.

Existing information suggests that protein hormones are filtered by the glomerulus and then reabsorbed in the proximal tubules (16,17). The radioactivity concentrated by the kidney cortex probably reflects this process.

The question as to whether or not the process of labelling HCG with ^{125}I alters the molecule so that it follows a different metabolic pathway from that of non-labelled HCG must be answered by further study. Nonetheless, our data and the data of Eshkol et al. (8) suggest that binding sites for trophic hormones may exist in target organs such as the ovary.

Supported in part by grants AM 05161 from the National Institutes of Health and contract AT(45-1)-1781, Atomic Energy Commission.

REFERENCES

1. McCullagh, D.R. and I. Schneider: Endocrinology 27:899, 1940.

2. Heller, C.G. and W.O. Nelson: Recent Progr Hormone Res 3:229, 1948.

3. Heller, C.G., et al.: Ann N Y Acad Sci 55:685, 1952.

4. McCullagh, E.P. and C.A. Schaffenberg: Ann N Y Acad Sci 55: 674, 1952.

5. Howard, R.P., R.C. Sniffen, F.A. Simmons, and F. Albright: J. Clin Endocr 10:121, 1950.

6. Lacy, D.: Effects of Ionizing Radiation on the Reproductive System. New York, Macmillan Co. 1964.

7.   Johnsen, S.G.: Acta Endocr (Kobenhavn) Suppl 90:99, 1964.

8.   Eshkol, A.: Recent Research on Gonadotrophic Hormones.
     Edinburgh, E. and S. Livingstone, Ltd., 1966, pp. 202-209.

9.   Sonenberg, M., A.S. Keston, W.L. Money, P.J. Fitzgerald
     and J.T. Godwin: Endocrinology 49:709, 1951.

10. Seki, M.: J Jap Obstet & Gynec 10:8, 1963.

11. Cox, P.L.: Anat Rec 109:285, 1951.

12. Reisfeld, R.A. and R. Hertz: Biochim Biophys Acta 43:540,
     1960.

13. Flodin, P.: J. Chromat 5:103, 1961.

14. Reichert, L.E. and A. Parlow: Endocrinology 74:236, 1964.

15. Greenwood, F.C. and W.M. Hunter: Biochem J 89:114, 1963.

16. Vilar, O., B. Alvarez, O. Davidson and R.E. Mancini: J
     Histochem & Cytochem 12:621, 1964.

17. Beck, L.V. and N. Fedynskyj: Endocrinology 81:475, 1967.

DISCUSSION

VILAR: Dr. Espeland, since the labeled HCG was present
in the corpora lutea, I would like to ask you if the
hormone was localized in the theca luteal cells as well
as in the enlarged granulosa lutein cells. If this was
the case, did the interstitial cells also show localization of labeled hormone?

ESPELAND: In this study we did not attempt to determine
which of the corpora luteal cells were concentrating the
labeled HCG. With regard to the interstitial tissue, the
localization of labeled HCG was negligible.

MANCINI: I would like to go back to Dr. Espeland's
paper and also to a comment made by Dr. Paulsen on the
same subject. A few years ago we published papers (J.
Histochem. Cytochem. 10: 194, 1962; ibid. 11: 80, 1963;
ibid. 12: 621, 1964) related to the fate of homologous
and heterologous rat serum proteins labeled with

fluorochromes, radioiodine or tritium and histologically revealed
by fluorescence microscopy or radioautographic- technique. From
10 minutes onward after a single intravenous injection, a fluorescent or radioactive material appeared in the vessels of many organs and extravascularly diffused in dermal skin, testis and ovary.
This material also diffused inside the seminiferous tubules, through
Sertoli cell cytoplasm, and in growing follicles through intercellular spaces of follicular cell layers reaching even the oocyte.
An appreciable amount of material was also seen in the macrophages
of liver, spleen and lymph nodes, in the proximal convoluting
tubules and to a lesser extent in the collecting tubules. Moreover, both ovine FSH and LH (NIH) preparations as well as other
pituitary hormones similarly labeled appeared in the kidney. In
general, the greater the heterologous origin or denaturation
induced by labeling, the larger the amount present in the kidney
and macrophages.

Therefore, I think that it may be somewhat risky to reach any
conclusions on the cellular or extracellular localization of
radioiodinated HCG in the ovary for the following reasons: It
is a heterologous and not defined chemical entity, more than one
protein contaminant is present and the cytological resolution of
the radioautographic technique using frozen sections either for
soluble or insoluble compounds is low.

FATE AND LOCALIZATION OF IODINE-LABELLED HCG IN MICE

ALIZA ESHKOL AND B. LUNENFELD, TEL-HASHOMER GOV. HOSPITAL

In our previous publications (1, 2) we have shown that HCG labelled with iodine did not differ significantly from the unlabelled hormone.

Among all the organs examined only the ovary had a capacity to affix HCG to significantly higher concentrations than that present in the circulation (2). Following a single i.v. injection of iodine labelled HCG, radioactivity fell in the circulation to approximately 50% within the first 30 min. and dropped to about 7% within 6 hours. During this period radioactivity in the ovary increased and remained high (Fig. 1).

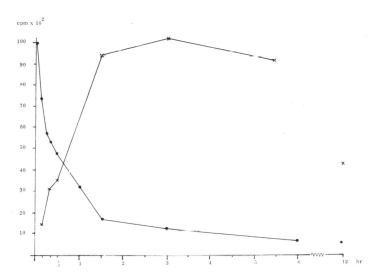

Fig. No. 1

Concentration of radioactivity in blood (● expressed as %) and in ovaries (✕ given in cpm x 10^2 mg tissue) following a single i.v. injection of labelled HCG.

The pattern of HCG exchange between ovaries and the circulation was investigated by neutralizing the injected HCG with antiserum at specific times. (The HCG-anti HCG complex is not concentrated by the ovary). Four phases of HCG uptake in the ovaries were identified: (a) during the first hour only inflow of HCG was detected; (b) between 60 and 90 min. inflow was greater than outflow (Fig. 2); (c) between 90 and 180 min. inflow was equal to outflow (2); (d) between 3 and 6 hours outflow was greater than inflow (Fig. 3).

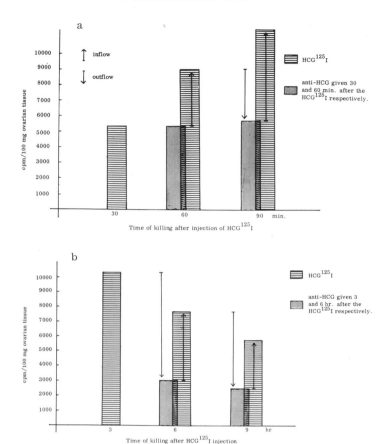

Fig. No. 2
Rate of inflow and outflow of labelled HCG to and from the ovary between: (a) 30
and 90 min.; (b) 3 and 9 hours.

The labelled HCG was confined mainly to the follicular envelopes as demonstrated by autoradiography (1).   The uptake was specific for HCG as demonstrated
previously (2).

REFERENCES

1.   Eshkol, Aliza and Lunenfeld, B.   International Symposium on the Pharmacol-
      ogy of Hormonal Polypeptides and Proteins, Milan, September 1967.
2.   Lunenfeld, B. and Eshkol, Aliza.   Vitamins and Hormones 25, 137, 1967.

DISCUSSION

PAULSEN: Dr. Lunenfeld, I was most interested in the work which demonstrated that the addition of gonadotropin antisera prevented the uptake and concentration of labeled gonadotropin by the renal cortex. You recall that Dr. Espeland in his studies showed that the renal cortex concentrated labeled HCG to a considerable extent. We would be interested to know whether or not you studied the effect of antisera on the binding of labeled gonadotropin by the kidney.

LUNENFELD: We did not specifically work with kidney cortex. We worked with the kidney as a whole organ; therefore I cannot give you a direct answer. I can only tell you that when we gave antiserum a very high concentration of iodine labeled HCG was found in the spleen, and the concentration in the kidney was somewhat lower than in the absence of antiserum. Another thing I would like to mention is the uptake by the thyroid. Thyroid uptake can be blocked by giving lugol to the animals or the thyroid can be left intact. In the latter case the uptake in the thyroid is exceedingly large. It is much higher than in the ovary and measurement of iodine in the thyroid actually gives you a possibility to assess approximately the rate of degradation or metabolism of HCG.

MIDGLEY: I would like to ask Dr. Lunenfeld whether he compared the immunochemical intactness of the labeled hormone in serum entering the ovary with that found in serum leaving the ovary. Is there a difference in the antibody binding ability of the hormone after passage through the ovary? I would also like to ask Dr. Lunenfeld how much hormone he injected into each mouse and Dr. Espeland how much he injected into each rat.

LUNENFELD: We tested the blood of the animals by the double antibody technique and found that the binding was similar to that of the uninjected labeled HCG. If I am not mistaken, between 60 and 70% of radioactive material was bound to the antiserum. As the gonadotropin is metabolized the freed iodine is trapped by the thyroid; thus radioactivity in circulation represents mainly the hormone. We performed the same experiment with lugol treated animals but I do not have the figures here.

MIDGLEY: I thought that in one experiment you compared the concentration of labeled hormone in ovarian arterial blood with that in ovarian venous blood. In this situation there is no chance for the hormone to enter the thyroid. I simply wanted to know whether the hormone was degraded on passage through the ovary.

LUNENFELD: We measured blood taken from the heart at different times; therefore it also contained material going into the ovary or other organs. When one extracts HCG from the ovary very small amounts are obtained which are almost impossible to measure. I cannot give you an answer to this. We can only call it inflow and outflow of radioactivity and not inflow and outflow of HCG. The dose used was approximately 1.5 units.

STEINBERGER: I should like to ask Dr. Lunenfeld a question with reference to the uptake of iodinated HCG by the ovary. The curve of changes in radioactivity in the ovary that Dr. Lunenfeld has shown brought to mind a curve published by Dr. Ellis (Endocrin. 68: 334, 1961) in a study where iodinated albumin was used to measure ovarian hyperemia for an LH bioassay. If such were the case, then wouldn't that affect the results of your study?

LUNENFELD: We did experiments having this in mind. Groups of mice were injected with iodinated albumin and Na ^{131}I, each of these in the presence of cold HCG. You see that after 1, 6 and 12 hours in all instances the ovary/blood ratios of radioactivity remained low and even the simultaneous administration of cold HCG did not increase the ratio, which rose significantly only when labeled HCG was injected. This, therefore, was not due to a higher blood flow.

NAFTOLIN: In our laboratories using plasma fractionation following labeled HCG injection Dr. Espeland has been able to show that HCG retains its iodine label for approximately 2 hours. He also showed that the thyroid uptake of radioactive iodine does not begin until about 2 hours after injection, and is then extremely rapid. Dr. Espeland then conceived the idea that priming the animals by inducing pseudopregnancy and thus augmenting the response could shorten the time of study enough so that the thyroid would not interfere. In addition, this procedure resulted in a large number of corpora lutea which took up the radioactive HCG. I should like to ask Dr. Lunenfeld what was the timing in relation to his autographs. Most of his previous studies have been carried out in the region of 6-12 hours after injection.

LUNENFELD: The autograph was made 90 minutes after the injection of HCG.

PARLOW: Some years ago we did a biological experiment intending to determine the distribution of LH and FSH in various tissues following a single massive intravenous dose of LH in normal female rats. We were unable to detect by bioassay means any LH activity in the ovary. We concluded from our study that less than 10% of the injected LH was localized in the ovary. We then repeated the experiment with pseudopregnant rats having heavily luteinized ovaries and found by bioassay that 25% of the LH was localized in the ovary.

BOGDANOVE: In Dr. Espeland's report, injected HCG was found only in the kidney and corpus luteum. I found this most interesting in relation to studies we have been doing on the distribution volumes of injected ovine LH and FSH in the rat. Surprisingly,

we found that the distribution volumes of these two exogenous
hormones were almost exactly the same as the plasma volume, or
RISA space, which suggests that very little of an intravenously
injected dose of gonadotropin goes to tissues other than the
blood. We must retain this reservation, however. If we are
dealing with heterologous hormones which have been subjected to
various "purifying" treatments, it is possible that some of the
characteristics of these hormones may have been altered. This
may include their capacity to be distributed in the same pattern
as native hormone. I think this is a very important point to
remember.

MANCINI: With regard to the comments of Dr. Parlow on the
amount of injected gonadotropins trapped by the ovary, I would
like to recall that we have had similar results with the rat
testis (J. Histochem. Cytochem. 13: 376, 1965). Animals injected
intravenously with a single high dose of ovine FSH or LH (NIH)
labeled with fluorochromes or ferritine and biologically checked
after tagging, showed at the microscopical and electronmicroscop-
ical levels that a smaller amount is detectable in the Sertoli
and immature Leydig cells respectively, when compared with that
in kidney and macrophages. These results were recently confirmed
by means of an indirect immunofluorescent technique injecting
unlabeled hormones. However, it appears obvious that our
observations should now be checked using homologous rat pituitary
gonadotropins.

IN VITRO ACTIVITY OF HUMAN FOLLICLE STIMULATING HORMONE

A. C. CROOKE, MD, FRCP, DIRECTOR AND M. RYLE, PhD, BIOLOGIST

THE UNITED BIRMINGHAM HOSPITALS, DEPARTMENT OF CLINICAL
ENDOCRINOLOGY, BIRMINGHAM AND MIDLAND HOSPITAL FOR WOMEN
BIRMINGHAM, 11, ENGLAND

In 1966 we set up a small team under Dr. Margaret Ryle to study the biological effects of gonadotrophins at the cellular level with the object of having techniques available which could subsequently be used to investigate modified or broken down parts of the hormone molecule as these became available.

Considerable progress has been made in recent years in understanding the mode of action of luteinizing hormone (LH) as a result of in vitro work. This has involved short periods of incubation, for up to four hours, used in metabolic studies. Comparable progress has not been reported with follicle stimulating hormone (FSH) and it seemed likely that the time scale of easily measured responses was longer. Attempts were therefore made to develop a procedure for maintaining ovarian tissue for several days in vitro and a number of responses were studied. These included morphological changes in the follicles and the uptake of ^{14}C-thymidine.

A systematically outbred strain of CFW mice were used (1). The mice were sexed at birth and groups of ten females born on the same day were reared by foster mothers. They were killed at 15 days old when they weighed 5.0 to 6.5 g. It was found that the ovaries of older mice were too large for satisfactory culture and those of younger mice were insufficiently sensitive to gonadotrophins.

One foster litter was used for each replicate set of experimental treatments. The experiments were of factorial design with three levels of FSH and three of LH. The mice were killed abruptly and the ovaries removed from their capsules and put on a stainless steel grid covered with lens tissue for support. The culture dishes which had been prepared in advance contained 5 ml. culture medium consisting of one part 5% crystalline bovine serum albumin to 19 parts Eagle's medium. This ensured that only known quantities of hormone were present. Highly purified FSH prepared by the method of Butt, Crooke, Cunningham and Wolf (2) and LH prepared by the method of Hartree, Butt and Kirkham (3) were added in various concentrations. Each dish was gassed in a small jar with 5% CO_2 in air and warmed to 37°.

After the ovaries were placed in the culture dishes they were regassed and returned to the incubator for up to four days when they were removed for morphological studies. Others were removed after 24 hours for the addition of ^{14}C-thymidine and culture was then continued for up to three days. Ovaries used for tracer studies were then rinsed with 9% NaCl and dissolved in 0.3 ml. hydroxide of hyamine–10–x at 37° for 6 to 8 hours. Six ml. scintillating fluid were then added (PPO-POPOP in toluene) and the ^{14}C was counted.

Follicles were examined histologically in some ovaries cultured for four days. All follicles with four or more layers of cells were counted. In a typical experiment there was an increase in the number of such follicles in ovaries cultured with 2.5 IU FSH but the significance of the difference from

ovaries without FSH could not be estimated because there was not a full replication of the experimental treatments.   There was, however, a significant (P <
0.01) increase in the proportion of such follicles with five or more layers.

        Cell division involves the formation of new DNA and radioactive thy-
midine, which is incorporated in new DNA, is widely used to investigate mitotic
activity.   In Dr. Ryle's experiments (4) it was found that the uptake of ^{14}C-
thymidine was significantly higher (P < 0.01) in ovaries cultured with FSH than
in control ovaries without FSH.   The percentage uptake of thymidine was not
large and 2.5 IU FSH per dish caused little greater uptake than 0.5 IU.   The
dose is therefore comparable with the effective dose in in vivo experiments.
In three out of five experiments LH had no effect but in two others it had a
small but significant effect (P < 0.025).   The precise conditions controlling
the effect of LH are as yet uncertain;   it is possible that it increases uptake
without increasing incorporation into DNA.   Work is now in progress to establish
the chemical and morphological location of thymidine retained in the cell in
these experiments.

        These preliminary experiments suggest that under suitable conditions
thymidine uptake can be used as a test for FSH activity at the cellular level
but it has not yet been used to investigate modified hormone.   It lends itself
to other fundamental studies, however, such as the "triggering" effect of FSH
and placed in a medium free from FSH it is possible to investigate how long the
effect of the hormone persists.

        In these experiments (5) sets of ovaries were cultured in dishes of
medium containing FSH, each culture dish being paired with another put up simultaneously without FSH.   After periods which varied from 12 to 40 hours in different experiments all ovaries in each set were transferred to fresh dishes with
no hormone. ^{14}C-thymidine was added to one pair of dishes at this time, to
another at six hours, to another at nine hours, etc.   After 24 hours incubation
with thymidine each culture was prepared for counting.   The difference between
the counts for the culture exposed to FSH and that for its paired control indicated the residual effects of the hormone after each time interval.   It was
found that the results from ovaries exposed to FSH for only 12 hours were somewhat inconsistent but became more regular and consistent after 20 to 40 hours.
The mean difference between untreated ovaries and those exposed to FSH for 20
to 40 hours was significant after intervals of 0, 6 and 9 hours (P < 0.02, <
0.05 and < 0.02 respectively) but by 12 hours it was no longer significant and
by 24 hours it had disappeared.

        The results suggest that FSH does not simply "trigger off" early
follicle growth.   The hormone must continue to be present if continued stimulation is to occur.   It is interesting that the duration of the FSH stimulus,
nine to 12 hours, is of the same order as that required for DNA replication in
various other mammalian cells.   Finally the effect is not cumulative since the
shapes of the curves after 40 hours in FSH are similar to those after 20 hours.

        This work was supported by a grant made to Dr. A. C. Crooke by the
Ford Foundation.

REFERENCES

1. Smith, M. and M. Ryle, Journal of the Institute of Animal Technicians, 19: 74, 1968.
2. Butt, W. R., A. C. Crooke, F. J. Cunningham and A. Wolf, J. Endocr. 25: 541, 1963.
3. Hartree, A. S., W. R. Butt and K. E. Kirkham, J. Endocr. 29: 61, 1964.
4. Ryle, M.   in press.
5. Ryle, M.   in press.

DISCUSSION

STEINBERGER: I would like to ask Dr. Crooke a technical question, if I may. What type of ovarian culture did you use - was it an organ culture; and if so, what system was employed? Also, I would like to know for how long a period of time the culture was exposed to the tritiated thymidine, and then how was the cultured material treated for counting.

CROOKE: This was a whole organ culture, which we felt was important for prolonged studies. We used a small strain of CFW mice and killed them at 15 days old. This age is important because the ovaries of older mice are too big and the cells in the centers show more pyknosis, while those of younger mice are not sufficiently responsive to FSH. They were cultured in modified Eagle's medium with 1:20 of 5% crystalline bovine serum albumin in saline aerated with 5% CO_2 in air at 37° for up to 4 days. Thymidine was introduced after the first 24 hours.

STEINBERGER: We have studied labeling of organ cultures with tritiated thymidine and found that the penetration rate of thymidine into the cultured fragment is relatively slow. It thus is obviously dependent to a large extent on the duration of exposure to thymidine in the medium. After a few hours of exposure one gets only a thin rim of labeling in the culture, with the central portion being completely unlabeled. Also, there is a definite gradient of label from the periphery toward the center. This comment is just to determine how accurately one can use this type of data for quantitative estimation.

CROOKE: The concentration of thymidine was 0.1 μC in 5 ml. medium. This gave counts of between 1,000 and 3,000 per pair of ovaries per minute. We have not yet done autoradiographs but hope to do so soon.

THE ROLE OF GONAD-STIMULATING HORMONE ON THE
DEVELOPMENT OF THE INFANTILE OVARY

B. LUNENFELD AND ALIZA ESHKOL, INSTITUTE OF ENDOCRINOLOGY, TEL-HASHOMER GOVERNMENT HOSPITAL AND DEPARTMENT OF BIOLOGY, BAR-ILAN UNIVERSITY, RAMAT-GAN, ISRAEL.

From birth to puberty the growing ovaries of mice undergo a sequence of developmental changes. Oocytes surrounded by only a few elongated cells - probably of stromal origin - (4) start growing. The cells surrounding the growing oocyte acquire a round shape and proliferate to form follicles with multiple granulosa cell layers during the first week of life. Spaces appear between the follicular cells which, at a later stage, confluence to form antra.

At any stage of follicular growth, follicles may discontinue their development; they degenerate and are either lysed and carried away by the vascular system, or the follicular cells change their shape and become part of the central stroma. Oocytes are either disposed of by escape through the ovarian membrane or, after lysis, are carried away by the vascular system. These developmental changes have been fully described by Peters and Pedersen (4).

Stimulation of ovaries to secrete uterotrophic steroids can be achieved by administration of gonadotropins to prepubertal mice only after the approximate age of 14 days. During early infancy ovaries of mice seem to be refractory to gonadotropic stimulation (1).

The aim of the first part of the present study was to investigate whether gonadotropins play a role in the development of the ovary in infancy, and in the second part some biochemical parameters following FSH stimulation were investigated.

Hypophysectomy at birth or in early infancy could have been a theoretical approach to the above question, but it is practically impossible since the animals either die or are killed or abandoned by their mothers or foster mothers (5). Moreover, by its very nature hypophysectomy might lead to inconclusive results, due to deprivation of other vitally important hormones.

We have demonstrated that an antiserum to rat pituitary gonadotropins (aRG) is capable of neutralizing circulating endogenous mouse gonadotropins. This continuous deprivation of gonadotropins even from birth is possible by continuous administration of such an antiserum. Moreover, such antiserum did not cross react with human gonadotropins (3) and therefore effects of human gonadotropins could be investigated in gonadotropin deprived mice.

This experimental design permitted a quantitative evaluation of follicular development between normal, gonadotropin deprived and animals deprived of endogenous gonadotropins and receiving human menopausal gonadotropins (HMG) or human follicle stimulating hormone (FSH) preparation devoid of luteinizing activity. For comparative quantitative evaluation, follicles were grouped according to the number of follicular cells surrounding the oocyte and according to the diameter of the oocyte in serially sectioned ovaries (in the section where the nucleolus was seen). In each experiment littermates served as controls.

On the first day of life all oocytes are already separated, elongated stroma cells are attached to many of the oocytes, and some of the oocytes have reached a diameter of 20 μ and are surrounded by a complete ring of 10-20 follicular cells.

By the seventh day follicular development had advanced and most of the growing follicles were surrounded by 20-40 cells, many by 40-60 cells and some were surrounded by 60-100 cells (Table 1).

When aRG was administered from the first day of life till day 7, follicular development was significantly retarded. Most of the follicles were encircled by up to 40 cells only, a few isolated follicles by 40-60 cells, but none were surrounded by more than 60 cells (Table 1).

Table No. 1

Counts of follicles per ovary according to the number of granulosa cells in section where the nucleolus of the oocyte was seen.

| | Number of follicles | | | | |
No. of granulosa cells	10-20	20-40	40-60	60-100	Total
Control	36	55	40	25	156
aRG	84	96	5	0	185
aRG + FSH	82	130	54	11	277
aRG + HMG	54	112	54	18	238

The total number of growing follicles is not significantly different from those of control animals. The number of small follicles, i.e. those surrounded by 10-20 or 20-40 cells is elevated in aRG treated animals, whereas those surrounded by 40-60 cells are significantly reduced and follicles surrounded by 60-100 cells are completely absent. This clearly indicates the necessity of endogenous gonadotropic stimulation for the progressive development of growing follicles.

Other striking differences between ovaries of control and aRG treated animals were: the observation that growth of oocytes was not inhibited and that in normal 7 day old animals the follicular cells were well defined and spaces started to be evident between them. In the aRG treated animals the follicular cells were crowded, not organized into definite layers and spaces between cells were absent.

The observations described above on the retardation of ovarian development cannot be ascribed to either FSH or LH (luteinizing hormone) deprivation, since the aRG contains antibodies to both hormones. To elucidate the role of FSH in early infancy, an FSH preparation devoid of LH activity (2) was administered (0.5 IU/ day) while the animals were deprived of their endogenous gonadotropins. The appearance of the ovary was similar to that of the control. From Table 1 it can be seen that the number of follicles with 40-60 granulosa cells in the FSH treated animals was similar to that of controls - 40 and 54 follicles respectively as compared to 5 in aRG treated animals. Follicles with 60-100 cells were only about half as compared to the controls, but it should be remembered that such follicles were completely absent in aRG treated mice. The appearance of the follicular cells resembled that of the controls, although probably the organization of follicular cells into concentric layers was less conspicuous than in the control animals.

When instead of FSH an HMG preparation - containing both FSH and LH (0.5 IU FSH + 0.5 IU LD/day) was administered to the gonadotropin deprived animals, no significant difference in follicular development was noted as compared to FSH treated animals. Moreover, it can be noted that in certain areas in the follicle the granulosa cells were well separated and spaces appeared between them.

Table 1 illustrates that on a quantitative basis, both FSH and HMG significantly increase the total number of growing follicles. No difference between FSH and HMG was found on follicular development, since as with FSH alone a complete restoration of multi-layer follicles was obtained. Similarly to FSH, also with HMG an increase of single layer follicles above control levels was noted; the number of young follicles was even higher than in the aRG treated animals. It can thus be speculated that FSH and HMG both stimulate the formation of young follicles and contribute to their further development.

When the duration of the above mentioned experimental conditions was prolonged to 14 days, the effect of gonadotropic deprivation described during the first week became even more pronounced. Also during this period FSH was capable of stimulating the formation of young follicles and contributed to their further development. During this second week of life it became evident that HMG treated animals showed different stages of antrum formation, while in control and FSH stimulated animals only "spacing" between granulosa cells was observed. It could thus be speculated that under the influence of LH folliculi fluid is elaborated, discharged into the intercellular spaces and finally antra are formed.

Furthermore, changes in the development of the theca were observed. These were more pronounced in the 14 day old animals than in the 7 day old animals. In

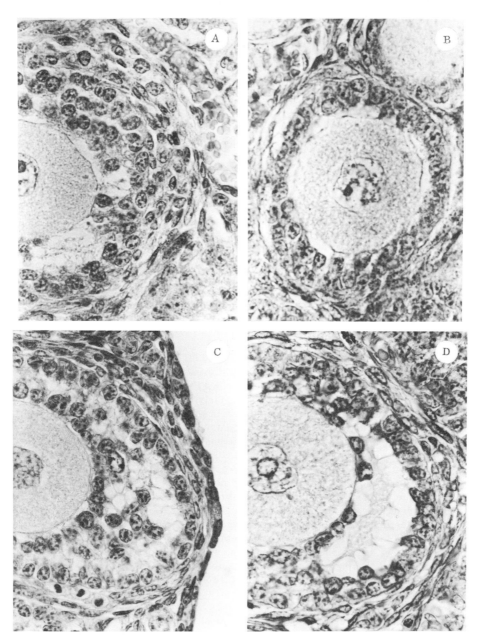

Fig. No. 1

the gonadotropin deprived animals the basal membrane between the granulosa cells
and the theca layer was often only partially present and sometimes almost invisible.
Strings of fibrous material were seen at some distance around the follicles, but only
a few thin cells appeared between them.   In the FSH treated animals this membrane
was more conspicuous and thecal layers surrounded the follicle.   In the HMG treated animals the membrane as well as the thecal cells were well developed and the latter
were more roundish in appearance; the whole layer occupied more space than in the
14 day old control littermates.

Vascularization was significantly less developed in the gonadotropin deprived
animals than in the normal controls.   When FSH was substituted vascularization
increased, but in the HMG treated mice this was even more pronounced than in the
normal 14 day old controls and erythrocytes were occasionally noted between the
theca cells.

Fig. 1 (900 fold magnification) illustrates some of the above described morphological observations in 14 day old littermate mice: (A) part of a follicle from a normal
control mouse; (D) treated with aRG; (C) treated simultaneously with aRG and FSH;
(D) treated simultaneously with aRG and HMG.

Both from the morphological observations and from data on total follicle counts
(Table 1) in each of the ovaries of control and treated animals, it became apparent
that gonadotropins are necessary for normal ovarian growth during infancy.   FSH
is the hormone responsible for granulosa cell proliferation and LH probably does
not contribute to this process, but has either a direct or indirect influence on inter-
granulosa cell spacing, antrum formation, development of theca and vascularization.

Some parameters in the sequence of events following stimulation by FSH and
leading to the morphological observation of granulosa cell proliferation were therefore investigated.   It could be demonstrated that 90 min. after a single injection
of "biologically pure" FSH (12 IU), rate of DNA synthesis increased exponentially,
reaching its peak at 240 min., decreasing thereafter, and returning to the initial
rate of synthesis 8 hours after the injection.   Increased rate of protein synthesis
was observed 30 min. after the increased rate of DNA synthesis was first noted
(Fig. 2).

Since FSH alone had the capacity to induce increased rate of DNA synthesis,
protein synthesis and proliferation of cells but not the production of uterotrophic
steroids (for which LH is required), the effect of HMG (containing both FSH and
LH) as well as the effect of HCG were investigated for their effect on nucleic acid
and protein synthesis.

When HMG was given, no increase in the rate of DNA synthesis was observed.
However, after the same dose of FSH alone, a significant stimulation was noted
(Fig. 3).   Furthermore, no increase in DNA synthesis was observed within the

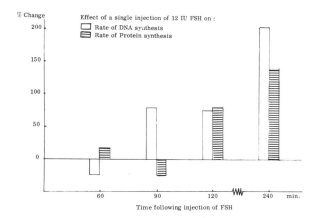

Fig. No. 2

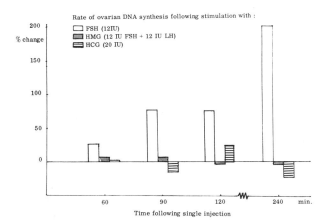

Fig. No. 3

first 120 min. following 10 IU HCG and a significant decrease was observed after
240 min. (C. Coriat*, A. Eshkol & B. Lunenfeld).

The pattern of RNA synthesis in this sequence of events leading to cell proliferation following FSH stimulation was as follows: A preferential accumulation of
labelled uridine was observed in the 28 S RNA region (presumably the precursor
of 50 S ribosomes) 45 min. after the injection of FSH.   Ninety minutes after FSH
injection a preferential accumulation of the label was found in the 16 S RNA region
(presumably the precursor of 30 S ribosomes).   At 180 min. after FSH injection,
the label was found unpreferentially in both regions, yet in a higher specific activity than in the control ovaries.

The sequence of events after injection of FSH proceeds as follows: The first
stimulation provokes an increased synthesis of the 23 S RNA, which will eventually
form the 50 S sub-unit of the ribosome.   Later the cell will begin to synthesize
its 16 S RNA, which is a precursor of the 30 S ribosomes (B. Hardy*, Y. Ash-
kenazi & B. Lunenfeld).

Sequential synthesis of the precursors of ribosomes was reported in various
cell populations (e.g., heLa cells, chick embryo).   Inhibition in the rate of protein synthesis by excess of 50 S ribosomes was observed in the poly U stimulating
systems.

Thus the following speculation can be made: The production of the 50 S ribosome is used in a dichotomal way - (1) its presence inhibits protein synthesis;
(2) upon synthesis of the additional sub-unit (the 30 S ribosome) followed by sub-
unit association (30 S + 50 S) forming the 70 S ribosomes, a signal is given to the
cell for general protein synthesis, division of cells, namely proliferation.

ACKNOWLEDGEMENTS

This study was supported by Ford Foundation Grant No. 67-470.

REFERENCES

1.   Ben-Or, S.   J. Embryol. exp. Morph. 2, 1, 1963.
2.   Eshkol, Aliza and Lunenfeld, B.   Acta endocr. (Kbh.) 54, 91, 1967.
3.   Lunenfeld, B., Eshkol, A., Baldratti, G. and Suchowsky, G.K.   Acta endocr.
     (Kbh.) 54, 311, 1967.
4.   Peters, H. and Pedersen, T. In press, 1968.
5.   Steinberger, E. Ciba Foundation Colloquia on Endocrinology 16, 191, 1967.

---

*   Part of M.Sc. thesis.

DISCUSSION

STEINBERGER: I was glad to see your data. They provide another confirmation for the fact that follicle stimulating hormone is a follicle stimulating hormone.

MARSHALL: How did you determine DNA and RNA synthesis and did you make these determinations in different cellular components of the ovary or in whole ovaries?

LUNENFELD: The role of DNA synthesis was determined by measuring incorporation of ^{3}H-thymidine into TCA precipitable material of the ovaries. The pattern of RNA synthesis was determined by fractionation of the total RNA into its different subunits and measurement of specific activity. The procedure was carried out following incubation in the presence of ^{3}H-uridine.

BELL: I should like to ask Dr. Lunenfeld for further details of his technique for counting follicular cells.

LUNENFELD: The ovaries are serially sectioned and in each fifth section follicles are counted according to the number of follicular cells around all those oocytes in which the nucleolus is seen.

SAXENA: Have you studied the effects of actinomycin and puromycin on RNA and DNA synthesis to show their relationship to protein synthesis in the ovaries?

LUNENFELD: We did not administer puromycin or actinomycin to the experimental animals nor did we do any such experiments in vitro, since our aim was to study directly protein and nucleic acid synthesis and not any other effects mediated through these.

ULTRASTRUCTURAL CHANGES OBSERVED AFTER HYPOPHYSECTOMY IN RAT TESTES

Oscar Vilar, M. D.

Centro de Investigaciones en Reproduccion, Facultad de Medicina, Universidad de Buenos Aires, Argentina.

Investigations carried out in rats by Smith (1) showed that after hypophysectomy, the seminiferous tubules are greatly re-duced in size. Only spermatogonia and degenerating spermatocytes are present, hence, it was postulated that functional activity could be restored with the administration of appropriate treat-ment. In other studies it was found that after hypophysectomy, all the cells of the germinal line (except spermatogonial cells) are absent in both monkeys (2) and humans (3). Cutuly and Cutuly (4), on the other hand, reported that the premiotic stages of spermatogenesis do not depend on hormonal stimulation while Clermont and Morgentaler (5) stated that in the hypophysectomized rat, the process of spermatogenesis may proceed as far as "step 7" of spermiogenesis without gonadotropin treatment. Little in-formation has been obtained in regard to the effect of hypophy-sectomy on the Sertoli cells which are known to be present for long periods of time after surgery (1). Studies on the immature testes of lambs showed that gonadotropins do have a particular action on Sertoli stem cells (6). Burgos and Vitale-Calpe de-monstrated that the sustentacular cells of toad testes were the main target of the acute effect of LH (7). Furthermore, it is known that, after hypophysectomy, the Leydig cells become smaller with an increased amount of cytoplasmatic fat content.

This study was undertaken to obtain information concerning the ultrastructure of the rat testes at varying periods of time after hypophysectomy. We anticipated that the study of the sub-cellular characteristics would enable us to better understand the sequential changes which occur in the male gonad as well as of the changes observed in the connective tissue structures of the tubular wall and the so-called sustentacular or Sertoli cells of the seminiferous epithelium.

MATERIAL AND METHODS

Holtzman adult male rats were used for this study. Animals were killed in groups of three each according to the following time intervals: 2, 3, 5, 7, 10, 15, 21, 28, 31, 35, 42, 49, 58, 77, 89, 99, 136 and 149 days after hypophysectomy. Testicular specimens were obtained while the animals were under anesthesia and fixed in 2.5% buffered gluteraldehyde (8). Post fixation was also carried out in 2% uranyl acetate - followed by dehydra-tion and embedding (9). Silver and gold sections were stained with lead citrate (12) and observed under either a Siemens

Elmiskop or an RCA EMU 3F electron microscope.

RESULTS

Interstitial tissue. Three days after hypophysectomy, the Leydig cells exhibited degenerative changes in the cytoplasm; the nuclei showed degeneration and, these cells disappeared rapidly from the intertubular spaces. Repeated observations taken at different intervals of time throughout the study showed no evidence of transformation of Leydig cells into other cell types. Consequently, we could not confirm the observations made by other investigators in that a differentiation of Leydig cells into fibroblasts does take place. After two weeks, however, scarce traces of fibroblasts and collagen fibers could be seen in the intertubular spaces.

Tubular wall. Anatomically, the tubular wall of the hypophysectomized rat presented the same components found in the normal animal. .The cellular layers and collagen fibers showed no change. The structural formation of the tubular wall itself, however, differed from the normal in the following respects: the basement membrane was of normal thickness but contained numerous folds. It also appeared to be detached from the germinal epithelium, especially in areas where the tubular diameter decreased (this would account for the apparent thickening observed under the light microscope). We did not, however, observe any hyalinization of the tubular wall, even five months after hypophysectomy.

Germinal epithelium. Three days after hypophysectomy, the Sertoli cells showed numerous localized dilatations of the endoplasmic reticulum resembling small and medium-sized empty vacuoles which gave the cytoplasm of these cells a sifted appearance. Only seven days after operation they began to show segregated portions which appeared as either multi-layered membranous bodies, myelin-like structures, or as clusters of dense lysosomal bodies. These changes increased in intensity during the first month following operation and then disappeared. The Sertoli cells were small and atrophic. Furthermore, the amount of cytoplasm began to decrease at a much greater rate than the nucleoplasm until the composition of the cell consisted of nothing more than a shriveled nucleus surrounded by a thin layer of cytoplasm. The nucleolus became small losing its typical complexity and appeared rather homogeneous. Spermatogonial cells showed no alteration at any time during the study. Neither the cytoplasm nor the nuclei exhibited morphological changes at the end of five months. Type A spermatogonia appeared normal in number whereas mitotic divisions decreased considerably. Type B spermatogonia were also found to be normal in number but mitosis was absent at the end of forty-two days. The germinal epithelium exhibited a progressive reduction in the number of spermatocytes, and at the end of five months very few spermatocytes could be found. In a few cases where meiotic spermatocytes were observed, it was found that pituitary tissue was present.

The absence of spermatocytes seems to have elminated the existence of the so-called "resting spermatocyte" (10). Electron microscopy revealed that in the normal germinal epithelium no resting stage was interposed between the last spermatogonial mitosis and the meiotic prophase of spermatocyte I. A few spermatocytes, however, with obvious signs of degeneration were traceable in many cases but the majority of these had separated from the Sertoli cells and were seen in the lumen of the semi-niferous tubules. Maturing spermatids did not undergo degener-ation nor phagocytosis by the Sertoli cells but, instead, com-pleted their maturation and were seen in the lumen of the semi-niferous tubules. Golgi phase spermatids did not show regres-sive changes either and persisted in the germinal epithelium as long as there were available spermatocytes. It was quite evi-dent, however, that spermatids undergoing the "cap phase" began degenerating seven days after hypophysectomy and were completely eliminated when the number of early spermatids were no longer present. The moment this massive degeneration of spermatids began to take place seemed to correspond to steps 6-8 of Clermont's report (10). Furthermore, the necrotic cells ap-peared to be engulfed by the cytoplasm of the Sertoli cells but unlike normal cells, did not undergo the expected phagocytosis.

DISCUSSION

This study demonstrates that the early effects of hypo-physectomy on the rat testes are: disintegration of Leydig cells and progressive atrophy of the Sertoli cells. Disintegration of the cap phase spermatids and the sloughing of spermatocytes and early spermatids occurred a few days following hypophysectomy. However, this phenomenon was not very extensive. These changes were associated with decreased mitosis of spermatogonia A, and with absence of mitosis of spermatogonia B which caused progres-sive diminution of the tubular content with consequent decrease in tubular diameter. Nevertheless, the cell content of the semi-niferous tubules did not revert to the prepuberal stage, for the ultrastructure of the germinal epithelium several months after hypophysectomy was similar to that observed in cultured frag-ments of normal rat testes (13).

The detachment of the basement membrane was probably in-duced by mechanical forces created by the lack of proper ana-tomical relationships between the tubular cell content and the diameter of the tubular wall. It is still unknown if the changes observed in the germinal epithelium result from the effect of hypophysectomy upon the Sertoli cells. It should be noted that the Sertoli cells may exert a possible nursing role, and that during the process of development, Sertoli cell maturation pre-cedes the appearance of spermatocytes. The structure of its nucleolus suggest an active capacity of the Sertoli cells to synthesize ribonucleic acid (RNA). It could be postulated that this could influence the division and differentiation of spermatogonial cells. It is worth noting that the nucleolar changes observed in the Sertoli cells after hypophysectomy are similar to those induced by actinomycin (11) which is an active inhibitor of RNA synthesis.

ACKNOWLEDGMENTS

The author wishes to thank Mrs. Lynn Clark and Miss Maria Coumroglon for their technical assistance. This work was supported by U.S.P.H.S. grant No. HD 01039 and by the Consejo Nacional de Investigaciones Cientificas y Tecnicas (Argentina).

REFERENCES

1.   Smith, P. E. Am. J. Anat. $\underline{45}$: 205, 1930.

2.   Albert, A. in W. C. Young (editor) Sex and Internal Secre-
     tion. Third Edition. The Williams & Wilkins Co. Baltimore
     1961.

3.   Mancini, R. E. et al. in Coloquio Internacional sobre
     Transtornos Funcionales de la Glandulas Sexuales. Sociedad
     Espanola para el Estudio de la Esterilidad. Madrid, Spain.
     1967. (Abstract).

4.   Cutuly, E. and E. C. Cutuly. Endocrinology, $\underline{26}$: 503, 1940.

5.   Clermont, Y. and H. Morgentaler. Endocrinology $\underline{57}$: 369, 1955.

6.   Courot, M. Ann. Biol. Anim. Biochem. Biophys., $\underline{2}$: 157, 1962.

7.   Burgos, M. H. and R. Vitale-Calpe. Am. J. Anat. $\underline{120}$: 227, 1967.

8.   Sabatini, D. D., K. Bensch and R. J. Barrnett, J. Cell. Biol.
     $\underline{17}$: 19, 1963.

9.   Vilar, O., A. Steinberger and E. Steinberger. Z. Zellforsch.
     $\underline{74}$: 529, 1966.

10. Clermont, Y. and C. P. Leblond. Am. J. Anat. $\underline{93}$: 475, 1953.

11. Kierszenbaum, A. L. and R. E. Mancini. Actas del Primer
     Congreso Sudamericano de Quimioterapia Antineoplasica.
     Buenos Aires, 1967 (Abstract).

12. Reymolds, E. S. J. Cell. Biol. $\underline{17}$: 208, 1963.

13. Vilar, O., A. Steinberger and E. Steinberger. Z. Zellforsch.
     $\underline{78}$: 221, 1967.

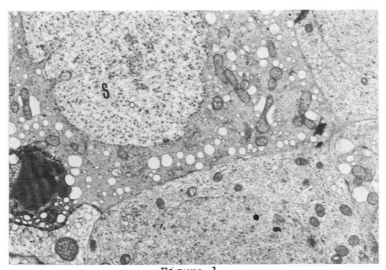

Figure 1
Rat testis 3 days after hypophysectomy. The cytoplasm of the
Sertoli cell (S) showed numerous small and medium-size vacuoles.
Two germinal cells show no changes. **x 11,000**

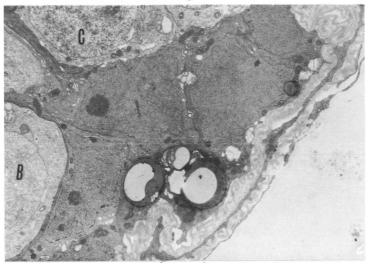

Figure 2
Rat testis 35 days after hypophysectomy. A spermatogonium B (B)
and spermatocytes in meiosis (C) show no alterations. The four
Sertoli cells appear smaller with a thin layer of cytoplasm
around the nucleus containing lipids and membranous bodies. The
basement membrane presents numerous folds. x 5,000

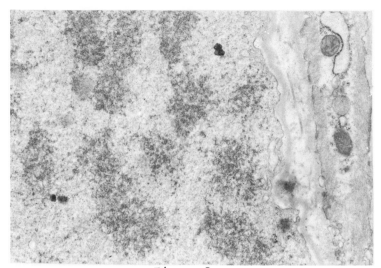

Figure 3
Rat testes 49 days after hypophysectomy.   Mitosis of spermatogonia
A are seen rather frequently. x 15,000

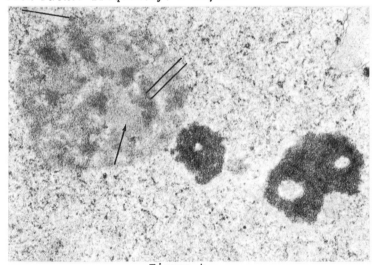

Figure 4
Sertoli cell 2 days after hypophysectomy. The nucleolar complex
shows normal features. Two heterochromatic bodies (chromatin)
are associated with the nucleolus as usual. The nucleolus itself
presents its typical heterogeneous components: granular (black
line), dense (double line) and amorphous (arrow). x 21,000

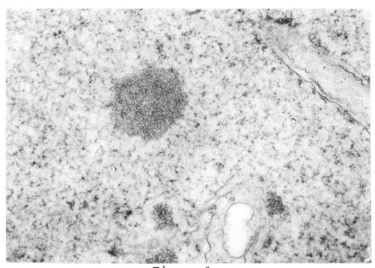

Figure 5
Sertoli cell 58 days after hypophysectomy. The nucleolus is
small and its typical heterologous internal structure is lost.
x 30,000

EFFECT OF LH IN THE SEMINIFEROUS TUBULE
AT THE SUBCELLULAR LEVEL

Burgos, M. H., Vitale-Calpe, R. and Russo, J.

Instituto de Histologia y Embriologia, Facultad de Ciencias
Medicas U. N. C. Mendoza, Argentina.

The role played by luteinizing hormone (LH) on spermatozoa
release is still unknown. This rather complicated and obscure
mechanism has escaped observation in mammals but has been
studied in amphibia since 1945 (1 and 2). In this report we
have compiled evidence in favor of the postulation that LH is,
in fact, the hormone of spermiation.

SPERMIATION IN AMPHIBIA

With the aid of electron microscopy, we have explored the
action of LH on the seminiferous tubules of the toad Bufo
arenarum Hensel specificallis, on its effect on the Sertoli
cells.

Under light microscopy the Sertoli cells appeared elongated,
paler, vacuolated and with rupture of the apical cytoplasm.
Figure 1 illustrates the sequence of changes which occurred in
the Sertoli cells of the toad after the administration of a
single dose of LH (1 mg). The first drawing, A, depicts a
resting Sertoli cell with late spermatids of spermatozoa implanted
in the deep recesses of the apical cytoplasm. Drawing B shows
the cell during the first stage of spermiation: note the marked
increase in size due to the swelling of the endoplasmic reticulum.
The tips of the spermatozoa have been pushed away from the nuclear
zone. Drawing C, shows the Sertoli cell undergoing the second
stage of spermiation at which time the swelling of the apical
cytoplasm has progressively effaced the apical recesses and has
pushed the spermatozoa further toward the tubular lumen. At the
same time, the distended endoplasmic reticulum had collapsed.
The last drawing, D, shows the third and final stage of the
spermiation process. The extreme swelling of the apical cytoplasm has resulted in the formation of dome-shaped projections
(or at other times, irregular cytoplasmic blebs). With the
rupture and disintegration of the apical cytoplasm, the spermatozoa, fluid and cellular debris have discharged into the lumen.
The nucleated basal portion of the Sertoli cell, however, is
protected by the overlapping of the residual membranes (3).

A similar study was performed in another amphibian
Leptodactylus chaquensis, after the administration of a single
dose of either LH or HCG (Fig. 2). It was found that fifteen
minutes after the injection of the gonadotropins, the testicular
weight of the toad increased significantly. This change, how-

ever, was mainly due to an increase in the toad's water content
as shown in Fig. 3.   The measurement of sodium content also
showed an increase from 46 in the controls to 64 in the experimental testis (Fig. 4) expressed as milliequivalents (mEq)
percent.

The enzymatic study of testis homogenates of control and
experimental toads, similarly treated with either LH or HCG,
revealed significant changes in the activity of some enzymes.
The specific activity of Na†K† (sensitive ATPase) as well as of
Mg †† (dependent ATPase) decreased by approximately 50% (Fig. 5).
Acid phosphatase activity was similarly lowered by the gonadotropins to about 50%. Also, the respiratory activity, measured
by oxygen consumption, showed a marked depression (50%) as
compared to control values (Fig. 6).

SPERMIATION IN MAMMALS

The absence of visible, periodically occurring events in the
reproductive process of the male, as well as the considerable
inertia exhibited by the testis in its response to gonadotropins,
makes these studies very difficult.   In the female there are
cyclic variations in the ratios of FSH, LH and LTH secreted.
There is as yet, however, no evidence to confirm that the rhythm
in the male involves anything more than quantitative changes in
the level of gonadotropin secretion (4).

During copulation in rats (5) an acute release of LH,
similar to the ovulatory surge seen in humans occurred in both
sexes, as indicated by an increase in plasma LH and a decrease
in pituitary LH.   In male hamsters, preliminary experiments
showed a similar release of LH during copulation in the order
of 5 µg per mg. of pituitary tissue during the first hour (6).
Based on these observations we have studied the testicular
response to endogenous LH in the hamster one hour after the
initiation of mating.   One testis was processed for electron
microscopy and the other for chemical determinations.

I.   Electron Microscopy

Spermatogenic stages which have Sertoli cells associated
with late spermatids were studied by comparing normal controls
and experimental animals. As shown in Figure 7, there were
significant changes in the cytoplasm of the Sertoli cells of
the copulating animals: a) increase in length; b) change in
the cytoplasmic matrix; c) opening of channels and cisternae
of the smooth endoplasmic reticulum; d) swelling of the apical
cytoplasm with unfolding of the apical recesses which contained
the late spermatids and spermatozoa and e) release of spermatozoa together with cell debris from the apical cytoplasm of the
Sertoli cell and residual bodies of the spermatids.

II. Chemical Determinations

No differences were found to exist in either the weight or water content of the testis of copulating or LH and HCG treated hamsters when compared to controls. The enzymatic activity of ATPase and acid phosphatase (Fig. 8), however, showed a decrease of approximately 50%, which is comparable to the enzymatic depression observed in amphibians. Similar results for ATPase and acid phosphatase activity, as well as a marked decrease in the oxygen consumption (Fig. 9) were obtained from mice after copulation or HCG treatment.

CONCLUSIONS

From the comparative study regarding the mechanism of action of LH in the seminiferous tubule at the subcellular level, it was postulated that the main target of LH is the Sertoli cell cytoplasm. The cytoplasmic swelling and the un-folding of the apical recesses, which was accompanied by the release of spermatozoa, can be considered as the counterpart of ovulation.

This aspect of the intimate action of LH appears to be related to blockage of the sodium pump; such blockage could be responsible for the swelling of the Sertoli cells and subsequent release of spermatozoa.

ACKNOWLEDGMENT

This work was supported by Grant M63.121 from the Population Council.

REFERENCES

1. De Robertis, E.D.P., M. H. Burgos and E. Breyter, Rev Soc Argent Biol, 4: 21, 1945.

2. _____, Proc Soc Exper Biol, 61: 20, 1946.

3. Burgos, M. H. and R. Vitale-Calpe, Am J Anat, 120: 227, 1967.

4. Davidson, J. M., In Martini, L. and W. S. Ganong (eds). Neuroendocrinology vol. 1, Academic Press, N.Y., 1966, p. 565.

5. Taleisnik, S., L. Caligaris and J. J. Astrada, Endocrinology. 79: 49, 1966.

6. Donoso, A. and R. C. Santolaya, Personal communication.

THE MECHANISM OF SPERMIATION IN THE TOAD

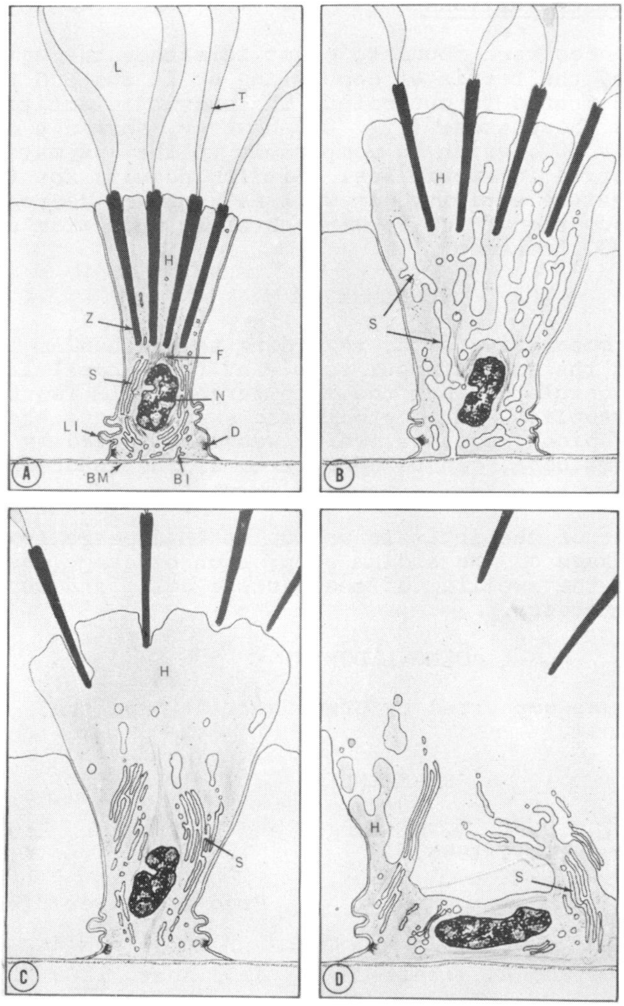

Figure No. 1

Figures A to D are drawings of Sertoli cells which summarize the different stages of the release of spermatozoa in the toad Bufo arenarum.

(Figures 1 to 6 from Burgos, M.H., and R. Vitale-Calpe, Am.J.Anat: 120:227, 1967)

THE MECHANISM OF SPERMIATION IN THE FROG WITH LH OR HCG

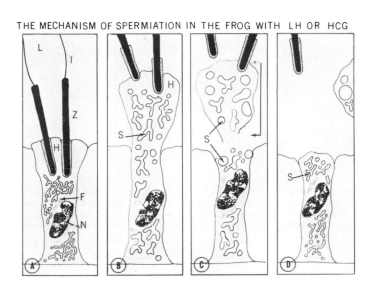

Figure No. 2

Figures A to D are drawings of Sertoli cells which summarize the
different stages of the release of spermatozoa in Leptodactylus
chaquensis.

TOAD TESTIS WATER CONTENT

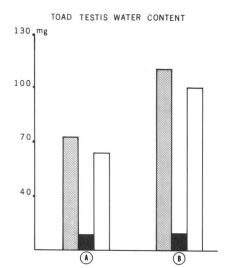

TOAD TESTIS SODIUM AND
POTASSIUM CONTENT

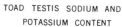
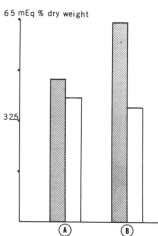

Figure No. 3
Changes in water content. Grey column represents the total weight of
both control (A) and experimental
testes (B); black column the dry
weight and white column the water
content.

Figure No. 4
Total sodium content (grey
column) increases from A
(control) to B (experimental).
Potassium content (white column decreases to a less significant degree.

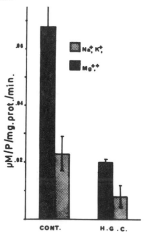

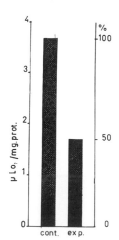

Figure No. 5.
ATPase activity in the testis of
control and experimental Toads.

Figure No. 6
Oxygen consumption of testis from control and experimental Toads.

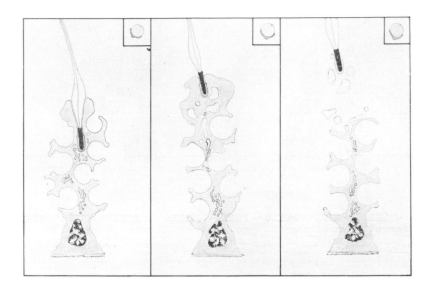

Figure No. 7

Figures A to C are drawings of Sertoli cells which summarize the
stages of release of spermatozoa in the hamster.

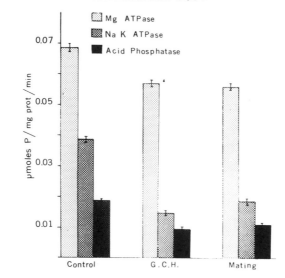

Figure No. 8

ATPase and acid phosphatases activity in the testis of control and experimental hamsters.

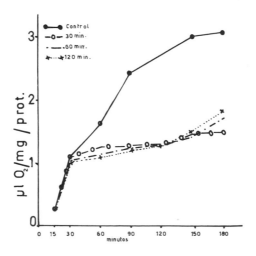

Figure No. 9

Oxygen consumption of testis from control and experimental mice.

DISCUSSION

RYAN: What does hyaluronidase do in the testis? Does LH affect hyaluronidase activity in the testis and does this have any bearing on the removal of sperm from the testis?

BURGOS: I have not tested hyaluronidase in my work.

STEINBERGER: About ten or twelve years ago we were interested in the effect of various hormones, including the gonadotropic hormones, on the levels of hyaluronidase in the normal testes of adult rats. We were unable to detect any effects (Endocrin. 56: 429, 1955; Endocrin. 60: 105, 1957). Dr. Burgos has singled out the Sertoli cell as the target organ for ICSH. If this is the case, how does one explain the relatively normal spermatogenesis in testis of hypophysectomized animals maintained on testosterone? A question also to Dr. Vilar - could you say whether or not you think that the Sertoli cells are a target site of hormonal action, as are the Leydig cells? Dr. Burgos, if I understood you correctly, you state that LH exerts its effect on the testes by direct action on Sertoli cells affecting the release of spermatozoa; in other words, the mechanism dealing with the release of spermatozoa from the Sertoli cells is under direct control of LH. But if that were the case, how would you explain that in hypophysectomized animals, maintained on testosterone, the spermatozoa are released and are capable of fertilization.

BURGOS: I think the question is very interesting and shows two points related to the action of copulation. One point is that during copulation release of spermatozoa which occurs at the level of the seminiferous tubules can be controlled by puncturing the reti testes and detecting at this level the outflow of fluid 30 minutes after injecting LH. This has nothing to do with the spermatozoa released during copulation from the tail of the epididymis. The spermatozoa mature in the epididymis for almost 14 days and pass from the head to the tail. This number of spermatozoa is ejaculated during copulation. At the same time LH is released in plasma and induces a new release of spermatozoa which travel from the testes to the head of the epididymis.

McARTHUR: I wonder if Dr. Burgos is familiar with the studies of Desjardins and his collaborators (P.S.E.B.M. 126: 23, 1967). They measured the levels of a variety of tropic hormones in the pituitaries of female rabbits after coitus. The FSH levels did not change, but many other levels declined. The LH concentration fell, and so also did that of ACTH and prolactin.

BURGOS: We have injected ACTH, TSH anti diuretic hormone and estrogens in the toad and we have produced a release of spermatozoa. This is a very specific action in the toad. We have not tested it in mammals as yet, but we are beginning to do so now. The

concentration of spermatozoa that we see in the tail of the
epididymis can be explained by an action of epinephrine independent
of the interaction of the testes whether the hypophysis is present
or not. By the injection of epinephrine or stimulation with
electrodes one can get release of these spermatozoa. This is an
independent mechanism and is like emptying a cavity that holds
mature spermatozoa. A point that is interesting to explore is the
release of spermatozoa which go from the seminiferous tubules to
the head of the epididymis. As far as it is known, nobody has
studied this mechanism carefully. We have derived a system and
I have a slide to show this. A complicated mechanism is used to
anesthetize the animals as we want to eliminate any factor that
will block release of LH or the action of LH in the tissues. The
hormone was injected through the saphena vein. We opened the
scrotal region and exposed the superior pole of the testis. We
then localized the efferent duct which goes from the testis to
the head of the epididymis. We made a puncture there and measured
the volume ejected during the observation. On injecting LH we
observed a very sharp rise in volume of fluid coming from the
tail. These conditions have therefore been used to observe the
response of the testes to LH in a way similar to the toad. The
toad has no epididymis but we can collect spermatozoa released
by LH in the cloaca of the toad. We have found a similar means
of studying the effect of the hormone by puncturing the rete
testis in the hamster. We have also done this in the rat, guinea
pig and other animals.

STEINBERGER: In the rat it takes about twelve days for the
spermatozoa to pass through the epididymis. One can hypophysectomize a rat and maintain it with testosterone for many
months. The animal will still produce spermatozoa and fertilize
a female. Consequently, the effect cannot be on release from
the epididymis since the spermatozoa must be coming from the
testis in such hypophysectomized animals.

BURGOS: With respect to Dr. Steinberger's question, in hypophysectomized or intact animals, if the animal is maintained with
androgen it is capable of ejaculating all spermatozoa during
copulation which reach the tail of the epididymis. No one has
found the mechanism of release of spermatozoa in hypophysectomized
animals.

RAO: I wish to present briefly the results of our studies on the
selective destruction of the follicle-stimulating and luteinizing
principles in human chorionic gonadotropin, using heat and hydrogen
peroxide, respectively. We have observed that HCG has at least
two antigens not present in either the serum or urine of normal
women. The HCG solution, at pH 7.6, was heated to $100°C$ for 30
min. in order to identify the hormone-specific antigen. Heating
the hormone to $100°C$ for 30 min. destroyed one of the antigens
but failed to completely inactivate the biologically active part
of the hormone. The ovaries of immature female mice injected
with the heated hormone were hyperemic and showed an increase in

weight as compared to controls, but no hemorrhagic follicles could be observed. It was further observed that the heat stable antigen gave an immunological cross-reaction with LH of pituitary origin (kindly supplied by Doctors A. E. Wilhelmi and L. E. Reichert). A positive Ächheim Zondek test could be obtained by injecting the heated and hydrogen peroxide-treated hormone at different sites. A similar result was obtained by injecting urinary FSH (HMG) and pituitary LH (Wilhelmi) at different sites. The heat stable antigen was biologically assayed for LH activity using the OAAD test in Swiss mice of our colony. The results indicated that the heated hormone retained LH activity. The biological studies carried out with the hydrogen peroxide-stable antigen indicated that the treated hormone possessed a follicle-stimulating principle as determined by the increase in uterine weight of mice primed with HCG. Histological observations of the ovaries of the mice injected with hydrogen peroxide-treated hormone indicated that there was a stimulation in the growth of ovarian follicles. The controls and the HCG-treated animals showed no such stimulation. It seems likely that oxidation with hydrogen peroxide destroys the luteinizing activity of HCG, probably by oxidizing - SH groups in the hormone. Heat, on the other hand, seemed to have destroyed the follicle-stimulating activity of HCG.

ROSEMBERG: Dr. Rao, you have used in your studies two bioassay systems; one to measure FSH and the other LH. The method used for LH measurement was the ascorbic acid depletion using the mouse as the experimental animal. You have referred to the method of Keller (Endocrinology 76: 165, 1965) who conducted this work, described in his paper, in our laboratories. This was published as a negative paper, that is, it was concluded that the OAAD assay could not be employed using the mouse as the experimental animal. With respect to the FSH assay, you used the Igarashi-McCann method (Endocrinology 74: 440, 1964). This method is not specific for FSH, especially when the materials tested contain large amounts of LH.

RAO: We utilized the Igarashi and McCann test to assay the follicle stimulating principle in HCG after destroying the LH activity of the hormone by treatment with 1 M H_2O_2 (Shahani, S. K. and Rao, S. S., Acta Endocr. 46: 317, 1964). This method, carried out in Swiss mice, fulfilled our requirements for the estimation of small amounts of the follicle stimulating principle present in HCG. The results were observed to be significant evidently as there was no interference with LH. In our work with HMG an excellent log dose response curve for the FSH activity of HMG was obtained when the LH moiety in the hormone was destroyed by treatment with 1 M H_2O_2 (Shahani, S. K. and Rao, S. S., Indian Jour. Exper. Biol. 4: 54, 1966) As for the ovarian ascorbic acid depletion test, the Holtzman strain of rats were not available and it was essential for us to try other strains of rats as well as mice to carry out the assay. The Swiss mice of our colony were found suitable for the OAAD assay as compared to 6 other strains.   The index of precision for the assay was good.

ROSEMBERG: I should like to emphasize that it is extremely important to test different strains of animals in one's own laboratory and if the experimenter feels that his or her method is reliable and specific, it is appropriate to go ahead and use it.   However, I wish to point out again that the Igarashi-McCann method is not specific for FSH.

CHAPTER 3

IMMUNOLOGIC ASSAY OF HUMAN AND ANIMAL GONADOTROPINS

THE SPECIFICITY OF ANTI-HUMAN CHORIONIC GONADOTROPIN (HCG)

BY SEVERAL IN VITRO PROCEDURES

A. M. REISS, J. B. HAWK AND R. D. JACOBS*
DEPARTMENT OF IMMUNOLOGICAL DEVELOPMENT
DIAGNOSTIC RESEARCH, ORTHO RESEARCH FOUNDATION,
RARITAN, NEW JERSEY, AND DEPARTMENT OF BIO-
CHEMISTRY, STATE UNIVERSITY OF NEW YORK,
SYRACUSE, NEW YORK

INTRODUCTION

It is well established that multiple immunologic determinant groupings occur in protein molecules and that these groupings are usually distinct from one another (1,2). Moreover, these determinant groupings have been found to be distinct from the areas of the molecule posessing biological or functional activity (3,4). Thus the possibility exists that the protein molecule may lose functional or biological activity without concomitant loss of immunological activity. Evidence to this effect has existed for HCG from the very beginning of the in vitro testing for pregnancy (5) and has been substantiated (6,7).

In spite of this, the international unit (IU) for biological activity has been adopted without qualification to describe the sensitivities possessed by the various immunological procedures and to report existing units of the hormone in clinical specimens. The practice, while potentially incorrect, remains acceptable as long as the designated standard is not unlike the test materials undergoing analysis.

If biologically inactive but immunologically active material occurs in significant amounts in the crude materials (and the accepted standard), a divergence of the in vivo and in vitro test results will occur as purification for the biologically active principles proceeds. In order to examine the extent of this divergence, four HCG powders were studied which ranged in biological activity from 2772 IU to 12,480 IU/mg. Each powder was tested by the following immunological procedures: inhibition of hemagglutination, inhibition of latex agglutination and quantitative complement fixation. The results of these studies are given and discussed.

*Supported in part by Ortho Research Foundation grant

MATERIAL AND METHODS

1. Preparation of antisera. HCG that assayed biologically at 9200
   IU/mg was used as the immunogen in rabbits. The individual sera
   were heated at 56° C for 30 minutes to destroy the complement
   activity. Each serum was characterized by the reactions obtained
   with latex-HCG prior to pooling. The antiserum pool was checked
   for specificity by complement fixation using human serum, and
   urinary preparations of varying degrees of purity known to contain or to lack biological activity.

2. Inhibition of hemagglutination. HCG was chemically coupled to
   stabilized red cells according to the procedure of Arquilla and
   Stavitsky (8). The maximum dilution of the antiserum pool was
   prepared which yielded a four-plus pattern of agglutination with
   the chemically coupled red cells in the absence of soluble HCG
   and no agglutination in the presence of 1 to 2 μgs of crude HCG
   powder.

3. Partial absorption of the anti-HCG pool. The antiserum pool was
   absorbed with stated amounts of HCG powders for 1 hour at 37° C
   followed by an overnight interval at 4° C.

4. Inhibition of latex agglutination. The maximum dilution of the
   antiserum pool was chosen which yielded a four-plus slide agglutination with latex-HCG in the absence of soluble HCG and no
   agglutination in the presence of 3 to 4 μgs of crude HCG powder.

5. Complement fixation. The method described by Plescia et al. (9)
   was used with the exception that optimally diluted antiserum,
   guinea pig complement and buffer were combined in bulk immediately
   prior to performance of the test and added in a single addition
   to each of the experimental tubes. All tests were performed in
   triplicate.

6. Bioassay. The ventral prostate assay in immature hypophysectomized rats was used to measure HCG biological activity according
   to the method of Albert et al. (10). Estimates of relative
   potency were obtained in terms of the second International Standard
   for HCG*. Statistical analysis of the data were obtained with
   the aid of a computer program.

*Kindly supplied by the Division of Biological Standards, Medical
Research Council, National Institute of Medical Research, Mill Hill,
London, England

RESULTS

Inhibition of hemagglutination. The biological activities of the
four urinary powders are shown in Table No. 1 together with the
amount of each powder required to neutralize the prestandardized
in vitro system in terms of IU of HCG/ml and μgs of powder/ml.   On
the basis of the amount of the purest powder required to neutralize
the system, the expected amounts of the other powders that would be
required for neutralization were calculated from their respective
biological activities.   If the biological assay had not been carried
out, the potency of powder A would have been calculated at about 6700
IU/mg or 2.4 times the actual potency.

Whereas the immunological potencies in terms of μgs/ml are linearly
related to the log of the biological activity, this type of relationship does not exist in terms of IU/ml.

Table No. 1

Comparison of biological activity of HCG and amount of powder required
in vitro for inhibition of hemagglutination.

HCG Powder	Biological Activity IU/mg	Immunological Activity		Expected[+] μgs/ml
		Experimental		
		IU/ml	μgs/ml	
A	2772 (2037-4100)*	3.4	1.24	3.03
B	6000 (5041-8280)	4.5	0.75	1.40
C	9200 (7400-12,400)	6.1	0.66	0.91
D	12,480 (9800-15,810)	8.4	0.67	----

*95% confidence limits
+expected values based on amount of powder D required

In an effort to further substantiate these findings, partial absorption of aliquots of the antiserum pool with powders A and C,
respectively, was carried out.   The partially absorbed serum samples
were then assayed for residual hemagglutination titers.   These
findings are shown in Table No. 2.

Table No. 2

Hemagglutination titers before and after partial absorption of
anti-HCG with powders A and C, respectively.

Powder used for absorption	Amount of powder used/ml antiserum		Endpoint of titer*
	IU	μgs	
none	0	0	1:15,000
A	249	90	1:15,000
A	748	270	1:3,000
C	828	90	1:12,000
C	2484	270	1:400

*Titer performed as arithmetic dilutions: 1:1000, 1:2000 or 1:100,
1:200. Possible error: ± 1 arithmetic dilution.

It can be seen that the reduction of the titer endpoint of the antiserum pool is not related to the amounts of powder in terms of IU's
that were used for absorption. As may be anticipated from the results obtained by inhibition of hemagglutination, less of the purer
powder was required to bring about a decrease in antibody concentration.

The antiserum partially absorbed with 270 μgs of powder A was then
used in the inhibition of hemagglutination system for reassay of
the four powders. The results were similar to those shown in Table
No. 1 which suggested that the biologically inactive but immunologically active materials present in powder A were not selecting out a
unique population of antibodies. The partially absorbed antiserum
sample appeared to be no more discriminating then the unabsorbed
antiserum.

Inhibition of latex agglutination. Table No. 3 shows the results
obtained when the carrier particle for the affixed HCG was latex
instead of a stabilized red blood cell.

Table No. 3

Comparison of biological activity of HCG and amount of powder required in vitro for inhibition of latex agglutination.

HCG Powder	Biological Activity IU/mg	Immunological Activity		
		Experimental		Expected[+]
		IU/ml	µgs/ml	µgs/ml
A	2772 (2037-4100)*	8.8	3.19	6.17
B	6000 (5041-8280)	8.0	1.33	2.85
C	9200 (7400-12,400)	10.6	1.15	1.86
D	12,480 (9800-15,810)	17.1	1.37	----

*95% confidence limits
+expected values based on amount of powder D required

The results are similar to those obtained by inhibition of hemagglutination, in that much less of the crude powder A was required
than would be expected by a factor of 1.9. Had the biological
assay not been carried out, the activity of powder A would have
been calculated at about 5377 IU/mg.

As was true of the hemagglutination data, the immunological activities in terms of µgs/ml are linearly related to the log of the
biological activities but this type of relationship does not exist
in terms of IU/ml.

Quantitative complement fixation. The advantages of a direct
testing system over an indirect one are readily apparent. Whenever
an inhibition or competitive system is used, cognizance must be
taken of the possibilities that:

a.   the chemical coupling process is not random, and

b.   a certain number of antigen reactive sites are obliterated
     either as a direct result of the process or indirectly by
     steric considerations.

In the present study, the optimum concentration of antiserum and
complement for maximum discernment of the respective antigens was
first determined. Appropriate amounts of the respective powders
were then chosen which fixed complement in the ascending portion
of each of their fixation curves. The slopes shown in Figure No. 1
are the result of combining statistically weighted data from three
separate experiments.

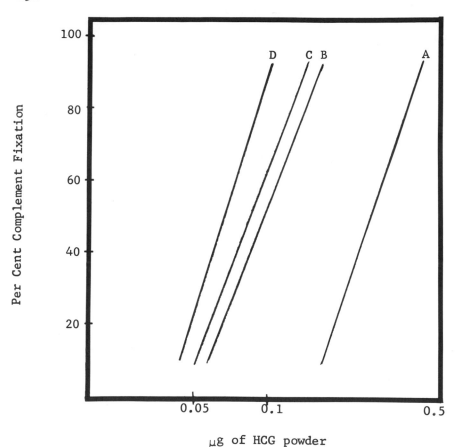

Figure No. 1

Ascending slopes of HCG powders as determined by complement
fixation.

Sample	Combined slope	Estimated Standard Error
A	202.89	7.69
B	175.74	5.77
C	181.27	3.10
D	211.99	6.54

It is apparent that the lines are essentially parallel which suggests, but does not prove, that the antigens in each preparation
may be the same.   The slope of each line together with the estimated
standard error appear in the legend.

The immunologic activity of each powder when compared with powder
D is shown in Table No. 4.   The amount of each powder in µgs/ml required to obtain 50% fixation is also given in order that a direct
comparison of the results may be made with those obtained by inhibition of agglutination.

Table No. 4

Immunological activity of HCG powders as determined by complement
fixation.

| HCG Powder | Dose-Response* in IU/mg | 50% Fixation Endpoint | | |
| | | Experimental | | Expected* |
		IU/ml[+]	µgs/ml	IU/ml µgs/ml
A	3095 (2820-3407)[‡]	0.721	0.260	0.824 0.297
B	8748 (8424-9098)	0.576	0.096	0.824 0.137
C	9610 (8574-10,758)	0.791	0.086	0.824 0.090
D	---- ----	0.824	0.066	----- -----

*Activity based on powder D possessing 12,480 IU/mg
[+]Activity in IU/ml based on biological activity (See Table No. 1)
[‡]95% confidence limits

As in the previous results the µgs of powder/ml required to reach
the endpoint is consistently decreased as the biologic potency is
increased.   It may be noted that powder B when tested by the latex-
HCG procedure as well as by complement fixation showed a sensitivity
greater than powder A in terms of IU/ml.   It is possible that inert
materials were removed during the fractionation of powder B while
the ratio of biologically inactive to biologically active molecules
was increased beyond the ratio found in powder A.   This possibility
is reflected in the dose-response data obtained by complement fixation which shows powder B as the only powder whose in vitro potency
is not contained completely in the range of activity established by
bioassay.

The 50% fixation endpoint shows that 1.1 times less of HCG powder A is required than would be expected from the results obtained with powder D.

The immunologic activities in terms of μgs/ml are related to the log of the biological activities but, as shown by the previous in vitro data, no obvious relationship exists in terms of IU/ml.

DISCUSSION

It is always the aim of fractionation procedures to increase the potency of the biologically active component while decreasing the amount of inert materials as well as inactive hormone. Antisera which cannot distinguish active from inactive hormone will err significantly if the aim of the fractionation procedure is not fulfilled.

Of the three in vitro test methods used, complement fixation was superior to the two indirect procedures. One might suspect that the system is inherently more discriminating in that at least two γG immunoglobulin molecules in correct propinquity are required per antigen molecule before fixation of complement can occur.

The data shows that a relationship between immunological and biological potency does exist but that this relationship is in terms of μg of HCG powder/ml and not in terms of IU's.

It remains to be determined whether or not all of the biologically inactive but immunologically active material is of gonadotropic origin.

ACKNOWLEDGMENTS

Appreciation is due to Mr. T. Ho for his help with the statistical evaluations.

REFERENCES

1. Lapresle, C., Ann Inst Pasteur 89: 654, 1955.

2. Maurer, P.H., Ann N Y Acad Sci 131: 374, 1965.

3. Imura, H., L.L. Sparks, G.M. Grodsky, and P.H. Forsham, J Clin Endocr 25: 1361, 1965.

4. Rosen, F.S., P. Charache, J. Pensky, and V. Donaldson, Science 148: 957, 1965.

5. Wide, L., Acta Endocr (Kobenhavn) Suppl 70, 1962.

6. Hobson, B., and L. Wide, Acta Endocr 46: 632, 1964.

7. Borth, R., M. Ferin, and A. Menzi, Acta Endocr 50: 335, 1965.

8. Arquilla, E.R., and A.B. Stavitsky, J Clin Invest 35: 458,
        1956.

9. Plescia, O.J., M. Amiraian, and M. Heidelberger, J Immunol
        78: 147, 1957.

10. Albert, A., J. Kobi, J. Leiferman, and I. Derner, J Clin
        Endocr 21: 1, 1961.

DISCUSSION

LUNENFELD: Dr. Reiss, this is only semantics but I would suggest that we do not use the term mono-specific antisera. I do not think that mono-specific antisera actually exist. Antisera are a big group of antibodies and I would be very careful in the use of the word mono-specific.

REISS: Dr. Lunenfeld, I can only re-echo what you have just said. I too believe that mono-specific anti-HCG does not exist at the present time. Even when we are able to produce antisera that recognize antigenic determinants close to the biologically active site we may not always parallel biological activity. However, we will have advanced from our present position in which we are detecting materials that may not even be gonadotropic in origin. Whether these materials that are chemically very similar to chorionic gonadotropin are detected immunologically because they possess determinants that are similar to those of HCG or because they persist as contaminating substances in all HCG powders is still not established. We have absorbed anti-HCG sera with specially prepared normal urinary powder as well as with what we call a standardized biologically inactive urinary powder. These absorbed antisera do not react with the absorbing powders, random urinary powders and normal human sera when tested by double diffusion and complement fixation procedures. These antisera do react with urinary powders containing HCG. When such absorbed antisera is tested by double diffusion in agar using samples of HCG at different levels of purity up to 9000 IU/mg., a single precipitin band of complete identity is observed within the first 24 hours with all the HCG samples. After 48 hours, two additional bands appear which also show complete identity with all the samples of HCG. This simply re-emphasizes the caution that must be used when one is speaking of immunological specificity within the HCG system.

MIDGLEY: I would like to direct a couple of comments to Dr. Reiss and Dr. Robyn and others who have presented studies dealing with non-radioimmunoassay use of antibodies. The experience of the radioimmunoassay workers is that individual rabbits produce unique antisera. A person doing radioimmunoassays will often screen 30 to 100 or more antisera to find one single antiserum that is suitable for radioimmunoassay use; i.e. one that gives a good correlation between biological and immunological activities, gives good dose response relationships, results in a sensitive assay, etc. In this screening process, one cannot help but be struck by the tremendous differences between antisera with regard to their species cross reactivity, nonspecificity, differences in avidity, etc. It is obviously impossible for individuals doing neutralization studies and often difficult with other immunological studies to screen this number of antisera. Thus, while it is possible to form conclusions based upon the study of relatively few antisera, it might be dangerous to generalize about how these results might pertain to results obtainable with other antisera. It is apparent that hormones have multiple over-lapping antigenic sites, and that some of these sites are shared by other completely unrelated hormones. A spectrum of anti-bodies can be found in a single antiserum with varying degrees of avidity for these sites and for sites found in totally un-related molecules which might have contaminated the immunizing material. Dr. Reiss, in your first slide on the results obtained by complement fixation, I thought you made the point that bio-logical activity and immunological activity were not correlated, and yet I thought I saw a good correlation in results. Did I mis-read your slide?

REISS: The degree of correlation between immunological and biological procedures depends to some extent upon the procedures themselves. While the results obtained by complement fixation correlate better with the results of the biological assay than either of the other two immunological procedures, there is a common trend in evidence for all of the in vitro procedures. Since the accuracy of an immunological technique is greater than that of a biological technique, the immunological potency and the confidence limits should lie completely within those obtained biologically. When one looks at the results with Powder B, one can see the overestimation as determined by complement fixation. The confidence limits are higher than and lie completely outside those obtained with the biological procedure.

MIDGLEY: I just do not interpret your data as indicating such a trend. The data did not indicate to me that as the purity of the hormone increases, the ratio of biological to immunological activity changes significantly.

REISS: The data I have presented shows that a relationship between immunological and biological potency does exist but that this relationship is in terms of micrograms of powder/ml.

and not in terms of IU's/ml.

MIDGLEY: There is obviously some misunderstanding between us
which is probably better resolved at another time. I would like
to refer to an illustration published by Brody and Carlstrom
(Acta Endocrinologica 43: 485, 1963). It was an immunoelectrophoretic study of crude HCG with antisera absorbed in two
different ways. At the top two bands formed when the antiserum
was saturated with human serum. These can be contrasted with a
single band seen at the bottom when the antiserum was absorbed
with a urinary extract. A crude HCG was studied with non-
absorbed anti-HCG serum and the same antiserum after exhaustive
absorption with human serum and children's urine concentrated by
ultrafiltration (Arch d'Anat Micr. In press, 1968). Although
the non-absorbed antiserum gave multiple precipitin bands with
the crude HCG preparation, the absorbed antiserum gave only a
single precipitin band. A single precipitin band was still seen
after seven days of incubation.

BIOASSAY OF ANTIGONADOTROPIC SERA.

Robyn C. and Diczfalusy E.

SWEDISH MEDICAL RESEARCH COUNCIL REPRODUCTIVE ENDOCRINOLOGY RESEARCH
UNIT, KAROLINSKA SJUKHUSET, STOCKHOLM.

A bioassay method is proposed for the estimation of the gonadotropin neutralizing potency of antisera (1). The method is based on
pilot assays (Fig. 1) followed by proper bioassays (Fig. 2). The
definition of the proposed unitage is derived from the terminology
suggested by Zondek and Sulman (2):1.0 antiunit (AU) is equivalent
to the amount of antiserum which neutralizes the specific biological
activity of 1.0 I.U. contained in an International Standard preparation or its equivalent in another reference preparation. This
definition is subject to the qualification that the condition of
simple additivity for the Hormone (H) and the Antiserum (AS) must
be fulfilled (3). Preliminary data (illustrated in Fig. 3) seem to
indicate that the antigonadotropic potencies obtained at different
levels of neutralization (between 33 and 90%) are in reasonably good
agreement with each other and as a first approximation fall within
the fiducial limits of error of the potency estimates obtained at
50% neutralization.

ASSAY OF THE HUMAN CHORIONIC GONADOTROPIN (HCG) AND LUTEINIZING HORMONE (LH) NEUTRALIZING POTENCIES (4).

The anti-HCG and anti-LH potencies were estimated in assays
based on the increase in weight of the accessory reproductive organs
of intact immature male rats and on the increase in weight of the
ventral prostate of hypophysectomized immature rats.

The antigonadotropic sera were obtained following immunization
of rabbits with HCG, human menopausal gonadotropin (HMG) and human
hypophysial gonadotropin (HHG) preparations. These antisera were
then assayed against the laboratory standard of HCG, the Second
International Standard of HCG and a highly purified HCG preparation.
The antigonadotropic potencies of the various antisera showed a
close agreement when assayed in intact or hypophysectomized animals
against the different HCG preparations.

When anti-HCG sera were assayed in intact or hypophysectomized
animals against the laboratory standard of HMG, the anti-LH potencies were approximately three times higher than those obtained when
the antisera were tested against HCG preparations (Fig. 4). In an
attempt to account for this discrepancy, the laboratory standard of
HCG and the Second International Standard preparation of HCG were
assayed in both systems against the laboratory standard of HMG and
the Second International Reference preparation of HMG, respectively.
The potency of 1.0 I.U. of HCG corresponded to that of 2.5 to 2.9
I.U. of L.H. If this difference is taken into consideration, the

discrepancy in antigonadotropic titers disappears. However, when anti-HCG and anti-HHG sera were assayed in intact or hypophysecto-mized animals against an HHG preparation, the anti-LH potencies were much lower; in the case of anti-HCG sera, thirty times lower than those obtained in the assays conducted against the laboratory standard of HMG. Since these discrepancies in antigonadotropic titers cannot be explained by differences in the gonadotropic potency of the preparations used, it is concluded, that major dif-ferences exist in the antigenic properties of human LH of pituitary and urinary origin.

ASSAY OF THE HUMAN FOLLICLE STIMULATING HORMONE (FSH) NEUTRALIZING
POTENCY (5).

The anti-FSH potencies were estimated in assays based on a modified ovarian weight augmentation test (6), using HCG or LH of ovine origin for augmentation. When HCG was used for augmentation, the FSH neutralizing potency of antisera depended on the sequence in which HCG, FSH and the antiserum were combined (Fig. 5). When HCG was mixed with the antiserum prior to the addition of FSH, this resulted in a significant decrease in the FSH neutralizing potency. When HCG was injected separately from the FSH-antiserum complex, the FSH neutralizing potency increased. However, the FSH neutralizing potency of all antisera was significantly higher when LH of ovine origin, rather than HCG was used for augmentation.

All anti-HCG sera exhibited a considerable FSH neutralizing potency, even when prepared by immunization with HCG preparations of high specific activity (Fig. 6). These high FSH neutralizing potencies were in contrast to the low FSH activity of the HCG preparations used for immunization (Table 1).

Anti-HMG sera possessed little, if any FSH neutralizing potency. These poor FSH neutralizing potencies were in contrast to the high FSH activity of the HMG preparations used for immunization (Fig. 7 and Table 1).

The FSH neutralizing potency of an anti-HHG serum was at least 5 times higher when assayed against HMG preparations than when assayed against an HHG preparation (Fig. 7).

The data presented indicates that HCG preparations extensively compete with FSH for antibodies neutralizing FSH activity. This suggests that there is a cross-reaction between FSH and HCG preparations.

The data also indicates that there are significant differences in the antigenic properties of human pituitary and urinary gonado-tropins. It is concluded that the establishment of specificity of immunoassay methods for human gonadotropins cannot be based exclu-sively on immunological evidence. Also, the absorption procedures used to improve the biological specificity of antigens and anti-sera are of limited value unless carried out in a strictly quan-titative manner following the establishment of the profile of the gonadotropic and antigonadotropic activities present.

The expenses of this investigation were defrayed by Research Grants from the Ford Foundation, from the Swedish Medical Research Council and from AB Leos i Halsinborg Stiftelse for Forskning.

REFERENCES

1. Robyn C., E. Diczfalusy, and D.J. Finney, Acta Endocr (Kobenhavn) 1968, In Press.
2. Zondek B., and F. Sulman, Proc.Soc. exp. Biol. 36:708, 1967.
3. Robyn C., P. Petrusz, E. Diczfalusy, and D.J. Finney,: in preparation.
4. Robyn C., and E. Diczfalusy, Acta Endocr (Kobenhavn): 1968 (a), In Press.
5. Robyn C., and E. Diczfalusy, Acta Endocr (Kobenhavn): 1968 (b), In Press.
6. Steelman S.L., and F.M. Pohley, Endocrinology 53: 604, 1953.

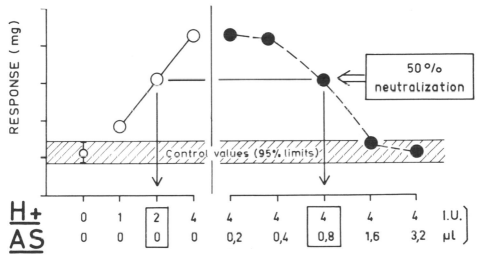

Fig. 1

Scheme of a pilot assay to obtain a provisional value of the anti-gonadotropic potency. Open circles represent the mean value of five individual responses to the Hormone (H) alone. Filled circles represent the mean value of five individual responses to the Hormone (H) + Antiserum (AS) combination. A dose of Hormone (H) inducing near maximal response (in this case 4 I.U.) is injected together with increasing amounts of Antiserum (AS). The amount of antiserum causing 50% reduction in Hormone (H) activity is in this case o.9 µl. (From Robyn C., E. Diczfalusy, and D.J. Finney. Acta Endocr.58: 593, 1968)

BIOASSAY OF ANTIGONADOTROPHINS

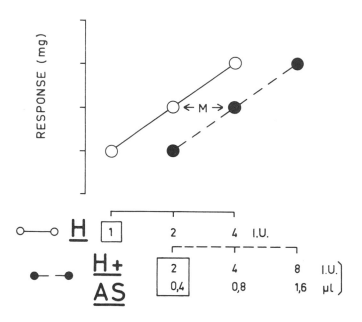

Fig. 2

A 3 + 3-point bioassay of the antigonadotropic potency of an antiserum.   Open circles represent responses (5 animals) to graded
doses of the Hormone (H), filled circles indicate responses to the
Hormone (H) + Antiserum (AS) combination. M, is the logarithm of
the relative potency.
(From Robyn, C., E. Diczfalusy, and D. J. Finney, Acta Endocr. 58:
593, 1968)

NEUTRALISATION

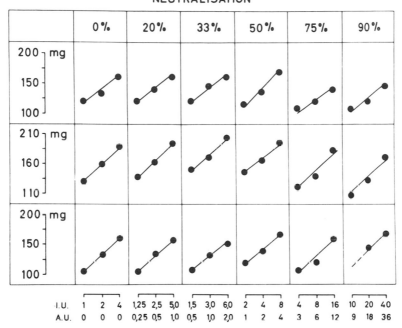

Fig. 3

Weights of the accessory reproductive organs of intact immature
male rats (mg) injected with different combinations of human
chorionic gonadotropin (HCG) and one of these antisera against
HCG. Each point represents the mean value of 6 animals.
I.U. = International Units, A.U. = Anti-Units.

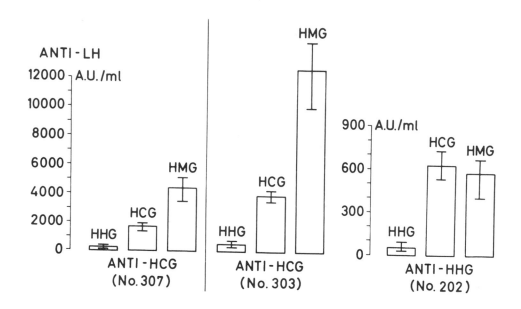

Fig. 4

The human luteinizing hormone (LH) neutralizing potency of two
anti-human chorionic gonadotropin (anti-HCG) and one anti-human
hypophysial gonadotropin (anti-HHG) sera tested against the
laboratory standards of HCG and human menopausal gonadotropin (HMG)
as well as against an HHG preparation. The end point in the assays
is the total weight of accessory reproductive organs in intact
immature male rats. The columns indicate the antigonadotropic
potencies expressed in Anti-Units (AU) per ml and the brackets
indicate the 95% fiducial limits of error.

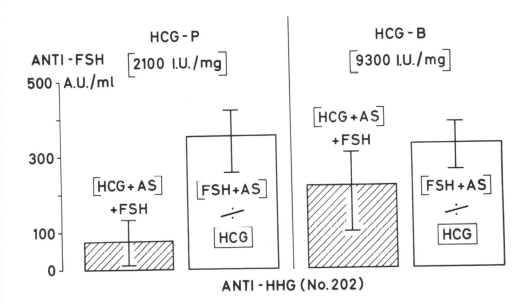

Fig. 5

Human follicle stimulating hormone (FSH) neutralizing potencies
of an anti-human hypophysial gonadotropin (anti-HHG) serum.   The
FSH neutralizing potency is assayed in a modified Steelman-Pohley
system using two human chorionic gonadotropin (HCG) preparations
of different specific activities (2 100 and 9 300 I.U. per mg.)
for augmentation.   When HCG was mixed with the antiserum prior
to the addition of FSH (human menopausal gonadotropin-HMG), the
FSH neutralizing potencies were significantly lower than when HCG
was injected separately from the FSH-antiserum complex.   The
brackets represent the 95% fiducial limits of error.

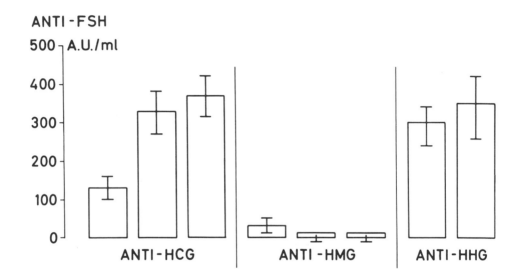

Fig. 6

Human follicle stimulating hormone (FSH) neutralizing potencies of
three anti-human chorionic gonadotropin (anti-HCG) sera, three
anti-human menopausal gonadotropin (anti-HMG) sera and two anti-
human hypophysial gonadotropin (anti-HHG) sera when assayed in a
modified Steelman-Pohley system using HCG for augmentation. The
brackets represent the 95% fiducial limits of error.

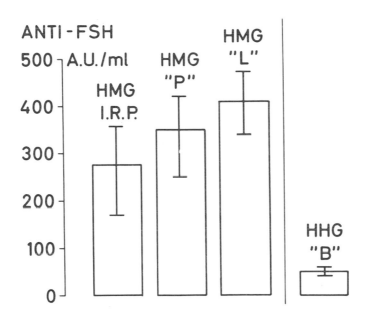

ANTI-FSH of ANTI-HHG (No. 202)

Fig. 7

Human follicle stimulating hormone (FSH) neutralizing potencies of
one anti-human hypophysial gonadotropin (anti-HHG) serum assayed
in a modified Steelman-Pohley system using human chorionic gonadotropin (HCG) for augmentation. The brackets represent the 95%
fiducial limits of error.
HMG "P" and HMG "L" are laboratory standard preparations.
HMG "I.R.P." is the 2nd International Reference Preparation.
HHG "B" is a human hypophysial gonadotropin preparation.

Table No. 1

Gonadotropic (GO) profile of the antigens used for immunization
and antigonadotropic (Anti-GO) profile of the antisera obtained
following immunization.

	GO – PROFILE			ANTI – GO – PROFILE			
Antigen	LH I.U. / mg	FSH I.U. / mg	LH/FSH	Antiserum	A –LH/ml	A – FSH/ml	A – LH / A– FSH
HCG–P	7 950	5.3	1 500	301	3 200	330	10
HCG–Z	16 000	6.2	2 600	303	12 100	370	33
HCG–B	23 300	7.4	3 150	307	4 400	130	34
HMG–12	130	20.0	6.5	103	39	30	1.3
HMG–L	6	78.0	0.1	104	2	6	?
HHG–B	150	100	1.5	201	590	300	2.0
HHG–Z	270	150	1.8	202	560	350	1.6

DISCUSSION

FAIMAN: I should like to ask how one can talk about the anti-FSH activity of anti-HCG serum using the Steelman Pohley assay. If there is anti-HCG activity, then the HCG used for augmentation is neutralized and the diminished response could be explained by this fact without involving neutralization of FSH. Perhaps if a considerable excess of HCG were used as an augmenting dose, and if there were adequate controls, some conclusion could be reached concerning the neutralization of FSH.

ROBYN: Indeed, all anti-HCG and anti-HHG sera possess a considerable HCG neutralizing potency. Therefore such antisera cannot be tested for their anti-FSH potencies without a proper adjustment for the HCG neutralized by them. On the other hand, HCG preparations possess some FSH-like activity. To explore the range in which excess of HCG can be administered without interfering with the potency estimate of the FSH activity, an HMG preparation injected together with the usual augmenting dose of 40 IU of HCG was assayed using the Steelman Pohley method in a 3 + 3 point assay against the same HMG preparation injected together with 400 IU HCG. The result of this assay indicated for the latter a relative potency of 1.25, with fiducial limits at 1.02 and 1.58 (λ = 0.09). Thus a tenfold excess of the augmenting dose of HCG results in a slight but significant increase in the FSH potency. Another difficulty is that when increasing doses of antiserum are administered together with graded doses of FSH, there is a gradually increasing degree of neutralization of HCG. Therefore in control experiments we have tested experimentally the hypothesis that an antiserum reduces the potency of the added excess of HCG to 40, 20 and 10 IU, in the presence of 1.5, 3.0 and 6.0 IU of FSH, respectively. This condition would result in a highly significant deviation from parallelism. On the other hand, if the hypothetical antiserum reduced the potency of the added excess of HCG to 160, 80 and 40 IU, this condition would not influence in any way the validity of the 3 + 3 point assay. Hence, in assays of the FSH neutralizing potency of antisera, the excess of HCG should be calculated on the basis of the anti-HCG potency so that the amount of unneutralized HCG in the presence of the highest dose of antiserum should be at least 40 IU and at the lowest dose of antiserum the HCG should be less than 400 IU.

THE INFLUENCE OF IODINE ISOTOPIC COMPOSITION ON HORMONE LABELLING

A. LEVY, R. GVION, A. ESHKOL AND B. LUNENFELD, ISRAEL ATOMIC
ENERGY COMMISSION, NUCLEAR RESEARCH CENTER - NEGEV, AND
INSTITUTE OF ENDOCRINOLOGY, TEL-HASHOMER GOVT. HOSPITAL, ISRAEL

For exploitation of radioimmunoassay, production of immunochemically intact labelled hormone of high specific activity is required; however, introduction of iodine atoms into the protein molecule is limited, since biological and immunochemical properties might be affected. Therefore high specific activity of iodine is of crucial importance.

One mC of iodine-131 equals 6.2×10^{-11} gram-atoms of iodine. If HCG labelling is taken as an example (assuming a molecular weight of 30,000), it can be calculated that 5 mcg of purified HCG contain 16.6×10^{-11} moles. Since the molar quantities used for labelling are of the same order of magnitude, the exact iodine isotopic composition should therefore be known.

Iodine-131 solutions contain I^{127} and I^{129}; this cannot be avoided owing to the production process -irradiation of TeO_2. Table I shows the relevant natural occurring isotopes of tellurium, and the main nuclear reactions taking place during irradiation. It can be seen that the contribution of $To^{127\,m}$ and $Te^{129\,m}$ to total iodine content is comparatively small, due to the low cross sections and their relatively long half lives.

Taking I^{129} as stable, and assuming irradiation time (t_1) longer than 2 days, and the time interval between irradiation and processing (t_2) greater than 6 hrs., the following equation is obtained:

$$\frac{\text{Inactive iodine}}{\text{Active iodine}} = \frac{19.1\, t_1 - 8.46\, e^{-\lambda_1 t_2}}{88\, (1 - e^{-\lambda_3 t_1})\, e^{-\lambda_3 t_2}}$$

where $\lambda_1 = \dfrac{0.693}{T_{\frac{1}{2}}}$ for Te^{127} and $\lambda_3 = \dfrac{0.693}{T_{\frac{1}{2}}}$ for I^{131}.

The ratio obtained for $t_2 = 0$ (end of irradiation; calculated using suitable equation) and $t_2 = 2$ days is described in Fig. 1. It can be seen that while an irradiation of 40 days reaches 97% of iodine-131 saturation, this results in a low ratio of active to inactive iodine (1:9). Irradiation for 12 days gives a ratio of 1:4 if processing takes place 6 hrs. after irradiation. In a separation process 6 hrs. after an irradiation period of 2 days, a ratio of 1:2.4 is obtained. If processing begins 48 hrs. after irradiation, the ratio will decrease for the same samples to about 1:4.7 and 1:3.2 respectively. Moreover, the longer the iodine-131 preparation is stored after production, the ratio of active to inactive iodine will

obviously decrease (e.g. an initial 1:9 preparation will, after 5 days, have a ratio
of 1:14).

Taking into account the low molar quantities of hormones used for labelling, the
data reported here shows that total iodine content should be taken into consideration
in any hormone labelling.   It may be that iodine-131 solutions with some specific
ratio should be prepared for this purpose.   The influence of the ratio of inactive
to active iodine on labelling yield is now under investigation.

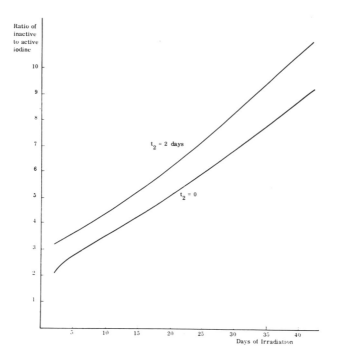

Fig. No 1.

Ratio of inactive to active iodine as obtained after varying periods of the target
irradiation and when the separation process is performed immediately ($t_2 = 0$)
and 2 days ($t_2 = 2$ days) after termination of the irradiation period.

Table No. 1

$$Te^{126} (18.71\%)^* \xrightarrow{\quad 0.09\ b \quad} Te^{127\,m}$$

$$\Big\downarrow T_{\frac{1}{2}} = 105\ d$$

$$\searrow_{0.8\,b}$$

$$\searrow Te^{127} \quad T_{\frac{1}{2}} = 9.4\,h \xrightarrow{\qquad} I^{127}$$

$$Te^{128} (31.79\%)^* \xrightarrow{\quad 0.015\ b \quad} Te^{129\,m}$$

$$\Big\downarrow T_{\frac{1}{2}} = 33\ d$$

$$\searrow_{0.13\ b}$$

$$\searrow Te^{129} \quad T_{\frac{1}{2}} = 72\ m \xrightarrow{\qquad} I^{129}$$

$$Te^{130} (34.49\%)^* \xrightarrow{\quad 0.008\ b \quad} Te^{131\,m}$$

$$\Big\downarrow T_{\frac{1}{2}} = 30\ h$$

$$\searrow_{0.22\ b}$$

$$\searrow Te^{131} \quad T_{\frac{1}{2}} = 25\ m \xrightarrow{\qquad} I^{131}$$

$$\Big\downarrow T_{\frac{1}{2}} = 8.04\ d$$

$$Xe^{131}$$

SOLID PHASE ANTIBODY SYSTEMS

A. C. CROOKE, MD, FRCP, W. R. BUTT, PhD, FRIC, S. S. LYNCH, BSc.

THE UNITED BIRMINGHAM HOSPITALS, DEPARTMENT OF CLINICAL ENDOCRIN-
OLOGY, BIRMINGHAM AND MIDLAND HOSPITAL FOR WOMEN, BIRMINGHAM, 11,
ENGLAND

INTRODUCTION

We have previously described a radioimmunoassay for human pituitary
follicle stimulating hormone (FSH) in which the antibody is attached to a
solid phase for the separation of free and bound antigen (1).   No antibody has
yet been obtained which does not also react to human luteinizing hormone (LH),
chorionic gonadotrophin (HCG) or thyrotrophin (TSH) and it has not been possible
to absorb these cross-reacting antibodies without also removing the antibody to
FSH.

The sensitivity of the method to FSH is approximately 0.5 mIU/ml.
(1 ng. of our pituitary FSH standard).   The minimum quantity of LH or HCG
giving detectable inhibition, however, is 15 mIU/ml.   Thus, in applying the
method to extracts of urine, interference from LH or HCG is only likely in exceptional cases as in pregnancy.   It was therefore considered worthwhile to
apply the method to urinary extracts in order to obtain information on any other
cross-reacting substances.   A preliminary account of this has been given (2).
The extracts assayed were obtained from 13 women undergoing treatment for infertility with human pituitary and urinary FSH.   The biological activities of
these extracts have been reported elsewhere (3).

MATERIALS AND METHODS

Antiserum

Rabbits were immunized with a crude extract of human pituitary gonadotrophin (CM 1 fraction) (4) using Freund's complete adjuvant.   In early work
antibodies were also raised to highly purified FSH obtained by starch gel electrophoresis (5,6) but the specificity of the antibodies was no better and the
practice was discontinued.

Antigens

Human FSH for labelling by the chloramine-T method (7) was a fraction
obtained by starch gel electrophoresis (5).   It was stored in solution at -10°
and showed no deterioration in quality over twelve months.   The labelled preparations were checked for damage from time to time by starch or polyacrylamide gel
electrophoresis.

Standards for radioimmunoassay were a CP 1 fraction (4) for pituitary
extracts and a batch of Pergonal (Searle Ltd.) for urinary extracts.   Both were
calibrated against the 2nd. International Reference Preparation for HMG (2nd.
IRP-HMG).

Solid phase system

Bentonite particles were coated with dialysed antiserum as described previously (1).

Incubations with the kaolin extracts were for 16 hours at 4°. The mixtures were then centrifuged and the supernatants were discarded. Labelled antigen was then added and each tube was counted in a Packard Auto-Gamma Counter. The tubes were left at room temperature for 3 hours, including counting time and were then centrifuged. The liquid was removed and the solid phase (bound antigen) was counted separately.

Recovery experiments

Pituitary (CP 1 fraction) or urinary (Pergonal) FSH was injected into 13 patients, as previously described (3). The material was administered either as a single injection or as three injections at 12 or 24 hour intervals. Urine was collected in 24-hour samples and each was extracted by the kaolin method. Biological assay was by the ovarian augmentation method in mice (8).

RESULTS

A typical inhibition curve for the 2nd. IRP-HMG is shown in Figure 1. The uptake of ^{131}I-FSH on control bentonite particles coated only with polyvinyl pyrrolidine was about 5 per cent and this has been allowed for in the results presented. The inhibition given with HCG is also shown and it will be noted that although the slopes of the two curves are similar the sensitivity to FSH and HCG in terms of mIU is considerably different. Pituitary FSH also gives a similar inhibition curve but the estimate of potency by radioimmunoassay is usually lower than by bioassay when compared with the 2nd. IRP-HMG (ratio of potencies, i.e., index of discrimination = 0.55).

Assay on control samples

There were 35 samples considered to be controls. These were obtained before injection with FSH or after all the injected material had been excreted. The mean estimate by radioimmunoassay was 15 IU/24 hours and 12.5 IU/24 hours by bioassay (Table 1). The correlation between the results was highly significant (r = 0.8, P = < 0.001) and the average index of discrimination was 1.2 (Figure 2).

Results after treatment with pituitary or urinary FSH

There were 45 samples obtained after treatment with CP 1 and 29 after Pergonal. The mean results are given in Table 1. Again there is a highly significant correlation between the two methods of assay.

Recovery of injected material

The recoveries of the injected material are given in Table 2. The recoveries of CP 1 estimated by radioimmunoassay tend to be higher than by bioassay. The average recovery for all patients was 8.1 per cent by bioassay and 11.7 per cent by radioimmunoassay.

The pattern of excretion of injected material as measured by both methods is summarized in Figure 3. The agreement appears to be excellent but it should be noted that there is a trend for the recovered material to appear slightly earlier as estimated by radioimmunoassay (Table 3). Thus the time

IMMUNOLOGIC ASSAY

taken for 50 per cent of the recovered material to be excreted was on the average 0.35 of a day less by radioimmunoassay than by biological assay. Over the whole series these differences are significant at the 5 per cent level.

DISCUSSION

A correlation between radioimmunoassay and bioassay of FSH is not practicable in serum because of the quantities that would be required for bioassay. However, there was available from another experiment a series of 109 kaolin extracts of 24 hour samples of urine which had been fully assayed biologically. These extracts provided a convenient series for comparison.

The present results suggest that kaolin extracts of urine are suitable for use in the radioimmunoassay of FSH. The correlation with bioassay is so good that it does not appear that any urinary material is extracted which interferes in the assay. Unpublished observations have indicated that unextracted urine is unsatisfactory and that the interfering substances are not removed by gel filtration or dialysis. Similar problems have arisen in attempting to assay other hormones in urine by radioimmunoassay (9, 10, 11).

A cross-reaction with LH, HCG and TSH is known to exist with all our antisera. However, in the present work interference from LH or HCG is not thought to be of significance. This is because of the different degrees of sensitivity in the assay (Figure 1).

It is interesting that although the pattern of excretion of injected material is similar as estimated by both methods, there is a significant difference in the half-life. This must indicate that the two methods are measuring different functions of the molecule. It is possible that a rapid inactivation of the hormone occurs and the product is detected by the immunological method but is biologically inactive. We have already shown that treatment with neuraminidase or with acid destroys the biological activity of FSH but not the immunological activity (2). Possibly neuraminic acid residues which occur in terminal positions in the molecule of FSH (12) are removed during metabolism and the inactive product is detected by radioimmunoassay.

The solid phase antibody method is a convenient, simple technique with relatively short incubation periods. It takes only 24 hours to perform and large numbers of samples can be examined simultaneously. Its sensitivity compares favourably with the double antibody systems described by others (13, 14, 15, 16).

We thank Dr. M. Morell and Mr. D. Whyman for their valuable operation. The work was supported by grants made to Dr. A. C. Crooke by Ford Foundation and the Medical Research Council. We thank Dr. J. K. Butler of G. D. Searle & Co. Ltd., for supplies of Pergonal.

REFERENCES

1. Butt, W. R. and S. S. Lynch, Excerpta Medica Foundation, I.C.S.No. 161, 134, 1968.

2. Butt, W. R. and S. S. Lynch, Clin. chim. Acta 22: 1968, in press.
3. Morell, M., A. C. Crooke and W. R. Butt, J. Endocr. 41: in press.*
*p. 571, 1968.

4. Butt, W. R., A. C. Crooke and F. J. Cunningham, Biochem. J. 81: 596, 1961.
5. Butt, W. R., A. C. Crooke, F. J. Cunningham and A. Wolf, J. Endocr. 25: 541, 1963.
6. Idem, Ciba Foundation Study Group No. 22, 85, 1965.
7. Greenwood, F. C., W. M. Hunter and J. S. Glover, Biochem. J. 89: 114, 1963.
8. Brown, P. S., J. Endocr. 13: 59, 1955.
9. Fraser, R., C. Lowy and A. H. Rubenstein, Excerpta Medica Foundation, I.C.S. No. 161, 14, 1968.
10. Girard, J., and F. C. Greenwood, J. Endocr. 40: 493, 1968.
11. Kulin, H. E., A. B. Rifkind and G. T. Ross, J. clin. Endocr. and Metab. 28: 543, 1968.
12. Butt, W. R., J. F. Jenkins and P. J. Somers, J. Endocr. 38: xi, 1967.
13. Faiman, C. and R. J. Ryan, J. clin. Endocr. and Metab., 27: 1711, 1967.
14. Midgeley, A. R., J. clin. Endocr. and Metab., 27: 295, 1967.
15. Franchimont, P., Excerpta Medica Foundation, I.C.S. No. 161, 99, 1968.
16. Saxena, B. B., H. Demura, H. M. Gandy and R. E. Peterson, J. clin. Endocr. and Metab. 28:, 519. 1968.

Table 1.

Comparison of bioassay and radioimmunoassay results

	No. of Samples	FSH IU/24 hr Mean (Range)		Index of Discrimination	Correlation	
		Bioassay	Radioimmunoassay		r	P
Control samples	35	12.5 (2.1-60.0)	15.0 (0.9-105.0)	1.20	0.8	<.001
After FSH	45	40.2 (5.9-379.0)	48.1 (3.5-237.0	1.20	0.67	<.001
After Pergonal	29	48.7 (7.9-168.6)	42.6 (4.5-138.0)	0.87	0.72	<.001

Table 2.

Comparison of recovery of injected FSH by bioassay
and radioimmunoassay

	No. of patients	Percentage of injected dose recovered Mean (Range)	
		Bioassay	Radioimmunoassay
Following single injection of CP 1	5	6.7 (1.7–17.2)	14.4 (4.3–29.6)
Three injections of CP 1 at 12-hrly intervals	2	12.3 (11.3–13.1)	17.4 (5.3–29.5)
Three injections of CP 1 or Pergonal at 24-hrly intervals	6	8.2 (4.3–15.3)	7.5 (4.4–18.5)
All treatments	13	8.1 (1.7–17.2)	11.7 (4.3–29.5)
Mean recovery after CP 1		8.0	14.0
Mean recovery after Pergonal		8.1	7.9

Table 3.

Comparison of time taken to excrete 50% of injected dose
by bioassay and radioimmunoassay

	No. of patients	Bioassay	Radioimmunoassay	Difference $\pm$ S.E.
Single injection of CP 1	5	1.22 (0.94–1.66)	0.87 (0.66–1.2)	0.35 $\pm$ 0.125
Three injections of CP 1 at 12-hrly intervals	2	2.08 (1.70–2.46)	1.56 (1.52–1.6)	0.52
Three injections of CP 1 or Pergonal at 24-hrly intervals	6	2.71 (1.80–3.33)	2.52 (1.80–3.0)	0.19 $\pm$ 0.065

Mean difference in half-life of injected material by the two
methods = 0.30 day (95% fiducial limits, 0.137–0.463)

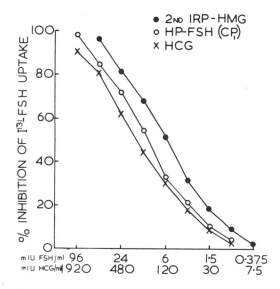

Figure 1.   Inhibition curves of FSH and HCG.

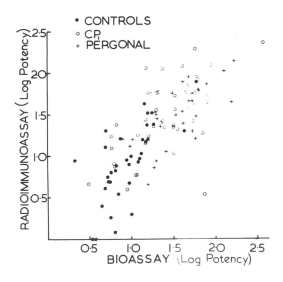

Figure 2.   Correlation between radioimmunoassay and
bioassay.

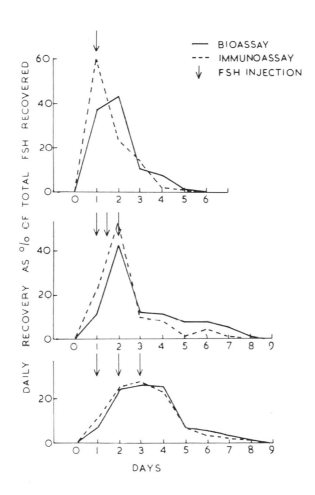

Figure 3.   Patterns of excretion of injected FSH as
            measured by radioimmunoassay and bioassay.

DISCUSSION

NAFTOLIN: Dr. Crooke, I wonder whether in your study of the injected material you did any LH assays on the urines you collected.

CROOKE: No LH assays were carried out. The amount of urine collected was too small for biological assays of LH as well as FSH.

TAYMOR: Dr. Crooke, what type of gonadotropin was indicated in the last slide? Was it an HMG or HPG? I am referring to the three curves of recovery after various techniques.

CROOKE: We used both gonadotropins but the differences between the excretion of pituitary FSH and Pergonal were not significant and the results were therefore pooled.

TAYMOR: In other words, you have not seen any differences between HMG and HPG?

CROOKE: No.

RADIOIMMUNOASSAY OF HUMAN CHORIONIC GONADOTROPIN (HCG) AND HUMAN
    LUTEINIZING HORMONE (LH) USING INSOLUBLE ANTIBODIES.

S. Donini, I. D'Alessio and P. Donini

Research Laboratories, Instituto Farmacologico Seroni, Rome (Italy)

INTRODUCTION

A new method for the radioimmunoassay of HCG and LH, based on
competitive inhibition of the binding between ^{125}I-HCG and anti-
HCG serum insolubilized by polymerization, has been developed.

MATERIALS AND METHODS

The HCG preparation used for radioiodination was obtained in
our laboratory (Donini, in press). The activity was 12,000 IU/mg.
and it was homogenous by disc electrophoresis and by immunoelectrophoresis.

The anti-HCG serum was produced in rabbits by three immunizing
injections of 2 mg. of HCG (3,000 IU/mg.) and repeated booster
injections of 1 mg. of the same HCG preparation. One ml. of the
anti-HCG serum neutralized 400 IU-HCG, as assessed by the inhibition of the mouse uterine weight increase. Each ml. of the anti-
HCG serum was absorbed successively with 0.2 ml. of normal human
serum (NHS) and 3.5 mg. of urinary extract from a hypophysectomized
patient.

Figure 1 shows that no line was visible against NHS or urinary
extract from a hypophysectomized patient after absorption of the
anti-HCG serum, whereas two lines against crude LH and HCG were
formed.

Fig. 1

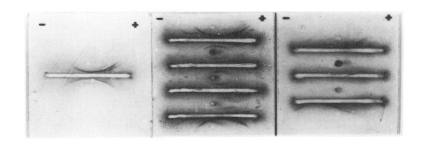

Agar immunoelectrophoresis of highly purified and commercial preparations of HCG and various materials, as specified below, against unabsorbed and absorbed anti-HCG serum. (A): Wells 1 and 2 were filled with normal human serum (N.H.S.) and highly purified HCG (Ell5ter-2) respectively. The trough was filled with unabsorbed antiserum. (B): Wells 1 to 5 were filled with HCG-JOBA, urinary extract from hypophysectomized man, N.H.S., serum from hypophysectomized man and roughly purified HMG respectively. Troughs A, B, C, and D were filled with unabsorbed antiserum. (C): Wells 1 to 4 were filled with HCG-JOBA, urinary extract from hypophysectomized patient, N.H.S. and roughly purified HMG. Troughs A, B, and C were filled with absorbed antiserum.

The antiserum was polymerized by the method of Avrameas (1), with slight modifications. To the lyophilized antiserum, dissolved in 0.2 M acetate buffer pH 5.0, ethylchloroformate was added drop by drop with gentle stirring. After 15 min. stirring, the gel formed was allowed to stand for 1 hr. at room temperature. The gel was then washed on a cellulose acetate filter (MF-100-Membran-Filter, Gottingen, Germany) supported by a glass fiber filter. The washings were performed under suction in the following order: Three washings with saline buffered at pH 7.0 with 0.1 I phosphate buffer pH 7.2; one washing with 0.1% Na_2CO_3; one washing with pH 7.0 buffered saline, repeated washings with 0.2 M glycine-HCl buffer pH 2.2, until the optical absorbancy of the filtrate at 280 mμ became less than 0.01 and several washings with pH 7.0 buffered saline, until the pH of the filtrate became 7.0. The polymerized anti-HCG serum (poly-anti-HCG serum) was then removed from the filter and homogenized in a Teflon homogenizer (A.H. Thomas Co., Philadelphia, USA); the suspension was made up to such a volume that the original antiserum was diluted 1:30. Then 1:10,000 (w/v) sodium azide was added. The protein recovery from the polymerization procedure was approximately 60%. The poly-anti-HCG serum, stored at 4° C., was stable for at least 4 - 6 months. The lyophilization did not reduce the binding capacity of the poly-anti-HCG serum. HCG (5 μg) was labeled with 2 mc [125]I (The Radiochemical Centre, Amersham, England) according to the method of Greenwood (2), except that 50 μg of chloramine-T and a 2 min. reaction time were used. The separation between ^{125}I-HCG and free ^{125}I was performed on a Sephadex G-50 (Fine) column 1 x 10 cm. The elution was carried out by 0.075M phosphate buffer pH 7.25 containing 0.075 M NaCl (elution buffer). The specific radioactivity of the ^{125}I-HCG was 70-150 μc/μg. The labeled HCG was further purified every 2 - 3 weeks by gel-filtration on a Sephadex G-200 column 1 x 50 cm.

The titration of poly-anti-HCG serum was carried out by incubating for 20 hrs. at room temperature under shaking, using a fixed amount of ^{125}I-HCG (approximately 30,000 cpm) with increasing dilutions of poly-anti-HCG serum. The titration curve was obtained by plotting the percentage of total radioactivity

bound against the log dilutions of poly-anti-HCG serum. The
dilution at which 20 - 30% of total radioactivity was bound to
the poly-anti-HCG serum was chosen for the assay. The assay was
carried out by incubating at room temperature for 20 hrs by
shaking 0.4 ml. of standard (International Standard of HCG or
2nd IRP-HMG) or unknown sample with 0.1 ml. of ^{125}I-HCG (30,000
cpm) and 0.2 ml. of poly-anti-HCG serum 1:320 (equivalent at
least to the 1:6400 dilution of the original unpolymerized antiserum). Each determinaton was performed in triplicate. The
elution buffer containing 0.1% bovine serum albumin (BSA) and
0.05% sodium azide was used as diluent. The separation between
bound and free ^{125}I-HCG was performed by filtration on Oxoid
Cellulose acetate filters, as described by Wilde (3). Results
were expressed as percentage of radioactivity bound, assuming
the radioactivity bound in control samples, where no competitive
unlabeled hormone was added, as 100% binding.

RESULTS

The freshly labeled HCG filtered through the Sephadex G-200
column showed three peaks of radioactivity (Fig. 2, left). From
the titration curves of poly-anti-HCG serum, obtained by incubating the poly-antiserum with the three fractions (Fig. 2,
right), it was concluded that the first peak was degradated
^{125}I-HCG, the second one was immunologically reactive ^{125}I-HCG,
and the third one was presumably free ^{125}I.

Fig. 2

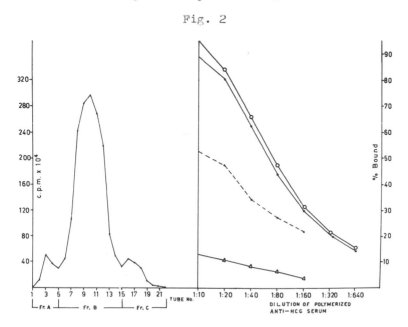

Legend to Figure 2:

Left: Elution diagram of freshly labeled ^{125}I-HCG from a Sephadex
G-200 column 1 x 50 cm., equilibrated and eluted with 0.075 M
phosphate buffer pH 7.25 + 0.075 M NaCl. Flow rate 2 ml/hr;
samples 1.75 ml/tube.
Right: Titration curves of polymerized anti-HCG serum with ^{125}I-
HCG before (⋅———⋅) and after purification on Sephadex G-200
(⋅− − −⋅ Fr.A; o———o Fr.B; ⌂———⌂ Fr.C).

When the ^{125}I-HCG, stored for 2 months at 4°C., was filtered
through the Sephadex G-200 column, the same elution pattern was
obtained, but the free ^{125}I-peak was much higher (Fig. 3).

Fig. 3

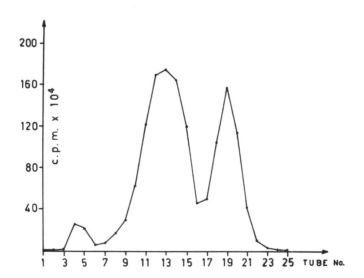

Gel-filtration on a Sephadex G-200 column (1 x 50 cm) of ^{125}I-HCG
stored at 4°C. for 2 months. Elution conditions as in Fig. 2.

(Fig. 4) shows the inhibition curve for the International
Standard of HCG, as compared to the inhibition curve for the 2nd
IRP-HMG, both obtained by incubation for 20 Hr. at room temperature.

Fig. 4

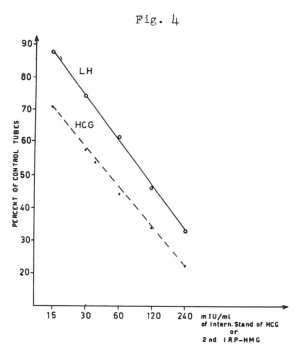

Standard curves for the International Standard of HCG (●---●)
and 2nd IRP-HMG (●———●).   The results are expressed as percentage
of radioactivity bound in control tubes where no unlabeled
hormone was added.   The incubation was at room temperature for
20 hrs. without preincubation.

The effect of 3 hr., of preincubation on the senstivity of
the LH assay is shown in Fig. 5.

Fig. 5

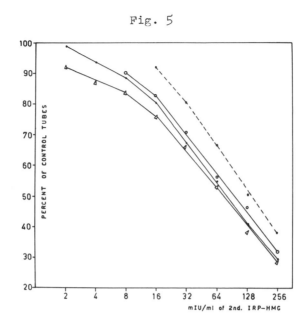

Effect of temperature and incubation time on the sensitivity of
LH assay. (•——•) 20 hr. at room temperature; (o——o) 20 hr. at
4° C.; (▵——▵) 3 hr. preincubation + 20 hr. incubation at room
temperature; (◂---◂) 1 hr. preincubation + 1 hr. incubation at
38° C.

It was possible to shorten the duration of the assay by a
"1 hr. preincubation plus 1 hr. incubation at 38° C." procedure,
although this produced a decrease in sensitivity (Fig. 5, dotted
line). Experiments are in progress to obtain higher sensitivity
by prolonging the preincubation and by using a higher dilution
of poly-anti-HCG serum and of the labeled hormone solution. A
good agreement between the bioassay and the radioimmunoassay was
found independently from the FSH/LH ratio and from the purity
grade of the preparations tested. Tables 1 and 2 show that the
bioassay/radioimmunoassay ratio ranged from 0.91 to 1.23 for LH
and from 0.65 to 1.18 for HCG.

Luteinizing activity of various gonadotropic extracts with different purity grade and FSH/LH ratio, as determined by the
ovarian ascorbic acid depletion bioassay and by radioimmunoassay.

Table 1

Preparation	FSH/LH ratio*	LH IU/mg		O.A.A.D. R.I.
		Bioassay (O.A.A.D.)	Radioimmunoassay (R.I.)	
E 183bis-7	-	41.8 (22.2- 105.0)**	41.0 (33.5- 49.2)	1.02
E 173bis-2	-	117.9 (75.9- 193.9)	95.6 (82.5- 108.8)	1.23
E 183bis-4	-	347.0 (179.8- 632.6)	379.6 (210.6- 521.1)	0.91
E 183bis-3	-	775.8 (4640-1589.0)	757.0 (522.2-1177.4)	1.02
E 181-2	0.019	103.0 (62.9- 187.0)	101.8 (38.9- 126.3)	1.01
E 178	0.069	81.3 (47.0- 149.0)	85.9 (62.8- 106.9)	0.95
P 28 E54C	0.96	58.3 (26.4- 109.0)	47.3 (36.9- 59.2)	1.23
E 185-B	1.46	1.78(0.60- 3.35)	1.79 (1.53- 2.08)	0.99
E 181-1	1.77	3.9 (1.5- 6.7)	4.0 (3.0 - 5.0)	0.97
P 37 E177C	2.08	31.3 (19.6- 49.3)	31.5 (24.1- 38.9)	0.99
E 161ter-4	259.3	4.3 (1.7- 7.8)	3.1 (2.4- 3.9)	1.39

* FSH/LH ratio is determined on the basis of biologic assays for both FSH and LH.

** In brackets the fiducial limits, P= 0.95.

Human Chorionic Gonadotropin determination: Comparison between
bioassay and radioimmunoassay.

Table 2

Preparation	Bioassay IU/mg*	Radioimmunoassay IU/mg-	Bioassay R.I.
HCG Serono, E 89-A	53.7 (42.9- 69.3)	62.1 (53.4- 73.9)	0.86
HCG JOBA, 766163	2029 (1800- 2277)	3130 (2564- 3767)	0.65
HCG Schering, P106/E	2981 (2610- 3408)	2513 (2184- 2889)	1.18
HCG Serono E145ter-2	11985 (10349-13730)	10854 (8763-13221)	1.10

* The activities are expressed as IU of 1st Int.Stand. of HCG.

The excretion pattern of urinary LH during two normal
menstrual cycles was studied (Fig. 6).

Fig. 6

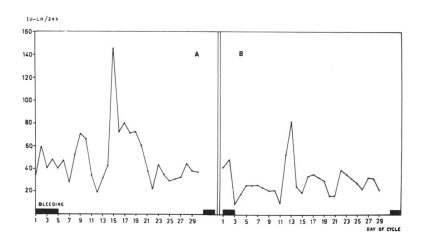

Excretion pattern of urinary LH during normal menstrual cycle.
Left: L. C. 27 year old, married. Right: L. A. 29 year old,
unmarried. The results are expressed as IU-LH, 2nd IRP-HMG/24 hr.

The results are in agreement with those previously reported
(4,5,6), but much higher than those obtained by biological
assays (7,8). The findings obtained by the radioimmunoassay on
the unprocessed urine from four adult men and from menopausal
women were 48 and 108 IU/24 hr., values much higher than those
obtained by bioassay and previously reported (6,9).

Fig. 7

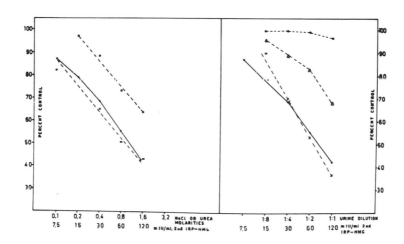

Left: The effect of increasing molarities of NaCl (×– –×) and
urea (o– – –o) on the reaction between ^{125}I-HCG and poly-anti-HCG
serum, as compared to the inhibition curve of 2nd IRP HMG (●———●).
Right: The effect of the dialysis and extraction by the kaolin-
acetone method on the inhibition by postmenopausal urine. The
doses of urine and extract are equivalent. The pH of urine was
adjusted to 7.2. The inhibition by urine before (×– – –×) and after
(o– – –o) dialysis and by urinary extract (▲– – –▲), was compared to the
inhibition curve of 2nd IRP-HMG (●———●).

We had some evidence that the sodium chloride and urea content
of urine and perhaps other substances inhibit the binding between
^{125}I-HCG and antiserum, as previously shown by Girard (10) for the
radioimmunoassay of HGH in the urine.

LH content of urines from 3 newborns was undetectable. The
urinary extract from a hypophysectomized patient was unable to
inhibit the binding between ^{125}I-HCG and poly-anti HCG serum, even
at the highest dose tested, i.e. a dose equivalent to 8 ml. of
urine.

Serum LH was also tested: the mean basal value in 4 women was
20.6 mIU/ml., whereas in 4 men 30.1 mIU/ml. were found. These
values agree with those reported by others (11, 12). Six assays
of the same crude urinary extract, performed at time intervals
during routine assays, showed a mean standard deviation of 21.3%.

The precision index (λ) of 50 assays ranged from 0.03 to 0.10 (mean λ = 0.06 $\pm$ 0.025 S.D.).

The proposed method can be applied to the radioimmunoassay of other hormones. Studies are in progress for the radioimmunoassay of FSH.

REFERENCES

1. Avrameas, S. and T. Ternynck, J Biol. Chem. 242:1651, 1967.
2. Greenwood, G. C. and W.M. Hunter, Biochem. J. 89:114, 1963.
3. Wilde, C. E., Hilary Orr, A. and K. D. Bagshawe, J. Endocr.
        37:23, 1967.
4. Bagshawe, K. D., Wilde, C. E. and A. H. Orr, Lancet 1:118, 1966.
5. Wilde, C. E., Orr, A. H. and K. D. Bagshawe, J. Endocr. 37:23,
        1967.
6. Nicolis, G. L., Wotiz, H. H. and J. Lester Gabrilove, J. Clin.
        Endocr. 28:547, 1968.
7. Rosemberg, E. and P. J. Keller, J. Clin. Endocr. 25:1262, 1965.
8. Stevens, V. C. and N. Vorys, Obst. & Gynec. Surv. 22:781, 1967.
9. Albert, A. J. Clin. Endocr. 26, 371, 1966.
10. Girard, J. and F C. Greenwood, J. Endoc. 40:493, 1968.
11. Catt, K. J., Niall, H. D., Tregear, G. W. and H. G. Burger,
        J. Clin. Endocr. 28:121, 1968.
12. Midgley, A. R., Endocrinology 79:10, 1966.

SPECIFICITY, SENSITIVITY AND PRECISION OF A
RADIOIMMUNOASSAY FOR FSH

MELVIN L. TAYMOR, M.D. AND TOSHIHIRO AONO, M.D.
FROM THE DEPARTMENT OF OBSTETRICS AND GYNECOLOGY, HARVARD
MEDICAL SCHOOL AND THE DEPARTMENT OF SURGERY (GYNECOLOGY),
PETER BENT BRIGHAM HOSPITAL, BOSTON, MASSACHUSETTS

INTRODUCTION

The specificity of the radioimmunoassay for FSH remains
in doubt because as yet we have been unable to obtain human
pituitary FSH, in sufficient quantity, and of sufficient
stability, completely free of LH, nonspecific proteins and
trace amounts of other pituitary trophic hormones. The
purpose of this report is to demonstrate that even without
pure material for labelling, absorption techniques can at
this time provide us with an assay system that appears to be
sufficiently specific, sensitive and precise for the assay of
FSH in human serum.

MATERIAL AND METHODS

The human pituitary FSH fractions utilized in this study
are shown in Table 1. Highly purified FSH, LER-828-2 and
partially purified FSH, LER-735-2, were generously supplied
by Dr. Leo E. Reichert (Emory University, Atlanta, Georgia)
from the National Pituitary Agency.

Table No. 1

Pituitary FSH Fractions Utilized

	UNITS/mg	
	NIH-FSH-S1	NIH-LH-S1
For labelling LER-828-2	138.0	0.21
For antiserum LER-735-2	5.3	0.067

LH contamination in these FSH preparations was reported
by Reichert to be 0.21 NIH-LH-S1 unit per mg for LER-828-2
and 0.067 NIH-LH-S1 unit per mg for LER-735-2. Labelling
with ^{125}I and the double antibody radioimmunoassay for FSH
were carried out according to techniques previously described (1).
The degree of purity of the antiserum following absorption with
human chorionic gonadotropin (HCG) and serum from normal children
(NCS) was tested in cellulose acetate immunodiffusion studies (2).

RESULTS

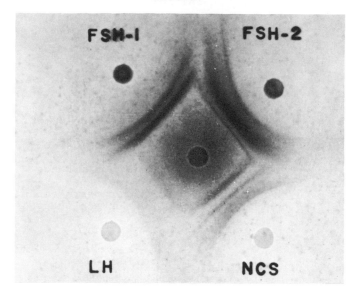

Figure No. 1

Cellulose acetate immunodiffusion study with unabsorbed anti-FSH in center well and two pituitary FSH preparations, one pituitary LH preparation, and serum from normal children (NCS) in outer wells. (From Aono, T. and Taymor, M.L. Am J. Obstet & Gynec 100:113, 1968.)

The fact that anti-FSH prepared from LER-735-2 contains antibodies against LH and non-specific protein is confirmed by immunodiffusion (Figure 1). After absorption with 5 ml of normal children's serum (NCS) and 0.5 mg of HCG (1,385 IU/ml) anti-FSH serum lines no longer appeared against NCS and LH (Figure 2).

Additional evidence for LH contamination of the RIA system, utilizing the previously described antiserum before absorption, is seen in Figure 3. Increasing amounts of HCG added to each tube progressively replaced the amount of labelled FSH in the precipitate. However, a plateau was reached when between 5 and 10 IU of HCG were added to each tube.

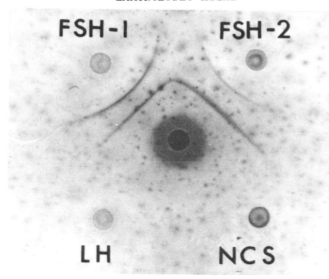

Figure 2. Cellulose acetate immunodiffusion study with absorbed anti-FSH in center well and two pituitary FSH preparations, a pituitary LH preparation, and serum from normal children (NCS) in outer wells. (From Aono, T. and Taymor, M.L. Am J Obstet & Gynec 100:114, 1968)

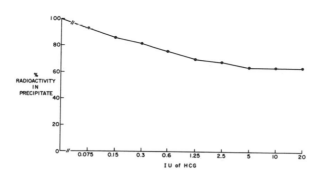

Figure 3. The ability of increasing amounts of HCG added to each assay tube to displace labelled FSH from unabsorbed anti-FSH.

GONADOTROPINS 1968

Table No. 2

Effect of absorption techniques on measurable FSH contamination in pituitary LH Fractions by RIA

Fraction	FSH IU/mg	
	DEAE-1-2	LER 822-2
Bioassay	0.5-5.8*	2.9
5 λNCS	34.6	60.6
5 λNCS, 500 IU HCG	9.6	19.5
5 λNCS, 750 IU HCG	11.6	14.5
5 λNCS, 1385 IU HCG	10.7	11.5
5 λNCS, 5 IU HCG/tube	12.9	17.9
5 λNCS, 10 IU HCG/tube	7.1	7.8

*See reference 3

The effects of different techniques of absorption upon the measurable FSH contamination of fractions rich in LH by radioimmunoassay are shown in Table No. 2. When anti-FSH was absorbed only with normal children's serum (NCS) the potency by radioimmunoassay was greatly increased over that reported by bioassay. When the undiluted antiserum was absorbed with progressively increasingly amount of HCG prior to use, the relationship between immune and bioassay improved. A maximum effect was reached when 1385 IU of HCG was added to each ml of undiluted anti-FSH. Further addition of HCG resulted in loss of the sensitivity of the assay. The best correlation between immuno and bioassay was achieved by adding 10 IU of HCG to each tube during the assay procedure.

Table 3. Comparison of Immunoassay and Bioassay (Indices of Discrimination)

	FSH Potency*		
	Immunoassay	Bioassay	I/B
FSH rich fractions			
LER 828-2	130.1	138.0	0.94
LER 780	52.7	53.4	0.98
LER 735-2	7.3	5.3	1.37
LER 677-4	0.61	0.61	1.00[+]
P-3-A-d-1	40.9	30.0	1.36
P-3-A-d-2	22.9	22.5	1.01
LH rich fractions			
LER 822-2	0.295	0.11	2.68
P-3-B	0.73	0.35	2.08

*Expressed as units of NIH-FSH-S1 per mg.
+LER 677-4 was used as the standard.
From Aono, T. and Taymor, M.D. Am J Obstet & Gynec 100:114, 1968.

A comparison of the immunologic and biologic potency of a
number of pituitary fractions is shown in Table 3. Four of the
FSH rich fractions were obtained from Dr. Reichert and two were
prepared in our laboratory. The FSH potency by bioassay varied
from 5.3 to 138.0 NIH-FSH-S1 units per mg. The potency
estimates by radioimmunoassay were remarkably similar to biologic
potency and the ratio of the immunoassay to bioassay, I/B, or
indices of discrimination were close to unity. On the other
hand, the immunologic FSH potency of two pituitary fractions
rich in LH appeared to be more than twice the biologic FSH
potency or actually twice what could be accounted for by
FSH contamination.

The failure to achieve unity in the indices of
discrimination casts some doubt on the specificity of the
assay system. However, previous studies reported from our
laboratory (1) indicate that LH will only effect the radioimmunoassay for FSH if the relative amount of LH is greater than 20
to 1 in terms of international units of the 2nd IRP. Since the
ratio of LH to FSH in serum is close to unity in terms of the
second IRP, it would appear that the degree of specificity
achieved by the technique herein described is adequate for
clinical testing.

As far as sensitivity is concerned, a standard curve
utilizing labelled FSH and antiserum absorbed as previously
described is shown in Figure 4. The assay is sensitive to
4 mIU/ml. Since as much as 0.4 ml of serum can be utilized in
the assay system, a concentration of FSH as low as 10 mIU/ml
of serum can be detected.

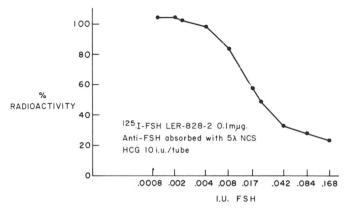

Figure 4. Standard curve for radioimmunoassay of FSH.

The precision of the assay has been expressed as the standard deviation, calculated according to Snedecor (4). The standard deviation (s) is given by the formula:

$$s = (\Sigma d^2/2n)^{\frac{1}{2}}$$

where d is the difference between results in a duplicate determination, and n is the number of duplicate determinations performed. The precision of the FSH assay system is shown in Table 4.

Table No. 4

Estimate of precision expressed as the standard deviation of results from their means

Range (mIU/ml)	S
- 4.9	†
5.0 - 9.9	†
10.0 -19.9	1.75 (136)*
20.0 -	1.97 (132)

*Number of duplicate determinations in parenthesis.
†Number of determinations was too small to derive S.D.(s).

DISCUSSION

Radioimmunoassay for FSH appeared to be sensitive and precise. In addition, relative specificity, sufficient for clinical purposes, can be achieved by appropriate absorption techniques.

The cellulose acetate studies point up the need to remove non-specific antibodies. In addition, until human pituitary FSH completely free from LH is available, it will be necessary to absorb anti-LH from the FSH antiserum.

The amount and method of added HCG may be critical. When HCG was added to a level of 1385 IU per ml of antiserum no lines appeared between the absorbed antiserum and LH. Nevertheless there was evidence for persistent anti-LH in the antiserum in radioimmunoassay results.

More complete absorption was obtained by adding 10 IU of HCG to each tube during the assay. In terms of absolute quantity it is easy to see why this resulted in more complete absorption. Since the antiserum was used in the dilution of 1:1000 this amounted to the use of 10,000 IU per ml of undiluted antiserum. When this amount of HCG was added to the crude antiserum the efficacy of the assay was effected.

The maximum recovery of radio activity in the tubes
which had no added FSH standard dropped to 30% from a previous
optimum level of 50%. This is difficult to explain, but it
is possible that the anti-FSH was being absorbed, as well as
anti-LH, either because of FSH contamination in the HCG or
due to a degree of cross-reaction between FSH, LH, HCG and
even non-specific proteins.

One can further theorize that if the HCG is added to
anti-FSH before addition of the labelled FSH to the system,
binding sites on the antibody will be used up. On the other
hand, these binding sites will be available to the labelled
FSH if this is added first to the antibody.

If cross reaction between FSH and LH is a reality it
appears to be a minimal one and apparent only in the presence
of high concentration of contaminating antibodies.

Finally, the variability in the approach to absorption
may account for many of the discrepancies noted in the
previous reports on the quantitative levels of FSH in the
human serum. The mean levels of FSH in the serum of
postmenopausal females, reported by both Midgeley (5) and
Faiman and Ryan (6), using the technique of adding 10 IU of
HCG to each tube, approximated the results obtained in our
laboratory. On the other hand, mean levels of FSH reported
by Saxena (7) who utilized less than 0.1 IU of HCG per assay
were considerably higher. In addition, it is possible that
the FSH curves reported by Saxena and by Odell (8), which
demonstrate a high FSH peak coinciding with the midcycle
peak of LH, are also influenced by participation of LH in
the reaction.

GRANT ACKNOWLEDGEMENT

Supported in part by grant FR-05489-05 of the USPHS and
a grant-in-aid from Hoffmann-LaRoche Inc., Nutley, New Jersey.

REFERENCES

1. Aono, T., and M.L. Taymor, Am J Obstet & Gynec
   100:110, 1968.

2. Tamada, T., M. Soper, and M.L. Taymor, J Clin Endocr
   27:379, 1967.

3. Hartree, A.S., Biochem J 100:754, 1966.

4. Snedecor, G.W., Statistical Methods 5th ed
   Iowa State College Press, Ames, Iowa, 1956.

5. Midgeley, A.R., J Clin Endocr 27:295, 1967.

6. Faiman, C., and R. Ryan, J Clin Endocr 27:444, 1967.

7. Saxena, B.B., H. Demura, H.M. Gandy, and R.E. Peterson, J Clin Endocr 28:519, 1968.

8. Odell, W.D., G.T. Ross, and P.L. Rayford, J Clin Invest 46:248, 1967.

DISCUSSION

REICHERT: The FSH utilized by Dr. Taymor was prepared in my laboratory. It was a lyophilized preparation which showed no evidence of heterogeneity when examined by polyacrylamide gel electrophoresis. Those of us concerned with the purification of human FSH are sympathetic with the need for FSH completely free of LH activity when examined in a sufficiently rigorous and objective manner. I think there is a good possibility that the FSH molecule contains inherent LH activity. Either this, or the LH-bioassay we employed to assess LH contamination, the OAAD assay, is not as specific as once believed but, rather, responds to certain very high FSH/LH ratios.

ROBYN: I should like to ask Dr. Taymor if the index of discrimination between immunoassay and bioassay was the same for urinary and pituitary gonadotropin preparations.

TAYMOR: We have assayed urinary FSH preparations and in general have found that we lose immunologic activity. The indices of discrimination were about 0.5 with urinary preparations. I think this is a similar experience to that reported by Dr. Faiman and Dr. Ryan.

ROSEMBERG: Dr. Taymor, in one of your slides you showed the index of discrimination for various preparations containing varying amounts of FSH and a fairly good amount of LH. Did you express the potency of these preparations in terms of NIH-FSH-S1?

TAYMOR: Yes it was.

NAFTOLIN: Since adsorption with children's urine or blood appears to remove some of the anti-LH potency of anti-FSH sera I wonder if anyone, perhaps Dr. Midgley, has used a very highly potent LH preparation to adsorb anti-FSH sera. Although this would be very precious material to use it might work. A danger exists that the LH may remove so much of the "anti-FSH" potency that the antiserum would no longer be potent enough to use in an FSH radioimmunoassay.

MIDGLEY: In my opinion, it has been clearly demonstrated that there are regions in molecules of human FSH, TSH, LH and HCG that are immunologically similar, being what might be called a "common core". Thus, the best that one can hope for, is that some animals immunized with FSH will respond to that portion of the molecule which is unique to FSH and that antibodies against the "common core" can be removed by absorption with other glycoprotein hormones possessing this common core such as HCG.

SAXENA: Contamination of FSH with LH, and LH activity of FSH due to possible similarities in the sequences of these two hormones, should be understood in their respective contexts. If the LH activity of the FSH molecule is due to overlap in the sequence, then an antiserum which is specific for only the FSH-portion of the entire molecule, may not be measuring the full biological activity of FSH in a radioimmunoassay. Further the inter and intra species response of rabbits or guinea pigs to some antigens may be variable. The purity of antigens used for labeling is,therefore, most important in the radioimmunoassay. I would like to ask Dr. Taymor to explain why his FSH-radioimmuno-assay becomes more specific when HCG is added after FSH. It would appear more logical to add HCG first in order to render the antiserum more specific for FSH. It is possible that some of the sensitivity of the assay may be lost but specificity would probably be improved.

COMPARISON OF RADIOIMMUNOASSAYS OF FSH AND LH IN DIALIZED, UNDIALIZED, AND EXTRACTED URINE WITH BIOASSAY METHODS.

VERNON C. STEVENS, Ph.D
DEPARTMENT OF OBSTETRICS
AND GYNECOLOGY
OHIO STATE UNIVERSITY

Radioimmunoassays of gonadotropins have provided methods suitable for studying concentrations of these hormones in human plasma. If these methods could be applied to urine measurements, the increased sensitivity could be used to correlate changes in plasma and urine levels in normal and pathologic states. The factors which affect the radioimmunoassay of urinary hormones must be evaluated before the application of these methods to such studies.

Simultaneous measurements of purified LH preparations by bioassays and radioimmunoassays have indicated a good agreement in potency estimates (1,2). Kulin et al (3) has, however, shown that measurements of unprocessed urine do not agree well with measurements of urine extracts. The latter measurements indicated much lower values than the urine values. Such differences could be attributed to losses of LH in the extraction procedure or by interfering substances present in the urine which were removed during extraction. It seems unlikely that extraction losses would account for the large differences found in the two measurements.

The concentration of NaCl and urea in urine has been shown to affect the radioimmunoassay of growth hormone (4). Since radioimmunoassays of growth hormone, FSH and LH are based on the same principles, there was good reason to believe that similar effects could be observed in assays of the latter two hormones. This study was designed to investigate the effect of salt concentrations on the assay systems and to compare levels of FSH and LH by radioimmunoassay in unprocessed urine, dialized urine and urinary extracts. Bioassay measurements were also made on some urinary extracts.

MATERIALS AND METHODS

Urine Collection and Processing

Urine pools were collected from males, premenopausal and postmenopausal women. No clinical data was obtained on patients contributing to each urine pool. Urine pools (1 - 4 liters) were stored at 4° during collection. Two 10 ml.

aliquots were taken from each pool. One of these was dialyzed against several changes of distilled water for 5 days at 4°C. Both aliquots were then frozen until radioimmunoassayed. The remainder of the pool was extracted by the kaolin-acetone procedure of Albert (5). In some pools, the extracts were further purified to Albert's fraction B after an aliquot of fraction A extract was taken. Amounts taken in each aliquot were equivalent to 25 ml. of the original urine. The remainder of the urine extract (Fraction A or Fraction B) was bioassayed for FSH or LH.

Bioassays

Potency estimates of urinary extracts for FSH were obtained using the ovarian augmentation assay (6) and for LH the ovarian ascorbic acid depletion test (7). The standard used in all assays was the 2nd International Reference Preparation for human menopausal gonadotropin (2nd IRP). The assay design of most samples was 2 x 2; however, some extracts with low potency were assayed by a 2 x 1 design (one point of unknown). Since most pools studied were from menopausal women, extracts equivalent to 200 - 600 ml. of urine per rat were used.

Radioimmunoassays

The double antibody techniques described by Midgley (1, 8) were used for immunological measurements. Purified human FSH* and LH** isolated from human pituitaries was used as the tracer antigen. Rabbit anti-HCG and antihuman pituitary FSH were used as antisera. Samples (0.1 - 0.25 ml.) were incubated at 4°C with the antisera for 24 hours before adding 0.1 uc. of the tracer I^{131} labeled antigen (100 - 250 uc/ug). After a 24 hour period of incubation with the labeled antigen, 0.20 ml. of the second antibody (sheep anti-rabbit gammaglobulin) was added. A third incubation of 72 hours elapsed after the addition of the second antibody. After centrifugation at 1000 x G for 30 minutes, the supernatants were decanted and the radioactivity of the precipitates was measured by an automatic gamma spectrometer. The 2nd IRP was used as a standard in both systems.

RESULTS

The effects of increasing concentrations of NaCl on the radioimmunoassay systems for FSH and LH are shown in Figures 1 and 2. The molarities indicated are concentrations in 0.5 ml. of volume used as samples. A significant inhibition of the binding of tracer antigen to antisera was observed by the addition of NaCl in both systems. In the experiments performed, the inhibition slopes resulting from NaCl were not parallel with those of the standard hormone.

---

*LER 780 Hormone supplied by the National Pituitary Bank, 8 S. Eutaw Street, Baltimore, Maryland.
**LER 822 Hormone supplied by the National Pituitary Bank, 8 S. Eutaw Street, Baltimore, Maryland.

Another experiment was performed in which 0.05 - 0.40 ml. of unprocessed male urine was assayed in both FSH and LH immunological systems. Equal volumes of the same urine after dialysis were also assayed. The results of these experiments are shown in Figures 3 and 4. It is readily apparent that assays of the unprocessed urine yielded response slopes not parallel to those of the standard hormone. Dialysis of the same urine resulted in smaller responses but with assay slopes similar to that of the standard.

In Tables 1 and 2 are shown values of FSH and LH concentrations in urine before and after dialysis. Each pool was assayed at a single dose and values shown represent a mean of 5 assays. A consistently lower value was obtained after dialysis for both FSH and LH (about 40%). In order to test for loss of FSH and LH from the dialysis bag, the dialysate water from 5 liters of urine was concentrated by freeze concentra-tion* (about 10 liters were reduced to 500 ml.). Aliquots from this solution showed significant inhibition of the I^{131} FSH and LH reaction to their respective antisera. Bioassay of this concentrate resulted in a toxic response to the assay animals.

Tables 1 and 2 also indicate the difference in potency estimates of dialized urine and extracted urine. An approximately 40% loss of FSH immunological activity was indicated by extraction to the Fraction A stage of purification. Only about 25% loss of LH was indicated. The FSH bioassay estimates of Fraction A materials, in general, agreed well with the radioimmunoassay values. The mean index of discrimination for FSH in Fraction A extracts was 1.06.

A further loss of immunological activity was observed by purifying extracts from Fraction A to Fraction B. The mean loss of FSH was about 23% and about 24% for LH. The LH bioassay estimates of Fraction B materials, in general, also agreed well with radioimmunoassay values. The mean index of discrimination for LH in Fraction B extracts was 1.12. The index of precision FSH and LH bioassays varied from 0.06 - 0.24.

Loss of biological activity by dializing urine was also tested. Eight liters of postmenopausal urine was divided into 4 equal parts. Two of these were dialized 5 days against several changes of distilled water and then extracted by the kaolin-acetone method of Albert (5). One of these pools was further purified to Fraction B. The two undialized pools were extracted in the same way (one to Fraction A and one to Fraction B). Fraction A extracts were assayed for FSH and Fraction B extracts for LH. The FSH activity in the dialized pool was 9.8 IU/liter and in the undialized pool 6.6 IU/liter. The LH activity in the dialized pool was 5.3 IU/liter and in the undialized pool 2.1 IU/liter. Thus, the responses in the bioassays were greater in the dialized urine pools than the undialized for both FSH and LH. These differences were significant (P = .01).

---

* Accomplished using a model 3-100 freeze concentrator, Virtis Research Instrument Co., Gardniner, N.Y.

DISCUSSION

Data obtained in this study indicate that radioimmunoassays of unprocessed urine for FSH and LH will not provide meaningful excretion values. The effects of salt concentration on assay responses are obvious. Certainly the salt content of random urine samples would vary markedly. There is evidence that extraction by the kaolin–acetone method yields material suitable for meaningful estimates by radioimmunoassay. This study has shown that simple dialysis of urine samples produces dose response slopes parallel to that of the standard hormone. Materials lost or retained in urine after dialysis were not completely revealed by this study. The evidence would indicate that biologically active gonadotropins are not lost, in fact, bioassay responses of extracted dialized urine were higher than unextracted urine responses. Perhaps some gonadotropin inhibitor affecting the bioassays was removed by dialysis. The 25–40 per cent difference in FSH and LH values between dialized urine and Fraction A extract indicates a loss in the extraction procedure than seems unreasonably high. Whether dialysis is sufficient purification of the urine to remove interfering substances before performing radioimmunoassays, is still open to question.

REFERENCES

1.   Midgley, A.R., Jr Endocr 79: 10, 1966
2.   Odell, W.D., Ross, G.T. and Rayford, P.L., J Clin Invest 46:248, 1967
3.   Kulin, Howard E., Rifkind, Arleen B. and Ross, Griff T., J Clin Endocr 28: 543, 1968
4.   Girard, J. and Greenwood, F.C., J Endocr 40: 493, 1968
5.   Albert, A., Kobi, J., Leiferman, J. and Derner, I., J Clin Endocr 21: 1, 1961
6.   Steelman, S.L., and Pohley, F.M., Endocr 53: 604, 1953
7.   Parlow, A.F., In Albert, A., ed. Human Pituitary Gonadotropins, Springfield, Ohio, 1961, p.300
8.   Midgley, A.R., Jr., J Clin Endocr 27: 295, 1967

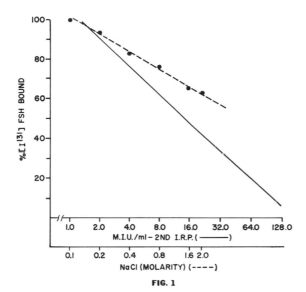

FIG. 1

Effect of sodium chloride on binding of [I^{131}] FSH to antiserum

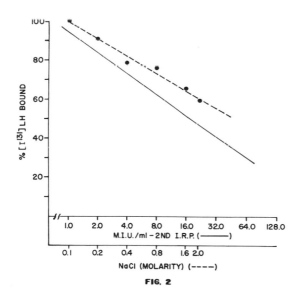

FIG. 2

Effect of sodium chloride on binding of [I^{131}] LH to antiserum

GONADOTROPINS 1968

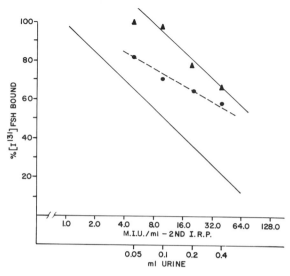

FIG. 3

The effect of dialysis on inhibition by urine. Comparison of standard
FSH (——) to urine (•--•) and dialyzed urine (▲—▲).

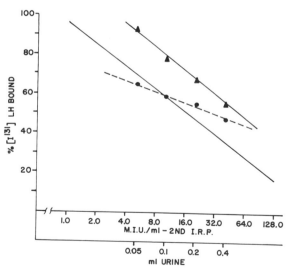

FIG. 4

The effect of dialysis on inhibition by urine. Comparison of standard
LH (——) to urine (•--•) and dialyzed urine (▲—▲)

TABLE 1

RADIOIMUNOASSAY & BIOASSAY OF FSH IN POOLS
OF URINE, DIALIZED URINE & URINARY EXTRACTS
FROM VARIOUS SOURCES.

	I.U.'s - 2ND I.R.P. (FSH) / LITER OF URINE			
POOL	URINE	DIALIZED URINE	EXTRACT FRAC. A	EXTRACT FRAC. B
1	10.2	6.2	2.2	2.0 (<1.0)
2	16.4	10.0	1.6	1.2 (<1.0)
3	32.6	21.4	9.5 (6.2)	—
4	24.0	15.6	5.4 (9.2)	—
5	18.6	9.2	2.6 (1.0)	—
6	42.4	20.7	15.7 (16.8)	—
7	86.0	60.0	45.2 (49.0)	—
8	69.0	31.2	18.5 (15.2)	—
9	59.7	22.6	7.2	—
10	116.8	75.6	45.0	36.2
11	97.2	56.0	33.0 (35.1)	25.7
12	68.6	29.9	15.2 (15.0)	10.5
13	110.2	81.6	47.1	36.4
14	98.2	56.2	40.2	30.0
15	136.0	100.2	57.0	—
16	110.0	76.2	45.2	—
17	122.0	102.5	60.0	—
18	127.0	90.3	54.6	—
19	80.0	28.5	16.5 (6.9)	14.5
20	50.0	12.5	7.5 (4.5)	4.5

( ) BIOASSAY VALUES

TABLE 2

RADIOIMUNOASSAY & BIOASSAY OF L.H. IN POOLS
OF URINE, DIALIZED URINE & URINARY EXTRACTS
FROM VARIOUS SOURCES.

	I.U.'s - 2ND I.R.P. (LH) / LITER OF URINE			
POOL	URINE	DIALIZED URINE	EXTRACT FRAC. A	EXTRACT FRAC. B
1	16.0	14.0	4.3	2.2
2	15.7	13.4	3.4	1.7
3	7.2	6.3	1.6	—
4	26.3	22.0	10.2	—
5	17.9	13.6	9.4	—
6	176.0	100.2	69.2	56.0 (32.0)
7	172.0	97.6	66.4	50.0 (42.6)
8	136.0	75.0	45.0	36.4 (39.0)
9	157.2	32.3	56.4	42.1 (45.6)
10	80.6	47.0	42.0	38.6 (26.0)
11	65.9	37.1	30.6	25.2 (21.6)
12	72.7	46.1	38.3	30.5 (29.0)
13	76.5	44.0	36.0	28.1 (31.6)
14	70.0	40.6	33.8	23.2 (27.0)
15	99.9	45.0	30.7	—
16	101.6	56.2	35.2	—
17	100.0	59.7	39.6	—
18	92.3	48.6	35.4	—
19	102.6	62.3	30.0	16.6
20	110.3	73.4	26.8	15.5

( ) BIOASSAY VALUES

IMMUNOLOGICAL STUDIES WITH HUMAN HYPOPHYSEAL GONADOTROPINS

P.-J. Czygan, D. Krebs, F. Lehmann, G. Bettendorf

Abteilung Fuer Klinische Und Experimentelle Endokrinologie Der
Universitaets-Frauenklinik Hamburg-Eppendorf, Germany

Because of the difficulties arising during the isolation of
pure FSH and LH by chemical procedures, several authors have tried
to use immunological methods for the characterization and purification of gonadotropins of various species. The preparation of
pure fractions can be regarded as a basis for studies concerning
their biological and biochemical mode of action. Lunenfeld et al.
first succeeded in isolating biologically pure FSH from HMG by a
combination of chemical (ion exchange chromatography) and immunological methods. A great number of reports in the literature do
not completely confirm their opinion concerning the immunological
and biological identity of FSH- and LH-Fractions prepared from
the same species but of different origin. For instance, there
are only a few data which show the difference between chorionic
gonadotropin, postmenopausal gonadotropin and hypophyseal LH.

In our experiments with immunological and biological methods,
we have studied the correlation of human hypophyseal gonadotropin,
human menopausal gonadotropin (Pergonal) and human chorionic gonadotropin (HCG); rabbit antisera were prepared against two antigens: HCG and HHG. The immunological activities of the antisera
could be controlled during immunization by heart puncture and
after bleeding by the agar gel-diffusion-test, by immunoelectrophoresis and by the hemagglutination test. Fig. 1 demonstrates
the number of precipitin lines after immunoelectrophoresis.

It is well-known that there is a cross-reaction of anti-HCG
to HHG and vice versa. Furthermore, both antisera produced
precipitates to HMG and an LH-enriched human pituitary preparation.
By stepwise absorption with human serum and the reverse antigen
the number of lines could be reduced to three in both cases and
the cross-reaction disappeared. Thereafter, both antisera precipitated the HMG antigen, but only AS-HHG reacted with hypophyseal
LH. The absorbed anti-HCG failed to give precipitates to this LH.
To prove whether these findings were due to a real antigenic
difference or to an antigen excess in absorbing the antisera, we
performed a hemagglutination test. For this study we only used
anti-HCG serum because of its capacity for binding the LH activity
in gonadotropin preparations. As indicator, tanned sheep
erythrocytes coated with (1) HCG, (2) and (3) two HHG preparations
of different FSH/LH ratios (0.35 and 0.2) and (4) HMG-Pergonal
were used. Unspecific reactions could be excluded by controls.
Fig. 2 shows a very high titer using HCG and HMG as antigens.

Precipitin-Lines afte Immuno-electrophoresis of Gonadotropins						
Antiserum	Antigen					
	HCG	HHG (FSH)	HMG	HHG (LH)	LH (borine)	Human Serum
AS -HCG unabs.	6	2	–	1	0	1
" abs. HS	5	2	–	–	–	0
abs. Peduex	5	–	–	–	–	–
abs. HHG	4	0	–	0	–	1
abs. HS,HHG Peduex	3	0	3	0	–	–
AS· HHG unabs.	2	7	–	–	–	6
" abs. HS	1	4	–	–	–	0
abs. HCG	0	6	–	–	–	5
abs HS+HCG	0	3	2	2	0	0

Figure No. 1

Number of precipitin lines in immunoelectrophoresis. Different gonadotropic antigens against AS-HCG and AS-HHG.

Haemagglutination Test with Anti-HCG-Serum											
AS - HCG	Cells coated with	Titer 1/									
		8	16	32	64	128	256	512	1024	2048	4096
unabsorbed	HCG	+	+	+	+	+	+	+	+	+	±
	HHG(E3)	+	+	+	+	+	+	±	–	–	–
	HHG (N4)	+	+	+	+	+	±	–	–	–	–
	HMG (Perg)	+	+	+	+	+	+	+	+	±	–
absorbed with 0,15 ml Human Serum	HCG	+	+	+	+	+	+	±	–	–	–
	HHG (E3)	+	+	+	+	+	±	–	–	–	–
	HHG (N4)	+	+	+	+	+	±	–	–	–	–
	HMG (Perg)	+	+	+	+	+	+	±	–	–	–
absorbed with 0,15 ml HS and 2,5 mg HHG(E3)	HCG	+	+	+	+	+	+	–	–	–	–
	HHG (E3)	–	–	–	–	–	–	–	·	··	
	HHG (N4)	–	–	–	–	–	–	–	–	–	
	HMG (Perg.)	±	–	–	–	–	–	–	–	–	

Figure No. 2

Titers in hemagglutination test with gonadotropin-coated cells.
AS-HCG unabsorbed, AS absorbed with human serum, AS-HCG absorbed
both with human serum and HHG in excess.

       After absorption with human serum in excess only the titers
of HCG and HMG of the urinary preparations were reduced, while
the HHG-reactions did not change. This must have been due to a
higher degree of protein contamination in the urinary material.
The third line represents an absorption in excess with both human

serum and HHG pointing out a persistence of anti-HCG/HCG reaction after high absorption.

The next figure (Fig. 3) demonstrates the hemagglutination test with AS-HCG after stepwise absorption with HHG.

Haemagglutination Test with Anti-HCG-Serum											
						Titer 1/					
AS - HCG	Cells coated with	8	16	32	64	128	256	512	1024	2048	4096
absorbed with 0,01 mg HHG (E₃)	HCG	+	+	+	+	+	+	+	±	-	-
	HHG(E₃)	+	+	+	+	±	-	-	-	-	-
	HHG (N₄)	+	+	+	+	+	-	-	-	-	-
	HMG (Perg)	+	+	+	+	+	+	+	±	-	-
absorbed with 0,1 mg HHG (E₃)	HCG	+	+	+	+	+	+	+	±	-	-
	HHG (E₃)	+	+	±	-	-	-	-	-	-	-
	HHG (N₄)	+	+	-	-	-	-	-	-	-	-
	HMG(Perg)	+	+	+	+	+	+	+	±	-	-
absorbed with 1,0 mg HHG (E₃)	HCG	+	+	+	+	+	+	±	-	-	-
	HHG (E₃)	±	-	-	-	-	-	-	-	-	-
	HHG (N₄)	-	-	-	-	-	-	-	-	-	-
	HMG (Perg)	+	+	+	+	+	+	±	-	-	-

Figure No. 3

Titers in hemagglutination test with gonadotropin-coated cells. AS-HCG absorbed with 0.01, 0.1 and 1.0 mg HHG (E_3)

The titer of HHG absorption was, as expected, reduced from 256 to 64 after 0.01 mg., to 16 after 0.1 mg. and to zero after 1.0 mg. absorption. In contrast, the HCG and HMG titers remained nearly the same. This finding correlated with the results of immunoelectrophoresis which indicated that the loss of cross-reaction between HHG and AS-HCG after absorption leads to an antibody only against urinary gonadotropin material.

In a third experiment, (Fig. 4), we used HMG in the same protein amounts for absorption. With 0.01 and 0.1 mg. only a loss of activity in the urinary extracts HCG and HMG became obvious. HHG-coated cells did not change their behavior against the anti-body. The absorption with 1.0 mg. Pergonal resulted only in a small loss of activity with HHG and in a higher one with HCG (titer 128). With HMG the hemagglutination disappeared completely. From these data we conclude the following two facts:

1. According to the absorption test with HHG we can suspect some different immunological properties of urinary and hypophyseal gonadotropins.

2. Despite good parallelism between HCG and HMG in most of the reactions there is one marked difference after high

absorption of AS-HCG with HMG. The remaining agglutination activity to HCG-coated cells may indicate an immunological difference between the chorionic gonadotropin molecule and that of menopausal gonadotropin.

Haemagglutination Test with Anti-HCG-Serum											
						Titer 1/					
AS - HCG	Cells coated with	8	16	32	64	128	256	512	1024	2048	4096
absorbed with 0,01 mg HMG (Pergonal)	HCG	+	+	+	+	+	+	+	+	±	-
	HHG(E3)	+	+	+	+	+	±	-	-	-	-
	HHG (N4)	+	+	+	+	+	-	-	-	-	-
	HMG (Perg)	+	+	+	+	+	+	+	+	±	∓
absorbed with 0,1 mg HMG	HCG	+	+	+	+	+	+	+	±	-	-
	HHG (E3)	+	+	+	+	+	±	-	-	-	-
	HHG (N4)	+	+	+	+	+	-	-	-	-	-
	HMG (Perg)	+	+	+	+	+	+	+	±	-	-
absorbed with 1,0 mg HMG	HCC	+	+	+	+	+	±	-	-	-	-
	HHG (E3)	+	+	+	+	±	-	-	-	-	-
	HHG (N4)	+	+	+	+	-	-	-	-	-	-
	HMG (Perg)	±	-	-	-	-	-	-	-	-	-

Figure No. 4

Titers in hemagglutination test with gonadotropin-coated cells. AS-HCG absorbed with 0.01, 0.1 and 1.0 mg HMG-Pergonal.

It is remarkable that no strong difference occurred in the immunology of E3 and N4, although these substances were prepared by different methods.

After demonstrating their immunological specificity and potency, we tried to prove the effect of antisera on the biological activities of the antigens tested and to study correlations between biological and immunological sites of these proteins. First it seemed necessary to acquire some general information on the anti-gonadotropic capacity in biological terms. This question was examined by a series of tests with rats according to the following schedule. Increasing concentrations of antisera were incubated with equal doses of gonadotropins and the precipitate was removed by centrifugation. The supernatant was injected into 4 animals in each group. Control experiments were done with antirat liver serum which had no influence on the biological effect of gonadotropins. We tested LH activity in the ovarian ascorbic acid depletion test and FSH activity by the increase of uterus and ovarian weight in immature intact rats. In the beginning, we did not use the augmentation test because a reaction of the anti-HCG residue and the HCG injected for augmentation could not be excluded. In the next two figures, (Figs. 5 and 6) the results of unabsorbed AS-HCG after reaction with 100 µg HHG (65.8 I.U. FSH, 200 I.U. LH, II. IRP) are given.

The antigonadotropic efficiency of the antibodies on the
animal organs could be demonstrated.

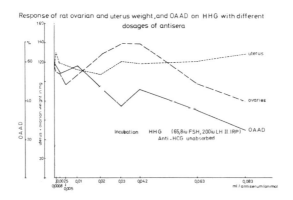

Figure No. 5

Response of rat ovarian and uterus weight and OAAD on HHG-E$_3$ (65.8
I.U. FSH, 200 I.U. LH, II IRP) after incubation with different
dosages of AS-HCG unabsorbed.

To examine this effect in detail, incubation was done with
smaller amounts of HHG (Fig. 6).

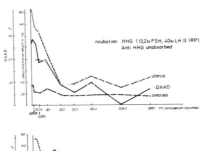

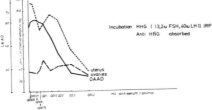

Figure No. 6

Response of rat ovarian and uterus weight and OAAD on HHG-E$_3$ (13.2 I.U. FSH, 40 I.U. LH, II IRP) after incubation with different dosages of AS-HCG both unabsorbed and absorbed with HS and HHG.

With 0.02 ml unabsorbed antiserum maximal inhibition of the biological FSH and LH effect could be observed. The reaction with absorbed antiserum deviated from this in that (1) the antibodies lost some general activity and (2) the LH decreasing capacity occurred at dose levels in which FSH effect remained still unchanged.

Although these findings can be taken as proof for antigonadotropic activity, the tests used are representative only for the biological profile of antigonadotropins and not for a bioassay method. In a further experiment, we therefore compared the effect of untreated HHG with that of HHG incubated with AS-HCG in the Steelman-Pohley-assay (using 60 I.U. HCG per animal) and OAAD (Fig. 7).

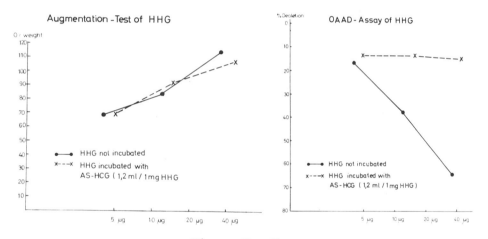

Figure No. 7

FSH and LH bioassay of HHG untreated and after incubation with AS-HCG unabsorbed (1.2 ml/mg HHG).

While the dose response curves of FSH are nearly congruent, indicating no detectable change of FSH activity by anti-HCG, the high LH response of untreated material is completely inhibited by antibodies to HCG at the dose range tested.

The results we can summarize as follows:

1. Unabsorbed AS-HCG reacts in immunological tests with both hypophyseal and urinary gonadotropins.

2. There is some parallelism in the antigenic behavior of HCG and HMG, but not with HHG.

3. The two hypophyseal gonadotropin preparations do not show differences in immunology in spite of the different procedure used and the different FSH/LH ratio contained in the preparations.

4. After stepwise absorbing the AS-HCG with HMG or HHG the corresponding reaction disappears, but some immunological activity against its homologous antigen remains.

5. Unabsorbed AS-HCG is active in inhibiting biological effects of human gonadotropins.

6. From the bioassay, we conclude that AS-HCG contains a high anti-LH activity and only a very low anti-FSH activity.

DISCUSSION

ODELL: I should like to make a general comment on the use of the immunoelectrophoretic system to identify so-called mono specific systems. We have used radioautographs in immunoelectrophoresis with labeled hormones, and have been able to show in some instances that a single line produced with an antigen - antibody precipitate may be associated with as much as 5% and perhaps more contamination of the antigen with another material. The discrimination of this method may not be very good.

CZYGAN: You are right. We did use the immunoelectrophoretic system only as a pilot test to explore cross reaction and to study the properties of our antisera against other antigens.

RADIOIMMUNOLOGIC STUDIES WITH MURINE, BOVINE, OVINE, AND PORCINE
LUTEINIZING HORMONE[1]

GORDON D. NISWENDER,[2] A. REES MIDGLEY, JR.,[3] AND
LEO E. REICHERT, JR.
DEPARTMENT OF PATHOLOGY, UNIVERSITY OF MICHIGAN, ANN ARBOR, MICHIGAN, AND
DEPARTMENT OF BIOCHEMISTRY, DIVISION OF BASIC HEALTH SCIENCES, EMORY
UNIVERSITY, ATLANTA, GEORGIA (L. E. R.)

INTRODUCTION

We have recently reported the development of radioimmunoassays (RIA) for rat
(1), bovine (2), and ovine (3) luteinizing hormone (LH) utilizing partially
purified preparations of LH from the homologous species for immunization of
rabbits and for radioiodination. Preliminary data suggests that a valid RIA
for porcine LH has also been developed in a similar manner. These assays
have been designated as the RR rat LH, BB bovine LH, OO ovine LH, and PP
porcine LH radioimmunoassays respectively. The first capital letter refers
to the species from which LH was obtained for immunization and the second
refers to the species from which the purified LH for radioiodination was
obtained. We have also reported the development of a highly sensitive RIA
for rat LH which utilizes a unique anti-ovine LH serum and radioiodinated
ovine LH (OO rat LH RIA) (4).

The purpose of this study was to determine the extent of species specificity
present in the above radioimmunoassay systems and to further investigate the
OO rat LH RIA and the possible uses of the OO LH system to quantitate LH from
other species.

MATERIALS AND METHODS

In the first series of experiments dose response curves with LH from sheep,
cattle, pigs, rats and humans as well as human chorionic gonadotropin (HCG)
and pregnant mares serum gonadotropin (PMS) were run in four different RIA
systems. The methods used to obtain the preparations of partially purified
LH and HCG used as standards have been described (1-5). PMS was obtained
commercially (Equinex, Ayerst Laboratories, New York, N.Y.) The purified
ovine, bovine and porcine preparations of LH used for radioiodination were
obtained from frozen whole pituitary glands by ammonium sulfate extraction
and fractionation, ion-exchange chromatography and gel filtration (6, 7).
Preparation of the antisera used in these studies and the methods used for
radioiodination and for the actual assays have been described in detail (2-4).

In a second series of experiments the effects of serum and antibody concentration
were determined in the OO rat LH RIA. The methods used have been reported

[1] Supported by research grants from the National Institute of Child Health and
Human Development (NIH-HD-02193) and USPHS Grant AM-03598. Publication #891 from
the Division of Basic Health Sciences, Emory University, Atlanta, Georgia
[2] Public Health Service Postdoctoral Fellow

[3] Career Development Awardee of the National Institute of Child Health and
Human Development

previously (4).

Results obtained in the first experiment with the OO LH RIA using antiserum from rabbit 15 suggested that this system might be suitable for measuring porcine and bovine LH as well as ovine and rat LH for which it had been previously used. A final series of experiments was conducted to test this possibility. The relative potency of bovine pituitary preparations with widely varying ratios of LH to FSH (follicle stimulating hormone) and LH to TSH (thyroid stimulating hormone) was determined in the BB bovine LH RIA and the OO LH RIA. A similar comparison was made between relative potencies of porcine pituitary preparations in a PP porcine LH RIA and the OO LH RIA.

RESULTS AND DISCUSSION

Results from the first series of experiments are shown in Figure 1. The quantity of LH-^{131}I bound to the antibody in the absence of competing unlabeled hormone (i. e. buffer control tubes) was considered to represent 100%. Dose response curves demonstrating the decrease in antibody bound LH-^{131}I which occurred with increasing levels of the various preparations in four different assay systems are shown. When antiserum from rabbit 15 was used in an OO LH RIA, porcine, ovine, bovine and rat LH and PMS gave dose response curves which were similar in shape and slope. They gave curves with steep slopes and appeared to be capable of completely inhibiting the reaction between the anti-ovine LH serum and the ovine LH-^{131}I. Of 36 rabbits immunized with various preparations of ovine LH only rabbit 15 produced an antiserum capable of cross reacting with rat LH and PMS. Human LH and HCG did not give smooth dose response curves. The slopes were very flat and the variation between points on the curves was considerable.

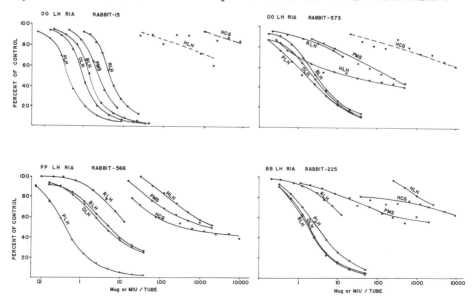

Figure 1
A comparison of four RIA systems with varying degrees of species specificity

The same preparations were also tested in another OO LH system using antiserum from rabbit 573, the antiserum which was used to develop the RIA reported previously for ovine LH (3). In this system ovine, bovine and porcine LH appeared to completely inhibit the reaction between the antibody and labeled hormone and the dose response curves were similar in slope and shape. Rat and human LH and PMS produced curves with flat slopes indicative of only partial cross reaction. The principle difference between the OO LH RIA systems shown in Figure 1 was that antiserum from rabbit 15 cross reacted with rat LH and PMS while antiserum from rabbit 573 did not.

In the PP LH RIA system the dose response curve obtained with porcine LH had a steep slope and complete inhibition of the reaction between anti-porcine LH serum and porcine LH-^{131}I was obtained with relatively small quantities of this hormone. Ovine and bovine LH gave dose response curves with similar shapes and slopes but did not give complete inhibition at levels which produced essentially complete inhibition in the other systems. The dose response curve for rat LH appeared to have a slope similar to those obtained with ovine and bovine LH but the highest level of rat LH used produced values which were still 60% of control values. Human LH, HCG and PMS gave curves which were flat and which appeared to level off at about 50% of control values suggesting only partial cross reaction.

Dose response curves obtained with bovine, ovine and porcine LH were all similar in the BB LH RIA. These hormones produced curves with steep slopes and all appeared to completely inhibit the reaction between the antibody and the labeled hormone at the levels used. Rat LH produced a curve with a flatter slope. Human LH, HCG and PMS again gave curves which were flat and leveled off at about 60% of control values.

In these experiments ovine, bovine and porcine LH produced dose response curves which were similar in all systems in which they were tested, with the possible exception of the PP LH RIA. These data suggest that ovine, bovine, and porcine LH molecules are immunologically similar and may suggest a structural similarity for LH from these species. Human LH and HCG did not give good dose response curves in any of the assay systems. Rat LH and PMS gave good dose response curves in the OO LH RIA system using antiserum from rabbit 15 but not in the others. Previous studies with the RR rat LH RIA revealed that ovine and human LH did not cross react completely in that system (1).

In developing the OO rat LH assay (4) dose response curves were obtained with preparations varying widely in their LH to FSH and LH to TSH ratios. It was apparent that the dose response curves were similar in shape and slope for all preparations tested. However, this finding was not evidence that this system was specific for LH. This evidence was obtained when estimates of the LH content of rat pituitary preparations as found by bioassay and the RR rat LH RIA (1) were compared to those obtained by the OO rat LH RIA. In the preparations tested the LH to FSH ratio varied 17,600 fold (B118 vs B180) and the LH to TSH ratio varied 3,400 fold (B156 vs B180), yet in all cases estimates of LH potency were consistent between bioassay and the two radioimmunoassays. These data demonstrated that FSH and TSH, the pituitary hormones most commonly a problem in LH radioimmunoassays, did not influence LH potencies obtained with the OO rat LH RIA.

In order to further characterize the OO rat LH assay system the effects of
serum were determined. Dose response curves, with rat LH diluted in buffer
and similar curves with 100 ul of serum from hypophysectomized rats added
to each tube, were compared (Figure 2). The radioactivity present in each
tube was plotted against the quantity of hormone present. The two curves
(one with serum and one without) can be superimposed upon each other which
clearly demonstrates that serum per se has no influence on the LH potencies
obtained with this assay.

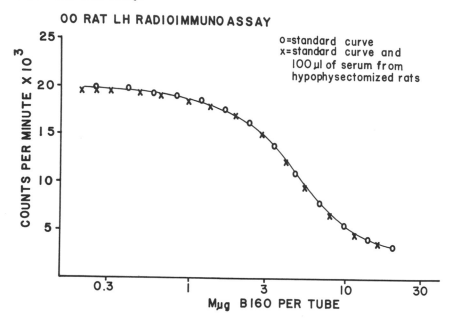

Figure 2

The OO rat LH radioimmunoassay standard curve, with and without the addition
of serum from hypophysectomized rats.

In another experiment the effects of varying the concentration of antibody
used in the OO rat LH RIA was studied. Figure 3 shows dose response curves
obtained with rat LH at 4 different antibody concentrations. There was a
substantial increase in the sensitivity of the assay as the concentration
of antibody decreased. The quantity of rat LH necessary to give values 80%
of that in control tubes was 9.4, 3.2, 1.2 and 0.7 Mug per tube at concentrations of 1:10,000, 1:20,000, 1:40,000, and 1:80,000 respectively. Thus,
a 13.4 fold increase in sensitivity was noted after dilution of the antibody
from 1:10,000 to 1:80,000. However, the decrease in the amount of total
radioactivity bound (69 vs. 28%) makes it impractical to use extremely high
antibody dilutions due to the significant increases in counting time
necessary for each assay. It should be noted that a 1:40,000 dilution of
the antibody resulted in an 8 fold increase in sensitivity over that noted
with a 1:10,000 dilution and 47% of the total radioactivity was bound

at this concentration.

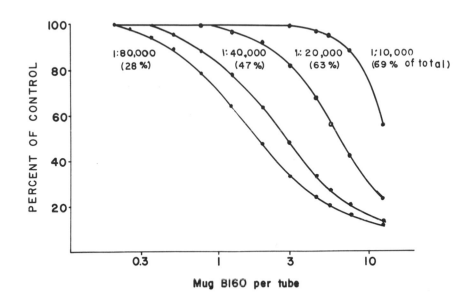

Figure 3
The effects of varying concentrations of antibody on the OO rat LH RIA
system.

The LH content of a homogenate of normal male pituitary glands (B314) and
of 3 rat serum preparations which contained low, medium and high quantities
of LH were determined at each of the 4 antibody dilutions used to obtain
the dose response curves. These results are shown in Table 1. Only that
area of the dose response curve where the radioactivity represented between
20% and 80% of that in control tubes was used to calculate relative potencies.
The curves for all rat preparations tested in this system have been shown to
be parallel within this range (4). However, values outside this range also
have some value and are reported in Table 1. A very good correlation
exists between the LH potencies obtained for the various preparations at
different antibody concentrations and with different quantities of the
preparation present in the assay tube.

The results of this experiment demonstrated that as the concentration of antibody used in the OO rat LH RIA is decreased the sensitivity of the assay increases. In addition, the relative potency of rat LH preparations, as estimated in this system, was not influenced by the concentration of antibody over the range used in this study.

Since the first series of experiments indicated that bovine and porcine LH cross reacted with anti-ovine LH serum from rabbit 15 in the OO LH RIA, a final series of experiments was carried out to determine if this system could be used for LH from cattle and pigs as well as that from rats and sheep. Table 2 contains the LH content of six bovine pituitary preparations as estimated by bioassay, the BB bovine LH RIA (2) and the OO bovine LH RIA. In the preparations tested the LH to FSH ratios varied as much as 164,000 fold (LER-943-2 vs. LER-892-2) and the LH to TSH ratios varied 64 fold (LER-814-2 vs. NIH-LH-B5). Excellent agreement was obtained between the RIA estimates of LH potency with the two systems. In addition potencies obtained with both RIA's agreed well with bioassay values. Since estimates of the LH content of bovine pituitary preparations obtained with the OO bovine LH RIA for preparations quite high in their TSH, FSH and growth hormone content agreed with bioassay values it appears these hormones do not influence the assay. These data suggest that a valid OO bovine LH RIA has been developed utilizing the anti-ovine LH serum obtained from rabbit 15.

Table 3 contains the relative potencies of 3 porcine preparations as estimated by bioassay and by the PP porcine LH and OO porcine LH RIA's. The agreement between the 3 estimates of LH potency is very good and the data suggest it is possible to quantitate porcine LH utilizing the anti-ovine LH serum from rabbit 15 and ovine LH-^{131}I.

These data in combination with data from a previous study (4) demonstrate that it is possible to utilize a unique anti-ovine LH serum, ovine LH-^{131}I, and appropriate standards as the basis for a single radioimmuno-assay to quantitate ovine, bovine, porcine and rat LH.

REFERENCES

1. Monroe, S.E., Parlow, A.F., Midgley, A.R., Jr., _Endocrinology_, In press 1968.
2. Niswender, G.D., Reichert, L.E., Jr., Midgley, A.R., Jr., submitted to _Endocrinology_.
3. Niswender, G.D., Reichert, L.E., Jr., Midgley, A.R., Jr., submitted to _Endocrinology_.
4. Niswender, G.D., Midgley, A.R., Jr., Monroe, S.E., and Reichert, L.E., Jr., _Proc.Soc.Exp.Biol.Med._ In press, 1968.
5. Midgley, A.R., Jr., _Endocrinology_ 79:10, 1966.
6. Reichert, L.E., Jr., _Endocrinology_ 71:729, 1962.
7. Reichert, L.E., Jr., N. S. Jiang, _Endocrinology_ 77:78, 1965.

IMMUNOLOGIC ASSAY

Table 1

Relative LH potencies of rat preparations in the OO rat
LH RIA with varying antibody concentrations

Preparation	µg or µl/tube	1:10,000	1:20,000	1:40,000	1:80,000
		Antibody Concentrations			
20%	-	-	14.0	7.6	5.4
80%	-	9.4	3.2	1.2	.7
B314 P	25	9.6[1]	9.7	10.9	8.2
	12.5	10.8	10.0	9.4	8.0
	6.25	-	11.2	-	-
	3.13	12.8	12.4	9.6	9.6
B315 S	500	-	-	-	-
B316 S	500	-	4.3	4.5	5.0
	250	-	4.4	4.6	4.5
B317 S	500	10.6	12.7	-	-
	250	10.4	11.2	13.2	14.0
	125	-	-	10.8	12.4

[1]Expressed as Mµg B160 per µg or µl

Table 2

Comparison of BB bovine LH and OO bovine LH radioimmunoassays

Preparation	TSH USP units per mg.	FSH* units per mg.	LH* bioassay units/mg.	LH BB bovine LH RIA units/mg.	LH OO bovine LH RIA units/mg.
NIH-LH-B5	.074 (3)**	.01 (1)	.87 (8)	1.26 (3)	.89 (2)
LER-943-2	.11 (3)	.0012 (1)	.83 (10)	1.01 (6)	1.08 (2)
LER-898-2	-	.38 (2)	.0016 (1)	.0019 (6)	.0009 (2)
LER-898-3	-	.07 (2)	.0016 (1)	.0014 (6)	.0008 (2)
LER-814-2	2.7 (2)	-	.50 (6)	.31 (6)	.51 (2)
NIH-GH-B12	.013 (3)	.001 (1)	.0085 (4)	.0056 (3)	.007 (2)

*FSH and LH relative potencies in terms of NIH-FSH-S1
and NIH-LH-S1, 1 unit = activity in 1 mg. of the standard preparation

**Numbers in parenthesis indicate number of assays

Table 3

Comparison of PP porcine LH and OO porcine LH radioimmunoassays

Preparation	TSH USP units per mg.	FSH* units per mg.	LH* bioassay units/mg.	LH PP porcine LH RIA units/mg.	LH OO porcine LH RIA units/mg
LER-786-3	-	-	.65	.67 (3)	.65 (2)
LER-778-4	.03 (3)**	-	.50	.53 (3)	.50 (2)
LER-441-2	.036	.76	.008	.007 (3)	.007 (2)

*FSH and LH relative potencies in terms of NIH-FSH-S1 and NIH-LH-S1
1 unit = activity in 1 mg. of the standard preparation
**Numbers in parenthesis indicate number of assay

RADIOIMMUNOLOGIC STUDIES OF RAT LH

A. R. MIDGLEY, JR., V. L. GAY, L. C. S. CALIGARIS[1], R. W. REBAR,
S. E. MONROE AND G. D. NISWENDER
DEPARTMENT OF PATHOLOGY, UNIVERSITY OF MICHIGAN, ANN ARBOR, MICHIGAN 48104

INTRODUCTION

Two radioimmunoassay methods for measurement of rat LH have been developed in our laboratory (1, 2, 3). The first of these, the RR rat LH radioimmunoassay, utilizes anti-rat LH serum and purified labeled rat LH. The second, a more sensitive OO rat LH radioimmunoassay, utilizes a highly selected anti ovine LH serum and purified labeled ovine LH. Rat LH standards are used in both assays. The specificity of these assays has been described. They each give anticipated LH relative potencies for pituitary preparations rich in TSH or FSH. Dilutions of sera give inhibition curves indistinguishable from those given by dilutions of preparations of rat pituitary LH. However, present data suggest that they each give concentrations of LH in samples of serum lower than one would anticipate on the basis of bioassay results. The reasons for this discrepancy are not clear.

The purpose of this report is to summarize briefly some of the changes we have observed in sera and pituitary glands of rats with these two radioimmunoassays. While these studies do not indicate why estimates of LH in rat serum are lower by radioimmunoassay than by bioassay, they do support the concept that the two radioimmunoassays are specifically measuring rat LH.

MATERIALS AND METHODS

Rats were purchased from Holtzman and Company and maintained in air-conditioned quarters in which the lights were on from 5 am to 7 pm daily. Samples of blood were obtained (through a permanent aortic catheter or by cardiac puncture) from non-anesthetized rats or from rats anesthetized with ether or pentobarbital. Serum was separated and stored frozen until time of assay. During sequential bleedings, 0.4 ml samples of blood were withdrawn; larger amounts were obtained terminally. Anterior pituitary glands, removed immediately after exsanguination, were sealed in air-tight parafilm envelopes, frozen on dry ice and stored at -50°C. The pituitary glands were later thawed, weighed on a Cahn electrobalance, homogenized in distilled water, and diluted in 0.01 M phosphate-buffered 0.14 M NaCl with 1% bovine serum albumin (PBS-BSA) for radioimmunoassay. Hypothalami were promptly dissected and homogenized in 0.2 ml of 0.1 M HCl. The acid extract was clarified by centrifugation and rapidly frozen for later examination. Some rats were hypophysectomized under ether anesthesia by a stereotaxic transauricular procedure (4). Some rats were castrated.

---

[1] Member: Carrera del Investigador Cientifico, Consejo Nacional de Investigaciones Cientificas y Tecnicas, Buenos Aires, Argentina. Instituto de Investigacion Medica, "Mercedes y Martin Ferreyra," Cordoba, Argentina.

In vitro incubations were performed according to the technique of
Piacsek and Meites (5). In brief, within a period of 10 minutes, 20
anterior pituitary glands were removed from adult male rats, divided in
half, and each half placed in one to two ml of modified Krebs-Ringer
buffer in individual flasks. The flasks were placed in a Dubnoff metabolic
shaker with 5% CO_2 in oxygen and agitated for various periods. The
"pre-incubation" media was then removed for radioimmunoassay and replaced
by one to two ml of media containing freshly neutralized cerebral cortical
extract (control flasks) or hypothalamic extract (experimental flasks).
After variable periods, the media was removed, rapidly frozen and later
radioimmunoassayed. The remaining pituitary tissue was processed as
described above for later radioimmunoassay. The standard for all radioimmunoassay determinations was B160, a partially purified rat pituitary
extract with a potency 0.17 times NIH-LH-S1 by ovarian ascorbic acid
depletion bioassay.

RESULTS

Response to Exogenous Steroids

Testosterone propionate (2.5 mg in oil) was given intraperitoneally to 3
adult rats 25 days after ovariectomy. The serum concentrations of LH fell
from a mean of 86 mµg B160/ml to 50 mµg B160/ml 2 hours after injection
and then continued to fall more slowly, reaching a low value of 25 mµg/ml
24 hours after injection. The next day LH concentrations had increased
to 45 mµg/ml.

A combination of estradiol valerate (50 µg in peanut oil) and progesterone
(25 mg in peanut oil) were given intraperitoneally to 4 adult rats 25 days
after ovariectomy. Within 30 minutes serum LH concentrations fell from a
mean of 97 mµg B160/ml to 64 mµg/ml and by 4 hours a mean concentration
of 41 mµg/ml was found. This concentration did not change appreciably
over the next 3 days.

A group of 10 adult male rats were given 2 mg of testosterone propionate
subcutaneously each day for 21 days. On the twenty-second day the rats
were orchidectomized. Serum concentrations of LH remained below 20 mµg
B160/ml for the first three days after castration. By the sixth day mean
serum concentrations of 37 mµg B160/ml were found and by the tenth day
these concentrations had reached 50 mµg/ml. Pituitary concentrations remained low for the first 6 days after castration but had increased 6 fold
by the tenth day.

Assessment of LH Releasing Activity in Hypothalamic Extracts

Preliminary results with in vitro incubation procedures have indicated that
the radioimmunoassays can be used to monitor synthesis and release of LH.
A pre-incubation period of one-half hour appears satisfactory, and by
determining the concentration of LH in these pre-incubation media damaged
pituitary halves can be identified. By discarding results from such
damaged pituitary glands, considerable improvement in precision can be
obtained. Results found to date have shown that pituitary tissue treated

with hypothalamic extract (one hypothalamic equivalent per flask) both synthe-sizes (increased total LH) and releases more LH than pituitary tissue treated with either media alone or with media containing cerebral cortical extract (P $<$0.01).

Various extracts have been injected intravenously into ovariectomized progesterone-estradiol-blocked, pentobarbital-anesthetized rats (6), and sequential samples (0.3 ml) of blood withdrawn after various intervals from an aortic catheter. Injection of PBS into 5 rats caused no appreciable change in concentrations of LH in serum over a 1 hour observation period. Injections of rat cortical extract produced a striking increase in serum concentrations of LH beginning between 20 and 30 minutes after injection. Thus, serum LH concentrations increased from preinjection levels of less than 40 mμg/ml to an average value of approximately 120 mμg/ml. In contrast to the delayed response produced by cerebral cortex, injections of varying concentrations of hypothalamic extract from castrated male rats resulted in a prompt (less than 5 minute) increase in concentrations of serum LH. This increase consisted of as much as 50 mμg B160/ml between 5 and 30 minutes after injection. Between 30 and 60 minutes after injection, serum LH concentrations increased an additional 30 mμg/ml.

Changes in Serum LH following Castration

In adult male rats, a 50 fold increase in serum LH concentrations (up to 100 mμg B160/ml) occurred during the first day after castration. This rapid initial increase produced serum LH concentrations which were nearly 50% of the average concentrations observed as late as 61 days after orchidectomy. The rate at which serum LH concentrations increased was clearly the greatest during the first 24 hours. Within the first month after castration LH release did not appear to consist of a stable or steady-state condition. Studies in individual rats, in which blood samples were collected by cardiac puncture, revealed large fluctuations in serum LH concentrations, both on a day-to-day and on an hour-to-hour basis. No evidence was found to suggest that these fluctuations were the result of a diurnal rhythm in LH release (7).

In contrast to the rapid response following orchidectomy, serum LH concentrations were not elevated above 50 mμg B160/ml during the first five days following ovariectomy of adult rats. A similar delayed response was seen in 8 animals ovariectomized on the day following vaginal opening. In the younger rats, serum concentrations of LH were low (30 mμg B160/ml) for the first five days after castration. By the sixth day, concentrations were elevated (50 mμg/ml) and by the eighth day they averaged 70 mμg/ml. Since serum LH concentrations in the adult castrates did eventually equal the concentrations observed following orchidectomy, it appears that a primary sex difference in response to castration is the rate at which high levels of LH are achieved (one day for the males vs nearly a week for the females).

Concentrations of LH in the Rat During the Estrous Cycle

Adult female rats exposed to a 14 hour photoperiod (5 am to 7 pm) were followed by daily vaginal smears for 2 or more cycles. They were sacrificed

at all stages of the estrous cycle, and the concentrations of both serum
and pituitary gland LH were measured by radioimmunoassay. Serum LH concentrations on the afternoon of proestrous in either 4 or 5 day cycling
animals were 50-to 100-fold greater than levels observed during other
times in the estrous cycle. LH peaks were found between 1 and 8 pm, the
majority occurring in the period 3 to 6 pm. All animals with elevated
serum LH concentrations had distended, fluid-filled uteri. No significant
elevation in serum LH concentration was found during the afternoon of
diestrus. The LH concentration in pituitary glands prior to the LH peak
was 2 to 3 times greater than that observed in pituitary glands following
the serum LH peak (8).

To obtain a further understanding of the nature of the LH peak, animals
were bled by serial cardiac puncture on the afternoon of proestrus. All
animals which showed an LH peak on the afternoon of proestrus were found
to have ova when sacrificed the next morning. The period of rapid pituitary
LH release in an individual rat was very brief, only 1 to 2 hours. During
this period, the serum LH concentration increased by approximately 100
fold. The fall in the serum LH concentration was likewise very rapid, and
the rate of disappearance of LH was very close to the half life of endogenous LH in the proestrous rat, namely 30 minutes.

Serum LH in the PMS treated Immature Female Rat

Following the injection of PMS into immature (21 day old) female rats, the
ovulatory "surge" of LH, presumed to occur on the second day following PMS
injection, was measured directly by radioimmunoassay (7). The duration
and magnitude of the LH release was similar to that reported for the
proestrous rat (8). Similar responses, in terms of increased serum LH
concentrations, were produced by two different doses of PMS; a) a 30 IU
dose selected for an optimal response in terms of number of ova produced,
and b) a 100 IU dose which produced few, if any, ova. These results
suggest that the well documented biphasic effect of PMS (9, 10) is not
due to interference with pituitary LH release.

Concentrations of LH Before and After Delivery

To determine the time, extent, and duration of LH release following
parturition, concentrations of LH were determined in anterior pituitary
glands and in sera drawn several times during the day from pregnant and
post-partum rats (11). A 14-hour photoperiod (5 am to 7 pm) was employed.
The pups were removed as soon as possible after delivery. In the pregnant
rat, only 5 of the 85 sequential samples collected in the 7 days prior to
delivery contained detectable concentrations of LH ($>$ 30 mμg B160/ml).
Serum LH was never found to exceed 52 mμg B160/ml during those 7 days.

Individual samples of sera from 42 animals showed elevated ($>$ 50 mμg/ml)
concentrations of serum LH as early as 7 am and as late as 2 am of the
day of delivery. With two exceptions, serum LH was not elevated during
either the first or the second day after delivery.

A relationship appeared to exist between the post-partum release of LH and
hours after delivery. Samples with elevated concentrations of serum LH were

seen as early as two hours after delivery and the highest percentages of elevated samples were between 7 and 11 hours after delivery. Sequential samples from individual rats showed that the onset of the rise in serum LH occurred between $3\frac{1}{2}$ and 11 hours after delivery in each case, and probably sooner than 8 hours after the end of delivery.

The release of LH was extremely rapid, at least a 15 fold rise in concentration (and perhaps as much as a 60 fold increase depending upon initial levels which were not detectable) occurred in as little as two hours in some cases. The initial fall in LH concentration was likewise extremely rapid. In fact, the return to lower levels ($<$ 100 mμg B160/ml) was as rapid as the rise in the concentration of LH. However, the shortest time observed for the serum LH to decrease by 50% approximated $1\frac{1}{2}$ hours. This is about 3 times as long as the disappearance rate observed during the decline of the peak in the proestrous rat.

There appeared to be a rise in the concentration of LH in pituitary glands the day before delivery and a significant decrease occurred during the first 10 hours after delivery. However, the concentration continued to decrease between 10 hours and 24 hours after delivery, eventually reaching a concentration only 1/3 that of pre-delivery levels.

Disappearance Rate of LH in Intact and Castrated Rats

Sequential bleedings from individual rats following hypophysectomy have indicated that the "half-life" for endogenous LH does not change appreciably between the first and the 35th day following orchidectomy (7). A similar (approximately 30 minute) half-life has been observed in individual female castrates one month after ovariectomy and (in preliminary experiments) in non-castrated proestrous and postpartum rats (7). With the possible exception of the intact male, in which adequate determinations have not yet been made, the 30 minute half life for endogenous LH thus appears to be relatively constant, at least in those situations in which serum LH concentrations are increased above 40 mμg B160/ml.

ACKNOWLEDGMENTS

The authors wish to acknowledge the technical assistance of Mrs. H. Hepburn, Mrs. K. Kersey, and Mrs. E. Schaefer.

These studies were supported in part by a research grant from the National Institute of Child Health and Human Development of the USPHS (NIH-HD) 2193.

REFERENCES

1. Parlow, A.F., S.E. Monroe, and A.R. Midgley, Jr., Fed Proc 26: 533, 1967.
2. Monroe, S.E., A.F. Parlow, and A.R. Midgley, Jr., Submitted for publication.
3. Niswender, G.D., A.R. Midgley, Jr., S.E. Monroe, and L.E. Reichert, Jr., Proc Soc Exptl Biol Med, In Press, 1968.

4. Gay, V.L., Endocrinology 81: 1177, 1967.

5. Piacsek, B.E. and J. Meites, Endocrinology 81: 535, 1967.
6. Ramirez, V.D. and S.M. McCann, Endocrinology 73: 193, 1963.
7. Gay, V.L. and A.R. Midgley, Jr., Unpublished.
8. Monroe, S.E., R.W. Rebar and A.R. Midgley, Jr., Fed Proc 27: 371, (abstract #886), 1968.
9. Callantine, M.R. and R.R. Humphrey, Endocrinology 77: 921, 1965.
10. Wilson, E.D. and M.X. Zarrow, J Reprod Fertil 3: 148, 1962.
11. Rebar, R.W. and P.K. Nakane, Fed Proc 27: 371, (abstract #887), 1968.

SOLID-PHASE RADIOIMMUNOASSAY OF
OVINE, BOVINE AND MURINE LUTEINIZING HORMONE

MAX S. AMOSS, JR. AND ROGER GUILLEMIN, BAYLOR UNIVERSITY COLLEGE OF MEDICINE, HOUSTON, TEXAS.

INTRODUCTION

The development of the principle of isotope dilution in immunological assays based on the decrease of the binding of radioactivity-labeled hormone to specific antibody in the presence of non-labeled hormone has led to methodology capable of detecting amounts of protein or polypeptide hormone in the range of 10^{-9} - 10^{-12} grams. Various techniques have been proposed for the separation of antibody-bound hormone from that which remains free in the incubation medium. The most widely used at the present are a) the charcoal separation technique (1), b) the double antibody method in which the soluble hormone-antibody complex is precipitated by the addition of excess amounts of anti-γ-globulin (2,3,4,5); c) solid-phase radioimmunoassay which is the newest technique introduced in this field and is based on the principle of the binding of the specific antibody to an insoluble matrix (6,7); the labeled and unlabeled antigen then complex to the antibody which is adsorbed to the insoluble polymer. It then becomes a simple task of removing the "free" antigen by a series of decantations and washings. It has been reported that antibodies to human chorionic gonadotropin and human growth hormone can be adsorbed to dextran polymers (8) and unsubstituted polymers of polystyrene and polypropylene (9) available in specially prepared disks. We are reporting on a similar method using as the solid phase matrix a commercially available polystyrene test tube which has greatly simplified the practical approach to this method; with this technique, utilizing the concept of disequilibration (10), it is possible to detect as little as 50 picograms of ovine luteinizing hormone.

MATERIALS AND METHODS

Hormone preparations.

a) Purification of ovine and bovine LH was performed by Dr. D.N. Ward (11). Potency of the ovine LH (designated AMO-5-835) as determined by the ovarian ascorbic acid depletion (OAAD) assay (13) is 2.21 times that of NIH-LH-S1 (11). The bovine LH (MSA-3-125) also supplied by Dr. Ward had a potency of 1.77 times NIH-LH-S11 (unpublished data).

b) Rat LH (DNW-8-37) was purified in collaboration with Dr. D.N. Ward according to a method which is reported separately (12). The potency of this preparation when compared to NIH-LH-S11 is 2.6 when studied by the OAAD bioassay.

c) These materials were dissolved in 0.1M phosphate buffer, pH 7.4, to obtain a concentration of 1 mg LH/ml and stored frozen in 50 μl aliquots (1 μg/μl) in sealed ampoules. One ampoule is opened for the iodination procedure which requires 5 μg; another 10 μg aliquot is taken and diluted with 0.1% BSA in 0.1M phosphate - 0.15M NaCl buffer, pH 7.4, to obtain a concentration of 1 μg/ml. This solution of hormone is used as a stock solution from which further dilutions are made on the day of the assay to be used in preparing samples for the standard curve which is part of each assay.

Production of antisera.
        All hormone preparations were mixed in a thick paste with an equal
volume of complete Freund's adjuvant to give a final concentration of 2 mg
hormone/ml mixture. White Leghorn roosters approximately 5-6 months old
were injected with 0.5 ml of this mixture once a week in the comb for 6 weeks.
One week after the last injection, 20 ml of heparinized venous blood were
withdrawn from each animal through the external jugular vein under ether
anesthesia and immediately centrifuged at 170 xg in the cold (+4⁰ C). Each
plasma aliquot was decomplemented in a 56⁰ C water bath for 30 minutes and
centrifuged at 40,000 xg for 20 minutes at 4⁰ C. The antisera were absorbed
2 times with serum (50 μl/ml) obtained from hypophysectomized rat (8 days after
hypophysectomy) and centrifuged after each absorption as above.

Biological inactivation of LH by anti-LH antibodies.
        One of the first experiments conducted after the production of anti-
sera was to determine whether the biological activity of purified sheep LH as
measured by the bioassay based on ovarian ascorbic acid depletion could be
inhibited by incubation of sheep LH with the antiserum to ovine LH obtained
as above. To 1 ml aliquots of NIH-LH-S11 (13.2 μg/ml) was added 1 ml of a)
undiluted antiserum, b) antiserum diluted 1:10, and c) antiserum diluted
1:100. The solutions were thoroughly mixed on a Vortex mixer, incubated for
30 minutes at 37⁰ C then kept at 4⁰ C overnight. The samples were then centrifuged at 2500 xg for 30 minutes at 4⁰ C. A control sample of LH standard
(without antiserum) was treated in a similar manner. Aliquots of these
various preparations were taken following centrifugation and injected in rats
prepared for the OAAD assay (13); the design was that of a multiple 4-point
assay conducted in randomized blocks; the doses of LH (control and antibody
treated) were 0.3 and 0.9 μg per rat; all calculations and statistical analyses
of the bioassays were conducted as in (13) using the program EXBIOL (14) on
an IBM 7094.

Radioiodination.
        The various hormones were radioiodinated with carrier free I125 (Iso
Serve) by a modification of the method of Greenwood (15,16) using chloramine-
T as an oxidizing agent. Specific radioactivities of approximately 80 μc/μg
protein were found to be optimal for this isotope and in accordance with
theoretical calculations, yielded an average of 1 atom of I125/molecule of
LH. By allowing the oxidation by chloramine-T to take place for only 15
seconds, "damage" of the molecule of LH was kept to less than 20% and a total
uptake of the added iodine averaged approximately 80%; this was determined by
chromatoelectrophoresis on Whatmann 2 MC paper using barbital buffer, ionic
strength = 0.05, the electrophoresis being carried out at 320 volts for 2
hours at 4⁰ C. After taking an aliquot for the chromatoelectrophoresis as
above, the remainder of the iodination mixture was placed on a 1 x 30 cm
column of Sephadex G-50 equilibrated in 1.5% bovine serum albumin (BSA) and
eluted with 0.1M phosphate buffer (pH 7.4) to achieve a separation of the
iodinated hormone from the free iodine and other inorganic reagents. The
iodinated hormone was diluted in 0.1% BSA in 0.1M phosphate buffer in 0.15M
NaCl (pH 7.4).

Radioimmunoassay.
        One ml aliquots of diluted antisera (the diluent is barbital buffer,
ionic strength = 0.1, pH 9.0) are added to polystyrene tubes 15 x 75 mm
(Falcon Plastics, Los Angeles, California, catalogue no. 2058) and incubated

overnight at 4° C. The antisera are decanted and saved and the tubes, now coated with the antibodies, are washed 2 times with normal saline and 1 time with 10% normal rabbit serum. Various volumes of diluent (0.1% BSA in 0.1M phosphate buffer - 0.15M NaCl) are now added to each tube so that the final volume (see below) will be 1 ml; known amounts of unlabeled hormone are then added in a range from 0.1 ng to 5 ng in solutions at 10 ng/ml or 100 ng/ml. Plasma samples (0.1 ml) are added to the remainder of the assay tubes. All standard hormones and unknowns are prepared in triplicate. In those instances where pituitary homogenates or pituitary incubation fluids are being assayed, 100 μl of hypophysectomized plasma is added. After careful stirring of all fluids (Vortex mixer) the tubes are placed in an incubator for 24 hours at 37° C. At this time the iodinated hormone is added, usually in a concentration which yields approximately 10,000 CPM/50 μl, and the tubes are again incubated at 37° C overnight (16 hours). The solutions are aspirated from the tubes which are then washed twice with tap water and counted in an automatic deep well scintillation counter. The digital count rate is fed directly from the scaler into an IBM key punch and the cards are then sent to an IBM 7094 computer which computes the equation of the standard curve (13) with the confidence limits of the slope and then proceeds to calculate the ng of LH/ml. This curve is obtained by plotting the ratio B_o/B on the ordinate (B_o: total number of counts bound to antibody in the absence of unlabeled LH; B: number of counts bound in the presence of a known amount of LH) and the doses of LH in ng, on the abscissa.

RESULTS

Biological inactivation of LH by anti-LH antibodies.

    The biological activity of LH as measured by the ovarian ascorbic acid depletion assay was completely suppressed in the solutions of LH incubated with both the undiluted antiserum and that diluted 1/10. In this experiment 13.2 μg of LH was rendered biologically inactive by incubating with an antiserum diluted 1/10. It will be shown that when using antibody dilutions of 1/10,000 in the radioimmunoassay measurements of concentrations of 1 to 10 ng LH can be made; thus considering either of the end points, it can be concluded that the amounts of LH complexed by the antiserum appear to be closely related. In other words, biological and immunochemical competence appear to be similar, with this particular antiserum when compared indirectly in these experiments.

Table 1.

Inactivation of ovine-LH by anti-OLH antiserum as determined by OAAD. Protocol #8408.

Treatment	No.of Rats	Adjusted Mean ± S.E.	P
Control	5	115.33±3.9	
0.3 μg NIH-LH-S11	5	102.18±3.9	*
0.9 μg NIH-LH-S11	5	85.02±3.9	**
0.3 μg NIH-LH-S11 + Undil Ab	5	123.58±3.9	-
0.9 μg NIH-LH-S11 + Undil Ab	5	118.37±4.2	-
0.3 μg NIH-LH-S11 + Ab dil 1/10	5	117.44±3.9	-
0.9 μg NIH-LH-S11 + Ab dil 1/10	5	116.13±4.0	-
0.3 μg NIH-LH-S11 + Ab dil 1/100	5	106.49±3.9	-
0.9 μg NIH-LH-S11 + Ab dil 1/100	5	84.31±3.9	**

Legend for Table 1. Adjusted mean ± S.E. = mean of ovarian ascorbic acid
content (in μg ascorbic acid) of second ovary adjusted by covariance to the
ascorbic acid content of the first ovary (13). S.E., standard error. P,
probability of statistical significance when compared to the control group
by the multiple comparison test of Dunnett; - not significant; * 0.05 level;
** 0.01 level.

Standard curves obtained with the solid-phase radioimmunoassay.

        Standard curves are shown in which ovine, bovine or murine LH is re-
acted with homologous antisera (Fig.1). The curves are plotted in two ways;
a) as the percentage of radioiodinated hormone bound to the adsorbed antiserum
(100% taken as that bound when no unlabeled LH is present) which approaches a
hyperbolic function over a small range of hormone concentrations, and b) the
reciprocal of the "percent-bound" which is a straight line function over the
same range of hormone concentrations. The latter method of plotting these
results produces equations that are easier to handle statistically although
it is possible with the proper mathematics to handle the hyperbola. When
dealing with the straight line function, the slope and its confidence limits
are given. To date the ovine LH preparation AMO-5-835 has given slopes ranging from 0.9 to 1.4 with overlapping confidence limits of the slopes between
assays done at different times. One is immediately impressed by the very low
slope obtained with the rat LH preparation DNW-8-37 even in the presence of
an antibody 10 times more concentrated than that of the anti-OLH. The same
low slope is seen with the bovine LH in which an antibody dilution of 1/25,000
was used. This may reflect a lower standard free energy of change (ΔF^o)
according to the terminology of Berson and Yalow (17). This phenomenon in no
way invalidates the assay and is merely a function of the antiserum that is
available at the present time.

Cross reactions of TSH, FSH and prolactin in the radioimmunoassay for ovine LH.

        Ovine NIH-TSH-S4 (LH contamination 0.015 units/mg by bioassay) was
reacted with anti-OLH using a tracer concentration of I^{125} which yielded 10,000
CPM or approximately 0.1 ng. The curve is plotted using ng of LH contamination as the ordinate (Fig.2A). If no cross reaction existed the slope should
be similar to that of a standard curve using purified LH. Since the slope for
the TSH standard curve is approximately 7 times greater than that of the LH
curve one must draw the conclusion that a cross reaction between ovine TSH and
ovine LH when using this homologous antiserum did exist. Subsequently, the antiserum was absorbed with increasing amounts of NIH-TSH-S4 in an effort to eliminate this cross reaction. Anti-OLH absorbed with 10 μg TSH/ml of antiserum
yielded a slope of 4.26 when tested as above and when a total of 17.5 μg/ml of
TSH was used for absorption a slope of 1.78 was obtained. If cross reaction to
a "common core" had existed, this decrease in slope would not have been seen.
The absorption with TSH, which precipitated some of the TSH antibodies, brought
about an increase in the anti-OLH titer; the usable dilution of antiserum increasing from 1/10,000 to 1/40,000. At present it requires 50 to 100 times
more TSH than LH, on a weight basis, to produce the same decrease in iodinated
LH bound to antibody even considering the LH contamination as given above.
Absorption of the antisera with TSH is continuing and will continue until the
cross reaction is eliminated.

        The same type of protocol was used with ovine NIH-FSH-S4 (LH contami-
nation - 0.006 units/mg by bioassay) (Fig.2B). In this case the slopes obtained from the purified OLH and the NIH-FSH-S4 are identical indicating that

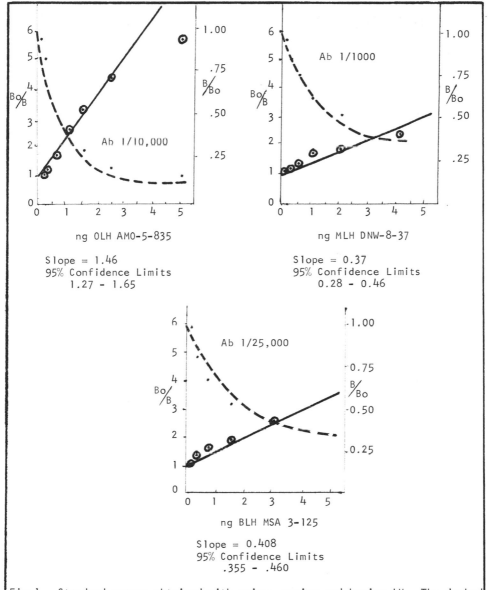

Fig.1. Standard curves obtained with ovine, murine and bovine LH. The dashed line is the curve obtained by plotting the percentage of I-125 bound to antibody using that bound at 0 LH as 100%. The solid line is the rectified curve found by dividing the I-125 bound at 0 LH by that bound at various doses of LH standard. (OLH=ovine LH, MLH=murine LH, BLH=bovine LH)

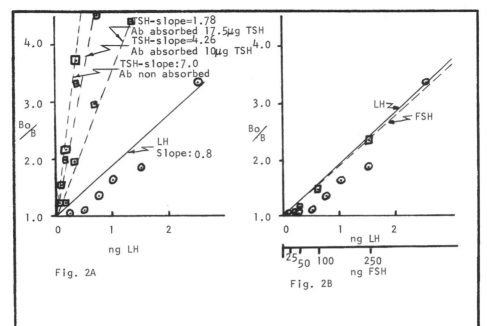

Fig. 2A

Fig. 2B

Fig.2. These graphs show the cross reaction between LH (AMO 5-835) and NIH-TSH-S4 (Fig.2A) or NIH-FSH-S4 (Fig.2B). Both the TSH and FSH are plotted in terms of their respective LH contamination.

no cross reaction with FSH exists when using this particular antiserum. More than 1000 times as much FSH as LH was needed to produce a minimal depletion in the percentage of iodinated LH bound to antibody, which could easily be accounted for by the LH contamination of the FSH used in the assay.

No cross reaction between LH and prolactin was apparent when as much as 1 µg of ovine prolactin (NIH-P-S5) was used, which is 10,000 times the concentration needed for a significant depletion in the amount of antibody bound I^{125} LH.

Correlation between bioassay (OAAD) and the RIA.
        In this study an experiment was designed in which the relative immuno-chemical reactivity between two LH preparations of known biological potency was studied. The two LH preparations involved were the highly purified ovine LH supplied by Dr. D.N. Ward, AMO-5-835 which is 2.21 times NIH-LH-S11 which is 0.81 times NIH-LH-S1 as determined by the same assay. In ascertaining the difference in immuno-reactivity between these preparations various dilutions of each were reacted in the radioimmunoassay as previously described. From data obtained on the decrease in antibody bound radioactive LH with the two preparations, the slopes were calculated. The AMO-5-835 preparation yielded

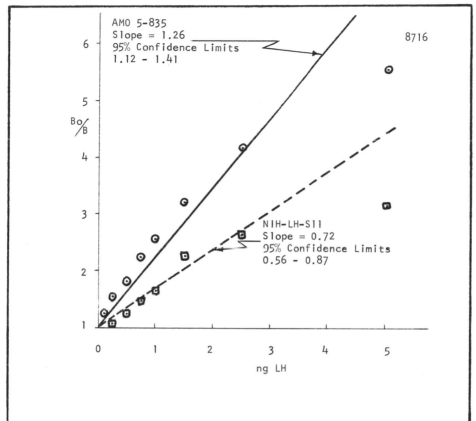

Fig.3. Standard curves obtained with highly purified ovine LH (AMO 5-835 - 2.2 x NIH-LH-S1) and NIH-LH-S11 standard. Antibody dilution was 1/10,000 and the amount of iodinated LH added was 0.05 ng.

a slope of 1.26 (1.12-1.41) whereas the NIH-LH-S11 gave a slope of 0.72 (0.56-0.87) as seen in Fig.3. The slope derived from the higher purity LH (AMO-5-835) is 1.75 times greater than that obtained with the NIH-LH-S11 standard, indicating that higher immunoreactivity as well as higher biological activity exists with the former preparation. That similar differences are to be found in biological potency and in immunological reactivity is further evidence for the valid use of the radioimmunoassay as a measure of LH in biological fluids.

Measurement of LH in sheep serum by the solid phase radioimmunoassay.
        Aliquots of 25, 50, 100, 200 and 400 μl from a pool of serum (ovari-
ectomized ewes) were assayed in triplicate and the LH concentration determined from a standard curve obtained with NIH-LH-S11. When ng of LH are
plotted against the volume of the aliquot a linear function with a slope of
exactly 1.0 is obtained. The TSH content of the serum as determined by bioassay was less than 0.08 mU/ml which would have no effect in the radioimmunoassay.

        Similar experiments are underway in which aliquots of pituitary homo-
genates are similarly studied to ascertain the existence of a linear function
between the amount of LH present and the dose of pituitary extract used. The
ratios of potency between the radioimmunoassay and the OAAD bioassay will also
be determined in the case of the extracts of the pituitary. This convenient
and simple parameter will not be meaningful when applied to measurement of
plasma LH, in view of the absence of specificity of the OAAD assay for LH when
using plasma (18,19,20).

Use of anti-OLH to determine murine LH.
        Based on the earlier observations in Li's laboratory (21) that a cross
reaction between ovine LH and rat LH could be demonstrated, experiments were
performed to determine whether this relationship would be shown with the antiserum produced here in chicken, and whether it would be of sufficient potency
to allow a sensitive radioimmunoassay of rat LH using anti-OLH. With an antiserum dilution of 1/5000, standard curves were obtained which yielded slopes
of 0.85 over a range of rat LH concentrations of 0.05 ng/ml to 2.5 ng/ml (Fig.4).
The increased slope obtained with the use of the anti-OLH antibodies over that

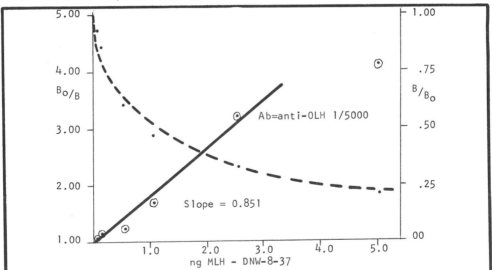

Fig.4.   Standard curves obtained by using anti-OLH antisera to determine murine
LH. The dashed line represents the curve obtained by plotting the percentage
of I125 LH bound to antibody. The solid line represents the reciprocal of the
"percent" bound.

found when using the anti-MLH antisera available at the present time (see Fig.1) shows that the heterologous system provides a more sensitive assay (than the isologous murine system) for the determination of rat LH. Theoretically, the use of a heterologous antiserum also decreases the probability of any "common core" cross reactions with other murine pituitary hormones. We are now using routinely the heterologous antiserum assay for rat LH until such time as a rat LH antiserum of equal or greater sensitivity becomes available.

CONCLUSIONS

The prime intent of this short note is to describe in detail the protocol used in a simple, routine, solid phase radioimmunoassay for rat LH, sheep LH and bovine LH. Experiments are reported in which the immunoassay for LH is more than 1000 times more sensitive than the bioassay now used by most investigators. The absence of cross reactions between FSH or prolactin and LH is shown and the ability to decrease the cross reaction with TSH by absorption of the antiserum with that hormone is reported; it is envisioned that a finite amount of TSH will be found which will bring about the precipitation of all of the TSH specific antibodies present. Similarities in both biological and immunochemical potencies of several ovine LH preparations have been observed; a linear relationship between the amount of serum tested in the immunoassay and the concentration of LH is reported. The use of an antiserum to ovine LH to determine murine LH is also reported; this heterologous system is shown to be more sensitive than the homologous system using the anti-MLH antisera presently available. The solid-phase radioimmunoassay as described offers a simple, sensitive and reliable assay for the determination of LH in biological fluids.

ACKNOWLEDGEMENTS

We would like to express our gratitude to Drs. Knobil and Neill, School of Medicine, University of Pittsburgh and to Drs. Schalch and Reichlin, School of Medicine and Dentistry, University of Rochester who generously provided advice and experience to one of us (M.A.) in the early phases of these studies. We are also indebted to Drs. Berson and Yalow, V.A. Hospital, Bronx, New York who, some years ago, instructed the other one of us (R.G.) in the principles and mechanics of radioimmunoassays.

Research supported by Research Grant AM 08290, Training Grant GM 956 and FR 00254 to Common Research Computer Facilities, Texas Medical Center, Houston, Texas.

REFERENCES

1. Herbert, V., K-S Lau, C.W. Gottlieb and S.J. Bleicher, J. Clin. Endocr.
    23:1375, 1965.
2. Odell, W.D., G.T. Ross and P.L. Rayford, Metabolism 15:287, 1966.
3. Faiman, C. and R.J. Ryan, Proc. Soc. Exp. Biol. Med 125:1130, 1967.
4. Midgley, A.R., Jr., Endocrinology 70:10, 1966.
5. Pelletier, J., G. Kann, J. Dolais and G. Rosselin, C.R. Acad. Sci. (Paris)
    April, 1968, in press.
6. Wide, L., R. Axen and J. Porath, Immunochemistry, Pergamon Press, 4:381,
    1967.
7. Catt, K.J., H.D. Niall and G.W. Tregear, Nature 213:825, 1967.
8. Wide, L. and J. Porath, Biochim. Biophys. Acta 130:257, 1966.
9. Catt, K.J. and G.W. Tregear, Science 158:1570, 1967.
10. Samols, E. and D. Bilkus, Proc. Soc. Exp. Biol. Med. 115:79, 1963.
11. Ward, D.N., M. Adams-Mayne, N. Ray, D.E. Balke, J.A. Coffey and M.
    Showalter, Gen. & Comp. Endocr. 8:44, 1967.
12. Ward, D.N., M. Amoss, C. Sweeney, W. Vale, J. Kleber and R. Guillemin,
    Workshop Conf. on Gonadotropins, San Jose de Vista Hermosa, Mexico, 1968.
13. Sakiz, E. and R. Guillemin, Endocrinology 72:804, 1963.
14. Sakiz, E., Proc. 2nd Intern. Cong. Endocrinology, London, vol. 1, p. 225,
    Aug. 1964.
15. Amoss, M.S., Jr., Ph.D. Thesis, Baylor University College of Medicine, 1968.
16. Amoss, M.S., Jr. and R. Guillemin, in preparation.
17. Berson, S.A., R.S. Yalow, S.M. Glick and J. Roth, Metabolism 13:1135, 1964.
18. Pelletier, J., C.R. Acad. Sci. (Paris) 258:5979, 1964.
19. Gibson, W.R., A.I. Frankel, G.W. Graber and A.V. Nalbandov, Proc. Soc. Exp.
    Biol. Med. 120:143, 1965.
20. Guillemin, R., Ann. Rev. Physiol. 29:313, 1967.
21. Trenkle, A., C.H. Li, K.K. Sadri and H. Robertson, Arch. Biochem. Biophys.
    99:288, 1962.

DISCUSSION

BOGDANOVE: I would like to expand on what Drs. Niswender and
Midgley have said about their 0:0 system for radioimmunoassay
(RIA) of rat LH. In the course of setting up this system in our
own laboratory, Dr. Makoto Yamamoto, Mr. N. D. Diebel and I have
encountered two rather unexpected findings which we think are
very important features of the RIA system. These findings are
illustrated by the accompanying table, which shows bioassay-RIA
comparison of 3 pools of material we prepared for use as working
standards for the RIA.

These materials, taken from ovariectomized rats, were: crude
anterior lobe homogenate (α), plasma (β) and serum (γ). I
should mention that we used distilled water to prepare the initial
pituitary homogenate (concentration $\cong$ 20 mg. wet weight/ml.);
subsequent dilutions were in saline (for bioassay) or phosphate
-buffered saline - 10% BSA (PBS-BSA, for RIA). We chose to
evaluate these 3 potential RIA standards because we were aware
of the possibility that serum, plasma and pituitary may produce
dissimilar dose-response curves in an RIA. Since we expected

that we might have to develop a set of conversion factors to correlate our RIA results not only with Midgley's findings but also with our own bioassay work, we included graded doses of Midgley's B 147c rat LH standard (not shown in table) in some of our RIAs and set up NIH-LH-S11 dose-response curves in every assay of each type.

| Assay | λ | Relative Potency* (Confidence Limits) | | | Ratio |
		α	β	γ	$\alpha:\gamma$
OAAD Parlow 2x2**	.28	10.3(4.9-18.9)			
2x1†	.12	7.84(5.5-11.0)	0.042(0.03-0.06)	0.043(0.03-0.06)	182:1
OAAD Bog-Gay 2x2	.12	5.5(4.2-7.3)	0.038(0.02-0.05)	0.034(0.02-0.05)	161:1
2x1	.10	6.3(4.5-8.5)	0.052(0.03-0.08)	0.039(0.03-0.08)	161:1
OAAD Bog-Gay 2x2	.22	6.8(3.8-11.6)	0.062(0.03-0.12)	0.097(0.05-0.17)	70:1
2x1	.23	6.1(2.6-15.9)	0.077(0.03-0.29)	0.071(0.03-0.23)	86:1
RIA-B-1		9.36	0.051	0.053	175:1
RIA-B-4		7.97	0.046	0.048	165:1
RIA-B-5		6.76		0.049	137:1
RIA-B-6		7.36			

λ: index of precision; *in terms of NIH-LH-S11; **two doses of standard and two doses of unknown; † two doses of standard and one dose of unknown.

The upper part of the table gives the results of 3 bioassays. The first row shows a conventional "Parlow" OAAD assay. Since such an assay has only a marginal capacity for estimation of serum LH activity, we could do only "3-point" (2 x 1) analyses on β and γ. We did do a "4-point" (2 x 2) analysis of α, but the results were not too satisfactory because of poor parallelism. The second row shows replication in a "Bogdanove-Gay" OAAD assay (Endocrinology 81: 1104, 1967). In this more sensitive assay, the $\alpha:\gamma$ ratio, by either "3" or "4-point" analysis, was 161:1 (actually, 161,000:1). The third bioassay was one of our poor ones (λ >.2). Comparison of it with the other two suggests that it gave falsely high estimates for the blood samples (β and γ), reducing the $\alpha:\gamma$ ratio. The lower part of the table shows 4 RIA studies of these same materials. The $\alpha:\gamma$ ratios derived from these assays (and others we have subsequently performed) are obviously indistinguishable from those obtained in the better two bioassays.

One reason we find this exciting is that in our analysis of LH
secretory kinetics (Endocrinology 82: 359, 1968) a great deal
hinges on the question of whether equal amounts of intrapituitary
(stored) and extrapituitary (circulating) LH have equal activities
in the assay system used. Unless they do, of course, the calculations Gay and I presented are invalid. While our present results
cannot prove that a molecule of LH stored in the pituitary has
the same biological activity as a molecule of LH in the circulation, they seem to increase greatly the probability that this is
so. To suppose otherwise we would have to assume that any acti-
vation (or inhibition) of the LH molecule, as it passes from one
compartment to the other, is of such a nature that it affects both
a biological and an immunological assay system equally.

These findings become even more remarkable when we consider the
fact that all the potency estimates shown in the table are given
in terms of NIH-LH-S11. These estimates were not obtained by
conversion but by reading the response directly against an NIH-
LH-S11 curve included in each of the assays shown. The fact that
the relative potencies of all 4 of these materials (NIH-LH, α ,
β and γ) are the same by both the OAAD assay and the O:O rat
RIA is perhaps fortuitous. However, it obviously means that we
can compare our RIA results and bioassay results without conversion,
since we can read the RIA findings, like the bioassay findings,
directly against the NIH standard.

I should add that we have confirmed these findings in an
experiment which included a study of whether centrifugation of
a pituitary homogenate affects its activity in either of these
assay systems. We found that removing the solid matter from a
distilled water (pH about 6 to 7) homogenate of anterior
pituitaries did not detectably reduce its potency, estimated by
direct comparison with NIH-LH-S11, in either LH assay system.
In other words, our routine extraction procedure probably makes
all the intrapituitary LH available for assay. This point lends
further confidence to our LH "turnover" calculations.

NISWENDER: Dr. Bogdanove has pointed out one of the advantages
of the O:O rat LH RIA. It is possible to use ovine LH standards
directly to quantitate rat LH in this assay system. The bioassay
potency of our standard preparation of rat LH is 0.17 NIH-LH-S1
units per mg., whereas the radioimmunoassay potency of this
preparation, using NIH-LH-S12 as a standard, is 0.173 NIH-LH-S1
units per mg. We feel that this relationship to the ovine
standards is indeed fortuitous for rat LH since this same relationship was not true when comparison of the ovine standard was made
with either bovine or porcine preparations.

RYAN: Dr. Niswender, I noticed those very nice titers that you
showed - one at 1:40,000 and another at 1:30,000 - and I wonder
whether they are initial or final titers? I should also like to
know whether these antisera will be available for other investigators.

NISWENDER: Those were initial titers. In other words we added 200 microliters of antiserum at a 1:40,000 dilution. The final reaction mixture had a total volume of 1 ml. so the final dilution was 1:100,000. As to the availability of the reagents, Dr. Midgley, Dr. Reichert and myself feel that we have developed these assays as research tools and that the reagents will be supplied to competent investigators as adequate supplies become available.

RYAN: That was an unfair question, but you gave a generous reply.

STEINBERGER: Dr. Midgley in the experiments where animals were treated with testosterone and estrogen, you report a drop in plasma LH level. Did you measure the pituitary levels of LH in these animals?

MIDGLEY: These were pilot experiments designed to determine whether LH measured by radioimmunoassay would respond to various treatments as one would anticipate. The measurements were made in sera obtained from sequential bleedings of individual rats. We did not sacrifice the rats to measure pituitary concentrations.

ODELL: I have one comment on Dr. Midgley's paper. You have stated that after castration the blood level of LH rises slowly. The same observation is true in the estrogen-suppressed human female. If a castrated woman is suppressed with estrogens and the drug is then discontinued, the LH levels remain low for perhaps 3 to 6 days before they begin to rise. I should like to ask, what are the effects of androgen and estrogen on LH in the normal female rat?

MIDGLEY: Unfortunately we have no data on that.

LUNENFELD: When you say that after delivery LH rises, what do you mean exactly by delivery? Just when delivery of the first animal starts or when it finishes? The second question concerns the LH rise before estrus - how do you determine pro-estrus - by vaginal smears or do you have other methods?

MIDGLEY: The estimate of time after delivery is inexact. It represents our best estimate of the time following delivery of the last pup. Quite obviously, the trigger for release of LH could be any one of numerous events occurring prior to, during or after delivery. Regarding your second question, we evaluated pro-estrus by examination of vaginal smears, by examining the uterus for the presence of ballooning, and by noting the absence of eggs in the fallopian tubes.

BURGOS: Do you have any data on the circadian variation of serum LH in the male?

MIDGLEY: We have no data regarding circadian rhythm of LH in the male rat. There is, as you know, a discrepancy between our data and that of Drs. Faiman and Ryan. We have not yet been able to demonstrate the existence of circadian rhythm in men. We do have data which indicate the existence of a diurnal rhythm in LH and FSH during the follicular phase of the human menstrual cycle.

BELL: Dr. Midgley, do you have any information on the time interval between the peak of LH in rats serum and the occurrence of ovulation or the presence of ova in the oviducts?

MIDGLEY: We have no direct information on this point. However, since we have found a peak in LH concentration in serum during the afternoon of pro-estrus as would be anticipated on the basis of numerous other studies, I would assume that our rats are behaving like other rats and are ovulating during the early morning of estrus.

ROBYN: Dr. Parlow has shown that there was no cross-reaction between human FSH and rat FSH. I wonder if it is the same for human LH and rat LH? Two years ago Monroe and Midgley (Fed. Proc. 25, 1966, 315) and more recently Leleux, Robyn and Herlant (C.R. Acad. Sc. Paris, 1967), have shown that it is possible to see, by immunofluorescence, the gonadotropic cells in the rat pituitary using antisera from rabbits immunized with human chorionic gonadotropin.

MIDGLEY: As Dr. Niswender mentioned, we have not been able to demonstrate a strong cross-reaction with human LH using any of the non-human gonadotropin radioimmunoassay systems available to us at the moment. These include the RR rat LH radioimmunoassay, the OO rat LH radioimmunoassay, the OO ovine LH radioimmunoassay, the BB bovine LH radioimmunoassay and the PP porcine LH radio-immunoassay. However, it is quite clear that antisera against human chorionic gonadotropin can cross react with rat LH. This cross-reaction is very weak and requires a highly sensitive test system such as immunohistochemical analysis. The reason that this method readily indicates the existence of weak cross-reactions is that there is nothing to compete with the interaction between the antigen in the tissue and the antiserum used for localization of the antigen.

RYAN: I think that this again illustrates the fact that radio-immunoassay systems, neutralization, hemagglutination and complement fixation systems are all different.

REICHERT: An important criterion for evaluating gonadotropin preparations is the FSH/LH ratio. Using the purification procedure described earlier and pituitaries from 293 castrated male rats treated after castration with testosterone propionate and thyroglobulin, it was possible to prepare a rat FSH fraction with an FSH:LH ratio greater than 160,000. No LH contamination could be detected by radioimmunoassay, being less than 0.00043 NIH-LH-S1 units/mg.

MIDGLEY: I would like to indicate that we have been able to obtain from one rabbit an antiserum against ovine FSH which appears to react sufficiently well with Dr. Reichert's labeled rat FSH to be useful in development of a rat FSH radioimmunoassay. To date, the dose response curves for all tested preparations, including serum, have been parallel. The relative potency estimates we have obtained on preparations varying widely in FSH/TSH and LH/FSH ratios are as we anticipated on the basis of prior bioassay results.

RYAN: It seems to me that there might be very good use of an immunoassay system that could be applied to the guinea pig, which has a long functioning corpus luteum. Has the assay system developed by Dr. Niswender been checked to see if there is any cross-reactivity of useful degree with the guinea pig?

NISWENDER: At the present time I have some guinea pig pituitaries and plan to check their cross reactivity in the OO LH assay using the antibody which cross reacts with rat LH. I am interested in the relationship between the uterus and the corpus luteum and the guinea pig is a suitable animal for studies of this sort. I am hoping that I shall be able to develop a radioimmunoassay for guinea pig LH.

LUNENFELD: Dr. Amoss, how much chloramine-T did you use in your labeling when the reaction period was only 15 seconds? What was your yield of labeling after the separation? And, what was the variation between the different tubes?

AMOSS: The concentration of Chloramine-T used in the iodination was 50 µg delivered in 20 µl of 0.05M phosphate buffer. Oxidation for 15 seconds results in approximately 80% of the added I^{125} coupled to protein. "Damage" to LH is never greater than 20% which means that of the 5 µg of LH iodinated, 4 µg of immunochemically active hormone remains. As for your final question, I can best answer it by giving you the results of a typical standard curve, each point done in triplicate, in which I will give the mean and the range of CPM. This happens to be a standard curve using NIH-LH-S11.

Treatment	Mean (CPM)	Range (CPM)
Control (no unlabeled LH)	4599	4292-4854
0.1 ng NIH-LH-S11	3866	3704-4032
0.25 ng "	2901	2724-3069
0.50 ng "	1846	1821-1880
1.00 ng "	1184	1139-1255
2.00 ng "	752	684-834
4.00 ng "	427	420-434
8.00 ng "	286	281-293

SAXENA: Dr. Catt visited our laboratory and demonstrated to us his radioimmunoassay techniques for LH and GH. Both discs and tubes could be used in the assay, but we encountered significant variation in individual discs used for each point. One must, therefore, use 8 to 10 discs per point to arrive at a reasonable average.

STEVENS: We have studied two radioimmunoassay systems for FSH and LH. One system utilized antigens from human pituitaries and the other used antigens from monkey pituitaries. Antisera for both systems were raised in rabbits from the respective FSH and LH preparations. The specificity of the human FSH assay was evaluated only by testing the ability of human LH to react in this system and the LH assay was evaluated only by testing the ability of human FSH to respond in the LH system. These experiments showed the assays to be specific. The monkey assays were likewise evaluated and found to be specific. Using these four assay systems we studied the ability of FSH and LH preparations from four different species to displace the labeled hormone in each assay system. In our studies with human FSH radioimmunoassay there was no significant displacement or competition with human I^{131} labeled hormone by monkey, baboon or rat FSH. However, in the human LH radioimmunoassay system there was significant displacement of the I^{131} labeled human LH by monkey, rat and particularly baboon LH. The response lines produced by increasing dosages of the LH preparations were not parallel with those produced by the human hormone. In the monkey FSH radioimmunoassay system there was no significant displacement of the labeled hormone by the unlabeled hormone from rat and human FSH preparations. However, there was a significant and parallel displacement by baboon FSH materials. A similar observation was found with the monkey LH radioassay system inasmuch as only slight displacement was seen by human and rat LH preparations but a significant and parallel response was seen with the baboon preparations.

In summary, it can be tentatively concluded, although the specificity of these systems needs to be studied in more detail, that neither the rat, monkey nor baboon preparations can be assayed in human radioimmunoassay systems. Nevertheless, it would appear that it is very probable that the monkey FSH and LH radioimmunoassay systems can be used effectively to measure baboon FSH and LH.

RAO: I wish to present very briefly a summary of our immunological and biological studies with human and animal gonadotropins. We have used HCG, HMG and human pituitary FSH and LH, kindly supplied by Dr. Wilhelmi, ovine, bovine, porcine LH and FSH obtained from the NIH and PMSG from the Organon Co. Immunological investigations with ovine (LH) were carried out to characterize the antigens present in the hormone and to study the antigens it has in common with the LH preparations of bovine, porcine and human origin, HCG, HMG and PMSG. Immunoelectrophoretic analyses indicated that ovine LH has an antigen that cross reacts with a precipitating antigen present in human, bovine and porcine LH, HCG and PMSG. Thus we observed cross reactions between the LH preparations of all species studied but the FSH of no two species showed any cross reaction. We had no rat FSH to study its cross reaction with the antiserum.

The effect of anti LH antiserum on the biological activity of gonadotropins was also investigated. These results have been published in the Indian J. Exp. Biol. 5: 135, 1967. The antiserum inhibited the endogenous LH activity of normal immature rats. Bioassays carried out in normal immature rats showed that the antiserum to ovine LH inhibited not only the activity of ovine, bovine and porcine LH but also that of PMSG. The antiserum also inhibited the endogenous LH of adult female mice. Daily injections of the antiserum into mice prevented the normal estrus cycle. The antiserum decreased the weight of ovaries, uteri, adrenals and pituitary glands in treated female mice. Injections of antiserum, started immediately after fertilization (day 1 to 4) prevented pregnancy by blocking implantation in all animals. Injection of the antiserum after implantation (days 6 to 8) resulted in resorption of all implantation sites. Antiserum to ovine LH administered on day 3 of pregnancy alone or in combination with estradiol, blocked implantation in all the treated mice.

SUMMARY OF SESSION

RYAN: Many points have been made in the formal presentations and discussion. I shall not attempt to catalogue each of them. Instead, I shall attempt to very briefly summarize our position.

Abundant evidence has been presented here and elsewhere concerning the multiplicity of antibodies produced by immunizing animals with relatively crude HCG preparations obtained from urinary extracts. Some of these antibodies can be removed by absorbing the antisera with human serum, some by absorption with pituitary extracts and some by absorption with extracts of children's urine. None the less, several apparently different antibodies are apt to remain even after exhaustive absorption. One wonders if this heterogeneity is not related to the use of HCG prepared from urine which may contain several metabolic derivatives of the hormone. A study of HCG derived from the placenta, rather than the urine, seems in order.

A very important point has been made that has bearing on several facets of the immunoassay of gonadotropins, and indeed of other biologically active materials. The sites on the molecule concerned with biologic activity need not, and indeed generally are not, identical to the sites concerned with immunologic reactivity. As we have heard, this fact has intruded into the immunoassay of HCG, the differences between pituitary and urinary LH and FSH, the immunoassay of LH in rat serum, and most obviously into comparisons of biologic and immunologic potency estimates. It has an important bearing on the selection of standards to be used in immunoassays and this will be discussed in considerable detail at another session. It is time that we

learned more about the composition of the hormone molecules with
which we are working. What portion of the molecule is concerned
with biologic activity, what portion with hormone specific immunoreactivity and what portion with species specific reactivity?
What portions of the molecules of FSH, LH, HCG etc. are similar?
What are the compositional and conformational differences between
the molecules as they exist in the tissue of origin, in the
blood and in the urine?

My last remarks (and perhaps the preceding ones) may very well
be regarded as gratuitous or even fatuous, but I shall make them
anyway. Each antiserum must be regarded as a unique reagent.
Two antisera prepared against the same lot of hormone, using the
same immunization schedule in the same species and strain of
immunized animal, may differ widely in their sensitivity, titer,
hormone specificity and species specificity. They may also
differ in the effects of pH and salt concentration upon binding
of antibody to antigen. Great caution must be exercised in
attempting to predict the results obtainable from a given antiserum from those obtained with other antisera made from the same
or similar antigens. Likewise, each immunologic end-point tends
to have some unique feature that makes extrapolation to a
different end-point rather hazardous. The lack of precipitating
antibodies, as seen by immunodiffusion or immunoelectrophoresis,
does not preclude the possibility that the antiserum may be useful for a radioimmunoassay. An antiserum that is ideal for a
radioimmunoassay may be rather useless in neutralizing biologic
activity. As we need to learn more about the nature of hormone
antigens, so too do we need to know more about the unique
features of these end-points used to measure antigen-antibody
reations.

CHAPTER 4

MEASUREMENT OF GONADOTROPIC ACTIVITY BY RADIOIMMUNOASSAY

RADIOIMMUNOASSAY OF FSH AND LH IN HUMAN SERUM: THE EFFECTS OF AGE, AND INFUSION OF SEVERAL POLYAMINES IN MALES*

ROBERT J. RYAN AND CHARLES FAIMAN
SECTION OF ENDOCRINE RESEARCH, MAYO CLINIC
ROCHESTER, MINNESOTA

We have previously described (1,2) specific radioimmunoassays for human follicle stimulating hormone (FSH) and luteinizing hormone (LH). We wish to report: (1) some observations on concentrations of these hormones in the serum of healthy young and old adult males, and (2) the effects of administration of histamine, putrescine and arginine upon release of these hormones.

Sera were obtained, during the morning hours, from 163 adult males (20 to 74 years of age) to investigate the effects of age on serum concentrations of LH and FSH. Some of these men were blood bank donors and some were individuals who came to the hospital for a routine annual physical exam. Figure 1 shows frequency distribution plots of serum concentrations of FSH and LH for males 20 to 49 years of age and 50 to 74 years of age.

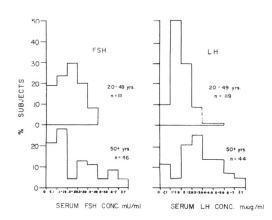

Figure No. 1: The distribution of serum concentrations of FSH and LH in two age groups of healthy males.

* Supported in part by a Grant from the U. S. Public Health Service (HD 03726).

Serum FSH in the younger group of males ranged from $<$ 0.10 to 0.49 mU FSH[†] per ml and had a median value of 0.21 mU/ml. Serum concentrations of FSH in **older** males tended to be higher, ranging from $<$ 0.10 to 1.45 mU/ml. The distributions of values for young and elderly males were tested by a chi-square analysis and were found to be significantly different (p $<$ .001). The data suggest that males over 50 years of age may segregate into two populations based on serum concentrations of FSH. Serum concentrations of LH showed a similar phenomenon. Males less than 50 years of age had concentrations ranging from $<$ 1.0 to 5.9 m$_\mu$g/ml[**] with a median of 1.9 m$_\mu$g/ml while those more than 50 years of age ranged from $<$ 1.0 to 13.8 with a median of 3.4 m$_\mu$g/ml. The difference between serum concentration of LH in younger and older males was statistically significant (p $<$ .001) again using a chi-square analysis. A higher concentration of LH in the sera of older males as compared to young males was previously reported by Schalch et al. (3). It was also previously noted by Ryan (4) that pituitary content of LH tended to be higher in the older male. It should be emphasized, however, that these increases in LH and FSH in the older male do not approach the magnitude seen in the postmenopausal woman.

Before performing some acute experiments in an attempt to alter serum concentrations of LH and FSH in males, we felt it advisable to investigate within day and day-to-day variations. We previously reported (5) a small but statistically significant diurnal variation in serum FSH but not in LH concentration in males. In order to ascertain the degree of day-to-day variation in serum concentrations of LH and FSH in males, morning blood samples were taken from 52 subjects on 2 or more days during a period of one week. The replicate values for each subject were averaged and the average was assigned a value of 100%. Variations were then calculated as a percentage. The 95% confidence limits for serum LH were $\pm$ 24% and for FSH $\pm$ 26%. Because of these small spontaneous variations, it would thus appear that the male is a suitable subject for certain types of physiologic experiments.

White et al. (6) reported that certain polyamines, including putrescine, histamine, lysine, spermine and spermidine, caused a decrease of pituitary FSH content in the castrate testosterone-treated male rat within 15 to 30 minutes. Putrescine was the most potent, being effective at a dose of 1 nanogram or less. We have examined the effects of histamine, arginine and putrescine on gonadotropin release in the human male.

Histamine: Four subjects were given an intravenous injection of 100 $_\mu$g of histamine phosphate. Blood samples were taken before and from 15 to 300 minutes after the injection. In each individual this dose of histamine was sufficient to produce a fall in blood pressure, a flush, and a mild

---

[†] The assay standard employed was a human pituitary preparation which had a bioassay potency of 100 NIH-FSH-S1 Units/mg. The immunoassay results were therefore expressed in terms of NIH-FSH-S1 Units. These values may be converted to milli International Units (mIU) by multiplying by a factor of 30.

[**] The standard employed was a human LH preparation with a potency of 3.35 NIH-LH-S1 Units/mg. A conversion factor of 8 may be used to express the data in mIU/ml.

headache.   As can be seen in Figure 2, there was no significant change in
serum concentrations of FSH or LH.

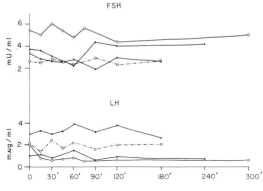

Figure No. 2:   The effects of intravenous administration
             of histamine phosphate on serum concentrations of LH
             and FSH in healthy males.

Arginine: Five subjects (3 male and 2 female) were given an intravenous infusion of 30 gm of arginine hydrochloride over a period of 30 minutes.   Blood samples were obtained 15 minutes and immediately before the
start of the infusion, upon completion of the infusion and at various times
thereafter.   The results are shown in Figure 3.

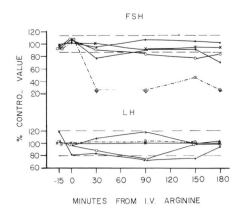

Figure No. 3:   The effects of intravenous infusion of
             arginine monohydrochloride on serum concentrations of
             FSH and LH in 3 healthy males and 2 healthy females
             (•——• and x——x).   The dashed lines represent
             the 95% confidence limits of the control values.

Although all of the subjects had significant increases in serum concentrations of insulin and growth hormone, none had a significant increase in serum FSH or LH. Indeed, several subjects had a decrease in serum FSH and LH concentrations. Schalch et al. (3) have also noted that arginine failed to induce a release of LH.

Putrescine: The effects of an intravenous infusion of putrescine on serum FSH and LH concentrations in 4 young men were studied in collaboration with W. F. White and R. Herting of Abbott Laboratories. Each subject was studied on three occasions at weekly intervals. The first study consisted of a 15-minute intravenous infusion of normal saline; in the second study a small dose of putrescine was delivered with the saline infusion; and in the third study a 16-fold increase in the dose of putrescine was administered with the infusion. Blood samples were taken twice before and at 30, 60, 180 and 240 minutes after completion of each infusion. The preinfusion serum concentrations were averaged and assigned a value of 100% and the post-infusion samples were expressed as a percentage of this control value. Data are illustrated in Figure 4.

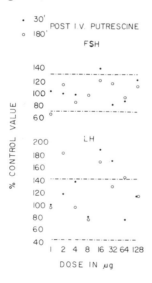

Figure No. 4: The effect of various doses of intravenously infused putrescine on serum concentrations of FSH and LH. The dashed lines represent the 95% confidence limits of values observed during a control infusion of normal saline.

The broken lines on the graph represent the 95% confidence limits of the values found during the infusion of saline alone. Doses of putrescine ranging from 1 to 128 µg had no significant effect on serum FSH concentrations. There were a few significant increases in serum LH concentrations, but a dose-response relationship was not evident.

It would thus appear that these polyamines when administered in a peripheral vein do not induce significant release of FSH or LH in the human.

REFERENCES

1. Faiman, C., and R. J. Ryan, J Clin Endocr 27:444, 1967.

2. Faiman, C., and R. J. Ryan, Proc Soc Exp Biol Med 125:1130, 1967.

3. Schalch, D. S., A. F. Parlow, R. C. Boon, and S. Reichlin, J Clin Invest 47:665, 1968.

4. Ryan, R. J., J Clin Endocr 22:300, 1962.

5. Faiman, C., and R. J. Ryan, Nature (London) 215:857, 1967.

6. White, W. F., A. I. Cohen, R. H. Rippel, J. C. Storey, and A. V. Schally, Endocrinology 82:742, 1968.

RADIOIMMUNOASSAY OF FSH AND LH IN BODY FLUIDS

B. B. SAXENA, H. M. GANDY, AND R. E. PETERSON
DEPARTMENTS OF MEDICINE AND OBSTETRICS & GYNECOLOGY
CORNELL UNIVERSITY MEDICAL COLLEGE
NEW YORK, N.Y. 10021

FSH AND LH IN URINE

The radioimmunoassay of human pituitary FSH and LH described for estimation of gonadotropins in plasma (1) has been extended to the measurement of FSH and LH in urine. Daily 24 hr urine specimens were obtained for one menstrual cycle in each of 3 normal women with cyclical menses. An 8 hr aliquot of each 24 hr specimen was used for measurement of 5β-pregnane-20α-diol (2) and total estrogens (3); the remaining 16 hr aliquot was extracted for gonadotropins (4). A fourth of the urinary gonadotropin extract was dissolved in and dialyzed against water at pH 7 for 6 hr at 4°C to remove urea and other salts. Ten to 20 μl of a 0.1% solution of the dialyzed extract was used for radioimmunoassay. The FSH and LH levels in daily 24 hr urine specimens are shown in Figs. 1-3.

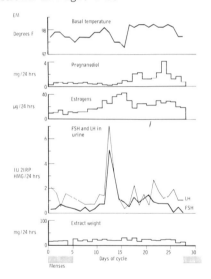

Figure 1

FSH and LH Levels in Urinary Extracts of E. M.

The patterns of FSH and LH in the urines of subjects E. M., and S. M. were characterized by maximal values for FSH and LH at midcycle. These findings were similar to the pattern seen in plasma samples obtained in women with cyclical menses (1). Individual variation in daily FSH and LH levels in the urinary extracts of three cycles is however noteworthy. Increase in 5β-pregnane-20α-diol in urine was noted following the midcycle elevation of FSH and LH whereas increase in total urinary estrogens occurred prior to the midcycle rise in FSH and LH.

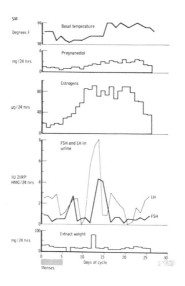

Figure 2

FSH and LH Levels in Urinary Extracts of S. M.

The pattern of FSH and LH excretion in the urine of the third subject, F. P. (Fig. 3) showed an additional rise in FSH and LH during Days 1 through 5 of the cycle. The total weight of the gonadotropic extract of 24 hr urine on each of these five days of the follicular phase of the cycle was significantly higher than on the remaining days of the cycle. Elevation of basal body temperature or increase in excretion of 5β-pregnane-20α-diol did not occur following the rise in excretion of FSH and LH on Day 5 as noted after the midcycle rise in excretion of gonadotropins. The possibility of some non-specific cross-reacting material in these extracts must be considered. The nature of the material in the urinary extracts of gonadotropins on Days 1 through 5 as measured by the radioimmunoassay can be better defined by bioassays which are in progress.

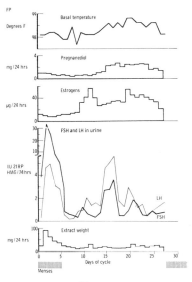

Figure 3

FSH and LH Levels in Urinary Extracts of F. P.

FSH AND LH IN PLASMA FOLLOWING CHLOMIPHENE CITRATE

Plasma concentration of FSH and LH as well as progesterone and its 20α-isomer have been measured in patient G. G. with primary amenorrhea (1, 5). G. G. had a history of absent secondary sexual characteristics until age 15; vaginal bleeding occurred at age 16 following administration of estrogens and progesterone. Subsequent vaginal bleeding occurred only after cyclical hormone therapy; this therapy was continued intermittently until age 25 when it was discontinued several months prior to her admission to the hospital for evaluation. The patient showed no important abnormal physical findings. Laboratory studies showed urinary 17-ketosteroids and 17-hydroxysteroids of 6 and 8 mg/24 hr respectively and the urinary gonadotropin titer was positive at 13 and negative at 52 mouse uterine units. The basal metabolic rate was -10. A roentgenogram of the chest and an intravenous pyelogram were within normal limits. The sella turcica measured 9 mm in horizontal diameter and 7 mm in depth on tommography. At exploratory laporatomy and curretage, the uterus sounded to 6 cm. Findings at curreting were consistent with an atropic endometrium. Both ovaries were 2 x 1 cm and characterized by the presence of a few small follicle cysts and a moderate number of primordial cells beneath the capsule. Spontaneous menstruation did not occur following ovarian biopsies. The patient was then given chlomiphene citrate, 50 mg/day for three days. Values for FSH and LH are shown in Fig. 4. It is of interest that rise in LH was noted 24 hours after the first dose of chlomiphene citrate. Elevation in plasma concentration of progesterone followed maximum elevation of FSH and LH.

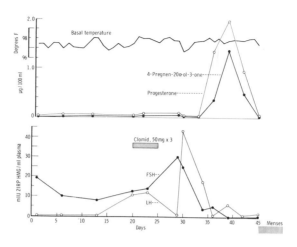

Figure 4

FSH, LH and Progesterone Levels in Peripheral Plasma of G.G. - Prior to and Following Chlomiphene Citrate

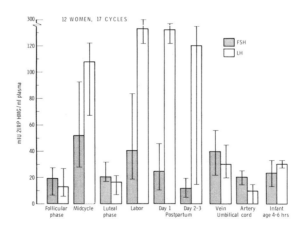

Figure 5

FSH and LH values in normal women, during labor and puerperium and in the new born. The mean and range are shown by bar and line respectively.

PLASMA FSH & LH DURING PREGNANCY, PARTURITION & IN NEWBORNS

Studies on plasma concentration of FSH and LH in normal men, women and children have been extended to include observations during pregnancy, labor and puerperium. FSH and LH were noted to rise as early as 2 weeks following the first missed menstrual period and remained elevated during pregnancy. LH levels during pregnancy may not be meaningful due to cross-reaction with HCG. FSH and HCG-LH values present in maternal plasma during stage II of labor are shown in Fig. 5. These values are compared to values found in women with cyclical menses. Values for FSH during labor ranged from 18. 5 to 84 mIU-2ndIRP/ml of plasma with a mean of 41. 6; LH ranged from 142 to greater than 250 mIU-2ndIRP/ml of plasma. Day 1 post partum values for FSH in these same patients ranged from 11. 2 to 46 mIU; LH values were similar to those noted during labor. By the 3rd post partum day, FSH values were similar to the range during the follicular and luteal phases of the menstrual cycle; LH values in 4 of the patients ranged from 15 to 42. 5 mIU but was greater than 250 mIU in the remaining patients.

Table I

	FSH*	LH*
Mother W. W.	84. 0	>250
Umbilical vein	56. 0	20
Umbilical artery	24. 6	trace
Baby boy W.	33. 5	33. 5
Mother L. G.	40. 8	> 250
Umbilical vein	22. 4	30
Umbilical artery	15. 1	9. 5
Baby girl G.	14. 0	28

* mIU 2nd-IRP-HMG/ml

The concentration of FSH and LH in umbilical venous and arterial plasma samples was considerably less than the concentration in the respective maternal plasma. FSH and LH venous concentration in the respective umbilical arterial plasma was always lower than the concentration in the umbilical venous plasma. Values for concentration of FSH and LH in plasma from the maternal-placental-fetal unit are shown in the Table above.

DIURNAL VARIATION OF FSH AND LH IN MEN

Plasma FSH and LH concentrations determined every four hours for 24 hours in 3 normal men, 25 to 30 years of age are shown in Figs. 6 and 7. These studies were performed in W. R. for two 24 hr periods. These subjects were ambulatory from 7 AM to 11 PM. In each subject, the highest values for FSH and LH were in the 4 or 8AM plasma samples. The 8 AM values for FSH and LH were significantly higher than the 8PM values for

each subject, however this was not always so in all subjects described earlier (1) in whom plasma samples were collected at 8AM and PM only (maximum concentration of FSH and LH may have occurred prior to 8 AM). The
FSH and LH determinations in 4 hourly samples (for 24 hrs) in 3 subjects
reported earlier (1) and 3 subjects shown here suggest a diurnal variation
in plasma concentration of gonadotropins.

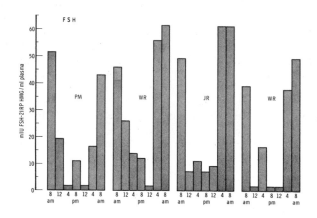

Figure 6

FSH Levels in Men

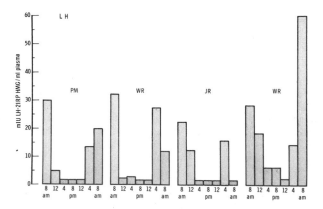

Figure 7

LH Levels in Men

ACKNOWLEDGEMENTS

We are indebted to Doctors L. Nocke and W. Nocke for preparation of the gonadotropic extracts and the steroid determinations in urine. This investigation was supported by grants from the National Institutes of Health (T1 AM-5350 and AM-07328); from the American Cancer Society (P-440) and from the Population Council of Rockefeller University (M67-27); from NIH grant AM - 11187.

REFERENCES

1. Saxena, B.B., H. Demura, H.M. Gandy, and R.E. Peterson. J. Clin. Endocrin. 28:519, 1968.
2. Nocke, L., and W. Nocke, Unpublished data
3. Brown, J.B., R.D. Bulbrook, and F.C. Greenwood, J. Endocrinol. 16:49, 1957.
4. Johnsen, S. Acta Endocrinol. (Copenhagen) 28:69, 1968.
5. Gandy, H.M. Unpublished data.

DISCUSSION

VANDE WIELE: Dr. Ryan, I assume that you were interested in the effect of putrescine because of the known high concentration in the hypothalamus of putrescine and related polyamines. Notwithstanding your negative results, I feel we should not exclude the role of these substances in the control of gonadotropic secretion. In view of the high concentration of putrescine in the hypothalamus I would guess that it is synthesized in situ and that its level is largely independent of concentration in peripheral blood. If so, infusion of putrescine, even in massive amounts, into a peripheral vein may not significantly alter putrescine levels in the hypothalamus. In relation to your arginine experiments I would like to add that we have measured plasma LH levels in patients during insulin-induced hypoglycemia. Even in patients who had a brisk growth hormone response there was no change in LH levels.

RYAN: I think Drs. Parlow and Schalch also noted that arginine infusion did not affect serum LH concentration. We did not study pitressin; we studied putrescine, which is not a nice name so we should perhaps call it 1,4 diaminobutane.

ODELL: If I read your slides correctly you detect no FSH in about 30 to 40% of normal males under the age of 40 and no FSH in about 25% of males over 40. This is less than 3 milliunits if I translated your values right.

RYAN: The figure you refer to, Dr. Odell, indicates that approximately 20% of the males, either young or old, have a serum concentration of FSH less than 0.1 mU or 3.0 mIU/ml.

This does not mean that 20% of these males have no measurable
FSH. Many of them have concentrations ranging between 0.6 and
3.0 mIU/ml. It should be pointed out that most of those who were
found to have undetectable concentrations were studied using the
antisera that we originally described (J. Clin. Endocr. Metab.
27: 444, 1967). During the past year we have been using an antiserum that is 5-6 times more sensitive and equally specific
(Protein and Polypeptide Hormones, M. Margoulies, Ed., Excerpta
Med. Fdnt., Amsterdam, 1968, p. 133) and very few adult males
have undetectable concentrations of FSH when this antiserum is
used.

ODELL: I think it is worthwhile then to call attention to a
discrepancy between your findings and our findings, with a
sensitivity of less than 5 milliunits per ml. and postulating
that all children let us say under the age of 6 have no detectable FSH. We find that all males have detectable levels of FSH
and furthermore, these levels can be appropriately manipulated
by a steroid hormone.

LUNENFELD: A question for both Dr. Ryan and Dr. Gandy. Did
you check the effect of clomiphene on FSH and LH excretion and
the kinetics of the effect? I saw in the slides which Dr. Gandy
showed that she checked the effect of clomiphene only 4 days
after clomiphene administration. I wonder whether data on day
to day values immediately following clomiphene administration
are **available.**

RYAN: We have studied the separate cis and trans isomers of
clomiphene and have noted differences. The cis isomer when
administered orally shows a log dose-response relationship between
the amount administered, over a range of 15 to 200 mg. per day,
and serum concentrations of LH. The first significant increase
in serum LH, with the cis isomer, occurred about the third day
of administration. The duration of effect varied with the dose.
With the higher doses the effect persisted for 7-12 days after
withdrawal of the drug. The responses of serum FSH to the cis
isomer were not clear. Some increases in serum FSH occurred,
but not consistently, with very small doses of cis-clomiphene,
i.e. 1 mg./day. At doses of 200 mg./day, all subjects showed a
significant increase in serum FSH. The trans isomer had no
effect on serum FSH in the doses we studied. It had some effect
on serum LH concentrations but was less potent than the cis
isomer.

CARGILLE: Drs. Jacobson, Marshall, Ross and I have studied the
effect of clomiphene citrate, a mixture of the cis and trans
isomers, on plasma FSH as measured by double antibody radioimmunoassay. Our subjects were seven anovulatory or oligo-
ovulatory women, in each of whom an ovulatory response to
clomiphene was diagnosed by a shift to a progestational endometrium. In three women, ovulation was documented by Dr.
Marshall by biopsy of a corpus hemorrhagicum at culdoscopy. In

all subjects, a rise in plasma FSH occurred in response to a five-day course of clomiphene. A peak was reached by the third or fourth day after the start of therapy, the mean rise being 53% above pre-treatment levels. This was followed by a progressive decline to a day 10 to 15 follicular nadir which was 43% less than the pre-treatment levels. Following this nadir a sharp peak of FSH lasting 1 or 2 days was seen in all 7 women. Luteal levels were lower than pre-treatment follicular phase levels. Thus the configuration of plasma FSH in a clomiphene induced ovulatory cycle resembles the pattern we have observed in a study of the normal menstrual cycle in 16 women with spontaneous menses. I would like to ask Dr. Gandy whether she studied daily samples in her group of clomiphene treated women. Perhaps her inability to identify a clomiphene induced peak subsequent to the initial rise in plasma FSH relates to less frequent sampling.

GANDY: Blood samples were not obtained daily.

TAYMOR: I would object to calling the increase in FSH in your last slide really a rise. This is one of the difficulties we have found with the study of FSH and LH levels following clomiphene. Minor changes in FSH do occur but I am not sure that we can call these actual rises or falls. There is a typical LH rise anywhere from 3 to 7 days after the last clomiphene tablet followed by an ovulatory cycle, but I find it difficult to concede that the variability of 3 or 4 mIU is a significant change in FSH.

RYAN: I am sorry that I did not specify that our experience with clomiphene was only with the separate isomers administered to males. We have had very limited experience with the racemic mixture as administered to women. In fact, we have only studied two normal young women with racemic clomiphene. One young woman was given the drug during the proliferative phase of the cycle and had a striking increase in both serum FSH and LH. The second was given the drug during the secretory phase of the cycle and had no response whatsoever.

BELL: In male subjects the effects of clomiphene on estrogen excretion may be long lasting. Harkness et al. (Harkness, R. A., Bell, E. T., Loraine, J. A. and Morse, W., J. Endocrinol. 31: 53-61, 1964), studied four normal men who were treated with 50 mg. clomiphene twice daily for 12 days. Elevated estrogen levels were noted for at least three weeks following withdrawal of the drug and in some cases for more than one month. Dr. Ryan, do you have any data on the long-term effects of clomiphene on LH levels in men?

RYAN: If you mean by longitudinal more than a week, we have no data.

SAXENA: Dr. Ryan has said that in older people the FSH and LH is higher and has also suggested that their gonadotropins may be different from those in younger people. In view of these suggestions could one use postmenopausal plasma for an FSH standard? The second question I would like to ask Dr. Ryan is whether men have a menopause similar to that which occurs in women.

RYAN: I would not speculate on either point. I do not think this is a different kind of FSH nor did I say so. I have no evidence to prove the point conclusively. I was saying that the population of older males may separate into 2 groups based on a high or low serum FSH concentration. As to your second point, I do not know how we define menopause, whether it is a "hot flash" or what. Certainly the male continues to be reproductively active, albeit perhaps less so, for quite a long time, and I am not sure what a male menopause would be.

STEINBERGER: Dr. Ryan, I would like to comment on the differences in gonadotropin levels which you observed among different subjects. As you indicated, the differences were greater in the older age group, and their mean value was higher than in the younger age group. I would like to suggest the possibility that the greater variation in the levels among individuals fifty years or older may be due to the fact that the chances of non-specific damage to the germinal epithelium would be greater and are thus reflected by the elevated levels. Using bioassay (Steelman-Pohley for FSH and ovarian ascorbic depletion technique for LH) we were able to correlate, at least to a degree, the elevated levels of both FSH and LH in the urine of the male with damage to the germinal epithelium in the presence of clinically normal androgenic function.

RYAN: I think that is an attractive hypothesis and I would like to believe that it is true.

CARGILLE: Dr. Bardin, Dr. Ross, and I have studied the response of normal men to a racemic mixture of clomiphene citrate. Three men received 200 mg./day for five days and responded with a rise in plasma FSH reaching a peak on days 4, 6, and 10 respectively. Elevated levels persisted for at least 5 but up to 9 days after cessation of therapy. A group of 7 normal men treated with clomiphene for 7 days, 100-200 mg./day responded with a progressive rise in plasma FSH reaching a level 131% above control values by the seventh day following the onset of therapy. The response of LH in the 10 men was very similar to that of FSH.

SERUM LEVELS OF FSH AND LH BY RADIOIMMUNOASSAY

MELVIN L. TAYMOR, M.D., TOSHIHIRO AONO, M.D.
AND CAROLYN PHETEPLACE, A.B.
FROM THE DEPARTMENT OF OBSTETRICS AND GYNECOLOGY, HARVARD
MEDICAL SCHOOL AND THE DEPARTMENT OF SURGERY (GYNECOLOGY),
PETER BENT BRIGHAM HOSPITAL, BOSTON, MASSACHUSETTS

The availability of sensitive and relatively specific radioimmunoassays for FSH and LH has opened the way for more detailed studies of the circulating levels of these hormones in normal and abnormal human reproductive physiology. The specificity of the LH assay system has been widely accepted. However, as Dr. Albert has previously noted, there are questions concerning the specificity of the FSH system. In our previous report we suggested that with adequate absorption techniques such a system is probably sufficiently specific for at least a clinical assessment of serum FSH levels. In addition there have been discrepancies in the actual levels of hormone that have been reported from different laboratories. These differences may ultimately be reduced by the use of similar antigens and antiserum and by refinement of standards. Pending these developments, there still may be value in placing our findings on the serum FSH, LH levels in various states on the record along with others previously reported.

Radioimmunoassays for FSH and LH were carried out by methods previously described (1,2). Pituitary fractions for labelling and antibody production are shown on Table 1. Iodination was carried out utilizing 125 I. The advantages of this isotope have been previously described (2).

Table 1. Gonadotropin preparations used for antigen and antibody production

Assay	Preparation	LH activity	FSH activity
LH	Ag: LH-DEAE-I-2	1660 IU/mg	0.5 IU/mg
	Ab: HCG-APL	20,000 IU/amp	--
FSH	Ag: LER-828-2	0.21 NIH U/mg	138.0 NIH U/mg
	Ab: LER-735-2	0.067 NIH U/mg	5.3 NIH U/mg

It was first considered of importance to investigate the day to day variation since previous bioassay studies have shown significant variation. Figure 1 shows the FSH and LH levels in the serum of one individual on four consecutive days. There was no significant day to day variation.

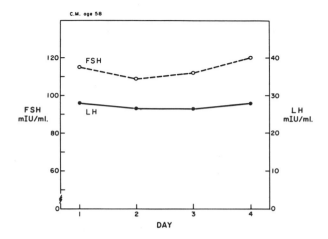

Figure 1. Daily serum FSH and LH levels
over a 4 day period.

     A study of diurnal variation is shown in Figure 2.
There does seem to be a tendency to lowered afternoon levels
of FSH as compared to morning levels, but the differences
are probably not significant. No demonstrable change
between morning and afternoon sampling could be demonstrated
for serum LH.

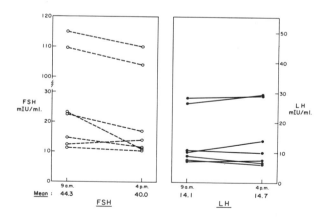

Figure 2. A.M. and P.M. levels of FSH and LH.

Serum LH levels for various groups of individuals are shown in Figure 3. The mean level from the sixth through ninth days of the follicular phase of the normal cycle was taken as a control level. This was 8.4 mIU in 11 normal cycles. This is shown as the bold line on the graph. Two standard errors are included within the lighter lines. There was of course a significantly higher level in post-menopausal females. Luteal phase levels during the normal menstrual cycle were similar to the follicular phase controls. Levels in males appear to be slightly higher but there was overlap of confidence limits. Levels in children were similar to those seen during the follicular phase of normally menstruating females. The mean level at the time of the ovulatory peak was somewhere between menopausal and follicular control levels.

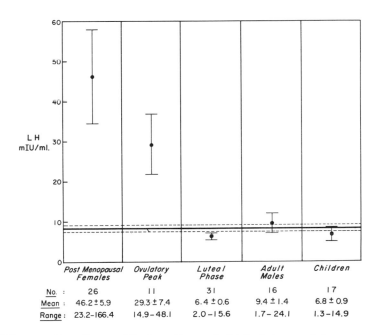

	Post Menopausal Females	Ovulatory Peak	Luteal Phase	Adult Males	Children
No. :	26	11	31	16	17
Mean :	46.2±5.9	29.3±7.4	6.4±0.6	9.4±1.4	6.8±0.9
Range:	23.2-166.4	14.9-48.1	2.0-15.6	1.7-24.1	1.3-14.9

Figure 3. Serum LH levels. Solid dots and brackets indicate mean plus 2 standard errors. Solid horizontal line indicates mean of follicular phase (8.2±1.1).

The FSH data is shown in Figure 4. The mean level for the mid four days of the follicular phase was 20.0 mIU. Considerably higher levels were noted in post-menopausal females. There was no significant difference noted during the luteal phase. The serum FSH levels in males were significantly lower than the control female values. Serum FSH levels in children were also significantly lower.

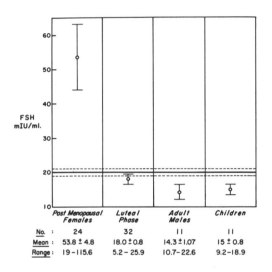

Figure 4. Serum FSH levels. Open dots and brackets indicate mean plus 2 standard errors. Solid horizontal line indicates mean of follicular phase (20 ± 1.2)

Figure 5 shows the mean serum FSH and LH levels from 11 normal menstrual cycles. The LH peak is taken as the point of reference. The clear cut midcycle LH peak, well documented by previous biologic and immunologic studies, is well demonstrated. The fiducial limits (2 standard errors) are quite small.

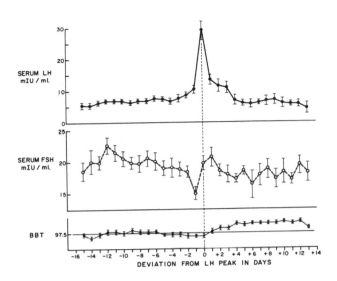

Figure 5. Mean FSH and LH levels in 11 normal
cycles. Brackets indicate 2 standard errors.

The individual FSH patterns were somewhat more variable,
resulting in the wider fiducial limits. Nevertheless, a
distinct pattern can be seen. FSH is relatively high in the
early and midportion of the follicular phase. There is a
significant lowering of FSH levels on the day prior to the
LH peak. FSH then again rises and there is a peak that may
or may not coincide with the LH peak. In our experience the
midcycle FSH rise usually comes a day after the LH peak.
FSH levels are variable during the follicular phase.

Supported in part by grant FR-05489-05 of the USPHS and
a grant-in-aid from Hoffmann-LaRoche Inc., Nutley, New Jersey.

REFERENCES

1. Aono, T., D.P. Goldstein, M.L. Taymor, and K. Dolch, Am J
    Obstet & Gynec 98:996, 1967.

2. Aono, T., and M.L. Taymor, Am J Obstet & Gynec 100:110,
    1968.

EFFECT OF ORAL CONTRACEPTIVES ON PLASMA FOLLICLE STIMULATING HORMONE

C. M. Cargille, G. T. Ross, and P. L. Rayford, Endocrinology Branch, National Cancer Institute, National Institutes of Health, Bethesda, Maryland

Introduction

Urinary excretion of follicle stimulating hormone (FSH) and luteinizing hormone (LH) measured biologically has been shown to decline in response to therapy with either estrogens, progestins, or combinations of these agents (1,2,3,4). More recently plasma LH levels measured by radioimmunoassay have been shown to be reduced by treatment with a combination of norethynodrel and mestranol, Enovid E (5).

We now wish to report measurements of FSH made by radioimmunoassay in samples taken daily in eight women during control cycles and cycles in which they received Enovid E. Some of these results have been reported (6).

Materials and Methods

Eight women between the ages of 18 and 23 with a history of regular menses, were studied in the hospital. Five mls of heparinized blood were drawn daily for two consecutive cycles, a control cycle and a cycle during which Enovid E was administered for 17 to 25 days beginning on the second day of menses.

Plasma LH was measured with a double antibody radioimmunoassay (7). Plasma FSH was measured by a similar method in which incubation of trace (Reichert 780-I^{131}*), rabbit antiserum (Cargille/Ross #24), and plasma (200 μl volume) was carried out for five days at 10 C prior to addition of the second antibody (sheep anti-rabbit gamma globulin). The 2nd International Reference Preparation for Human Menopausal Gonadotropin (2nd IRP HMG**) was found to be an appropriate standard since slopes of the dose response curves of this material and of plasma from normal men and from young and postmenopausal women were parallel. Estimates of within assay precision revealed that values in the normal female range have 95% confidence limits of 1.6 mIU/ml. Insignificant cross-reactivity (less than 1% by weight) has been found for highly purified preparations of LH and less than 3.5% for purified thyroid stimulating hormone. No cross-reactivity could be shown with purified preparations of growth hormone and adrenocorticotropic hormone.

---

*   R-780 FSH was prepared by L. Reichert, Emory University, Atlanta, Georgia. The FSH potency at the time of bioassay was 61 NIH-FSH-S1 U/mg by ovarian augmentation assay, although initial potency may have been higher. LH potency was 0.28 NIH-FSH-S1 U/mg by ovarian ascorbic acid depletion assay (courtesy of Dr. L. Reichert). Labeling with I^{131} was performed by the method of Hunter and Greenwood.

** Kindly supplied by D. R. Bangham, National Institutes for Medical Research, Mill Hill, London 7, England.

Results

Plasma FSH levels during a single menstrual cycle in one woman are depicted in Fig. 1. A plasma progesterone level of 7.2 mµ g/ml* during the luteal phase representing a 29-fold rise over the follicular level and a thermogenic shift were considered presumptive evidence for ovulation. Five characteristic features of the pattern of variations in plasma FSH during this cycle are the following: 1) an early follicular rise, 2) decline to a preovulatory nadir, 3) a midcycle peak, 4) decline to a luteal nadir, 5) a late luteal rise. Criteria utilized in our laboratory for delineation of these features are listed in Table 1.

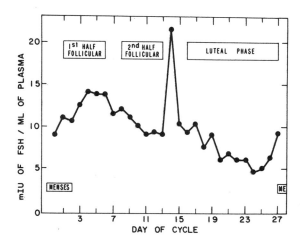

Fig. 1 Plasma FSH levels measured in daily sample during a normal menstrual cycle.

---

* Plasma progesterone was measured by Dr. T. Yoshimi by the method of Yoshimi and Lipsett (8).

Table 1

Laboratory Criteria for Five Features of Variation in Levels
of Plasma Follicle Stimulating Hormone in Normal Menstrual Cycles

Early Follicular Rise

1. The mean first half follicular level exceeds the mean second half follicular level.
2. The highest individual value of the follicular phase is in the first half of the follicular phase.

Preovulatory Nadir

1. The mean second half follicular level is less than the mean first half follicular level.
2. The lowest individual value of the follicular phase is in the second half of the follicular phase.

Midcycle Peak

1. A sharp FSH rise which occurs near the midcycle and
    a. exceeds the mean value of the second half of the follicular phase by 45% or more;
    b. exceeds any individual value in the second half of the follicular phase.

Luteal Nadir

1. The lowest value in the second half of the luteal phase if it
    a. is less than any other individual value in the second half of the follicular phase and
    b. is equal to or less than any other individual value in the first half of the luteal phase.

Late Luteal Rise

1. A progressive increase in three consecutive values subsequent to the luteal nadir, prior to or including the second day of the next menses.

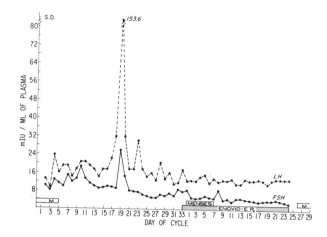

Fig. 2 Plasma FSH (solid line) and LH (dashed line) measured in daily samples during a normal menstrual cycle and during treatment with Enovid E.

Levels of FSH and LH for a woman during a control cycle and in response to Enovid E are depicted in Fig. 2. In addition to the five characteristic features for FSH noted in Fig. 1 and in Table 1, a tall mid-cycle peak is demonstrated for LH during the control cycle. Levels of both hormones were promptly suppressed following the administration of the oral contraceptive, Enovid E.

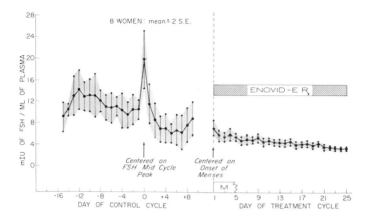

Fig. 3 Plasma FSH levels in 8 women during control cycles and in response to Enovid E. The shaded area depicts 2 standard errors of the mean (heavy line). Control cycles were aligned on the FSH mid-cycle peak. Treatment cycles were aligned on the first day of menses when Enovid E was started.

Fig. 3 depicts the mean ± 2 standard errors for FSH levels observed during control cycles and treatment cycles in all eight women studied. The control cycles were aligned on the day of the FSH mid-cycle peak. These women exhibited a marked early follicular rise of FSH and subsequent decline to a nadir in the second half of the follicular phase. The sharp mid-cycle peak is followed by further decline to a luteal nadir and a late luteal FSH rise prior to the next menses.

The treatment cycles were aligned on the day that menses began and Enovid E was first administered. A progressive decline to levels significantly less than those of the luteal phase occurred, the lowest values being near the limit of detection of the assay.

Discussion

The suppression of plasma gonadotropin levels observed in these studies probably reflects an effect of Enovid E on pituitary secretion rather than on the metabolic clearance rates (MCR) of either FSH or LH. Enovid E has been shown to have no effect on metabolic clearance rates for LH (9) and similar MCR for FSH have been shown in pre- and postmenopausal women (10) in whom different plasma levels of estrogen and progesterone might be expected.

Several inherent limitations reside in the design of these studies. Firstly, since Enovid E consists of a mixture of an estrogen and progestin, the separate effects of these two steroids on plasma gonadotropins cannot be determined. Secondly, if a dose response relationship exists for the combination of these steroids, it cannot be determined from these data since the dosage used suppressed plasma FSH and LH levels in all eight women tested. It is conceivable that certain doses of these agents either singly or in combination might be stimulatory. For example, Odell has shown that after an appropriate period of administration of estrogen to postmenopausal women, a single dose of progesterone resulted in an elevation of plasma LH similar to the midcycle peak of an ovulatory cycle (ll).

Despite these limitations it is apparent that the pattern of variation in FSH and LH observed during a normal menstrual cycle is obliterated in women receiving this oral contraceptive preparation. To the extent that ovulation depends upon the observed variations in plasma FSH and LH in the control cycles it seems reasonable to conclude that the contraceptive efficacy of this regimen inheres primarily in suppression of pituitary secretion of gonadotropins with consequent inhibition of ovulation.

Acknowledgements

The authors express their appreciation to Miss Jayne Smith for her excellent technical assistance.

Some of the reagents in these studies were supplied to the authors by the National Pituitary Agency during the course of collaborative studies on the feasibility of radioimmunoassay for FSH.

References

1. Stevens, V. C., N. Vorys, P. K. Besch and R. D. Barry, Metabolism 14: 327, 1965.

2. Vorys, N., J. C. Ullery and V. C. Stevens, Amer J Obstet Gynec 93: 641, 1965.

3. Stevens, V. C. and N. Vorys, Obstet Gynec Survey 22: 781, 1967.

4. Schmidt-Elmendorff, J. and H. Kopera, Excerpta Medica International Congress Series 133: 1049, 1967.

5. Ross, G. T., W. D. Odell, and P. L. Rayford, Lancet, Dec. 3, 1966, p. 1255.

6. Cargille, C. M. and G. T. Ross, Lancet, April 27, 1968, p. 924.

7. Odell, W. D., G. T. Ross and P. L. Rayford, J Clin Invest 46: 248, 1967.

8. Yoshimi, T. and M. B. Lipsett, Steroids ll: 527, 1968.

9. Kohler, P. O., G. T. Ross and W. D. Odell, J Clin Invest 47: 38, 1968.

10. Coble, Y. D., P. O. Kohler, C. M. Cargille and G. T. Ross, Clin Res 16: 264, 1968.

ll. Odell, W. D. and R. S. Swerdloff, Progesterone Induced Luteinizing and Follicle Stimulating Hormone Surge in Postmenopausal Women: A Simulated Ovulatory Peak, Proc Nat Acad Sci (in press).

DISCUSSION

MIDGLEY: I should like to make two comments: Firstly, I was
delighted to see the results that Dr. Cargille presented. I
think the absolute levels of FSH and LH, the patterns throughout
the menstrual cycle, and responses to various steroids were very
similar to those we have obtained. Secondly, we have examined
the effects of clomiphene, both the racemic mixture and the
individual isomers, in an accumulated total of 45 menstrual
cycles in 15 apparently normal women. These women were studied
using a single control cycle, a treatment cycle consisting of
50 mg. of either the individual isomers or the mixture twice a
day on days 5, 6 and 7 and then a single post-treatment control
cycle. Upon examination of the data from these samples we have
been unable to detect any consistent change in either FSH or LH
in the normal subjects. However, some of the patterns observed
in the post-treatment control cycles were quite bizarre. This
suggests that clomiphene might have been retained in the body
exerting effects in subsequent months.

MARSHALL: Whereas the data presented by Dr. Cargille on the 7
anovulatory or oligo-ovulatory women revealed a maximum FSH
response to clomiphene occurring on day 3 or 4, the maximum LH
response in these same cycles occurred on day 6 or 7. These
maximum responses are statistically significantly elevated above
control values and suggest a distinct difference in the response
of FSH and LH to clomiphene.

NAFTOLIN: In our laboratory Dr. Carpenter has also found that
as men reach the age of 50 their LH levels tend to rise. Since
Dr. Midgley and Dr. Cargille were in such close agreement when
they were measuring FSH and since Dr. Midgley could find no
change in LH or FSH following clomiphene administration to
normal females I should like to raise two points. Firstly,
could Dr. Cargille comment on dosages less than 200 mg. per day
and secondly did he use clomiphene in normal women?

CARGILLE: We have no definitive data with respect to clomiphene
dose response relationships in normal women. However, we have
measured plasma FSH daily in samples taken from one woman during
a control cycle and a cycle in which 100 mg of clomiphene citrate
was given daily for five days, starting on the 2nd day of menses.
An increased level of plasma FSH was evident from the third to
the eighth day following the start of clomiphene therapy when
compared to the control cycle. The significance of this apparent
response will remain unclear, however, until adequate studies
have been made of the variability in plasma FSH levels observed
in consecutive cycles in the same subject. As yet, we do not
have data relating to between-cycle variability in normal women.

MIDGLEY: If I may take that question instead, I should like to
say that our comments regarding clomiphene were restricted to
normal menstruating women. In the anovulatory subject we
obtained a number of different kinds of response consisting

either of what appears to be the sudden induction of a normal menstrual cycle with a peak where there had been no peak before or an immediate response identical to that which Dr. Cargille has reported. Our results in male subjects are also similar to his in that LH and FSH each rise about the second or third day after administration of clomiphene at 200 mg./day.

MARSHALL: The pattern of gonadotropin response to clomiphene which was described previously and which consisted of both clomiphene peaks and pre-ovulatory peaks has consistently been seen in ovulatory cycles. Three other patterns have been noted with anovulatory cycles: 1) clomiphene peaks without pre-ovulatory peaks, 2) generally increasing, but irregular gonadotropin levels, and 3) no alteration of gonadotropins.

BELL: I should like to ask Dr. Cargille two questions. First, what is the time relationship between the FSH and LH midcycle peaks in individual cycles, and secondly, what evidence do you have that the women had normal ovulatory menstrual cycles?

CARGILLE: In our study of spontaneous cycles in 21 normal women, clearly defined FSH and LH peaks were noted in 19 women. These peaks were coincident in 14 women whereas the FSH peak followed that of LH in four instances; in one woman a small FSH peak preceded the LH peak by two days. Evidence of ovulation in 15 women consisted of finding a luteal plasma progesterone value of more than 5 mμg/ml. in assays performed by Dr. Yoshimi using the competitive protein binding method of Yoshimi and Lipsett. Fourteen of these 15 women had significant increases of FSH and LH near the time of midcycle and in 13 instances they were coincident.

STEINBERGER: I was delighted to hear the discussions of Drs. Cargille and Taymor who have shown elegantly, utilizing the radioimmunoassay technique, the biphasic characteristics of FSH excretion in the normal menstrual cycle. This confirms our studies performed by the cumbersome method of total gonadotropin determination, using rat ovarian weight, which was published in the Am. J. Med. Sci. 237: 4 , 1964; and a study of FSH excretion using the Steelman-Pohley augmentation method, which was presented at the First Gonadotropin Workshop in Puerto Vallarta in 1965. In both studies we have shown two peaks of gonadotropin excretion; one during the time of menstrual flow, and the other during the estimated time of ovulation. These peaks were observed in well over a dozen cycles. Thus, we are very happy to see that the data obtained by bioassay is now confirmed using radioimmuno-assay techniques.

STEVENS: I would like to direct a question to either Dr. Cargille or Dr. Midgley concerning the agreement they have reached on the effects of contraceptive steroids in the first treatment cycle. Did either of the workers have an opportunity to perform culdoscopic examinations on any of these patients to get an idea of what the state of follicular development might be?

ODELL: We published reports of the effects of 100 mg. clomiphene per day in normal males over a year ago and the findings were as Dr. Cargille has reported. In addition might I say that a higher dose of clomiphene, viz. 300 mg., will suppress LH and FSH in postmenopausal women although the suppression is not nearly as dramatic as with estrogen. The effects of oral contraceptives on LH reported by Dr. Cargille also agree with those which Dr. Ross and I have already published. The menstrual cycle data has been obtained from the assay of a very large number of patients by Dr. Parlow and I, Dr. Cargille and Dr. Ross. We would say that in 80% of this group of patients the FSH peak coincides with the LH peak and in 20% it occurs at a different time. The pattern is much as Dr. Cargille has found using his independent FSH and LH assay systems.

SAXENA: With regard to the secretion pattern of FSH during menstrual cycle, I would like to consider one of the subjects, reported by Dr. Gandy and myself, who showed a peak for FSH and LH in the early follicular phase as well as at midcycle. It is of interest that the urinary gonadotropic extract during the early follicular phase weighed five to six times more than the extracts from other days of the cycle. Could one consider the possibility that in some subjects these extracts may contain some non-specific cross-reacting material and can one correlate peaks of FSH secretion with steroid excretion or secretion during the menstrual cycle?

CARGILLE: Plasma levels of FSH and LH in four spontaneous cycles have been correlated in our laboratory with daily measurements of plasma progesterone performed by Dr. Yoshimi. In no instance did the plasma progesterone rise prior to either the FSH or LH midcycle peaks. The intervals from the gonadotropin peaks to the onset of the progesterone rise were highly variable, ranging from 0 to 4 days.

ROSEMBERG: Changing the subject under discussion somewhat, I would appreciate it if we could consider metabolic clearance rates and production rates of FSH and LH. I am referring to data obtained in the human.

ODELL: If I recall correctly the metabolic clearance rate was about 24 ml. per minute and this was independent of the gonadal status of the women; whether castrate, eugonadal or suppressed with oral contraceptives. The production rates were 734mU/min. in eugonadal women, 387 mU/min in women receiving norethynodrel and menstranol, and 2400 in postmenopausal women. Using published data of Dr. Ryan on pituitary content, we estimated that pituitary LH turned over once every 24 hours (Kohler, Ross and Odell, J. Clin. Inv. 47: 38, 1968).

BETTENDORF: In collaboration with Dr. Bishof we have measured FSH and LH activity in single human pituitaries from females

who had died suddenly. Histological examination of the ovaries
and the endometrium was used to determine the day of the ovarian
cycle. Only those pituitaries in which the exact time of the
cycle could be determined were used. The FSH test was carried
out by the Steelman-Pohley assay and the LH activity was measured
by the OAAD technique. The glands were homogenized in saline
before injection. High LH activity was found during menstruation
and between days 11 and 13. During the early follicular phase
and following ovulation in the luteal phase the pituitary LH
activity was much less, the difference being statistically
significant. The FSH activity per mg. of pituitary tissue showed
a similar pattern, with high values during menstruation and a
decrease in the follicular phase. An increase which began in
the middle of the follicular phase continued up to the time of
ovulation, after which a decrease occurred giving low levels in
the luteal phase. By calculating the total activity per
pituitary the values of LH were higher in relation to FSH. The
ratio of FSH/LH was low during menstruation, higher in the early
follicular phase and then decreased up to the time of ovulation.
After ovulation a high ratio was found, lower values occurring
at the end of the luteal phase.

Specific FSH and LH activity in Human Pituitaries

Day of Cycle	IU FSH/mg.	IU LH/mg.	FSH/LH	n
1	1.012+0.283	41.1+7.1	0.0233+0.0105	5
3-5	0.599+0.182	2.36+1.58	0.339 +0.222	4
6-8	0.966+0.115	18.66+6.25	0.060 +0.033	5
11-13	0.925+0.283	39.0 +8.0	0.0229+0.011	3
15-17	0.52 +0.11	1.43+0.98	0.614 +0.303	3
18-20	0.53	15.9 +3.3	0.039	2
21-27	0.735+0.182	4.42+0.68	0.171 +0.022	4

Total FSH and LH Activity in Human Pituitary

Day of Cycle	IU FSH	IU LH
1	283 + 81	12,368+1929
3-5	172.9+ 73.03	745+ 687
6-8	292.0+ 77.5	5,598+2190
11-13	300 + 70	12,333+3820
15-17	162.6+ 64.1	335+ 129
18-20	160	4,755+ 940
21-27	209 + 56	1,097+ 237

MIDGLEY: I should like to ask Dr. Odell whether he felt it was safe to make a judgment on production rates and metabolic clearance rates. We know that problems exist with respect to what the proper standard for LH in serum and urine and in the pituitary gland might be. I think that until we get this problem worked out it would be very difficult to talk about numbers of molecules leaving the pituitary gland, going into serum, and finally being cleared into the urine. I would now like to ask Dr. Gandy whether or not her assay was reacting to HCG. I was surprised to see the relatively low levels, activity equivlent to 300 mIU of 2nd IRP/ml. of serum on the first day following delivery. We found activity much greater than this.

SAXENA: You are right, they are much higher than 300 mIU. Our assay was not designed to measure values above 300 mIU with accuracy.

ODELL: In answer to Dr. Midgley's question our production rate studies were carried out with labeled pituitary LH and the IRP as a reference preparation. This was all done in blood by infusing the radioactive hormone. We estimated that about 5% of the LH produced was excreted in the urine.

SAXENA: I would like to add to the comments of Dr. Midgley that the use of pituitary homogenates or impure preparations of FSH and LH may not be suitable for the measurement of half-life and metabolic clearance rates of these hormones.

CARGILLE: Drs. Coble, Kohler, Ross, and I have recently reported values for the metabolic clearance and production rates of FSH in pre- and postmenopausal women. We utilized ^{131}I labeled Reichert 780 FSH as tracer and used both a single injection and constant infusion technique. Our results for premenopausal women showed a control value of 10mIU/ml. and a metabolic clearance rate of 14.2 ml./min $\pm$ 1.1 (S.E.). Their production rate was 146 mIU/min $\pm$ 27 (S.E.). In postmenopausal women the control level was 172 mIU/ml. and the metabolic clearance rate was 12.6 ml.min $\pm$ 1.1 (S.E.). The production rate in postmenopausal women was 2141 mIU/min. $\pm$ 264 (S.E.). From these data it is evident that the metabolic clearance rates are similar in pre- and postmenopausal women. The observed differences in plasma levels appear to relate to the marked differences in production rate.

PLASMA LUTEINIZING HORMONE LEVELS IN MALES
ACUTELY EXPOSED TO HIGH ALTITUDE

Luis A. Sobrevilla, M. D. and A. Rees Midgley, M. D.

Instituto de Investigaciones de la Altura, Universidad Peruana
Cayetano Heredia, Apartado 6083, Lima, Peru, and Department of
Pathology, The University of Michigan, Ann Arbor, Michigan.

INTRODUCTION

During the middle part of the 16th century, caucasian low-
landers from the mediterranean arrived at the shores of Peru
and began to settle on the highlands of the Central Andean plateau. During that period, transient disturbances of human and
animal reproduction were observed and recorded (1). Many years
later, in 1940, Monge observed that there was transitory infertility in couples living at high altitudes who were native of
sea level. He began the experimental study of this phenomena
(2) which was recently reviewed by Donayre (3).

In 1965, our group reported that acute exposure of males to
high altitudes created changes in seminal characteristics (4)
and in the urinary excretion of testosterone (5). Since these
changes were not accompanied by detectable alterations in "total"
urinary gonadotropin excretion, as determined by the mouse uterine weight bioassay (6), it was decided to re-investigate this
problem using a radioimmunoassay technic for the estimation of
luteinizing hormone activity.

MATERIAL AND METHODS

Subjects. Ten volunteer healthy seamen aged 18 to 22 years,
born and raised at sea level, were studied for four weeks at the
Navy Hospital in Lima (590 ft.). All subjects demonstrated normal adrenal, thyroidal and gonadal function, normal values for
urinary testosterone excretion as well as normal seminograms.

Exposure to High Altitudes. The subjects were taken by
train to Cerro de Pasco, a mining town at 14,000 ft., where the
mean barometric pressure is 445 mm Hg and the arterial oxygen
saturation of the adaptive native is 82%. Departure from Lima
took place at 7 a.m. By 11 a.m. an altitude of 10,000 ft. had
been reached. The day of the trip was considered day one of exposure. The group arrived at Cerro de Pasco at 7 p.m. and was
lodged in heated quarters. The subjects remained at high altitude for four weeks.

Plasma LH Determinations. Venous blood was collected in
heparinized syringes seven days before exposure, on the second
and third day of exposure, and seven days after return to sea
level. All samples were taken between 8 and 9 a.m. The plasma

was promptly obtained by centrifugation and frozen. The frozen
samples were then sent to Ann Arbor, Michigan, USA, where the LH
determinations were carried out as previously reported (7).

RESULTS

Table I summarizes the data, while Fig. I shows the individual values and the Mean + S.E. There was a statistically
significant drop the morning of the third day of exposure.

TABLE I

Plasma LH in ten healthy sea level males acutely exposed to
14,000 ft.

	Baseline °°	2nd day °°	3rd day °°	Return °°
Plasma LH ° (Mean + S.E.)	10.50+0.51	10.06+0.59	8.84+0.62	10.06+1.25
P	-	N.S.	<0.05	N.S.

° LH in terms of 2nd-IRP-HMG, milli IU/ml.

°° All samples taken from 8 to 9 a.m.

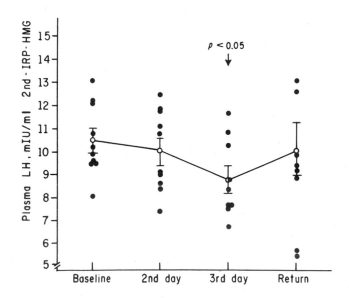

DISCUSSION

Plasma LH levels in the male have recently been determined by radioimmunoassay and, unlike FSH levels, they seem to change very little under normal conditions (8 and 9).

The plasma LH levels of our subjects did not change appreciably the second day of exposure, but a significant drop (p <0.05) of approximately 16% occurred the morning of the third day. Urinary testosterone excretion was found to decrease during the third day of exposure to altitude (5). This finding was confirmed in the present study. Since LH values were already low the morning of the third day, it is likely that the low urinary testosterone excretion is secondary to the decreased LH levels. On the seventh day of exposure the urinary excretion of testosterone was found to be normal. Hence, it is conceivable that plasma LH levels were also at the baseline level. In samples taken seven days after descent, LH levels were similar to the baseline values. Our previous finding of unaltered urinary excretion of "total" gonadotropins during the third day of exposure to high altitudes (6) could be due to the lack of precision of the bioassay used, or to a compensatory increase in the excretion of FSH.

Donayre et. al. have studied the seminal changes in this group of subjects (10). There was a statistically significant and continuous decrease in sperm count and motility, and an increase in abnormal forms. The pH became alkaline and the fructose rose while the citric acid did not change significantly. Samples were obtained the seventh, fourteenth, and twenty-seventh days of exposure. Since the fructose levels did not decrease, it appears that the seminal changes reflect both the alterations due to hypoxia and those secondary to hormonal changes.

Our group has previously reported the changes in adrenal (11) and thyroidal (12) physiology during the acute exposure of males to high altitudes. On the basis of those findings and the LH and testosterone data, it seems that the response to altitude exposure involves a prompt increase in the pituitary secretion of ACTH and TSH, lasting 2 to 4 days, while later during the third day there is a transient drop of LH secretion. Whether one of the variables is involved in exposure to high altitudes, or a combination of stimuli are responsible for the observed changes is difficult to answer, but further study of this area holds promise of a better understanding of the trophic hormone-gonad interrelationship.

ACKNOWLEDGMENT

Support was given in part, by grant T-66-89 from the Population Council, for which we are thankful. We are also grateful to the Peruvian Navy and their Commanders for their permission to let us study volunteer sailors, and to use the facilities of the Navy

Hospital in Lima. We are also indebted to the Director and
Medical Staff of the Social Security Hospital of Cerro de Pasco.
Miss Lilia Campos kindly typed the manuscript.

REFERENCES

1. Monge M. C., and C. Monge High Altitude Diseases, Charles
    C. Thomas, Springfield, Ill., 1966, p. 67.

2. Monge, M. C. and P. Mori-Chavez, Ann. Fac. Med. Lima 25: 34,
    1942.

3. Donayre, J., in: Life at High Altitudes, Pan-American Health
    Org. Publication 140, 1966, p. 74.

4. Donayre, J., R. Guerra-Garcia, F. Moncloa, and L. A. Sobrevilla
    Excerpta Med. Inter. Congress Series, No. 99, p. E 64.

5. Guerra-Garcia R., J. Donayre, L. A. Sobrevilla and F. Moncloa,
    Excerpta Med. Inter. Congress Series, No. 99, p. E. 62.

6. Sobrevilla, L. A., I. Romero, F. Moncloa, J. Donayre, and R.
    Guerra-Garcia, Acta Endocr. (Kbh),56: 369, 1967.

7. Midgley, A. R., Endocr.: 79: 10, 1966.

8. Odell, W. D., G. T. Ross and P. L. Rayford, J. Clin. Invest.
    46: 248, 1967.

9. Saxena, B. B., H. Demura, H. M. Gandy, and R. E. Peterson,
    J. Clin. Endocr.: 28: 519, 1968.

10. Donayre, J., R. Guerra-Garcia, F. Moncloa, and L. A.
    Sobrevilla, J. of Reprod. and Fertility, (In Press).

11. Moncloa, F., J. Donayre, L. A. Sobrevilla and R. Guerra-
    Garcia, J. Clin. Endocr., 25: 1640, 1965.

12. Moncloa, F., R. Guerra-Garcia, C. Subauste, L. A. Sobrevilla
    and J. Donayre, J. Clin. Endocr. 26: 1237, 1966.

DISCUSSION

BURGOS: I would like to ask Dr. Sobrevilla a question. How long can a subject remain at high altitude without any change in the sperm count and how many counts have been made in each person. Do you have any explanation for the decrease in the number of spermatozoa. Does the drop in LH have any relation-ship?

SOBREVILLA: Sperm samples were taken on the 7th, 14th and 27th days of stay at high altitude. With reference to your question on the mechanism of production of these changes, the fructose levels did not fall as we expected, although the days on which fructose was measured were not the same as those on which the fall in testosterone and LH occurred. Since the subjects were exposed for a month, and the spermatogenic cycle is rather long, we cannot quite relate the seminal changes with the brief hormonal alterations.

SERUM HLH LEVELS IN OVARIAN AND SYSTEMIC
VEIN BLOOD BY RADIOIMMUNOASSAY

Naftolin, F., Espeland, D., Tremann, J.A., Dillard,
E.A. and Paulsen, C.A.
University of Washington and U.S.P.H.S. Hospital
Seattle, Wash.

The effect of the pituitary tropic hormones upon their
respective target organs is well established. But the effect,
if any, of the target organ upon its tropin remains to be conclusively demonstrated. Today we will present studies on the
human ovary that suggest a role of this target organ in the
metabolic fate of its tropin, luteinizing hormone (LH). This
hormone causes morphologic and biochemical changes in the
ovary. Studies of _in vitro_ and _in vivo_ ovarian metabolism
have suggested that LH effects steroidogenesis by causing an
increase in ovarian 3',5'-cyclic adenylic acid (1,2). The
sequence is compatible with the general theory of hormone
action through a common mediator (3).

Investigators have asked whether the gonadotropins are
in any way trapped or altered while exerting their effect on
the ovary. Earlier experiments have been limited by methodology. Thus, studies of organ weights and gonadotropin levels
after hemicastration, during parabiosis and after subcapsular
splenic implants of ovaries in castrated animals have not
yielded clearly interpretable results (4-12). Seidlin, in
1940, exposed a commercial gonadotropin extract ("Gonin",
Cutter Laboratories) to macerated hog ovaries and found a
decrease in the "Gonin's" ability to stimulate enlargement of
the immature rat ovary. However, utilizing exposure of
"Gonin" to macerated muscle, he obtained similar results (13).
Decay curves of fluorescent labelled gonadotropin (14) as well
as renal clearance of both pituitary (15,16) and chorionic
gonadotropins have been accomplished but shed little light
regarding the role of the ovary, if any, in blood levels of
gonadotropin.

Recently protein hormones have been labelled with
isotopes, followed after injection and found to localize
significantly in various organs (17-19). Our group (20) has
confirmed the work done by Eshkol (21) that demonstrated the
preferential uptake of HCG ^{131}I by the **immature mice ovary.**

With the development of radioimmunoassay for protein
hormones, blood levels of LH have been measured in physiologic
situations by ourselves and others (22-25). This may allow

further elucidation of the effect of passage through the ovary upon gonadotropin. The following experiment was designed.

MATERIALS AND METHODS

Fifteen patients, age 23-50, were operated upon for non-ovarian pelvic pathology such as uterine fibromata. Ten were untreated and five had received estrogen-progestin therapy. At surgery simultaneous antecubital and ovarian venous blood samples were taken. Visualization of ovarian venous radicals directly draining the ovary was utilized to avoid the admixture of blood from the uterine venous drainage. In two patients simultaneous specimens were drawn from the antecubital vein and ovarian artery. All bloods were appropriately paired and handled identically i.e. sera frozen at -20° and run as pairs in the same assay. All samples were run in duplicate in at least two (2) assays. A radioimmunoassay modified after the double antibody method of Midgley (23) was employed. This is an HCG anti-HCG system that utilizes the cross reaction between HCG and LH. The standard curve of Second International Reference Preparation (2nd IRP) 1-128 mIU/ml is linear against a log dose plot from 2-64 mIU/ml, therefore, levels of 2 mIU/ml were considered valid. The precision of each assay exceeds 95 per cent.

Venous serum HLH from six normal males who were to undergo elective non-endocrine surgery such as hernia repair was studied before, during and after the day of surgery. Various anaesthetics were used. Preparation and assay of samples were as above.

RESULTS

All nine untreated women with levels greater than 2 mIU/ml showed a difference between systemic and ovarian venous LH (Table 1). Five of the nine had a relative lowering of ovarian venous LH in the range of 11-24%. Three of the patients had a relative lowering of the ovarian venous LH of 5-10%. Since this was less than double the error of the method these differences were classified as "not significant" when considering the individual cases. Evaluation of the entire group by the Sign Test showed the consistent lowering of ovarian venous HLH to be highly significant. One patient more than doubled the concentration of LH in the blood leaving the ovary.

All of the treated patients had low values of LH as expected (Table 2). This group also showed a consistent relative decrease in the amount of LH leaving the ovary and when considered in the group made the statistical significance even greater.

In one case, the paired values were identical and in the other
there was a 10% higher level in the artery to the ovary.
(**Table** 3). The LH levels in the six operated males
fluctuated randomly in the normal range throughout the period
of observation (Figure **1**).

Table 1

PER CENT DIFFERENCE BETWEEN SYSTEMIC AND OVARIAN VENOUS LH

Untreated Women - Age, 26-49 years

	Serum LH mIU/ml		
	Systemic	Ovarian	△%*
E.R.	20.5	18.2	12
G.D.	39.2	29.8	24
E.G.	13.3	11.8	11
N.A.	3.2	2.5	22
L.C.	5.7	4.8	16
B.P.	2.5	2.4	N.S.
E.M.	10.0	9.5	N.S.
E.F.	4.8	4.4	N.S.
J.J.	3.3	6.9	116

* p= < .01

Table 2

PER CENT DIFFERENCE BETWEEN SYSTEMIC AND OVARIAN VENOUS LH

Steroid Treated Women-Age 29-50 Yrs.

	Steroid Treated Agent	Serum LH mIU/ml		
		Systemic	Ovarian	△%*
M.H.	Norlestrin	3.1	2.1	38
N.D.	Norinyl	2.6	2.3	12
M.W.	Deluteval	2.6	2.2	17

*p= < .01

Table 3

SIMULTANEOUS   ANTECUBITAL VEIN
AND OVARIAN ARTERY LH (mIU/ml)

	Venous	Arterial
L.S.	7.6	7.6
C.H.	14.5	16.0

Figure 1

EFFECT OF SURGICAL STRESS ON SERUM
HLH LEVELS (mIU/m.)

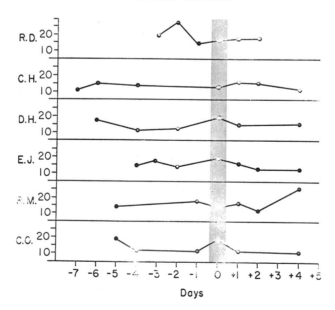

DISCUSSION

Human ovarian vein LH levels have not been reported previously. Paired samples of blood to and from the ovary drawn simultaneously should demonstrate any metabolism of tropin by the ovary. Because of spasm and associated hemodynamic changes during attempts at aspirating the ovarian artery the study was constructed as above. Simultaneous ovarian artery and systemic vein LH levels confirm the validity of using the systemic venous blood as the analog of the afferent loops in this system. Ney and Liddle have demonstrated changes in circulating adrenocorticosteroids during surgical stress (26). This is due to increase of ACTH secretion and raises the question of a similar effect of surgical stress on LH levels. However, the random distribution of pre-,intra- and post-operative LH levels in normal males undergoing elective surgery shows that LH is not responsive to surgical and anaesthetic stress per se.

In nine of twelve women studied, the difference between systemic and ovarian venous levels was greater than double the error of the method. A consistent lowering of LH concentration in blood leaving the ovary was found. No pattern relating to age, time of cycle or treatment with estrogen-progestin mixtures can be defined in this preliminary data since the relative decrease in ovarian venous LH levels is similar in all of the subjects studied, with a single exception. This one patient with an increased LH concentration in ovarian venous blood was a 37 year old multigravid female in good health who had uterine fibroids and menorrhagia. Five months prior to surgery she had had a carcinoma of the breast with axillary node metastases removed and was tumor free at the time of laparotomy. None of the patients had a positive history, physical signs or laboratory tests indicative of endocrine abnormality. All levels of LH were in the normal range.

SUMMARY AND CONCLUSIONS

The data reveals a consistent and significant lowering of LH in ovarian venous serum (11-38%). This constitutes preliminary evidence that LH is metabolized by the ovary in women.

ACKNOWLEDGEMENTS

The skilled technical assistance of Mrs. Sue Stevens is gratefully acknowledged.

REFERENCES

(1) Savard, K. in "Recent Research on Gonadotrophic Hormones, Bell, E.T. and Loraine, J.A. (eds.) London, Livingston, E. and S., 1967, p. 202.

(2) Savard, K., March, J.M. and Rice, B.F., **Rec.** Progr. Hormone Res., 21:285, 1965.

(3) Sutherland, E., Øye, I. and Butcher, R., Rec. Progr. Hormone Res., 21:623, 1965.

(4) Achilles, W., and Sturgis, S. Endocrinol., 49:720, 1951

(5) Bruzzone, S., Lipshutz, A. and Niedmann, L. J. Endocrinol. 8:187, 1952

(6) Heller, C. and Nelson, W.O. Rec. Progr. Hormone Res., 3:229, 1948

(7) Junck, E., Heller, C. and Nelson, W., Proc. Soc. Exp. Biol. Med., 65:148, 1947

(8) Lipshutz, A., Fuente-Alba, A. and Vivaldi, T. Compt. Rend. Soc. de Biol., 120:323, 1935

(9) Lipschutz, A., Ponce De Leon, H., Waywood, E. and Gay, O., Rev. Can. De. Biol., 5:181, 1946

(10) Selye, H. Proc. Soc. Exp. Biol. Med., 43:404, 1940

(11) Wijnans, M., Acta Physiol. Pharm. Neerl., 3:199, 1954a.

(12) Wijnans, M., Acta Physiol. Pharm. Neerl., 3:214, 1954b

(13) Seidlin, S.M., Endocrinol., 26:696, 1940

(14) Kulangara, A. and Pincus, G., Endocrinol., 71:179, 1962

(15) Apostolakis, M. and Loraine, J., J. Clin. Endocrinol. Metab., 20:1437, 1960

(16) Kohler, P.O., Phang, J.M., Fullner, W.W., Ross, G.T. and Odell, W.D. J. Clin. Endocrinol. Metab., 28:613, 1968

(17) Sonenberg, M., CIBA Symposia Endocr., 4:229, 1952

(18) Sonenberg, M., and Money, W. Rec. Progr. Hormone Res., 11:43, 1955

(19) Seki, M., J. Jap. Obst. Gyn. Soc., 19:8, 1963

(20) Espeland, D.H., Naftolin, F. and Paulsen, C.A. Unpublished data.

(21) Eshkol, A., in "Recent Research on Gonadotrophic Hormones, Bell, E.T. and Loraine, J.A. (eds.) London, Livingston, E. and S., 1967, p. 202

(22) Bagshawe, K., Wilde, C. and Orr, A., Lancet, 1:1118, 1966

(23) Midgley, A.R., Endocrinol., 79:10, 1966

(24) Odell, W., Ross, G. and Rayford, P., Metabolism, 15:287, 1966

(25) Paulsen, C.A., Gordon, D.L. and Carpenter. Unpublished data.

(26) Ney, R.L., Naokata, S., Nicholson, W.E., Island, D.P. and Liddle, G.W. J. Clin. Invest., 42:1669, 1963

CHAPTER 5

USE OF STANDARDS IN GONADOTROPIN ASSAY

USE OF STANDARDS
GENERAL CONSIDERATIONS

Eugenia Rosemberg, M. D.

Medical Research Institute of Worcester, Inc.,
Worcester City Hospital, Worcester, Massachusetts

We have long recognized the important role played by the World
Health Organization (WHO) in the establishment and distribution
of international standards and international reference preparations. The availability of standards and reference preparations
ensures the uniformity of the potency of preparations manufac-
tured and used throughout the world and facilitates and unifies
research throughout the world.

The exact definition of the various categories of standards
distributed by the WHO (DRB-PH-68/72S) are not well known.
These are as follows: International standard is a preparation
to which an international unit* is assigned on the basis of an
extensive international collaborative study. The standard is
intended for use in the estimation of potency of a test sample
by direct comparison of the two materials in a biological test
system. A collaborative study is usually made to ensure that
the proposed preparation would be suitable as an international
standard in the hands of different workers and, if appropriate,
by a number of different assay methods.
    International reference preparation may serve a function
similar to that of the international standard but is established
either without the full international study which precedes the
establishment of an international standard, or when a collaborative study has shown that the preparation is, for some reason,
not entirely suitable to serve as an international standard.
In some instances, an international unit is assigned to an
international reference preparation, especially when an early
definition of such a unit is desirable to prevent the emergence
of a multiplicity of systems for designating potency.

---

* The international unit (IU) is defined as the specified biological
activity contained in a defined weight of a current international standard.
The standard is the material as it exists in the ampoules; the "material"
thus includes the active ingredients together with all the other constituents
such as moisture and in some instances carrier and buffer salts. The potency
of the international standard should be taken as the number of IU stated on
the label, although the unit is still formally defined in terms of weight.

    International biological reference reagents are used for
specific laboratory tests for the identification of micro-
organisms. They are highly specific for the organism concerned
and since they are used mainly for the purpose of qualitative
identification, unitage is not usually assigned to them.
    Working standards are not normally provided by WHO. An
international working standard may, however, be made available
from the Division of Biological Standards, WHO, in a special
instance where the benefit of having one is exceptional. The
assumption is made that the ampoules of the working standard
are equivalent to the international standard itself. Assays
are carried out on each batch to verify its potency, but it is for
individual national control authorities to decide whether to
adopt the working standard as an official national standard.
    Research standards are set up by the Division of Biological
Standards, WHO. Research standards do not have the official
status of standards, reference preparations or reference reagents.
Research standards are set up with the same care and precautions
as the international standard, although these are not necessarily
subjected to the same extensive international collaborative
assay. In some cases, a research standard may, in due course,
become officially established by the Expert Committee of
Biological Standardization of the WHO as an international standard
or as a reference preparation.

A brief review of the historical development of standards for
gonadotropins seems in order. For many years, the bioassay of
pituitary gonadotropins suffered from the lack of suitable
reference materials. Consequently, results of bioassays could
only be expressed in terms of various "animal units" arbitrarily
established in different laboratories. Moreover, the use of
"animal units" made it very difficult to compare results obtained
in one laboratory with those obtained in another.

In the early 1950's, two reference standards were prepared by the
kaolin-acetone methods: one from the urine of menopausal and
postmenopausal women which was referred as HMG-20 A (1), and the
other, from the urine of normal males which was referred as
AMW (2). A collaborative study was undertaken to establish the
activity of AMW in terms of HMG-20 A (3) and to provide advanced
information bearing on the question as to whether the establishment of an international standard could serve a useful purpose.
As a result of this study, the establishment of an international
standard for human pituitary gonadotropins in urine was strongly
recommended. These two preparations (HMG-20 A and AMW) served
as local laboratory standards on a temporary basis.

In 1957, the WHO Expert Committee on Biological Standardization
(WHO Tech. Rep. Series #147, p. 9, 1958) recognized the need
 for the establishment of an international standard for human
menopausal gonadotropin and requested the National Institute
for Medical Research, London, to obtain a quantity of material

to be used as the International Reference Preparation for Human
Menopausal Gonadotropin. To fulfill this purpose, a batch of a
relatively crude material (HMG-24) was made in a fashion similar
to that used in the preparation of HMG-20 A. However, at that
time, the available methods for the bioassay of gonadotropins
were not considered sufficiently specific and quantitative to
make it possible to establish a standard with an international
unitage (WHO Tech. Rep. Series #172, p. 9,, 1959). Accordingly,
the material was established as an International Reference
Preparation for Human Menopausal Gonadotropin and became known
as the 1st IRP (WHO Tech. Rep. Series #187, p. 9, 1960).
Because of the lack of official unitage, the potency of gonadotropin preparations tested against this standard was expressed
as mg. equivalent of the 1st IRP.

These preparations (HMG-20 A, AMW and 1st IRP) provided the
first yardstick of communication among scientists. However, they
were relatively crude preparations. With the advancement of the
chemical and biological characterization of gonadotropins, it
soon became evident that a purer and more potent standard was
needed. Moreover, in 1959, the supply of the 1st IRP was nearly
exhausted. After lengthy deliberations at Gatlinburg in 1959
and in Copenhagen in 1960, it was decided that a urinary gonadotropin extract (Pergonal 23) purer, more potent and less toxic
than the 1st IRP be considered as its replacement and subjected
to full international study. The characterization of this
material [Proposed International Standard (PIS)] was carried
out utilizing bioassay methods specific for follicle-stimulating
(FSH) and luteinizing (LH) hormone activities, and also by non-
specific methods. The 1st IRP was used as the reference
material.

After completion of the international study, the Expert Committee
on Biological Standardization, WHO, at its 17th Session, which
was held in Geneva in September 1964, established the Proposed
International Standard (PIS) as the Second International Reference
Preparation of Human Menopausal Gonadotropin (2nd IRP) (WHO/BS/
723). The Committee assigned a potency of 40 IU of FSH activity
and 40 IU of LH activity to each ampoule of the 2nd IRP. It was
stated (DRB/DF/82) that 1 IU of FSH activity of the 2nd IRP was
equivalent to the activity present in 7 mg. of the 1st IRP; and
1 IU of LH activity of the 2nd IRP was equivalent to the activity
present in 2 mg. of the 1st IRP.

The adoption of the 2nd IRP facilitated the expression of results
in assays measuring FSH and LH activity, respectively. It was
not established as a standard for general gonadotropin assays
(rat ovarian weight or mouse uterine weight methods). If,
contrary to official intent, the 2nd IRP is employed as the
standard for general gonadotropin assays, the method used for
reporting results would be arbitrary. The Seventeenth Report of
the WHO Expert Committee on Biological Standardization (WHO Tech.

Rep. Series # 293, 1964) indicates that the International Unit
of FSH or LH activity corresponds to the activity contained in
0.2295 mg. of the 2nd IRP. Consequently, 40 IU, which is the
labelled potency would contain 9.18 mg. Presumably, half of
this would be lactose and half active material, or possibly,
the ampoule of the 2nd IRP is composed of 4.18 mg. of active
material and 5.0 mg. of lactose.

Many investigators who have used this standard in general
gonadotropin assays have reported results in terms of mg. of
the 2nd IRP. However, because of lack of information regarding
the exact quantity of active material (plus carrier) contained
in each ampoule of the 2nd IRP, some investigators expressed
their results based on the assumption that each ampoule contained
5 mg. while others considered the weight of the material to be
10 mg. All that can be recommended at present is that investigators always make clear, each time the 2nd IRP is used in
general gonadotropin assays, exactly what convention they are
employing in expressing their results.

In 1959, the National Institutes of Health (NIH), Public Health
Service, Bethesda, Maryland, U.S.A., through the Endocrinology
Study Section made available purified pituitary FSH and LH
preparations of animal origin. These preparations were not
established as official standards. Rather, they were distributed
by the NIH to provide a service to the scientific community at
the national level. Because the 2nd IRP was not made available
until 1964, these preparations became extensively used, nationally
and internationally, as reference material in specific assays
for FSH and LH activity.

The most widely used have been those obtained from sheep
pituitary glands. The first batches released for distribution
were NIH-FSH-S1* and NIH-LH-S1* which were standardized against
the Armour pituitary preparations pig FSH 264-151-X and ovine LH-
227-80 for FSH and LH activity, respectively. Subsequent
batches of sheep pituitary NIH-FSH and NIH-LH materials have
been standardized against the first batch. No official
unitage has been assigned to these preparations. Consequently,
results of assays have been expressed as mg.** equivalent of
the respective NIH-FSH or NIH-LH batch used.

---

* S1: sheep batch #1; ** designated by some investigators as a unit.
  Information regarding potency of the various batches and degree of
  contamination with other hormones is provided by the Endocrinology
  Study Section, NIH.

Recognizing the need for a reference preparation to be used in assays measuring general gonadotropic activity, the Endocrinology Study Section, NIH made available in 1965 a preparation obtained from the urine of postmenopausal women. This material was designated NIH-HPG-UPM-1. No unitage was assigned to it. Consequently, it was suggested that results of general gonadotropin assays be expressed in mg. equivalents of NIH-HPG-UPM-1. Because one vial of this preparation contained sufficient amount of material to conduct specific FSH and LH assays, its FSH and LH activity (expressed in IU's of the 2nd IRP), was also indicated.

The availability of the NIH preparations and of the 2nd IRP provided means for quantitation of bioassay results. However, the information thus far reported in the literature is rather confusing due to the fact that results have been expressed in terms of various NIH reference preparations or the official WHO standard.

A list of conversion factors is presented to facilitate comparison of specific activity of the preparation described in this report.

CONVERSION FACTOR			ASSAY	SOURCE
1 mg. 1st IRP	~	0.004 mg. NIH-FSH-S1	AR *	Rosemberg, E. et al (J. Clin.
1 mg. 1st IRP	~	0.009 mg. NIH-LH-S1	VPW**	Endocr. 24: 673, 1964)
1 mg. NIH-FSH-S1	~	9.2 rat units	AR	
1 mg. NIH-LH-S1	~	26.5 rat units	VPW	Albert, A. Mayo Clinic Proc. 40:
1 mg. NIH-LH-S1	~	166.0 rat units	OAAD†	216, 1965.
1 mg. 1st IRP	~	0.14 IU 2nd IRP	AR	DRB/DF/82
1 mg. 1st IRP	~	0.5 IU 2nd IRP	VPW	
1 mg. NIH-HPG-UPM-1	~	7.1 IU 2nd IRP	AR	Subcommittee on
1 mg. NIH-HPG-UPM-1	~	4.4 IU 2nd IRP	VPW	Gonadotropins NIH
1 mg. NIH-HPG-UPM-1	~	5.1 IU 2nd IRP	OAAD	(unpublished observations)
1 mg. NIH-FSH-S1	~	26.5 IU 2nd IRP	AR	Rosemberg, E.
1 mg. NIH-LH-S1	~	51.3 IU 2nd IRP	VPW	Present paper.
1 mg. NIH-LH-S1	~	588.0 IU 2nd IRP	OAAD	

*AR: augmentation reaction assay (4); ** VPW: ventral prostate weight assay (5); † OAAD: ovarian ascorbic acid depletion assay (6).

The most important principle governing the use of standards is
that a standard should be as alike   the material tested as
possible. Moreover, the physiologic characteristics of the
assay systems used should be understood if conversion factors
are used. To illustrate these   facts, let us consider the
assay of gonadotropin preparations of human urinary origin using
as standard a preparation of animal pituitary origin.

The LH activity of 3 preparations made from postmenopausal urine
[Pergonal batches 25-EX-1899 and 25-EX-1938 and PM (fraction
C)], of 1 preparation made from male urine [M (fraction C)], and
1 made from the urine of eunuchs [E (fraction C)],were assayed
with ovine NIH-LH-S1 as standard. Two bioassay systems, the
VPW and OAAD methods, were employed (7).

Table 1

RELATIVE POTENCY OF URINARY GONADOTROPIN
PREPARATIONS IN TERMS OF NIH-LH-S1

| Preparations | Relative Potency* | | ID** |
	VPW	OAAD	$\frac{VPW}{OAAD}$
Pergonal 25-EX-1899	0.30	0.027	11.1
Pergonal 25-EX-1938	0.34	0.028	12.1
PM (fraction C)	0.30	0.027	11.1
M (fraction C)	0.05	0.004	12.5
E (fraction C)	0.53	0.043	12.3
Mean			11.8

* In terms of NIH-LH-S1; **Index of Discrimination;
(from: E. Rosemberg, E. A. Solod, and A. Albert. J.
Clin. Endocr. 24: 714, 1964).

It was found that the VPW method indicated the presence of 12
times more activity in the 5 urinary gonadotropin preparations
than did the OAAD method. This was indicated by the index of
discrimination (ID) $\frac{VPW}{OAAD}$. In the search for an explanation of
this discrepancy, the OAAD and the VPW methods for assay
of LH activity were analyzed with respect to sensitivity,
accuracy and interference by other hormones. The discrepancy
was explained on the basis of differences in the chemical and

physical nature of the hormones, and to the effect of over-all rate
of metabolism of the LH in the ovine LH standard, and in the urinary
extracts. Also, discrepancies in relative potency (RP) obtained
by these two methods have been related to the concept that the
OAAD is an "acute biochemical response" and the VPW a "chronic
growth response" (8). A similar observation was made testing an
LH preparation obtained from human pituitary glands (R-469-2, kindly
supplied by Drs. L. E. Reichert, Jr., and A. Wilhelmi), in both
the VPW and OAAD methods using ovine NIH-LH-S1 as standard (9).

Another example is seen in the assay of ovine NIH-FSH-S1 and NIH-
LH-S1 and the 2nd IRP (a gonadotropin preparation obtained from
human urine).

Table 2 shows the assay characteristics and dosages used for the
comparative study of these hormones using three assay systems:
AR, VPW and OAAD.[†]

Table 2

ASSAY CHARACTERISTICS OF 2nd IRP, NIH-LH-S1
AND NIH-FSH-S1

Assay System	2nd IRP				NIH-LH-S1				NIH-FSH-S1			
	Dose IU	No. of Rats	Mean Slope (±SE)	λ	Dose mcg	No. of Rats	Mean Slope (±SE)	λ	Dose mcg	No. of Rats	Mean Slope (±SE)	λ
AR (10)*	2-4-8 3-6-12	126	247 (47)	0.14					100-200 75-150-300 120-240-480	119	235 (42)	0.14
VPW (6)	1.2-2.4-4.8 1.6-3.2-6.4	84	22.7 (4.3)	0.21	24-48-96 25-50-100	83	16.3 (3.6)	0.22				
OAAD (21)	0.4-1.6-3.2 0.6-1.8-5.4	231	-19.2 (5.5)	0.34	1-4 1-3-9 1.5-4.5	186	-34.0 (9.7)	0.22				

* Number of assays.

Table 3 shows the specific activity of the ovine preparations in
terms of the 2nd IRP

Table 3

SPECIFIC ACTIVITY OF NIH-FSH-S1 AND NIH-LH-S1, IU 2nd IRP/mg.

Assay System	No. of Assays	No. of Animals	Assay Characteristics		Weighted Mean Potency Ratio (95% CL)	
			bc	λ	NIH-FSH-S1 (IU/mg)	NIH-LH-S1 (IU/mg)
AR	10	245	239	0.14	26.5 (24.3-28.8)	
VPW	6	167	18.6	0.21		51.3 (43.9-59.9)
OAAD	21*	417	-26	0.30		588 (500-714)

* Lack of parallelism : 4 assays.

Index of Discrimination $\frac{OAAD}{VPW}$: 11.5

The index of discrimination, in this case $\frac{OAAD}{VPW}$, is of the same order of magnitude as that presented in Table 1.

The actual RP values obtained using the VPW and OAAD methods are different and therefore confusing. However, if the reference material used is identified, it is possible to calculate a common biopotency. Let us assume that an unknown urinary gonadotropin preparation has been tested in the VPW assay using ovine NIH-LH-S1 as standard. To convert this value into IU's of the 2nd IRP, the RP number should be multiplied by 51.3 (conversion factor NIH-LH-S1/2nd IRP, VPW assay), and by 11.5 (ID factor $\frac{OAAD}{VPW}$ Table 3).

It should be noted that when urinary gonadotropin extracts are assayed by means of the OAAD and VPW methods in terms of a reference material of urinary origin, the ID is approximately unity (7). Consequently, comparison of LH activity contained in urinary extracts by means of these two assay methods should be conducted using as standard the 2nd IRP and not the ovine NIH-LH preparations.

When gonadotropic substances are compared using fundamentally the same technics and essentially the same assay animals, variability between laboratories can be minimized. The conversion factors presented in this report are applicable only if it can be demonstrated that bioassay conditions in different laboratories are basically the same.

The use of one hormone as a standard for another hormone represents a violation of the principle of similarity. It is known that a protein molecule may lose functional or biologic activity without concomitant loss of immunologic activity. Therefore, with the advent of immunological technics for the measurement of gonadotropic activity in body fluids, the establishment of proper standards is of paramount importance. It is hoped that future developments in this field would lead to the preparation of gonadotropin standards of the same source and species as the material to be assayed biologically or immuno- logically. Only then, the use of conversion factors, which, if extended is extremely hazardous, would be avoided.

This work was supported by Grant AM-07564, USPHS, National Institutes of Health, Bethesda, Maryland. We are indebted to the Endocrinology Study Section, NIH, Bethesda, Maryland, for the generous supply of NIH-FSH-S1 and NIH-LH-S1 used in this study. We are also indebted to Dr. D. R. Bangham, Department of Biological Standards, Medical Research Council, Mill Hill, London, for the gift of the 2nd IRP.

REFERENCES

1. Loraine, J. A., and J. B. Brown. J. Clin. Endocrinol. 16: 1180, 1956.

2. Albert, A. Proc. Staff Meet. Mayo Clinic. 31: 341, 1956.

3. Albert, A., R. Borth, E. Diczfalusy, J. A. Loraine, B. Lunenfeld, J. W. McArthur, and E. Rosemberg, J. Clin. Endocrinol. 18: 1117, 1958.

4. Steelman, S. L., and F. M. Powley, Endocrinology 53: 604, 1953.

5. McArthur, J. W. Endocrinology, 50: 304, 1952.

6. Parlow, A. F. In: Albert, A. (Ed) Human Pituitary Gonadotropins: A. Workshop Conference, Charles C. Thomas, Publisher, Springfield, Illinois, p. 300, 1961.

7. Rosemberg, E., E. A. Solod, and A. Albert J. Clin. Endocrinol, 24: 714, 1964.

8. Parlow, A. F., and L. E. Reichert, Jr., Endocrinology 73: 377, 1963.

9. Albert, A., C. Hanten, E. Rosemberg, and G. Bulat. Endocrinology 77: 588, 1965.

10. Rosemberg, E., and I. Engel. J. Clin. Endocrinol. 21: 1063, 1961.

---

† p. 389: The details of the assay methods used as performed in our laboratories have been described (7 and 10).

REPORT OF THE NATIONAL PITUITARY AGENCY COLLABORATIVE STUDY OF THE RADIOIMMUNOASSAY OF FSH AND LH: CONSIDERATION OF STANDARDS

A. Albert, M. D.
Mayo Clinic and Mayo Graduate School of Medicine
Rochester, Minnesota

Principles governing the appropriate use of standards in assays, whether the assays are biological, chemical, immunological or microbial, have been laid down for a long time. Nonadherence to these principles usually leads to complexities and, more often than not, to erroneous interpretations and conclusions. The confusion in the reported values of radioimmunoassays of gonadotropins, particularly of human follicle stimulating hormone (hFSH) and human luteinizing hormone (hLH) in serum and urine is an example of difficulties that may arise from nonadherence to general principles. This is well shown by the report (1) of the recent collaborative study conducted by the National Pituitary Agency (NPA) on the bioassay and radioimmunoassay of hFSH and hLH. Only that part of the report pertinent to the use of standards will be discussed.

Essentially, the NPA study determined by both bioassay and radioimmunoassay techniques the FSH and LH content of four human pituitary tissue extracts differing widely in FSH/LH ratio and of three highly purified (immunochemical grade) preparations (one, of hFSH and two preparations of hLH). In addition, radioimmunoassay was conducted on serum from four patients with different levels of gonadotropic function as determined clinically. The standard used was the Second International Reference Preparation (2nd IRP) for Human Menopausal Gonadotrophins (from the urine of postmenopausal women). However, the study was designed (complete dose-response curves for each of the preparations were obtained in the radioimmunoassay) so that any of the 7 pituitary preparations could be assayed in terms of any or all of the remaining preparations.

Table 1 shows the results obtained by bioassay for the 7 pituitary preparations; all values are International Units/milligram (IU/mg) for FSH and LH activity, the 2nd IRP being employed as standard. Table 2 shows the radioimmunoassay values for FSH and LH of the 7 preparations with the 2nd IRP as the concomitant standard. It is immediately obvious, if the bioassay values are regarded as true values, that the radioimmunoassay is overestimating the FSH and LH present in these preparations. The degree of overestimation is shown in Table 3 where the 7 preparations are arranged in descending order of their FSH/LH ratios. The disparity between the bioassay and the radioimmunoassay estimation of FSH is given by the FSH radioimmunoassay/bioassay (Imm/Bio) ratio; the disparity seems to be inversely related to the purity of FSH. The LH radioimmunoassay/bioassay ratio, however, is constant for the first five preparations; the ratio may perhaps be somewhat greater for the two immunochemical grade LH preparations.

Many factors could be responsible for these discrepancies. One
possibility, however, is that the 2nd IRP, while satisfactory as
a bioassay standard, is not satisfactory as a radioimmunologic
standard. The 2nd IRP is a urinary gonadotropin extract, and its
use as a standard in an immunologic system for pituitary extracts
presumes equilivance of bioreactive and immunoreactive determinants.
However, the overestimation of both FSH and LH by the radioimmunoassay could be largely accounted for on the hypothesis that the 2nd
IRP had lost about one half of the FSH and about four-fifths of the
LH immunoreactivity. Were this a reasonable hypothesis, then correction of the overestimation could be made by using LER 907, for
example, as the standard. When the relative potencies are calculated
from the dose-response curves of LER 907 expressed as milli IU (or
by any of several methods of calculation), the agreement between the
radioimmunoassay values and the bioassay values becomes much closer
as shown in Table 4. Comparison of the Imm/Bio ratios for both FSH
and LH using the two standards (2nd IRP and LER 907) shows the extent
to which the disagreement between the bioassay and radioimmunoassay
has been reduced. What disparity remains is probably related to
other immunologic factors. The bioassay FSH/LH ratios and the radioimmunoassay FSH/LH ratios, shown in Table 5, are also much closer to
each other using LER 907 as standard than using the 2nd IRP as
standard.

A fundamental principle in assay is that, when only impure materials
are available, the standard be as alike the material being assayed
as possible. This alikeness means biological, chemical, physical
and immunological alikeness. As a recent example of the continuing
importance of this principle in the bioassay field, a disparity of
some 12-fold in the assay of urinary LH was found when the assays
were done by the ventral prostate weight method (VPW) and by the
ovarian ascorbic acid depletion method (OAAD). The discrepancy was
understandable on the basis that it was attributable to physical and
chemical differences and possibly also metabolic differences in the
standard used (NIH-LH-S1, an ovine pituitary LH) and the material
(urinary LH) tested (2,3). In any case, the discrepancy disappeared
when a urinary standard was used for assay of urinary LH. Similarly,
the NPA study showed that the use of the 2nd IRP (urinary) as a
radioimmunoassay standard is associated with overestimation of the
FSH and LH content of human pituitary tissue extracts. It is known
(4) that a human pituitary tissue standard is associated with
radioimmunoassay underestimation of the FSH and LH present in human
urinary extracts. Conversely, the NPA study confirmed that a
pituitary tissue extract (LER 907) is satisfactory, or almost so, as
radioimmunoassay standard for FSH and LH in pituitary tissue extracts;
and recently, it has been shown that the urinary 2nd IRP is a
satisfactory standard for the radioimmunoassay of FSH and LH in
urinary gonadotropic extracts, and index of discrimination(radio-
immunoassay/bioassay) being unity (5). These examples emphasize
the importance of the similarity principle in the use of standards
in a single assay system (bioassay) and even more dramatically in
two assay systems as fundamentally different as bioassay and radioimmunoassay.

In this connection, the proposal made in the NPA report to use LER 907 as a standard in the radioimmunoassay of serum FSH and LH violates the principle of similarity. It would seem more appropriate to use a serum standard for serum FSH and LH. Since there is no available serum standard, it became a matter of necessity to choose an interim standard. The choice of LER 907 as an interim and temporary standard was largely arbitrary. It was, however, supported by a calculation made on the radioimmunoassayable FSH and LH in the postmenopausal serum (Table 6). The mean FSH concentration in the sample of postmenopausal serum by radioimmunoassay was 78 mIU FSH activity per ml and the mean LH content was 107 mIU/ml, using the 2nd IRP as standard. The radioimmunoassay FSH/LH ratio is thus 0.7; the reported bioassay (2nd IRP standard) FSH/LH ratio of postmenopausal serum is 1.8 (6). When the radioimmunoassayable FSH and LH in the postmenopausal serum was recalculated using LER 907 as the standard, the values were 43 mIU FSH/ml and 23 mIU FSH/ml. The radioimmunoassay FSH/LH ratio is now 43/ 23 or 1.9, which is close to the bioassay ratio. Also, the biologic characteristics of serum FSH and LH are closer to those of FSH and LH in pituitary tissue than they are to those in the urine (7). It should be re-emphasized that LER 907 is suggested as only a temporary radioimmunoassay standard for serum FSH and LH and should be replaced by a more suitable one when available.

The remaining comments are not derived from the NPA study, but are comments on the use of standards in general. Once the appropriateness of a standard is settled, consideration must be given to certain practical matters: replacement of standards, stability, convenience, and expression of results. The first obvious practicality is whether or not an appropriate standard is available for distribution. Distribution implies that a large amount, large enough to last a long time, of standard can be prepared so as to avoid numerous replacements. When the standard contains only one bioreactive material, it is not difficult to match the bioactivity of a subsequent batch with the original. But when the standard contains two biologically active materials such as FSH and LH (which may interact in certain assay systems), the potency matching presents a greater challenge. The difficulty is compounded when, in addition to matching biologic potency, the immunoreactivity of the subsequent batches has to be equilibrated with the original. In the case of a standard containing only one or at least one major,bioreactive material, successful matching for both bio and immunopotency can be accomplished, as in the case of the Second International Standard for HCG. If the standard contains two biologically active materials (FSH and LH), then four matchings have to be made-- two for bioactivity and two for immunoreactivity. This may be difficult but it might be successful if large quantities of representative source material were used and multiple chemical manipulations avoided.

The stability of standard must be known. If stability fails for one or the other type of activity, then a new set of problems arises. Perhaps in the long run, separate standards may be needed for different types of assay systems such as the bioassay and radioimmunoassay.

Two more practical aspects are convenience and thrift in the use of
a standard. In the case of FSH and LH, the number of commonly used
and acceptable bioassays is small and their sensitivities are known.
The activity is so great for radioimmunoassays that the amount of
standard for this technique is not a problem. It would seem reasonable then to vial only that comfortable amount of standard needed
to conduct a bioassay. If the supply of standard is small, it would
be thrifty to vial a suitable minute portion to use in radioimmunoassay. Having a standard in two different amounts or in two kinds
of vials, for different types of assay, is not unreasonable. The NIH
urinary standard for general gonadotropin bioassays (NIH-HPG-UPM-1)
was vialed in two amounts--one for use in the mouse uterine weight
assay and another in the rat ovarian weight assay, as a thrifty
measure. The preparations of 5300 IU HCG per vial as in the Second
International Standard (IS) for HCG is not a shining example of
thrift and convenience. It is possible to subdivide the contents of
one vial of the 2nd IS for HCG into say 53 vials, each containing
100 IU, freeze them immediately, and use the subdivided standard as
needed over a period of a few months for bioassays perhaps, but
strictly, this subdivided material is no longer the International
Standard.

Another practicality has to do with the unitage proposed for a
standard and ways of reporting values. The pituitary gonadotropin
bioassay field suffered for a long time because of the painful lack
of any standard. Those interested in clinical research or diagnostic
work made use of several local urinary preparations such as AMW and
HMG-20A on a temporary basis. Because of the pressing need, the first
IRP (urinary) was prepared in a fashion similar to that for HMG-20A,
but it was quickly shown that this reference preparation was unsatisfactory. Chemical manipulation had apparently destroyed a
good protion of the FSH content of the 1st IRP (8,9). Another
urinary preparation--the 2nd IRP--was then made, and this was now a
satisfactory standard (except perhaps for the OAAD assay because of
toxicity) for the estimation of urinary FSH and LH, and, as a matter
of fact, for the estimation of FSH and LH in other body fluids and
in pituitary tissue extracts including pituitary extracts of many
species. The assignment of International Units, i.e.--one vial 2nd
IRP= 40 IU FSH activity= and 40 IU LH activity--gave a common measure
and a common language, and values can be reported as International
Units or milli International Units of FSH or LH activity per unit
quantity of the sample to be assayed. The advent of the radioimmunoassay technic makes it necessary to exert a constraint in the reporting of FSH and LH values. The constraint consists simply of designating the value reported as a bioassay value or a radioimmunoassay value, and designating the standard used. The designation is
made in parentheses. As an example, a bioassay determination of the
urinary excretion of FSH, would be reported as 10 IU/24 hrs(bioassay;
2nd IRP standard). Reporting radioimmunoassay values is a bit more
complicated but easily follows the convention. In the case of urine,
since the 2nd IRP appears to be a suitable standard, the radioimmunoassayable FSH and LH excretion, as an example, would be 10 IU FSH/
24 hrs and 5 IU LH/24 hrs (radioimmunoassay; 2nd IRP standard).
The NPA report suggests that radioimmunoassays of FSH and LH in
pituitary tissue and in serum be reported as weight of LER 907
standard. An example for the radioimmunoassay of FSH in a
pituitary tissue extract would be: FSH= 50 mg standard/gram (radio-

immunoassay; LER 907 standard). An example for the radioimmunoassay of FSH in serum would be 100 micrograms standard/100 ml (radio-immunoassay; LER 907 standard). Ultimately, the reporting for both bioassay and radioimmunoassay values should be, when appropriate, in terms of weight of chemically pure FSH and LH. It may even be necessary in the future to include in the parentheses the sequential or conformational designation of the antigen used to prepare the anti-serum and maybe a code number for the antiserum. In the interim, however, the suggested convention, something like it or even better, would serve a useful purpose.

Finally, the use of one hormone as a standard for another hormone represents an unnecessary, confusing and potentially dangerous violation of the principle of similarity. The case in point is the use of the 1st and probably the 2nd I.S. for HCG in bioassay and in immunoassay for LH. While some LH bioassay systems-the OAAD system, for example--may fulfill the validity criteria for the bioassay, other biologic systems may not. Similarly, the use of the I.S. for HCG or commercial preparations of HCG of varying grades of bio-logically active purity as standard with or without the 2nd IRP as a second standard in the LH radioimmunoassays presumes complete cross reactivity between LH and HCG. This has not yet been established as a general rule. Besides, reporting LH values in terms of IU HCG seems to be without any basic redeeming features, and adds only to Babel of assay values.

FOOTNOTE

Aided by Grant AM 01738 from the National Institutes of Health.

Table 1

BIOASSAY OF PITUITARY GONADOTROPIC PREPARATIONS

Preparation	FSH		LH		FSH/LH	
	SA*	95% CL	SA*	95% CL	Ratio	95% CL
Extracts: LER 907	20	(18-21)	48	(35-67)	0.4	(.3-.6)
LER 1033-1A	190	(167-216)	58	(45-74)	3.3	(2.5-4.3)
LER 1033-2	2.2	(1.9-2.5)	333	(257-430)	0.007	(.005-.009)
LER 939-4	16	(14-17)	70	(54-91)	0.23	(.17-.30)
Immunochemical: LER 869-2	2,782	(2,317-3,341)	92	(81-110)	30.2	(23.8-38.4)
LER 960	1.9	(1.6-2.3)	923	(808-1,039)	0.002	(.002-.003)
AFP DEAE-2-2	2.1	(1.1-4.1)	981	(866-1,096)	0.002	(.001-.004)

*SA = specific activity, International Units (IU) per mg (2nd IRP standard).

Table 2

FSH AND LH RADIOIMMUNOASSAYS OF PITUITARY PREPARATIONS
Results From Eight Laboratories

Preparation	FSH* Mean ± SE	LH* Mean ± SE
LER 907	38 ± 3	219 ± 13
LER 1033-1A	252 ± 12	227 ± 15
LER 1033-2	18 ± .7	1,929 ± 262
LER 939-4	55 ± 5	384 ± 15
LER 869-2	2,136 ± 169	633 ± 16
LER 960	12 ± 1	11,122 ± 915
AFP DEAE-2	11 ± .4	12,134 ± 1,239

*IU/mg (2nd IRP standard).

Table 3

SUMMARY OF BIOLOGIC (BIO) AND RADIOIMMUNOLOGIC (IMM) ASSAYS*

Preparation	FSH/LH ratio			FSH			LH		
	Bio	Imm	Bio/Imm	Bio	Imm	Imm/Bio	Bio	Imm	Imm/Bio
LER 869-2	30.2	3.4	8.9	2,782	2,136	0.77	92	633	6.88
LER 1033-1A	3.3	1.1	3.0	190	252	1.33	58	227	3.91
LER 907	0.42	0.17	2.5	20	38	1.90	48	219	4.56
LER 939-4	0.23	0.14	1.6	16	55	3.44	70	384	5.49
LER 1033-2	0.007	0.009	0.8	2.2	18	8.18	333	1,929	5.79
LER 960	0.002	0.001	2.0	1.9	12	6.32	923	11,122	12.05
AFP DEAE-2-2	0.002	0.001	2.0	2.1	11	5.24	981	12,134	12.37

*IU/mg(2nd IRP standard).

Table 4

COMPARISON OF RADIOIMMUNOASSAY
OVERESTIMATION OF FSH AND LH
(IMM/BIO RATIOS) USING TWO STANDARDS

Preparation	FSH			LH		
	2nd IRP	LER 907	$\frac{IRP}{907}$	2nd IRP	LER 907	$\frac{IRP}{907}$
LER 869-2	0.8	0.5	1.6	6.9	1.3	5.3
LER 1033-1A	1.3	0.7	1.9	3.9	0.8	4.9
LER 907	1.9	1.0	1.9	4.6	1.0	4.6
LER 939-4	3.4	1.8	1.9	5.5	1.2	4.6
LER 1033-2	8.2	4.5	1.8	5.8	1.5	3.9
LER 960	6.3	3.9	1.6	12.1	2.8	4.3
AFP DEAE-2-2	5.2	2.8	1.9	12.4	2.8	4.4
Mean			1.8			4.6

Table 5

COMPARISON OF FSH/LH RATIOS USING TWO STANDARDS

Preparation	2nd IRP standard			LER 907 standard		
	Bio	Imm	$\frac{Bio}{Imm}$	Bio	Imm	$\frac{Bio}{Imm}$
LER 907	0.42	0.17	2.5	0.4	0.4	1.0
LER 1033-1A	3.3	1.1	3.0	3.3	2.9	1.1
LER 1033-2	0.007	0.009	0.8	0.007	0.02	0.4
LER 939-4	0.23	0.14	1.6	0.23	0.34	0.7
LER 869-2	30.2	3.4	8.9	30.2	10.9	2.8
LER 960	0.002	0.001	2.0	0.002	0.003	0.7
AFP DEAE-2-2	0.002	0.001	2.0	0.002	0.002	1.0

Table 6

FSH AND LH IN POSTMENOPAUSAL SERUM

Technique	Standard	FSH*	LH*	FSH/LH
Bioassay	2nd IRP	144	79	1.8
Radioimmunoassay	2nd IRP	78	107	0.7
Radioimmunoassay	LER 907	43	23	1.9

*mIU/ml.

REFERENCES

1. Albert, A., E. Rosemberg, G. T. Ross, C. A. Paulsen and R. J. Ryan, J Clin Endocr (in press).

2. Rosemberg, E., E. A. Solod and A. Albert, J. Clin Endocr 24:714, 1964.

3. Albert, A., I. Derner, E. Rosemberg and W. B. Lewis, Endocrinology 76: 139, 1965.

4. Faiman, Charles and R. J. Ryan, Proc Soc Exp Biol Med 125: 1130, 1967.

5. Faiman, Charles and R. J. Ryan, and A. Albert, J Clin Endocr (in press).

6. Keller, P., Acta Endocr (Kobenhavn) 53:225, 1966.

7. Albert, A., In Clinical Endocrinology I. E. B. Astwood, editor, Grune and Stratton, Inc., New York, 1960, pp. 605-617.

8. Albert, A., Human Pituitary Gonadotropins: A Workshop Conference, Charles C. Thomas, Springfield, Illinois, 1961, 434 pp.

9. Albert, A., Acta Endocr Vol. 52, Supplement 106, 1966, 64 pp, Periodica, Copenhagen.

CORRELATION BETWEEN BIOASSAY AND IMMUNOASSAY OF HUMAN LUTEINIZING HORMONE

W. D. Odell+, L. E. Reichert* and R. S. Swerdloff+, +UCLA School of Medicine, Department of Medicine, Harbor General Hospital Campus, Torrance, California and *Emory University, Department of Biochemistry, Atlanta, Georgia.

In 1964 we first described a radioimmunoassay system for human chorionic gonadotropin (HCG) [1]. Wide [2] originally described an immunologic cross-reaction between luteinizing hormone (LH) and HCG for antisera against HCG. We [3, 4] and others [5, 7] utilized such antisera to develop radioimmunoassays for LH. In order to assist in validation of the assay system we attempted to correlate potency estimates obtained by immunoassay and by the ventral prostate weight increment bioassay [8]. The standard or reference preparation used was a laboratory reference preparation of human menopausal gonadotropin which was derived from urinary sources. All but one of the materials chosen for study were quite by accident also urinary in origin.

The ratio of the potency estimates obtained by radioimmunoassay divided by that obtained by VPW bioassay was 0.8 (95% limits: 0.3 to 1.3). Table I presents data calculated for this publication. There was fair agreement between potency estimates in the two assay systems. More recently, we have taken a closer look at the correlation between immunoassay and bioassay potency estimates, using pituitary gonadotropin preparations for study. Two specific bioassays for LH were used: 1) The ventral prostate weight increment in the immature, hypophysectomized, male rat (VPW assay) [8], and 2) The ovarian ascorbic acid depletion assay (OAAD assay) [9, 10]. The second international reference preparation of human menopausal gonadotropin (2nd IRP-HMG) was used directly as a standard in both the radioimmunoassay and in the VPW assay. This material was usually toxic in the OAAD assay. Frequently the dose response curve of the 2nd IRP-HMG was not parallel to those for human pituitary preparations. For these reasons the NIH-LH-S1 (an ovine pituitary preparation) which did show parallelism to human pituitary preparations was used in the OAAD assay as a reference. To express potency estimates in terms of the 2nd IRP-HMG, two translation values were used. Rosemberg and Lewis [11] obtained a relative potency of 500 (NIH-LH-S1/2nd IRP-HMG) using the OAAD bioassay. Donini, et al. [12] obtained a relative potency of 1538 using the same assay. The reason for this discrepancy is unknown. We have, therefore, used both values to translate our OAAD data. Table II presents the potency estimates obtained for eight pituitary LH preparations ranging in potency by bioassay from 20 to 4,599 IU/mg. Note the degree of agreement between the two bioassays. Potency estimates obtained by radioimmunoassay were 1.7-13.5 times higher than those obtained by bioassay when results were stated in terms of the 2nd IRP-HMG (urinary preparation). However, if results were stated in terms of a pituitary reference

there was considerably better agreement between potency estimates by bioassay and immunoassay. Table III gives these data.
For the VPW assay, no significant difference from immunoassay
results (RIA/VPW = 1.2) were obtained. For the OAAD assay, bioassay potencies were slightly less than immunoassay potencies,
even when results were expressed in terms of a pituitary reference (RIA/OAAD = 1.9).

To further study this phenomonon additional studies were
performed. Twenty mg of a partially purified human LH (containing 0.72 NIH-LH-S1 units/mg) were administered in a single intravenous injection to a healthy mongrel dog. Plasma samples
were obtained at 20-30 minute intervals for 5½ hours and the disappearance of LH quantified by both VPW bioassay and radioimmunoassay. The 2nd IRP-HMG was used as a reference preparation in
both assays. For the bioassay, there was only sufficient material for a 1x2 design. Figure 1 presents the results. The
slope of the disappearance line using the bioassay data was
-0.00249 (95% limits: 0.00168-0.00330). The slope using the
immunoassay data was -0.00179 (-0.00145-0.00213). These were
not significantly different (p >0.05). However, as is shown in
Figure 2 when values were stated in terms of the 2nd IRP-HMG
(urinary origin) those obtained by immunoassay were about two
times greater than by bioassay. Moreover, such values when
stated relatively in terms of one of the pituitary samples, were
not significantly different (Figure 1).

From these data one may conclude: 1) That bioassay and
radioimmunoassay potency estimates obtained for urinary preparations using a urinary reference preparation are in agreement;
2) That bioassay and radioimmunoassay potency estimates obtained for pituitary preparations using a pituitary reference preparation are in agreement*; and 3) Bioassay potency estimates of
pituitary preparations are smaller than radioimmunoassay potency
estimates when a urinary reference preparation is used.

Figure 3 schematically presents the interrelations of the
assay system, reference preparation, and unknown samples. Two
hypotheses may be advanced to explain these data: 1) The bioassay measures something in the urinary reference preparation
not measured by radioimmunoassay. 2) The radioimmunoassay
measures something in the pituitary preparation not measured by
bioassay. Note that the possibility that the radioimmunoassay
is responding to immunologically active, biologically inactive
material in the urine would not explain these data. Which of
the two hypotheses is true remains unknown.

We conclude that the 2nd IRP-HMG may not be a suitable reference preparation for quantitating pituitary materials. It is
presently unknown whether the 2nd IRP-HMG is a valid standard
for serum or plasma samples.

*This statement is true for the VPW bioassay. Immunoassay poten-
cies were still slightly higher than bioassay potencies when
the OAAD assay was used. The reason for this is not known.

REFERENCES

1. Paul, W. and W. D. Odell: Nature, 203:979, 1964.

2. Wide, L., P. Roos and C. Gemzel: Acta Endocr., 37:445, 1961.

3. Odell, W. D., G. T. Ross and P. L. Rayford: Metabolism, 15:287, 1966.

4. Odell, W. D., G. T. Ross and P. L. Rayford: J. Clin. Inv., 46:248, 1967.

5. Franchimont, P.: Annals d' Endocr., (Paris), 27:273, 1966.

6. Midgley, A. R.: Endocrinology, 79:10, 1966.

7. Bagshawe, K. D., C. E. Wilde and A. Hilary Orr: Lancet, 1:1118, 1966.

8. Greep, R. O., H. B. VanDyke and B. F. Chow: Proc. Soc. Expt. Biol., 46:644, 1941.

9. Karg, H.: Klin. Wschr., 35:643, 1957.

10. Parlow, A. F. in Albert, A. (ed.): Human Pituitary Gonado-tropins. Charles C. Thomas, Springfield, Illinois, 1961, page 301.

11. Rosemberg, E., W. B. Lewis: J. Clin. Endocr. and Metab., 26:788, 1966.

12. Donini, P., D. Puzzuoli, I. D'Alessio, B. Lunenfeld, Aliza Eshkal and A. F. Parlow: Acta Endocr., 52:169, 1966.

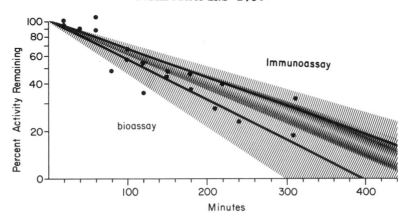

FIGURE 1:   Disappearance of partially purified HLH from the
plasma of a dog after a single intravenous injection.   The disappearance was measured by ventral prostate weight bioassay and
by LH radioimmunoassay.   Each dot represents the result at a
single time.   The mean slope is depicted by the heavy black line
and the 95% confidence limit of these slopes by the shaded area.
The slope obtained from the bioassay data is not significantly
different from the slope obtained from the immunoassay data.

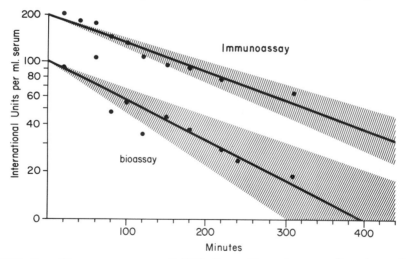

FIGURE 2:   Disappearance of HLH from the plasma of a dog after a
single intravenous injection.   These data were obtained from the
same studies illustrated in Figure 1.   The second IRP-HMG was
used as a standard on both assay systems.   Note that the international units measured by immunoassay averaged two-fold higher
at each time interval than those obtained by bioassay.

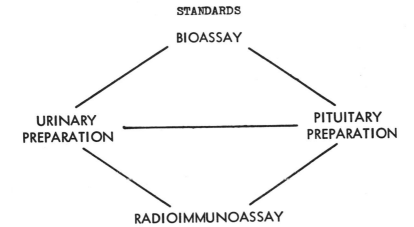

STANDARDS

BIOASSAY

URINARY
PREPARATION

PITUITARY
PREPARATION

RADIOIMMUNOASSAY

FIGURE 3: Schematic presentation of the relationship between
a urinary reference preparation and a pituitary unknown preparation, as measured in the two different assay systems.

TABLE I

BIOASSAY-IMMUNOASSAY POTENCY ESTIMATES FOR URINARY HLH
PREPARATIONS USING A URINARY REFERENCE PREPARATION

Preparation Number	Potency by VPW Bioassay * µg/24 hours	Immunoassay Potency* µg/24 hours	RIA/VPW
1	683	570	0.8
2	450+	207	0.5
3	1,125+	720	0.6
4	412+	660	1.6
5	0.75	0.45	0.6
6	250	100	0.4
		Mean:	0.8
	95% Limits:		(0.3-1.3)

* In terms of laboratory reference preparation
+ Only sufficient material for 1x3 bioassay design

T A B L E   I I

BIOASSAY-IMMUNOASSAY POTENCY ESTIMATES FOR PITUITARY HLH PREPARATIONS USING A PITUITARY REFERENCE PREPARATION

Preparation No.	Potency* by VPW Bioassay IU/mg	Potency A* by OAAD Bioassay IU/mg	Potency B* by OAAD Bioassay IU/mg	Potency* by Radioimmunoassay IU/mg	RIA/VPW△	(A)† RIA/OAAD+	(B)† RIA/OAAD+
1	28	62	20	263	9.4	4.2	13.2
2	63	126	41	232	3.7	1.8	5.7
3	168	231	75	940	5.6	4.1	12.5
4	228	431	140	1,364	6.0	3.2	9.7
5	691	569	185	2,466	3.6	4.3	13.3
6	1,692	1,476	480	2,834	1.7	1.9	5.9
7	3,959	2,614	850	11,453	2.9	4.4	13.5
8	4,000	4,599	1,495	10,506	2.6	2.3	7.0
				Mean:	4.4	3.3	10.1
				95% Limits:	(2.3-6.5)	(2.4-4.2)	(7.1-13.0)

*International Units/mg of the 2nd IRP-HMG. For the OAAD bioassay NIH-LH-S1 was used directly as the standard. Two translation values are available to express these results in terms of the 2nd IRP-HMG: 1) 1538, and 2) 638. Potency A was obtained by using 1538, potency B by using 638 [11, 12].

△Potency by immunoassay ÷ by VPW bioassay.

+Potency by immunoassay ÷ potency by OAAD bioassay.

†Ratio A was obtained by using Potency A by OAAD.

†Ratio B was obtained by using Potency B by OAAD.

TABLE III

BIOASSAY-IMMUNOASSAY POTENCY ESTIMATES FOR PITUITARY HLH
PREPARATIONS USING A PITUITARY REFERENCE PREPARATION

Pre-para-tion	Relative Potency by VPW Bioassay	Relative Potency by OAAD Bioassay	Relative Potency by Immuno-assay	RIA/VPW	RIA/OAAD
1	0.45	0.49	1.02	2.3	2.1
2	1	1	1	---	---
3	2.7	1.8	4.2	1.6	2.3
4	3.6	3.4	5.9	1.6	1.7
5	10.9	4.5	10.6	1.0	2.4
6	27.0	11.7	12.1	0.5	1.0
7	62.8	20.7	49.1	0.8	2.4
8	63.7	36.5	44.7	0.7	1.2
			mean:	1.2*	1.9*
			95% limits:	0.6-1.8	1.4-2.4

*RIA/VPW is not significantly different from RIA/OAAD

(p >0.05)

DISCUSSION

ROSEMBERG: The problems related to the establishment of standardized reagents for use in radioimmunoassays of follicle stimulating
and luteinizing hormones are numerous. It is hoped that today's
deliberations will be fruitful and will bring forth specific recommendations. It will be of extreme importance to hear Dr.
Bangham's views not only with respect to his personal position on
this subject but also to learn from him the particular interests
of WHO in this area.

BANGHAM: A meeting such as this, called to exchange experimental
findings of laboratories from many parts of the world, must view
with consternation the tables of factors relating the biological
activity of one gonadotropin to another. These tables list
"potency ratios" based on comparisons of various gonadotropic
substances, most of which have already been shown by biochemical,
biophysical or immunochemical criteria to differ from one another.
They are therefore comparisons of unlike substances. The value of
these figures is limited because they apply to the specific
occasion (assay procedure, animals, laboratory and time) on which
they were obtained.

One of the basic principles on which bioassay depends is that like
is compared against like; that the test sample is identical with
the standard (or so similar to it that it behaves as a dilution of
the standard itself). The parallel line assay is still the only
universally applicable way of estimating relative potency. If log
dose-response lines are not parallel, the best one can do is to
"match" the effects of the two substances at a given response
level.

Where two hormone molecules have a common physiological effect, I
think it is too readily assumed that a bioassay which reflects
that specific effect is not influenced by differences in the
molecule other than at the active site. Non-parallelism, heterogeneity of estimates within or between laboratories, or within or
between assay methods, and differences in the shape of the dose-
response curve can often only be seen when combining the results
of many assays. A research worker does not normally test his
cumulated data (on the same two materials) for significant heterogeneity. But he is nevertheless perplexed when he cannot get
the same answer as another laboratory, or by another assay method,
or from one year to another. For example, one laboratory compared
the 2nd International Standard for Chorionic Gonadotropin with the
2nd IRP of Human Menopausal Gonadotropins by two ICSH-specific
methods and obtained estimates of relative potencies on each of
two occasions 3 years apart; although the figures were consistent
('homogeneous') each time the substances were tested, the mean
estimates differed significantly. The reason for this must be
due to the differences and variability with time of the biological
substrate used in the assay, both within and between strains of

mice or rats.

The limitation of 'conversion factors' is that although they may be useful within a laboratory at a given time, they cannot be assumed to apply in another laboratory until that laboratory has shown by direct proof with its own animals and procedure that it happens also to obtain the same figure, at another time.

Evidence to prove biological heterogeneity with statistical certainty is often only compiled as a result of large elective collaborative studies in which the same preparations, in homogeneous and stable form, are compared. I have come to believe that such collaborative exercises for the sole purpose of demonstrating biological evidence of heterogeneity are in most instances a fruitless waste of effort if substantive biochemical or biophysical evidence already exists that two hormones are different. Such exercises tend to delay official steps to set up new separate standard(s) and meanwhile laboratories and literature fill up with figures which have local and temporary meaning only. Moreover in the long run the labor of proving biologically that two different materials cannot be compared exceeds the work of setting up a proper standard which will have to be done ultimately anyway. In practice preparations of the same hormone all too frequently differ enough (in degree of purity or due to the method of purification) to show significant invalidity, as collaborative international studies will testify. Some 'hormones' may even exist as families of molecules, such as chorionic gonadotropin in urine. While this is something we must accept, there is little reason to continue trying to assay one recognizably different hormone against another.

Ideally, then, we should have an individual standard available for each substance; (a solemn thought - we have been asked for a standard for sturgeon FSH). However, the problem of setting up suitable standards for all forms of gonadotropin with the resources available is a real dilemma, both for the official agency, such as WHO, and also for the individual research laboratory. Some compromise is inevitable, and can be workable for a time. Under certain conditions (body weight gain over 8 - 10 days in hypophysectomized young rats) it appears one can bioassay human growth hormone against bovine growth hormone (the International Standard). Overt discrepancies may not appear when only one or two assay methods are used by everyone and/or when the assays are so imprecise that invalidity stays hidden. Sooner or later, however, another assay method will be introduced, e.g. radioimmunoassay, which does discriminate and for which a species specific standard for the hormone (e.g. HGH) must be provided.

Incidentally, the antisera used in radioimmunoassay systems should also be regarded as an undefinable unreproducible variable substrate which, like the animal used in bioassay, cannot be completely defined in chemical and/or physical terms. A collaborative study to determine whether a preparation is suitable to serve as a standard for general use should thus include assays with several different antisera and the results should show that the same relative potency is obtained with each. If only one antiserum is used in this type of study, the results may validate that standard for use with that particular antiserum; but without experimental evidence, one cannot assume that the same relative potency will be obtained with other antisera. Hitherto international standards for hormones (e.g. HCG and HMG) have been set up for biological assays, and they may well prove not to be suitable for immuno-logical assays. Setting up a standard for a radioimmunoassay is an exacting task because the standard should contain a minimum (if any) of denatured material. In replacing the standard in due course, it would be virtually impossible to reproduce exactly the nature and amount of a denatured contaminant, and it is thus a laborious task to find out how to prepare material and test its suitability.

Ideally then, there should perhaps be internationally accepted standards available for human pituitary FSH and ICSH, urinary FSH and ICSH and chorionic gonadotropin, since there is already evidence that these are biochemically different. But what of gonado-tropins in serum? Are they also immunologically different? Should there be a reference preparation of serum from postmeno-pausal women for radioimmunoassay? I would be interested to learn your views. I think there is much to be said for separate prepa-rations of highly purified FSH and ICSH from both pituitary and from urine, with which people can characterize (i.e. test the specificity of) their antisera.

With the responsibility borne by the World Health Organization and the Food and Agriculture Organization of the United Nations, in world nutrition it may also be as well to have standards for certain gonadotropins of the more important food-producing animal species. Ideally, with adequate foresight and resources, these standards could be provided early enough to forestall the spread of conversion factors. I personally believe that the provision of a standard early in the research career of a hormone is of greater value to science than establishment of one long after its impor-tance in world medicine has achieved official recognition. A standard provided thus early accelerates the development of proper assay methods, thus putting quantitation on a sound basis, and also prevents the proliferation of invalid comparisons which con-fuse and can actually hinder research progress. The question of whether there should be a centralized supply (for example through WHO) of antisera and possibly purified antigens suitable for isotope labeling is not quite a 'standards' problem. In the interests of conserving very precious and rare materials, there is little doubt that it would greatly facilitate research and clinical work and therefore should be done, but it may be that this supply problem should be handled at national level in a few countries, providing that they are willing to share with those who have not.

The allocation of unitage to each new standard and adaptation to
the use of the new units is really a matter of intellectual
acclimatization. Each tetracycline and each penicillin (that is
biologically assayed) has its own unit, and there is no attempt
to 'match', compare or assay one in terms of another. A physician
knows the effect of 10 units of each different type of insulin
preparation, but there has been no attempt to assay one kind
against another. That is not to say that one should not try to
rationalize the procedure in some way such as by making one unit
approximately equal to say 1 mg. of what one may believe at the
time is pure hormone.

The best method of expressing results of estimations by radioimmunoassay is much under discussion at the moment. It is to be
hoped that WHO will very soon make formal recommendations on how
to do so. The 20th Report of the Expert Committee on Biological
Standardization of WHO contains the suggestion that meanwhile the
standard and method used should in each case be stated in record-
ing results. Much confusion will be avoided if scientists will
conform with such recommendations.

Lastly, to put the record straight, the International Unit of an
International Standard is defined as the biological activity contained in a given weight of the current International Standard.
The standard is the material as it exists in the ampules; the
material thus includes the active ingredients together with all
other constituents such as moisture and in some instances, carrier
and/or buffer salts. Moreover, many WHO hormone standards are
filled into ampules in "equal" (+ 1%) quantities and freeze dried.
The potency should be taken as the number of units per ampule
stated on the label, (although the unit is still formally defined
in terms of weight). It is thus wrong to speak of an ampule of
the 2nd IRP of HMG as containing 5 mg. of this or 10 mg. of that.
It is intended that the entire contents of these ampules be dissolved in a known amount of water or solution; no attempt should
be made to weigh out portions of the freeze dried plug. For all
practical purposes each ampule contains 40 I.U. of FSH of human
postmenopausal urinary FSH, and 40 I.U. of human postmenopausal
urinary ICSH.

I do hope the report of this meeting will have the effects firstly,
of encouraging scientists to use a standard (where one exists) of
the same hormone, source and species as the material they wish to
assay; and secondly, of stimulating the production of new standards for each appropriate form and species of these very interesting hormones.

ROSEMBERG: Dr. Bangham, with the increasing emphasis placed on
the measurement of gonadotropic activity in body fluids utilizing
radioimmunoassay techniques, I should think that it would be
extremely profitable to discuss the problem of standardization of
preparations needed for radioimmunoassay of FSH and LH. The NPA

collaborative study presented by Dr. Albert as well as Dr. Odell's data, points to the fact that we may be in need of the following: Standardized antiserum for FSH and LH, respectively; immuno-chemical grade hFSH and hLH to be used in the iodination procedure, and a standard, preferably obtained from pituitary tissue, as a reference preparation for pituitary gland extracts and temporar-ily as a reference preparation for serum gonadotropins. With respect to the provision of a standard preparation for urinary extracts, the 2nd IRP seems satisfactory for the radioimmunoassay of FSH and LH in human urine.

ALBERT: Dr. Bangham, the World Health Organization is an official body which has long standing commitments and responsibilities in the area of assay. I think that before talking about the very specific qualities of the materials needed for standards, one should ask whether WHO is prepared to undertake the task of pre-paring standards and reagents needed for radioimmunoassay. There is a great urgency for standards in the United States and, I am sure, also in England and other countries. It seems to take a long time for WHO to produce standards. An indication of the urgency in the United States is the entry of an unofficial and nonperma-nent body (the National Pituitary Agency) in this field. Consider-ing the technical experience and knowledge necessary to prepare and distribute standards, which the NPA does not have, it does not seem right that the WHO should default on its traditional respon-sibilities because of inertia. This field is perhaps not as im-portant as the provision of smallpox virus, or cattle problems; nevertheless, it is an important area of clinical investigation related to world population problems. Dr. Bangham, we would like you to convey this sense of urgency to the WHO. If you are will-ing to do this, we, in the United States, could provide some interim materials. We would like to have official standards and reagents for radioimmunoassay eventually and this group, I am sure, would be happy to offer suggestions on procedure.

BANGHAM: Dr. Albert, you covered an important point which I shall convey to Geneva. In explanation, if not defense, let me say that our attitude has been that a biological standard is a biological yardstick. Therefore, if we are going to make a yardstick, it is worth making it carefully and accurately. This does involve a lot of work, both in the technical preparation of materials and also in the considerable exercise of characterizing them by biological methods. It is difficult to skip corners if you are setting-up a standard that is going to be a useful one and last some time; the value of a standard is in a sense proportional to the care taken in setting it up and characterizing it. Whether WHO will agree to set up all these new standards will be influenced by the opinions of such groups of experts as you. If you say there is a need for International Standards for this or that, your opinion will carry weight in Geneva.

ROSEMBERG: I think that we could be of assistance to Dr. Bangham if we took a vote on this matter. The question I am posing to this audience is this: Do we favor the view that the WHO should prepare these materials? Those in favor, please raise your hands. Dr. Bangham, the decision, in favor of this view, has been unanimous. I assume that there is general agreement regarding the need for these reagents. Hence, I think we could now initiate discussion of specific problems.

McARTHUR: It seems to me that immunoassay may present a philosophical problem to the WHO. Its Division of Standards is charged with the responsibility of furthering the standardization of hormones intended for therapeutic use. In this context, is not the biological (rather than immunological) activity of paramount importance? What if the two types of activity cannot be equated?

BANGHAM: Yes, indeed. The WHO has been primarily concerned with the standardization of materials administered to man, but undoubtedly materials used either in diagnosis or to make a quantitative estimation of the suitable dose of a drug also require standardization. I think that the materials being discussed here will come within this category. Radioimmunoassay itself has acquired such an enormous field of application in clinical medicine, that it must be considered by WHO.

STEVENS: Other speakers have commented on standards to be used in immunoassay systems. Some work carried out in our laboratory, independent of that of the radioimmunoassay task force, has indicated that the relative potency of preparations of urinary and pituitary origin agree quite well with that presented by Dr. Albert and summarized by Dr. Odell. However, throughout the discussions, we have talked about radioimmunoassays as one assay system, namely, one in which the antigens used were of pituitary origin, and the antibodies used were raised either to HCG or purified FSH or LH. However, we have used radioimmunoassay systems in our laboratory with highly purified FSH and LH materials from urine. There are discrepancies involved. It has been shown and summarized by Dr. Odell that using the pituitary immunoassay system for measuring urine, gives good agreement with biological values using the 2nd IRP urinary standard. However, when an HMG radioimmunoassay system is used with a urinary standard, higher than biological measurements are found. In fact, the values, when expressed as I.U. per day, approximate more closely to the production rate values reported by Dr. Odell in his clearance rate studies. The issue, therefore, seems to be more involved than a standard reference preparation. The materials to be used in the radioimmunoassay system also merit consideration.

JOHNSEN: I would like to ask Dr. Bangham if any kind of material is available from the WHO for the time being. I have a similar question for Dr. Albert: Will the NPA be ready to provide enough material to the WHO to set up these standards?

BANGHAM: It just so happens that we have a few thousand ampules of freeze-dried preparations of highly purified human pituitary

FSH and ICSH and also of TSH. By bioassay, we have so far not been able to detect contamination of the ICSH with FSH, or the TSH with either FSH or ICSH.

ALBERT: I cannot speak for the NPA. I am but one member of the Medical Advisory Board. However, the past performance of the NPA is, I think, very favorable to Dr. Johnsen's suggestion. Growth hormone has already been provided by the NPA to the WHO. Dr. Wilhelmi offered one-half of the total supply of LER 907 to the WHO.

BANGHAM: I must immediately acknowledge the enormous generosity of the NIH and its Committees in providing quantities of rare and costly materials used either as formal international standards or as research standards. The WHO can only provide these services because of the generosity of laboratories which contribute materials, often rare and very precious, and also because of the generous collaboration of laboratories and experts around the world who carry out the work of characterizing them.

MIDGLEY: I think we have to accept the premise that all radio-immunoassays in all laboratories will differ even if we have the same reagents, but less so if the reagents are the same. It is important to determine to what extent the assay in one laboratory compares with the assay in another laboratory. Two assays, performed in similar fashion with the same reagents, can agree completely on the relative potencies for a series of pituitary preparations and yet disagree completely regarding estimated contents in serum. Differences of this sort can be ascribed to trivial causes such as inadvertent omission of an absorption step, use of an improper amount of an anti-globulin serum, differences in length of incubation, etc. Therefore, I think it is essential for each investigator to evaluate his immunoassay by noting whether or not it agrees with assays reported by others. This requires that he have available in his laboratory the same reference serum which is used in other laboratories. This reference serum should have an LH and FSH content high enough so that it can be diluted to give a dose-response curve. A second reference serum preparation should also be available with a value low enough so that the investigator will be required to use it at a reasonable volume in each assay. In addition, investigators should have a urinary reference preparation and at least one pituitary reference preparation so that potency comparisons can be made between the various materials. I would like to suggest that we consider for distribution, a preparation such as the 2nd International Reference Preparation of Human Menopausal Gonadotropin for the urinary material, a pituitary preparation such as LER-907 and two pools of serum. One of these could be from postmenopausal women and the other from men or women in the late luteal phase of the cycle. These preparations should be for reference use only to determine whether or not the assay is performing as described by others. If, as should occur, the radioimmunoassay gave

parallelism between preparations of pituitary, urinary and serum
origin, it would not matter which one was actually used as the
standard.

TAYMOR: What evidence do we have, other than a physiological one,
that a serum standard will be better for serum than the pituitary
standard that has been utilized?

ALBERT: None. There is no evidence one way or another on this
point.

RYAN: Although we have had a philosophical discussion, in point
of fact there are no data, at the present time, to say whether the
hormone that exists in serum is the same as that we measure in the
pituitary or in urine. It is essential then, at least until we
obtain more information, that we have a serum standard, and I agree
with Dr. Midgley that a postmenopausal serum should be employed.
I will go a step further and suggest that the postmenopausal serum
standard be a lyophilized extract rather than whole serum. I think
that the extraction procedure should be made as simple as possible.
The reasons for using an extracted lyophilized serum are several:
(1) It would minimize degradation of the gonadotropin by serum
enzymes that might otherwise occur with long storage and varying
temperatures and thus minimize the possibility of a varying
standard, and (2) it would facilitate the packaging, shipping and
storage of the standard so that it would not need to be handled
as frozen material. I think the extraction procedure per se, if
designed in an experimental way, might provide evidence as to what
ultimately may be the best standard to employ.

McARTHUR: I should like to endorse what Dr. Ryan has said. We
(and others) are developing methods for extracting gonadotropins
from serum, and are hopeful that stable preparations of FSH and
LH, suitable for use as standards, can be obtained.

TAYMOR: Dr. Ryan and Dr. Midgley have reemphasized the differences
between urinary and pituitary gonadotropins. Still there is no
evidence that there is a difference between pituitary and serum
gonadotropins. Before we ask the WHO to embark upon a project of
developing a standard with all the complications of preparation
and storage, I believe that we should have that evidence, and
until then, we should use the pituitary preparation as a temporary
standard. I think that your task force will quickly answer this
question in the same way that it has so well answered the question
for pituitary and urinary preparations. The WHO should not embark
upon such a project unless it is absolutely necessary.

ALBERT: I believe the NPA is going ahead with the preparation of
a serum standard and will have a field trial of it. This information may be available before anything is done at WHO. We would
then be able to provide WHO with some information. Let us assume
that a serum standard proves to be valid and useful. We would
then like it to be official and it is only the WHO who can make it so.

There is no reason why, if a sufficient amount of a serum standard were prepared by NPA, a goodly amount of it would not be given
to the WHO.

FAIMAN: I agree with the recommendation that a serum or plasma
standard would be good to have. I have reservations about a serum
extract. Although there are advantages of an extract of serum, in
terms of stability and distribution, there is a major problem.
This involves the principle which we discussed this morning --
namely, that the assay standard and unknown should be as similar
as possible. If one wishes to use extracted material as a standard, then to be correct, one should use an extract of the unknown
serum sample. I do not think this is advisable, and think we
would rather have a raw serum or raw plasma standard.

ROSEMBERG: Dr. Faiman, if the NPA will sponsor a pilot study to
determine whether or not a serum standard is necessary for radioimmunoassay work, I am sure that the experimental design used
will be such that it will answer all the points you have raised.

MIDGLEY: Data are now available indicating that assays can be in
excellent agreement for pituitary preparations but disagree with
samples of serum. For example, compare the early results obtained
by Dr. Odell for human FSH with those which we obtained. We
agreed very closely for the content of FSH in pituitary preparations.
With serum samples, his early estimations were much higher than
ours, however, these differences were resolved when he added serum
from a heterologous species to every tube in his standard curve.
Thus, there can be problems unique to serum which may not be related to the hormone content at all. Therefore, I will second
what Dr. Faiman has said, that we need to have available a serum
reference preparation, and that this serum preparation should not
be an extract but as close to native serum as is possible. Only
in this way will two investigators be able to determine that their
assays are behaving in a similar fashion.

ODELL: I should like to speak against the necessity just at the
moment of going to all the trouble of preparing a serum reference
preparation. First of all, I think that we all must agree that
the relative potencies of all hormones studied and discussed in
these meetings so far, by immunoassay or bioassay, are in agreement. I stress that this is the relative potency; it is the
absolute potency that differs. Secondly, I refer to Dr. Midgley's
point. If we look at all the immunoassay systems that we use in
our laboratories: LH, TSH, FSH, growth hormone, etc., the presence
of serum itself consistently has an effect on the immunoassay
serum, serum known to be free of human hormone. The widest
discrepancy between buffer alone and serum is in the HFSH assay,
where serum may cause a 10 - 12% difference in counts precipitated
(100% being defined as c.p.m. precipitated with antibody and
FSH-I^{131} alone in the immunoassay tube). When a standard such as IRP
HMG is set up in serum, the curve is shifted to the left and the
"100%" tubes contain 10 - 12% less counts.

Therefore, for example, if a postmenopausal serum is used as a reference standard, when low volumes of 10 or 15 lambda are used, and compared with 400 or 300 lambda of normal male serum, a discrepancy occurs caused by the serum itself. Insofar as the relative potencies of one sample to another, these are exactly the same by immunoassay and bioassay. Under suitable conditions, the IRP gives a parallel dose-response curve to serum samples. The 2nd IRP is already available and being freely distributed by Dr. Bangham. I would submit that until we have further data, we use the IRP in the immunoassay for measuring serum samples. Further, it would be unwise at this time to prepare another intermediate standard, such as the NPA is discussing. This would mean that in two years, or perhaps less, we will have to re-convert a third time around.

CARGILLE: The proposal that the WHO provide an International Reference Serum with an FSH potency determined by radioimmunoassay presents several problems. Drs. Rodbard, Ross, and I compared several anti-FSH sera and found that values for the same plasma sample differed by as much as threefold depending upon which anti-serum was used for the determination. Dr. Odell reported on the basis of results with his anti-FSH serum that when the IRP #2 HMG standard was prepared with a constant volume of dog plasma in each tube, lower values were obtained than when the standards were pre-pared in buffer. Using our own #24 antiserum, we have observed that the relative abilities of guinea pig, monkey, and bovine plasmas to displace counts in an FSH radioimmunoassay differ. Thus, different degrees of influence might be exerted upon FSH values by the use of plasmas from these different species as diluents for the standard, depending upon the antiserum being used in the assay. Even within the same species, plasmas from individual animals vary in the extent of their effect upon our FSH assay. It would appear necessary for WHO to provide an anti-FSH antibody, a reference standard, and instructions as to the diluent for the standard if different laboratories are to obtain potency estimates for an Internation Reference Serum comparable to the FSH potency assigned by WHO.

ALBERT: Could we get the opinion of the group about a serum standard? Would anybody object if the NPA went ahead with a study similar to the one seen today and then perhaps contact the WHO?

ODELL: I do not object to the study being done, but have you already decided that a serum standard is therefore desirable?

ALBERT: No. I think that the study, as Dr. Ryan pointed out, is one way of telling whether it is desirable or not. The point is that Dr. Taymor asked for evidence and there seems to be no information on this problem.

ODELL: So, after the study, a decision will be made.

ALBERT: Yes, I should think so. Perhaps Dr. Bangham has enough material for thought in Geneva. Are there any other suggestions?

ODELL: I should like to ask if we have general agreement for what I think is implied but not stated in the discussion. This is that the use of animal standards, not human standards, to measure human materials in bioassays and where possible in immunoassays, is to be deplored. Can we fully agree on this?

ALBERT: I think as a general principle, we all agree to this.

TAYMOR: I would like to draw attention to one of Dr. Odell's slides in which indices of discrimination have been presented. In that slide, the top 4 preparations, particularly the FSH assays, were quite good and only the last two, where there was a high LH:FSH ratio, did the index of discrimination go **away**. In the first place, is it fair to use this data in your calculations, and secondly, this brings up the question of how the anti-FSH distributed by the NPA was handled, and how it was adsorbed. Was it adsorbed before dilution or was it adsorbed during the assay? We believe that there is some advantage in adsorbing the anti-FSH during the assay procedure.

MIDGLEY: The anti-human FSH serum which was given to the NPA unfortunately was accepted and adsorbed in two separate lots. One third was adsorbed in our laboratory several months ago by adding HCG to the antiserum, incubating it for one-half hour at $37°$ C. and then for two days at $4°$ C. The antiserum was then centrifuged, merthiolate was added, and the clarified supernatant was placed in vials, frozen and returned to the NPA for distribution. This should have been the only antiserum available; unfortunately, you may have obtained some antiserum prior to adsorption. The remaining two-thirds of antiserum has now been adsorbed in a similar fashion and sent to the NPA for distribution.

TAYMOR: We utilized our own antisera developed from the same pituitary FSH preparation LER-735-2. Our previous report suggests that adding HCG to individual tubes may have some advantage. In addition, there have been a number of comments upon the necessity for having a pure preparation for antibody production. This is theoretically fine, but the NPA is going to be faced with distributing large quantities of antiserum and I believe that we will have to accept less pure preparations both for labeling and for antibody production and use adsorptive techniques at least for a time. Finally, we believe that I-125 has additional advantages in the preservation and storage of important materials. For example, we have used the same pituitary FSH for labeling and the same Hartree LH preparation for labeling for over two years, starting with one or two milligrams of this material, because we have been able to iodinate every six weeks. I think that this is another feature that the NPA task force should take into consideration.

REICHERT: The NPA has available sufficient hFSH for 300 investigators, assuming a distribution of 100 micrograms per investigator.

Because of the lability of highly purified FSH, we have not stock-
piled this hormone. However, adequate amounts of precursor are
available to meet the demands of the forseeable future. We also
have relatively large quantities of LER-735-2 equivalent materials
for use as antigens.

BANGHAM: I should like to raise the practical problem(s) of what
can be done for hospitals that for routine clinical practice need
to assay gonadotropins, and how the results of these assays should
be expressed. It should be said again and again that estimates of
relative potency with the mouse uterus weight assay are influenced
by the proportions of FSH and ICSH present in the materials assayed;
the method is not specific for either hormone, nor for a direct
arithmetical summation of the two. The urine extracts made in
hospitals presumably contain different proportions of FSH and ICSH
and as you know international units exist only for FSH and ICSH,
respectively, in the 2nd IRP of HMG. Nevertheless, the assay is
useful in that it is sensitive, simple and has a steep log dose-
response slope. It is, I understand, the most practicable gonadotropin assay for routine work in hospitals, at least until a
radioimmunoassay service becomes available. In the absence of an
international or national working standard (which) would have to
be enormous), one suggested way of handling this problem is as
follows: the great majority of these assays are for routine
clinical purposes for situations in which the clinician needs to
know simply if there is much too much, much too little, or about
a 'normal' amount of gonadotropins present. In the (much fewer)
instances when quantitive estimates of the specific gonadotropins
are required they can be assayed by specific methods. It is
suggested that hospitals obtain quantities of an extract of human
postmenopausal urine to use as their standard. This they can
calibrate by the mouse uterus assay in terms of the IRP (and here
I confess I do not know what figure other than 40 they would take
from an ampule of the IRP to assign a unitage to their own house
standard). But, if these units were called local mouse uterus
units, this unscientific term could be associated with what is an
unscientific (in the sense that it is here not specific) assay
procedure. The limitations of this assay need not interfere with
its usefulness in clinical practice but they should be understood
by clinicians.

ROSEMBERG: Dr. Bangham, it is indeed regretable that confusion
has arisen because many people were unaware of the fact that the
2nd IRP was never intended as a standard for general gonadotropin
assays. Perhaps we could suggest that in reporting results when
employing these assay systems with the 2nd IRP as the standard,
specific information should be given as to the procedure used in
the assignment of unitage to the 2nd IRP in each particular case.
SUMMARY OF SESSION
ALBERT: It might be well to summarize and recapitulate some of
the main points brought forth during this session. It was generally agreed that for the bioassay of human FSH or LH, the human
urinary 2nd IRP (established by the WHO as a biological standard)

is functioning well. FSH or LH in biologic fluids of man should
be assayed by specific FSH or LH bioassays using the 2nd IRP (or
a local equivalent preparation calibrated carefully against the
2nd IRP), and not by any other gonadotropic materials currently
available as standards. No clear evidence was advanced that it
was not possible to bioassay FSH or LH in pituitary gland extracts, blood or urine in terms of the 2nd IRP in spite of the
fact that pituitary tissue, blood or urine are not exactly alike.

The 2nd IRP is used correctly when the entire contents of a vial
are transferred quantitatively for appropriate test dilutions.
It is not used correctly when small quantities of the vialed
material are removed and weighed prior to preparing dilutions.
The 2nd IRP seems reasonably stable and it should not be difficult
to replace it. The toxicity of the 2nd IRP in bioassay systems,
such as the OAAD, is a drawback and reduction in toxicity would
be desirable when it is necessary to replace the 2nd IRP with a
new batch. Since the International Unit for FSH or LH is the FSH
or LH activity in 0.2295 mg. of the 2nd IRP, which is the material in the vial, it is not correct to express assays in terms of
the presumed concentration of the constituents of the 2nd IRP
(active material versus lactose carrier). The 2nd IRP was never
intended as a standard for general gonadotropin assay systems
(rat ovarian weight or mouse uterine weight methods) either by
expressing results of such assays in I.U. or in terms of mg. of
"active" material. If, contrary to official intent, the 2nd IRP
is used as a standard for general gonadotropin assays, some unit
other than International Unit of FSH and LH must be designated.
The idea of preparing a separate standard (not the 2nd IRP) for
hospital performance of the mouse uterine weight assay was discussed inconclusively. Such a standard would have been very
valuable 5 - 10 years ago. It would still be valuable depending
on how soon radioimmunoassay of FSH and LH in serum becomes
generally available. The convenience of obtaining small amounts
of blood for the measurement of gonadotropic activity by radioimmunoassay versus the inconvenience of collecting 24 - hour
urines and processing them for the subsequent bioassay would lead
to the abandonment of the urinary gonadotropin assay in favor of
serum radioimmunoassay as a diagnostic procedure.

For radioimmunoassay standards, many problems were raised, most
of which could not be resolved because of lack of data. In
retrospect, it might have been wiser to set up separate biologic
and immunologic units. This could still be done, now or in the
future, but would represent a drastic change in the current
direction which is to relate biologic and immunologic potency.
From available information, it appeared that biopotency and
immunologic potency were not necessarily equivalent, but that
metabolism of FSH or LH could give rise to varying immunologic
potencies of these hormones in pituitary glands, blood or urine.
For this reason, it was thought that the law of similarity must
be applied in full force. Radioimmunoassay of FSH and LH in

extracts of urine requires the 2nd IRP as a radioimmunoassay
standard, as was clearly demonstrated. For radioimmunoassay of
pituitary gland FSH and LH, a pituitary extract standard, such as
LER 907, (distributed by the NPA) is required. This also seemed
clear. However, there was no information as to whether a serum
standard for radioimmunoassay of serum FSH and LH was required.
Consequently, it was agreed that an appropriate study be made to
determine whether a serum standard was necessary.

In summary, general agreement was reached on five points: (1)
The 2nd IRP is a satisfactory standard for bioassay and radioimmunoassay of FSH or LH in urinary extracts. No difficulty in
replacing the 2nd IRP as a bioassay standard was visualized.
More information on the stability of the 2nd IRP as a radioimmunoassay standard is needed. It was not certain that the immunoreactivity of the 2nd IRP could be matched with equal ease. (2)
A pituitary extract standard, LER 907 or a similar preparation,
could very easily be established as an International Radioimmunoassay Standard for FSH and LH in pituitary gland extracts. This
preparation could also be used for radioimmunoassay of serum FSH
or LH. Absolutely pure FSH or LH from pituitary or other sources
would of course be of value, but presently seems to be out of
reach. (3) A standardized FSH and LH antiserum should be sought.
(4) Distribution of immunochemical grade hFSH and hHLH was
recommended. (5) A pilot study was recommended to determine
whether an official serum standard was needed for radioimmunoassay
of serum FSH or LH.

ROSEMBERG: It should be remembered that, for many years, investigators in this area did not have available any reference preparation and animal units were then used. The advent of national and
international preparations which were used as reference materials
(with whatever unitage was assigned to each) created a world of
confusion. It was necessary somehow to correlate one preparation
with another. This was done in many instances, by using conversion factors. We all recognize that conversion factors are of
limited value, and when used indiscriminately, hazardous. However,
we do indeed appreciate the value of animal units and conversion
factors -- in their place -- and when nothing better is (or was)
available. Some comparison of results, even an approximation, is
better than no comparison at all.

Of course, variability between assay methods, between laboratories
and between assay animals should be minimized. The standard used
should be derived from the same species as the gonadotropin being
tested and should not deteriorate with time. When necessary and
applicable, quantitation can be achieved by a variety of statistical techniques other than the customary parallel-line assay
(Cornfield, J.:J. Pharm. and Exp. Ther. 144:143, 1964; Cox, C.P.,
and P.E. Leaverton, J. of Pharm. Sciences 55:716, 1966).

It is my firm belief that the past has provided us with enough
experience to avoid future shortcomings. Moreover, advances in

the chemistry, biology and immunologic aspects of gonadotropin
research would, I am sure, exert the most helpful influence in
the preparation of future standards. The principle of similarity
in the use of standards for the purpose of assay (biological or
immunological) should be emphasized. We should advocate strongly
the use of comparative assays and units and appropriate standards
when they exist.

CHAPTER 6

GONADOTROPIN THERAPY.
STUDIES IN FEMALE SUBJECTS

INTRODUCTORY REMARKS TO THE SESSION

EUGENIA ROSEMBERG

We are indeed fortunate to have many of the leading investigators
in this area present at this Meeting. It is hoped that from the
exchange of ideas and reasoning together during this session, we
should be able to formulate specific recommendations regarding
the use of human gonadotropins as therapeutic agents in female
infertility.

The use of human pituitary (HPG, HHG) and urinary (HMG) gonadotropins combined with human chorionic gonadotropin (HCG) for
the purpose of inducing ovarian stimulation leading to ovulation
has been well documented since 1958 and 1960, respectively.
(Gemzell, C. A., E. Diczfalusy, and K. -G. Tillinger J. Clin.
Endocr. 18: 1333, 1958; Lunenfeld, B., A. Manzi and B. Volet.:
1st Int'l. Cong. Endocr. Period. (Copenhagen) Abstract # 295,
p. 587, 1960). This mode of therapy can be applied to specific
cases of female infertility. As we all know, apparent ovarian
overstimulation resulting in a number of multiple births had
occurred. The most disturbing occurrence has been that of
ovarian enlargement and cyst formation which, in severe forms was
also associated with ascites and pleural effusions and sometimes
with changes in blood volume and clotting time. It is quite
clear that to obtain better control over treatment is an absolute
necessity.

Under physiological conditions, ovarian response is dependent
upon the proper interplay of the effects of follicle-stimulating
(FSH) and luteinizing (LH) hormones which bring about follicular
growth, rupture of the follicle and structural formation of the
corpus luteum. Various factors influence the type of ovarian
response to exogenous gonadotropins.

1. Ovarian responsiveness to endogenous gonadotropin
stimulation is dependent upon the ability of the ovarian tissue
to respond to gonadotropin stimulation. Hence, in order to make
proper comparisons as to the effectiveness of gonadotropin
therapy, the patient population should be clearly defined. It
is worth remembering that ovarian unresponsiveness to endogenous
gonadotropin stimulation could be due to a relative deficiency
in the endogenous production of FSH and LH at levels required
to induce normal ovarian function.

2. Ovarian response to exogenous gonadotropins may be dependent
upon the "total" dosage of FSH activity administered prior to
HCG addition to the therapeutic regimen. Moreover, the amount
of LH activity contained in HMG preparations used clinically
may influence the degree of ovarian response. It is still not
known whether in order to induce adequate ovarian stimulation
an absolute amount of FSH activity is more critical than an
"optimal" FSH:LH ratio. Presently, the FSH:LH ratios of
available HMG preparations vary from batch to batch. We should,
if possible, arrive at some conclusion on this matter.

BIOLOGIC ACTIVITY OF POSTMENOPAUSAL GONADOTROPIN
PREPARATIONS IN TERMS OF THE 2nd IRP

Batch #	IU equiv./2nd IRP/ampoule		Ratio FSH:LH
	FSH	LH	
P-22-C*	27.3	42.5	0.64
P-25-EX-1899	108.8	73.8	1.47
P-25-EX-1938	118.5	63.8	1.86
P-25-EX-1958	110.0	34.4	3.20
P-25-EX-1990	84.5	93.8	0.90
P-25-EX-2015	63.0	63.1	1.00
P-25-EX-2040	74.3	130.6	0.57
P-25-EX-2074	72.8	103.2	0.71
P-25-EX-2089	85.4	123.2	0.69
P-25-EX-2119	81.6	28.3	2.90
P-25-EX-2127	75.0	84.0	0.89
HMG** 1942	71.0	35.0	2.0
HMG 2010	64.0	20.0	3.2
HMG 2127	66.0	6.0	11.0
HMG 2138	74.0	2.7	27.4
HMG 2167 (2197)	73.0	1.4	52.0
HMG 2225	81.0	23.0	3.5
HMG 2282	82.0	28.0	2.9
HMG 2316	78.0	28.0	2.8

* Pergonal (Cutter). ** HMG (Ortho).

3. It is important to remember that patients vary in their
individual sensitivity to similar doses of gonadotropin. We
should discuss the value of conducting a "sensitivity" test
with HMG or HPG alone prior to initiation of a full course of
medication with pituitary gonadotropins and HCG.

4. We should also remember that the metabolism and excretion rate of administered gonadotropins may play a role in ovarian responsiveness to exogenous gonadotropins. This subject has been discussed at this Meeting.

5. As HCG is the hormone which has been employed to "trigger" ovulation, we should define the optimal dose to be used as well as the timing of its administration during a course of treatment with HMG or HCG.

6. We should make every effort to evaluate the various systems of treatment which have been proposed and used in the past few years.

Finally, it would be of great interest to compare the effectiveness of human pituitary LH preparations and HCG in the induction of ovulation.

EFFECT OF ANTIOVULATORY COMPOUNDS ON THE OVARIAN RESPONSE TO HMG AND HCG. -LUTEOTROPHIC HORMONES IN THE HUMAN.

CARLOS GUAL, M.D., JOSE A. BERMUDEZ, M.D. AND AUGUSTO DIAZ-INFANTE Jr., M.D. DEPARTMENT OF ENDOCRINOLOGY, INSTITUTO NACIONAL DE LA NUTRICION. MEXICO.

For many years several groups of investigators have presented controversial evidence trying to explain the mechanism of action of oral contraceptives in the human. In this regard some authors have suggested a central effect on the hypothalamo-pituitary system (1, 2, 3, 4), while others claim a direct effect on the ovaries by diminishing the responsiveness of the gonad to endogenous or exogenous gonadotropins (5, 6). These hypothesis are mainly based on: a) The action of anti-ovulatory steroids in amenorrheic patients with low or no detectable urinary gonadotropins whose ovaries responded to exogenous human gonadotropins; and b) The action of human gonadotropins in normal menstruating women treated cyclically with oral anti-ovulatory compounds. Apparently, differences in case selection are not responsible for such contradictory effect. It was therefore desirable to resume the problem and to test these possibilities in normal and hypopituitary patients (Sheehan's syndrome and primary "hypothalamic" amenorrhea). Finally it looked interesting to present recent data on the luteotrophic effect of HCG in patients with demonstrated pituitary insufficiency.

MATERIAL AND METHODS.

CASE REPORTS.

Case 1: C.M., age 40, with previously normal ovarian function and confirmed fertility; was treated cyclically for 72 months from day 5 to day 24 of the menstrual cycle, with a daily dose of 2 mg. norethisterone + 0.08 mg. of mestranol. Withdrawal of therapy restored ovulation which was again inhibited by a combined dose of 2.5 mg. linestrenol + 0.08 mg mestranol. In the last treatment cycle an attempt to induce ovulation was made by the administration of human menopausal gonadotropin (HMG) and human chorionic gonadotropin (HCG). Further on, different antiovulatory (combined and sequential) and gonadotropic schemes were tested for a total of nine menstrual cycles.

Case 2: M.R.P., age 35, with previously normal ovarian function and several pregnancies was treated cyclically for 18 months with a sequential regimen consisting of 0.08 mg. mestranol, from day 5 to day 25, associated with 2.5 mg. linestrenol on the final seven days of therapy. In the last treatment cycle, HMG and HCG were injected as in Case 1.

A total of six menstrual cycles were studied.

Case 3: M.A.M., age 34, with a history of thyroid, adrenal and ovarian insufficiency of 3 years evolution, was diagnosed as Sheehan's syndrome and controlled with 25 mg. cortisone + 130 mg. of Proloid. Ovulation was induced with HMG and HCG, followed by associated sequential antiovulatory therapy (0.08 mg mestranol + 2.5 mg. linestrenol). In some induced ovulatory cycles, HCG was injected to assess its possible luteotrophic effect, from day 7th to day 16th of the luteal phase.

Case 4: M.T.D., age 31, with a history of primary amenorrhea and sterility, associated with severe hypoestrogenism and no detectable urinary gonadotropins. Gonadotropin therapy arose a normal ovarian response, being anovulatory. When sequential therapy was added after 4 successive induced ovulatory cycles. Further gonadotropin therapy alone, resulted in pregnancy.

GONADOTROPIN THERAPY.

HMG was purchased from Cutter Laboratories, Berkeley, California, as Pergonal ampoules corresponding to 75 IU FSH and 75 IU LH of the 2nd IRP. Also, Humegon ampoules, each containing 75 IU FSH and 300 IU LH of the 2nd IRP were obtained from N.V. Organon, Holland. Ampoules with 5000 IU of Human Chorionic Gonadotropin (Ecluton) were supplied by N.V. Organon, Holland.

Three ampoules of Pergonal or Humegon were injected intramuscularly starting the 7th day of the menstrual cycle for 8 to 10 consecutive days. Ten thousand IU HCG (Ecluton) were injected intramuscularly as a single dose administered 48 hours after the last injection of HMG. In some instances daily doses of 5000 IU HCG were administered along with HMG for the last 4 or 5 days of therapy.

ASSESSMENT OF OVULATION.

Ovulation was assessed by indirect means, mainly based on basal body temperature charts (BBT) and daily urinary pregnanediol determinations. Pregnanediol was estimated by the method of Goldzieher and Nakamura (7), modified and standardized at our laboratory (8). Interpretation of results were made on the basis of our previous experience (9) in which pregnanediol values were found consistently under 1.3 mg/24 hs, in anovulatory cycles and the follicular phase of the menstrual cycle. An active corpus luteum gives a maximum of 6 or 7 mg/24 hours on day 6 preceding the succeeding menstrual flow. Since pregnanediol excretion does not exhibit circadian rhythm (10), only night urine collections were made and reported as 24 hours values.

RESULTS.

A. NORMAL WOMEN UNDER PROLONGED ANTIOVULATORY THERAPY.

The ovarian response in Case 1 (C.M.) is presented in the next two figures. Fig. 1 shows the last treatment cycle of 72 months antiovula - tory therapy, with pregnanediol data consistent with anovulatory cycles. Withdrawal of inhibitory therapy, ensued a 47 day cycle in which an ovulatory rise of urinary pregnanediol was observed. On the third cy - cle, restitution of combined antiovulatory therapy was accompanied by low pregnanediol levels which characterizes anovulatory cycles. In the fol - lowing cycles, three different schemes of HMG + HCG administration were used along with the antiovulatory drugs. In none of these cycles, ovulatory rise in pregnanediol excretion was observed. In the next cycle, no treatment was given and a 39 day ovulatory cycle was observed. It should be pointed out that the pregnanediol excretion reached a maximum of 11.1 mg./24 hours. This value is not usually found in the normal ovula-

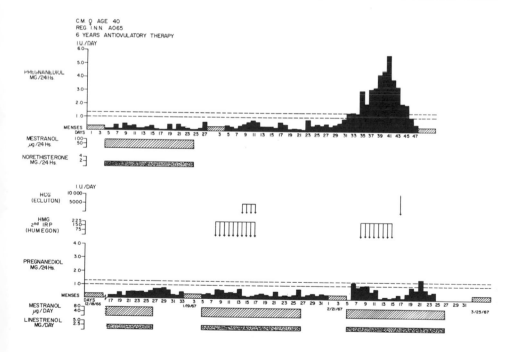

Figure No. 1.

Ovarian response to exogenous gonadotropins in a normal patient under combined and sequential antiovulatory therapy.

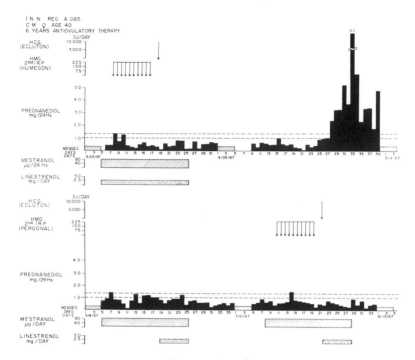

Figure No. 2.

Ovarian response to exogenous gonadotropins in a normal patient under combined and sequential antiovulatory therapy.

tory women studied at our laboratories. It is quite possible that this high pregnanediol value is compatible with multiple corpora lutea formation. Finally, sequential antiovulatory therapy was followed by a typical anovulatory response. Association of HMG + HCG with antiovulatory steroid therapy, was not accompanied by a pregnanediol rise as seen in the previous cycle. It is therefore evident that antiovulatory therapy interferes with the ovarian response to gonadotropic stimulation.

       The results obtained in Case 2 (M.R.P.) are shown in Figures 3 and 4. In the first three menstrual periods, different schemes of HMG + HCG stimulation were used simultaneously with an antiovulatory sequential regimen. Although an ovarian response was not observed in the first two cycles, a discrete pregnanediol rise was detected in the third. This doubtful ovulation was confirmed in the fifth cycle in which a typical ovulatory response was obtained. From these data, it appears that in some cases, successive exogenous gonadotropic stimulation is able to induce ovulation, still when administered stimultaneously with antiovulatory steroids.

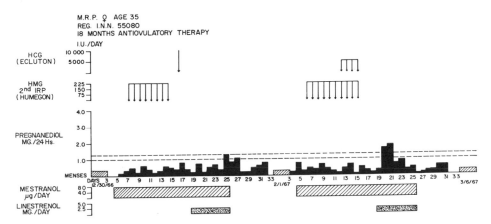

Figure No. 3.

Ovarian response to exogenous gonadotropins in a normal patient under
sequential antiovulatory therapy.

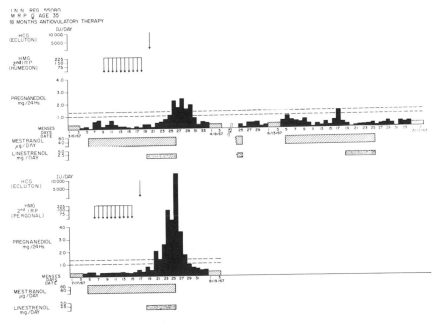

Figure No. 4.

Ovarian response to exogenous gonadotropins in a normal patient under
sequential antiovulatory therapy.

B. PITUITARY AMENORRHEICS.

Figure No. **5**, shows the ovarian response to various courses of gonadotropic stimulation in a Sheehan's syndrome patient with 3 years of amenorrhea (Case 3: M.A.M.).   In the first two cycles, ovulation was demonstrated by a biphasic pregnanediol excretion with values up to 7 mg/24
hours. It should be pointed out that the luteal phase persisted through
fourteen days after the last injection of HCG. This finding should be interpreted in patients with pituitary insufficiency. Estrogen excretion consecutive to HMG therapy, was made evident by vaginal smears in which a
sharp increase of the karyopycknotic index was observed. In a third cycle,
simultaneous gonadotropic and sequential antiovulatory therapy, did not
induce ovulation as seen in previous cycles under stimulatory therapy alone.

In Figure No. 6, is shown the ovarian reaction to exogenous gonadotropins
in a patient with primary amenorrhea (Case 4: M.T.D.), treated simultaneously with sequential antiovulatory steroids. As in the forementioned
patient, ovulatory pregnanediol excretion was not observed. It is suitable
to mention that prior to this simultaneous therapy, five consecutive ovulatory cycles were induced by similar HMG + HCG courses.

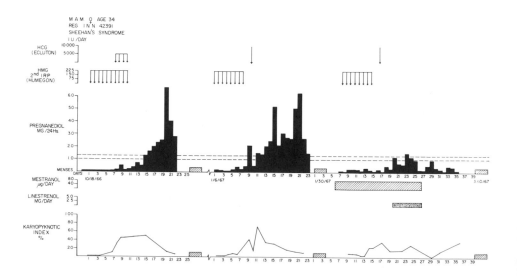

Figure No. 5.
Ovarian response to exogenous gonadotropins and simultaneous sequential
antiovulatory therapy, in a 3 years amenorrheic Sheehan's syndrome patient.

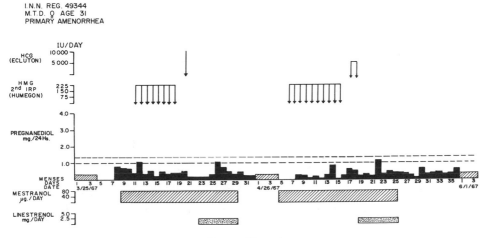

Figure No. 6.

Simultaneous gonadotropic and sequential antiovulatory therapy in a patient with primary amenorrhea.

Summarizing our observations, we have found that in most of the cases, sequential or combined antiovulatory therapy **is** able of inhibiting the ovarian response to HMG + HCG stimulation.

C. LUTEOTROPHIC HORMONES IN THE HUMAN.

Figure No. 7, shows the pregnanediol metabolic pattern of Case 4 (M.T.D., primary "hypothalamic" amenorrhea) in which an undoubtful ovulatory response to exogenous gonadotropins was observed and confirmed by a multiple pregnancy (2 products). In this case there were several features that can be summarized as follows: a) By previous cycles it was manifest that the luteal phase lasted for 14 days without further exogenous gonadotropic stimulation in a similar fashion as in other hypopituitary patients. b) According to our established laboratory techniques, we have found in this and in other cases, that pregnanediol levels over 10 mg/24 hours, are suggestive of polyovulation. c) After an initial rise in the pregnanediol excretion, a sharp drop was observed followed by a second elevation to a plateau around 20 mg/24 hours, which was mantained through the first nine weeks of pregnancy. It is possible that the second pregnanediol rise was a consequence of endogenous chorionic gonadotropic stimulation occurring after the 8th or 10th day of conception.

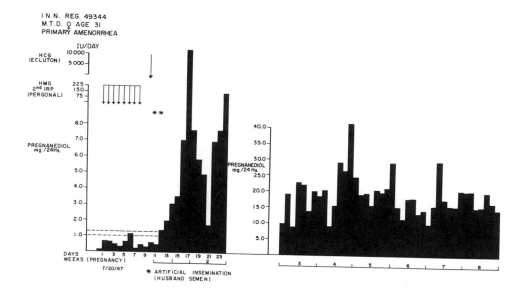

Figure No. 7.

Pregnancy consecutive to exogenous gonadotropic stimulation in a primary amenorrheic patient.

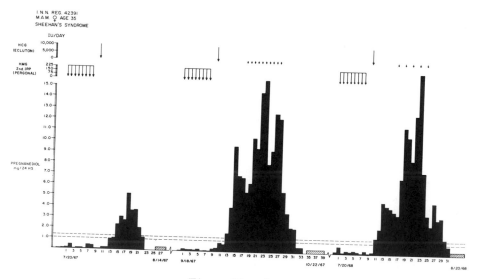

Figure No. 8.

Luteotrophic effect of HCG in hypopituitary patients (Sheehan's syndrome).

Figure No. 8, shows the luteotrophic effect of HCG in hypopituitary patients (Case 3, M.A.M.). In the first cycle, ovulation was induced with HMG + HCG with a luteal phase of 13 days in length. In the second cycle, ovulation was induced with a similar gonadotropic scheme, but extra HCG was injected in daily doses of 1000 IU from day 7th through day 16th of the luteal phase. In a third cycle extra HCG was also injected from day 7th through day 16th of the luteal phase, but 1000 IU were administered every other day. In these two cycles, the high pregnanediol excretion was suggestive of multiple ovulation. Withdrawal of HCG stimulation was followed by a fast decrease of urinary pregnanediol and normal menstrual bleeding. In both cases the luteal phase was prolonged 22 and 21 day respectively, evoking a pseudo-pregnant corpus luteum.

COMMENTS AND CONCLUSIONS.

It has been generally accepted that antiovulatory steroids have a definite inhibitory effect on the hypothalamo-pituitary system, manifested by a significant suppression of total gonadotropins in most patients under prolonged antiovulatory treatment. Nevertheless there is some evidence that steroid therapy may act also on the ovaries by diminishing the responsiveness of the gonad to endogenous or exogenous gonadotropins. In this regard our results suggest that mestranol alone or combined with a progestogen, have a direct effect on the ovaries by interfering the stimulatory action of exogenous gonadotropins, independently of any other possible inhibitory effect on the central nervous system. It was also found that in some cases, a repeated or increased gonadotropin administration, may overcome the steroid inhibitory effect; thus explaining in part the apparent contradictory results obtained by others. Similar observations were reported by Staemmler (11) and Staemmler and Staemmler (12), postulating a direct relationship between ovarian response and a gonadotropin-steroid dose ratio. Recently it has been reported (13) that anticonceptive progestogen therapy, interferes with progesterone synthesis in recent formed corpus luteum. Since in our patients ovulation was not detected by direct methods, it is not possible to assess this possibility that could explain many other apparently conflicting reports.

Of interest was the ovarian response observed in our hypopituitary patient. Previous experience on this matter, was reported by Bettendorf (14), who showed that hypophysectomized patients subjected to human gonadotropin stimulation, presented normal ovulatory cycles and successful pregnancies. In his cases, as well as in our patient, if was observed that once ovulation has taken place, it seems unnecessary to stimulate further the corpus luteum, to have a normal 14 days luteal phase. It is obscure how the luteal activity is maintained in absence of pituitary gonadotropins, but it is conceivable that extrapituitary luteotrophic factors may exist.

For many years it has been known that HCG is capable of prolonging the luteal phase in normal women, as was reported in 1938 by Browne and Venning (15) and confirmed later on by Brown and Bradbury (16), Segaloff et al (17) and more recently by Geller (18). Although in these experiments it was not excluded a synergetic action with some endogenous pituitary gonadotropins, it is evident as demonstrated in our hypopituitary patient (M.S.M.), that administrated HCG has a definite luteotrophic effect in absence of endogenous pituitary gonadotropins.

ACKNOWLEDGMENTS.

This work was supported by a Research Grant from The Ford Foundation. We are indebted to Organon Laboratories, The Netherlands, for a generous gift of HMG (Humegon) and HCG (Ecluton).

REFERENCES.

1. Bettendorf, G., Geburtsh.u.Freuenheilk. 22:928,1962.
2. Johannisson,E., Tillinger, K.G., and Diczfalusy, E., Fertil. and Steril. 16:292,1965.
3. Taymor, M.L. and Rizkallah, T., J. Clin. Endocr. 25:843,1965.
4. Starup,J. and Østergaard, E., Acta Endocr. (Kobenhavn) 52:292, 1966.
5. Lunenfeld, B., Sulimovici, S. and Rabau, E., J. Clin. Endocr. 23:391, 1963.
6. Hecht-Lucari, G., Int. J. Fertil., 9:205,1964.
7. Goldzieher, J.W. and Nakamura, Y., Acta Endocr. (Kobenhavn) 41:371,1962.
8. Rojo-Sanchez,B., Thesis.Universidad Motolinia, México, 1963.
9. Gual,C., In Greenblatt, R.B. (ed.) Ovulation, J.B. Lippincott,Co. Philadelphia, 1966, p. 310.
10. Gual, C., Proc. Fourth Panamer. Symp. Farmacology Therapeutics, ed. Excerpta Medica. The Netherlands (In press).
11. Staemmler, H.J.,Geburtsh.u.Frauenheilk. 20:758,1960.
12. Staemmler, H.J.,and Staemmler, H., Arch.Gynäk. 194:183,1960.
13. Østergaard,E. and Starup, J., Acta Endocr. (Kobenhavn), 57:386, 1968.
14. Bettendorf,G., Proc.Fifth World Congr.Fertil. Steril., ed. Excerpta Medica, The Netherlands, Int. Congress Series No. 133, Stockholm 1966, p. 46.
15. Browne, J.S.L. and Venning, E.H., Am.J. Physiol. 123:26,1938.
16. Brown, W.E. and Bradbury, J.T., Am. J. Obstet. Gynec. 53:749,1947.
17. Segaloff, A., Sternberg, W.H. and Gaskill,C.J., J. Clin. Endocr. 11:936,1951.
18. Geller,S., Europ. Rev. Endocrin. Suppl. 2, part 2, p. 397, 1967.

DISCUSSION

LUNENFELD: I am glad that Dr. Gual actually confirmed our
earlier results where we showed that administration of medroxy-
progesterone acetate together with ethinylestradiol blocked the
induction of ovulation by Pergonal. In our series we were unable
to achieve this block by administration of ethinylestradiol alone.
Again to confirm what Dr. Gual has said I would like to refer to
the results of our experiments with various treatment schedules.
Four patients were selected for this study. Three had primary
amenorrhea and one secondary amenorrhea of 8 years duration.
All had low or undetectable urinary gonadotropins and none had
evidence of endogenous estrogen production. The preparation
used was HMG (Pergonal) with a potency of 75 IU FSH and 75 IU LH
per ampoule. Each patient received two alternate treatment
courses: 1. The equally spaced treatment (according to Gemzell)
consisting of 2 ampoules of HMG daily for 8 days followed by
10,000 IU HCG 2 days later. 2. The single injection schedule
(according to Crooke) in which the total amount of HMG (i.e.
16 ampoules) was given at once and followed by 10,000 IU HCG
10 days later. The response was measured by serial estimations
of urinary estrogen and pregnanediol, basal body temperature and
cervical mucus crystallization (fern test). As judged by these
parameters the single injection scheme caused a significant
ovarian response and ovulation in only one out of the four
cases. The equally spaced schedule induced a measurable response
and probably ovulation in all instances.

In our clinical work we use the individually adjusted treatment
schedule in which the amount of HMG and the length of treatment
are determined in each course by the patient's response. This
scheme allows the treatment to be adjusted to the individual
needs of the patient and thus saves time and expense by combining
the "sensitivity test", induction of ovulation and pregnancy
in a single course. So far as results of gonadotropic therapy
(i.e. pregnancies) are concerned our treatment scheme seems to
justify itself fully. When the amounts of HMG required in
264 treatment courses given to 133 women were plotted the
individual dose requirements showed a distinct Gaussian-like
pattern. In the majority of treatment courses medium doses
(15-34 ampoules) were required, however in 13% of courses the
required amount of HMG was lower and in 33% higher (sometimes
as much as 70, 80 or 90 ampoules per course). If a predetermined
treatment schedule of 2-4 ampoules per day over 8 days was used,
that would cover the medium portion (54% of cases) but patients
falling into either end of the curve would not receive the
required amount of gonadotropins; 13% would probably be
hyperstimulated while 33% would probably not ovulate. The
individually adjusted treatment schedule therefore results in
ovulation and pregnancy in a number of cases which would otherwise fail to respond.

BETTENDORF: We had the same experience with HHG, (Human
Hypophyseal Gonadotropin) as Dr. Lunenfeld reported with

Pergonal. Injections of 150 IU daily were given and after 4 or
5 days the dosage was changed or not according to clinical
symptoms and estrogen excretion.

MARSHALL: We have some information concerning the effect of
estrogen given with HMG. Four patients were treated for two
cycles at HMG doses slightly greater than the FOD. In one
cycle ethinylestradiol, 0.05 mg., was given daily beginning
5 days prior to HMG and continuing for 10 days. In the control
cycle the same amount of HMG was given without the estrogen.
Ovulation occurred in all four of the control cycles, but did
not occur in any of the estrogen cycles. The difference is
statistically significant at the .05 level.

BETTENDORF: In the treatment of your case with Sheehan's
syndrome was the administration of HCG continued after ovulation
had occurred?

GUAL: We injected 1000 IU of HCG daily for 10 consecutive
days. The first dose was given one week after occurrence of
ovulation.

BETTENDORF: In other words you were able to prolong the luteal
phase.

GUAL: Yes.

BETTENDORF: Do you find that the length of the luteal phase is
12 days?

GUAL: In patients with the Sheehan's syndrome we found luteal
phases of 12 to 14 days in length.

BETTENDORF: Our experience with hypophysectomized patients is
very similar. Four such patients were given eight treatment
courses with HHG and in all cases clinical and analytical data
indicated that ovulation had been induced. In three hypophysectomized patients six treatment courses consisting of HHG
administration followed by HCG resulted in five ovulations,
including one patient who became pregnant three times. The
length of the luteal phase was 12 days.

A COMPARISON OF TREATMENT SCHEDULES FOR OVULATION INDUCTION WITH HMG

J.R. Marshall and A. Jacobson, Surgery and Reproductive Research Branches
National Cancer Institute and National Institute of Child Health and
Human Development, National Institutes of Health, Bethesda, Maryland

Introduction

A gonadotropin treatment schedule should be both efficient and
convenient. Historical tradition favors daily injections (1),
simplicity favors a single injection (2), compromise suggests three
spaced injections (3). Valid comparative information is scant (3).

This study compares four non-variable schedules in an attempt to
provide a basis for gonadotropin treatment schedule selection. While
ovulation and pregnancy occurred with each schedule, efficiency
depended upon the ovulatory thresholds of the patients treated.

Materials and Methods

Subjects were anovulatory or oligo-ovulatory women receiving cyclic
human menopausal gonadotropin (HMG) and human chorionic gonadotropin
(HCG) for ovulation induction. The HMG used was a single preparation
containing 75 I.U. FSH and 530 I.U. LH IRP#2 per ampule*. Indicated
doses are total number of ampules given during one cycle. The day HMG
was begun was arbitrarily called day 1. HMG was given according to
4 schedules; 1) a single injection given on day 1; 2) three injections
given on days 1,3 and 5; 3) three injections given on days 1,4 and 8;
4) daily injections given on days 1 through 8. HCG, was given as a
single injection of 10,000 I.U. on day 9 for the single injection
schedule or on day 10 for the triple and daily schedules. Ovarian size
was estimated by pelvic examination on days 1,9 or 10 and 21.

Treatment was begun with presumed subovulatory doses, and dose
was increased until ovulation occurred. The lowest and usually first
dose causing ovulation was called the first ovulatory dose or FOD and
was used as a measure of ovulatory threshold to HMG. Further treatment
and comparisons of dosage schedules used HMG doses usually slightly
greater than the FOD. Judgement of response as ovulatory or
anovulatory was made at the conclusion of each treatment cycle based
upon basal body temperatures (89%), cervical mucus (100%), urinary
pregnanediol excretion (15%) and endometrial biopsy (43%). Figures in
parentheses are the percentage of ovulatory cycles in which the given
indicator was useful in the diagnosing of ovulation and have been
obtained from our total experience with ovulation induction using
human gonadotropins. Endometrial biopsies were obtained more
frequently in the ovulatory cycles occurring early in each patient's
course of study, whereas the other indicators were relied upon more

* Provided by Organon, Inc., West Orange, New Jersey

frequently in later cycles when the patient's ovulatory response pattern had been recognized.

Gonadotropin schedules were compared using 1) pregnancy rates per ovulatory cycle; 2) ovulatory rates to equal HMG doses: 3) FODs determined in comparable groups of patients or in the same patient or; 4) if none of these were available, total response. Total response was defined as the rank sum of a series of individual comparisons of treatment dose, ovulatory versus anovulatory response and ovarian enlargements wherein differences in dose of less than 10% or in maximum ovarian diameter of less than 2 cm. were not considered meaningful. For comparisons in which total response has been evaluated the tabulations of the data have always been arranged so that a positive value was assigned when the first mentioned schedule of the pair being compared was considered more efficient.

Convenience was always considered as inverse to the number of injections.

Results

Pregnancy occurred with each of the 4 treatment schedules.

Meaningful pregnancy rates were available only from the single and the triple 1,4,8 schedules; groups were not segregated in terms of ovulatory threshold (Table I). Data is available from 41 ovulatory cycles which were not biopsied and which occurred in 28 women who ultimately conceived with HMG/HCG therapy. Pregnancy resulted from 61 percent of such cycles induced with the triple 1,4,8 schedule and from 39 percent induced with the single injection schedule. The probability of these distributions occurring by chance is $.30 > p > .20$. With larger groups differences of this magnitude could become significant, however, they are presently not so. Therefore, providing ovulation occurred, neither schedule was more likely to result in pregnancy.

Table I.   Pregnancy Efficiency of Single and Triple 1,4,8
            Schedules Determined from Non-Biopsied, Ovulatory
            Cycles Occurring in Women Who Conceived with
            HMG/HCG Therapy

	Pregnant	Non-Pregnant
Single	7 (39%)	11
Triple 1,4,8	14 (61%)	9

$.30 > p > .20$

In addition to pregnancy rates, comparisons were made using ovulatory rates, FODs or total responses. In making these comparisons it became clear that ovulatory threshold as measured by FOD was a significant determinant of response to HMG treatment schedule. As shown in Table II where total response is used as a basis of comparison, 7 out of 7 patients having FODs of greater than 25 ampules (1,875 I.U. FSH IRP#2) had a greater total response with the triple schedule, whereas 4 out of 4 patients having FODs of less than 25 ampules had equal or greater responses with the single schedule. These distributions were significantly different by Chi square with $p < .01$. Therefore, additional comparisons were made separately and in more detail in patients having FODs of greater than or less than 25 ampules (hereafter called high or low thresholds).

Table II.   Comparison of Total Response to Single and Triple 1,4,8 Injection Schedules in Patients Having First Ovulatory Doses (FOD) of Less Than and Greater Than 25 Ampules

Total Response	FOD < 25 AMPULES	FOD > 25 AMPULES
Single < triple	0	7
Single ⩾ triple	4	0

Comparisons of Schedules in Patients Having Low Thresholds

To compare the single and triple 1,4,8 schedules first ovulatory doses were determined in 2 separate groups of patients with low threshold and in paired cycles in 4 patients. Thus using the single injection schedule 10 patients had a mean FOD of 14.1 ± 1.6 ampules(S.F.) and using the triple schedule 23 patients had a mean FOD of 14.1 ± 1.1 ampules. The difference is not significant. Further, no significant difference was observed between regimes using paired cycles in 4 patients where the mean FODs for the single and triple 1,4,8 schedules were 14 and 16.3 ampules respectively. (Table III) Thus, the single injection schedule was at least as efficient as the triple 1,4,8 schedule in inducing ovulation in patients with low thresholds.

Table III.   Comparison of First Ovulatory Dose Obtained by Single
and Triple 1,4,8 Injection Schedules in Patients with
Low Thresholds

Patient	Single FOD	Triple FOD
J.S.	13	19
Z.M.	10	11
H.E.D.	10	12
H.C.	23	23
Mean	14	16.3

A direct comparison of the daily and the triple 1,4,8 schedule
in patients having low thresholds was not made in this study; however,
an indirect comparison was made using data from oligomenorrheic
patients, who almost always have an ovulatory threshold of less than
25 ampules. In 14 oligo-ovulatory patients the mean FOD was 13
ampules (range 6-24) which compares favorably with the mean dose of
17 ampules observed by Lunenfeld[4] to be effective in inducing
ovulation without hyperstimulation in similar subjects and as noted
before, again the 2 schedules compared did not appear to differ in
efficiency.

In summary among patients with low thresholds the single,
triple and daily schedules appeared to be equally efficient.

Comparison of Schedules in Patients Having High Thresholds

Using ovulatory rates or total response as the means of
comparison all schedules did not appear equally efficient in patients
having high thresholds.

To compare the single and triple 1,4,8 schedules among patients
with high thresholds 7 subjects were randomly treated in 2 cycles
with equal total doses of HMG given according to these two schedules.
Seven ovulated with the triple schedule whereas only 2 ovulated
with the single schedule (Table IV). This difference was
significant with p <.05. Thus, in patients having high thresholds
the triple 1,4,8 schedule was significantly more efficient than
was the single.

Table IV.   Comparison of Responses to Equal HMG Doses Given
             According to Single or Triple 1,4,8 Schedule in
             Patients with High Thresholds

Patient	Total Dose	Single	Triple
P.S.	64	Anovul	Ovul
M.M.	32	Anovul	Ovul
M.S.	50	Anovul	Ovul
M.B.	35	Anovul	Ovul
M.D.	60	Anovul	Ovul
R.L.	44	Ovul	Ovul
C.N.	52	Ovul	Ovul(twins)

$$p < .05$$

To compare the daily and triple 1,4,8 schedules 4 patients with
high thresholds were treated with similar total doses of HMG
according to these two schedules (Table V). On the basis of
ovulatory rates (3 ovulated with both whereas one, M.S., ovulated
only with the daily) no differences could be shown. On the basis
of total response the daily schedule was more efficient in all
4 patients, but this, too, is not statistically significant.
However, examination of the individual comparisons which make up total
response reveals none favoring the triple schedule, 5 ties and 7
favoring the daily schedule. When the ties are discarded as
providing no information this distribution is significant at the
.05 level by the sign test. Therefore, the daily schedule appeared
to be more efficient. Because of the small sample, this judgement
must be tentative. Additional comparisons should provide a more
definitive answer.

In summary among patients with high thresholds the daily schedule was suggestively most efficient, the two triple schedules were equally efficient and the single injection schedule was least efficient.

Discussion

This study indicates that patient ovulatory threshold is a significant determinant of response to treatment schedule and should be given consideration in schedule selection. Whereas the single injection schedule has good efficiency and may be preferred in patients having ovulatory thresholds of less than 25 ampules it is least desirable in patients with higher thresholds. In these latter patients both triple injection schedules appear equally efficient in inducing ovulation, but the daily schedule may be even more efficient than either of the triples. Whether this increased efficiency is great enough to offset the inconvenience of daily injections remains to be seen. Perhaps the physical loss of gonadotropins associated with their preparation for injection accounted for some of this difference. No schedule appeared to result in a more favorable therapeutic toxic ratio when used in equally effective doses.

An HMG preparation containing 75 I.U. FSH and 530 I.U. LH was used in this study. Whether other preparations with differing FSH/LH ratios would result in similar differences is not known. However, previous studies indicate that the responses to equal FSH doses of this preparation and one containing 75 I.U. FSH and 75 I.U. LH do not differ significantly but are both significantly greater than that seen with preparations containing 83 I.U. FSH and 23 I.U. LH (5). It would seem likely, therefore, that the findings reported here would be transferable to treatment with the more frequently used HMG preparations having a FSH/LH ratio near unity.

Dose of HMG (3) and HCG (6), FSH/LH ratio (5), patient diagnosis (7) and now HMG threshold and schedule have been recognized as significant determinants of ovarian response to gonadotropins. Unfortunately, this multiplicity of determinants has sometimes been neglected in the design of studies of gonadotropin pharmacology. HMG dose cannot be studied without regard to FSH/LH ratio, and treatment schedule cannot be studied without regard to patient threshold. In addition, because of the variability of response, efficiency cannot be judged from uncontrolled, case report type observations. Strict adherence to the statistical principles of randomization, controls, and tests of significance is essential.

In the study of ovulation induction with gonadotropins the only reliable indicator of ovulation is pregnancy. In the single situation in this study where pregnancy rates could be compared they appeared (but not significantly) to favor the schedule which was less favored when "ovulatory" rates were considered. In view of the many factors known to be operative in the interval between ovulation and successful implantation which might be influenced by

Table V.   Comparison of Total Response to Similar HMG Doses
             Given According to Daily or Triple 1,4,8 Schedules*

Patient	FOD †	Dose	Ovulatory Response	Ovarian Enlargement	Total Response
P.S.	64	+	=	+	+
K.N.	80	=	=	+	+
R.L.	34	+	=	=	+
M.S.	32	+	+	+	+

$\dagger$ Determined using 1,4,8 triple schedule

* Comparisons are arranged so that a positive value arises when
   the first mentioned schedule is considered most efficient, i.e.,
   a + arises when the daily dose was less than the triple dose,
   when ovulation occurred with the daily schedules but not with
   the triple or when the maximum ovarian diameter noted with
   the daily schedule was more than 2 cm. greater than the
   maximum ovarian diameter noted with the triple.

Comparison of the two triple schedules have been made in 5
patients having high thresholds (Table VI). No significant
differences were seen in this small series so that judgement must
be preliminary.

Table VI.   Comparison of Total Response to Similar HMG Doses Given
             According to Triple 1,3,5 and Triple 1,4,8 Schedules

Patient	FOD†	Dose*	Ovulatory Response++	Ovarian Enlargement++	Total Response++
P.S.	64	=	=	=	=
K.N.	80	=	=	=	=
R.L.	34	=	=	=	=
M.S.	32	+	=	=	+
M.M.	32	=	=	=	=

*   1,3,5 < 1,4,8; +
++ 1,3,5 > 1,4,8; +
$\dagger$ Determined using 1,4,8 triple schedule

gonadotropin therapy and since pregnancy is the desired end result of therapy, pregnancy rate would seem to be the most valid standard of comparison. Only until pregnancy rates are available should other, less suitable data be considered.

Conclusions

All 4 schedules tested were able to induce ovulation proved by pregnancy. Ovulatory threshold as measured by FOD was a significant determinant of response to treatment schedule. Among patients with low thresholds all schedules tested were equally efficient. Among patients with high thresholds the daily schedule appeared most efficient, however, the triple schedules were also efficient and were more convenient than was the daily schedule. Among patients with high thresholds the single injection schedule was least desirable.

References

1. Gemzell, C. and P. Roos, Am. J. Obst. Gynec. 94: 496, 1966.

2. Crooke, A.C., W.R. Butt and P.V. Bertrand, Lancet, 2: 514, 1966.

3. Crooke, A.C., W.R. Butt and P.V. Bertrand, Acta Endocrinologica, 53: supp. 3, 1966.

4. Lunenfeld, B. and E. Rabau, Proc. 5th World Congress Gynec. Obstet., Sidney, Australia, Sept. 1967.

5. Jacobson, A. and J.R. Marshall, Presented at 24th Annual Meeting, Amer. Fertil. Soc., San Francisco, Calif., March 1968.

6. Crooke, A.C., W.R. Butt, R.F. Palmer, R. Morris, R.L. Edwards, and C.J. Anson, J. Obstet. Gynec. Br. Commonwealth, 70: 604, 1963.

7. Butler, J.K., Proc. Royal Soc. Med., 60: 655, 1967.

DISCUSSION

VANDE WIELE: I feel that in discussing treatment doses we should take into account the clinical status of our patients. I am sure if we divided Dr. Marshall's patients into two groups, one with a low and one with a high FOD, we would find these groups to be different in terms of their estrogen secretion. Whereas most of the patients with a high FOD would have little residual estrogenic function, the majority of the patients with a low FOD would turn out to have adequate estrogens.

CROOKE: We are very much in agreement with Dr. Marshall. We have not made a distinction between sensitive and insensitive patients with respect to their responses to different ratios of FSH to LH or added HCG. My guess is that sensitive patients will do well with single injections of FSH having low LH content and insensitive ones will respond poorly. The latter will do better with multiple injections of FSH having a high LH content.

TAYMOR: Dr. Crooke, have you broken this down between HPG and HMG? This is very important for us because in the USA HPG is not available.

CROOKE: In this particular group, we have used both types of hormone. We have not broken down the figures any further but we have found no differences in other experiments in which HPG and HMG were compared except differences related to changes in ratio of FSH to LH.

ODELL: I must make a comment on the theoretical implications of the single treatment schedule. If a single injection of FSH will cause a follicle to grow and then a single injection of HPG cause the induction of ovulation it is possible that once follicle growth is initiated then it becomes autonomous, i.e. independent of the FSH levels. Dr. Gual's studies in the hypophysectomized human would also suggest this. This idea has been suggested by Dr. Steinberger many years ago and perhaps many other people, but it is a very interesting possibility. The same thing probably occurs with corpus luteum function as Dr. Short's studies would indicate in the sow and in the cow. Once the corpus luteum is formed it functions independently and dies whether the pituitary is there or not.

BETTENDORF: We have drawn similar conclusions from our data. When a functional corpus luteum is present it needs no further stimulation. This is true also in hypophysectomized subjects.

CROOKE: May I reply to that very interesting comment? In our in vitro studies we showed that FSH must be present for each successive generation of cell division, which seems to contradict the clinical results obtained with a single injection of FSH. We have been very puzzled by this, although, of course, we are looking at different animals and different regimes. It is possible that FSH is necessary for initial successive generations of follicles but when a certain stage of development is reached the process becomes autonomous.

PARLOW: With respect to the relative efficacies of FSH in a single and in repeated administrations I should like to revert to some laboratory data in the rat. The usual treatment regime for the HCG ovulation assay is to divide a particular dose over a period of three days using twice daily administrations, followed by autopsy and measurement of ovarian weight on the 4th day. If one administers the entire dose of FSH in a single injection and continues the HCG twice daily for a 3-day period one obtains exactly the same response in terms of ovarian weight increase. So there seems to be a parallel here between experiments in the rat and in the human. In relation to the duration of action of FSH we can cite another experiment. It is possible to administer the total dose of FSH intravenously and continue HCG injections twice daily for 3 days and still obtain a very effective FSH response in terms of ovarian weight increase in the rat. The intravenous dose must however be much larger than a subcutaneous dose. If the FSH is administered intravenously in a single dose and HCG administration is not begun until 1 day later a very good ovarian weight increase can still be produced.

VANDE WIELE: Before we draw any conclusions about the so-called autonomy of the ovarian follicle, I think we must be sure that we have ruled out the possible role of residual endogenous gonadotropic function. I have studied this problem in a number of patients who apparently had no residual gonadotropic function as a result of either surgical hypophysectomy or radiation therapy for a pituitary tumor. In each of such cases, when FSH stimulation was stopped there was a prompt decrease in urinary estrogens, leaving little evidence for speculation about autonomy of the ovarian follicle.

MARSHALL: We confirm the observations of Dr. Vande Wiele. We have treated two patients following hypophysectomy with the single, the triple, and the daily schedules each given in equal FSH and LH doses. Each patient ovulated with either the triple or the daily schedule, but did not ovulate with the single injection.

JOHNSEN: I think that all the physicians present would agree with me that the word "headache" is not a medical diagnosis. But neither are the terms "amenorrhea" or "anovulation". They just designate a symptom. Through all the many gonadotropin meetings that have been held, gynecologists have presented treatment of "amenorrhea". But what are they talking about? Do these patients have hypergonadotropic state, a normogonadotropic state or a hypogonadotropic state? Do they have a pituitary or a hypothalamic disturbance? Do some of them perhaps have a borderline adrenogenital syndrome? Or others perhaps enzymatic defects in the ovaries? Would it be possible to define patients in terms of the etiology of their ovarian disease?

ROSEMBERG: Dr. Johnsen is absolutely right. However, it is very easy for clinicians to talk about amenorrhea and anovulation. We think we know what we are talking about. It is possible that we will need definitions here. However, we could solve the problem by asking people to describe the type of patient and their reasons for arriving at the various diagnostic categories.

MARSHALL: I would like to respond to a comment which Dr. Rosemberg made a few moments ago about the importance of the FSH and LH content of the different gonadotropin preparations. We have compared the ovulatory response rates associated with 3 HMG preparations: HMG Ortho with 83 IU FSH and 23 IU LH/ampoule, Pergonal with 75 IU FSH and 75 IU LH; and Humegon with 75 IU FSH and 530 IU LH. Each patient's first ovulatory dose was determined using the high LH material. A comparison of preparations was then made using FSH doses which were just greater than the first ovulatory dose. Thus, each of the 9 patients received all 3 preparations at equal FSH doses, but at LH doses which varied depending upon the amount present in the preparation. Some patients received these preparations more than once. Six ovulations were noted with 9 cycles (67%) using the high LH material, 8 ovulations were noted with 12 cycles (63%) with the medium LH material and 0 ovulations were noted with 9 cycles (0%) with the low LH material. These differences were significant at the .01% level. Since these differences occurred when the FSH dose was held constant, we feel that they indicate the importance of the synergistic action of LH. It is interesting to note that when the total HMG dose of the low LH preparation was increased by about 50% it became as effective as the other two preparations.

LUNENFELD: As to the question of the difference between HPG and HMG we have conducted a collaborative study with Drs. Vande Wiele and Gemzell and I will summarize the results. Both preparations contained the same amount of FSH activity (93.5 IU per ampoule) but the LH content differed. The HPG preparation contained 213 IU LH per ampoule and the HMG 62 IU LH per ampoule. Eighty-four treatment cycles were studied. In occurrence of ovulation and pregnancy no significant differences between the two preparations were noted. With respect to urinary steroid excretion, the effect of both preparations was almost identical in some patients while in others, either HPG or HMG resulted in higher estrogen or pregnanediol levels. The inconsistency of these quantitative differences seems to indicate individual variations of response rather than differences in the effect of gonadotropins.

PAULSEN: We have data on two female patients with hypogonadotropic eunuchoidism which might be of interest to you. Both patients have received HMG (Pergonal)-HCG therapy in a regular cyclic fashion for about four years. The treatment schedule remained constant. Each month the patients received 2-3 ampoules HMG daily for nine days. The total dose given over a nine day period was 1350 to 1935 IU FSH and 1170 to 3070 IU LH activity. No medication was given on days 10 and 11. Then HCG, at a dose of 5,000 IU per day was administered on days 12 and 13. In one patient we have almost complete data for 43 treatment cycles. This includes urinary estrogen and pregnanediol excretion and basal body temperature recordings. We have evidence by these means that ovulation occurred during 22 treatment periods. Ovulation did not occur in 12 treatment cycles and our data were insufficient to draw any conclusions in the remaining 9 cycles. Thus even when similar doses of gonadotropins are administered repeatedly to a patient without endogenous gonado- tropin secretion ovarian response is quite variable. This type of information points to the difficulties involved in establishing strict dosage schedules for patients with secondary amenorrhea or anovulatory cycles.

FSH AND LH DOSE RESPONSE RELATIONSHIP IN OVULATION INDUCTION WITH HUMAN GONADOTROPINS

G. Bettendorf, M. Breckwoldt, Charlotte Neale

Abteilung Fuer Klinische Und Experimentelle Endokrinologie Der
Universitaets-Frauenklinik Hamburg-Eppendorf, Germany

During the last nine years, we have extracted gonadotropins
from human post mortem pituitaries and used them to treat anovulatory patients. Ovulation and functional corpora lutea could be
obtained using human hypophyseal gonadotropin (HHG) given either
alone or in combination with HCG. It is of interest that we were
also able to induce ovulation in hypophysectomized patients. In
1964 (11) we were able to show that a prerequisite for the successful clinical use of gonadotropins is adequate information as to the
specific FSH activity.

The HHG showed great variation in FSH and LH activity. The
FSH/LH ratio of the preparations was between 0.05 and 10. The
total FSH activity administered during one treatment was equivalent
to 200 - 10,000 I.U. and that of LH to 100 - 10,000 I.U. The
patients were divided into two main groups according to the level
of gonadotropin excretion. In addition, these two groups were
subdivided according to clinical status, such as primary or secondary amenorrhea, anovulatory cycles or status post hypophysectomy.
In our first treatment courses we used a definitive treatment
schedule and the same amount of gonadotropin was given in daily
injections. We then found that an individual treatment schedule
was more effective and less dangerous. The dosage and the time of
treatment was adjusted for every patient according to the individual ovarian response (1, 4, 5, 7).

In all groups ovulation could be induced. The ovulation rate
was 78% of all courses of medication. In the treatment of infertility patients, pregnancy was achieved 19 times in 16 patients,
that is 40% of patients treated and 18% of treatment courses.
Seven pregnancies resulted in single birth, two in twins, one in
quadruplets and one in quintuplets. Three of the pregnancies
ended in abortions and four of the patients are still pregnant.

During 44 courses of medication in 29 patients ovulation
could be induced in 70% by HHG without additional administration
of HCG (Fig. 2).

The ovulation rate in different types of ovarian insufficiency
(Fig. 3) showed no marked difference in response between the
various groups. Only patients with a primary amenorrhea and no
measurable gonadotropins had a somewhat lower frequency of ovulation. In this group, it was 60%; in all other groups around
80%. The incidence of ovarian enlargement in all groups was about

40%, but was much less in the patients who did not receive HCG.
Only in 16% of all patients treated was an ovarian enlargement of
more than 5 cm found and one acute Meigs-Syndrome occurred. In
ten patients we substituted human pituitary LH (N$_4$) for HCG. Ovulation could also be induced by this treatment and almost no ovarian
enlargement could be observed (10).

In each patient we found a wide range in the activity of both
FSH and LH which was necessary for induction of ovulation. On
comparison of the total FSH and the corresponding LH dose with the
ovarian response, we found no optimal combination in the range of
activity studied. Stimulation was possible with total activities
below 1000 I.U. of FSH and 500 I.U. of LH. On the other hand, we
had no responses with more than 4000 I.U. FSH and LH respectively.

There was a wide range both in FSH and LH of the activity
necessary for induction of ovulation in each patient (Fig. 4). In
the different groups of ovarian insufficiency we obtained the same
range of total activity. The single patient had no definite effective dose and the responsiveness often changed from one treatment to
the next (Fig. 5).

From these results we must conclude that the ovarian response
did not correspond to the ovarian status as far as we understood it.
In addition, each patient had no definite effective dose and the
responsiveness changed during different courses of medication. We
also could not find a definite total dose either of FSH or LH in
which ovarian enlargement and adverse reactions occurred predominantly (Fig. 6 - 7).

However, when we calculated the ratio of FSH/LH, there seemed
to be a combination which provoked less hyperstimulation than others
(Figs. 8 - 9). In the different groups of FSH/LH ratio, positive
reactions were seen in about 80% (Fig. 9). The numbers of pregnancies were too small to make any conclusions. But it is of
interest that a higher incidence of ovarian enlargement was found
in the group with the low FSH/LH ratio than in that with the high
one.

In summary, we could induce ovulation in all patients with
ovarian insufficiency and low or normal values of gonadotropin
excretion. We found no significant difference between pituitary
and urinary gonadotropin in the dosage range used. Calculating
the FSH/LH ratio, the material with a ratio of between 0.3 and 1
seemed to be optimal for ovarian stimulation and in preventing
overstimulation. The additional administration of HCG is an important factor in producing ovarian enlargement. However, we could
not find a correlation between the dose of HCG injected and the
percentage of adverse reactions (Fig. 10). For each patient to be
treated with human gonadotropins, a certain schedule with respect
to dosage and time of administration must be found. Each treatment
with gonadotropins is still a clinical and endocrinological experiment in which we must try to find a better understanding of the
pharmacology of gonadotropins. Two facts are important for further
development. We must first find better criteria for the status of

endocrine function in patients before treatment and for the response during medication and secondly, obtain more purified human FSH and LH preparations for clinical studies.

REFERENCES

1. Apostolakis, M., Bettendorf, G., Voigt, K.D.: Acta Endocrinol. 41, 1962, 14
2. Bettendorf, G., Apostolakis, M., Voigt, K. D.: Proc. III. World Congr. Figo, Wien 1961, 76
3. Bettendorf, G.: Int. J. Fertil. 8, 1963, 799
4. Bettendorf, G., Breckwoldt, M.: Arch. Gynakol. 199, 1964, 423
5. Bettendorf, G.: Int. J. Fertil. 9, 1964, 351
6. Bettendorf, G., Breckwoldt, M., Knoerr, K., Stegner, H.-E.: Dtsch. Med. Woschr. 41, 1964, 1952
7. Bettendorf, G., Breckwoldt,M.: Fortschr. Geburtsh. Gynak. 21, 1965, 31
8. Bettendorf, G., Napp, J.-H., Ahrens, D.: Geburtsh. Frauenheilk. 26, 1966, 1281
9. Bettendorf, G.,: Excerpta Medica 109, 1966, 4
10. Bettendorf, G., Breckwoldt, M., Czygan, P.-J., Groot, K.: Gynaecologia 163, 1967, 134
11. Diczfalusy, E., Johannisson, E., Tillinger, K.-G., Bettendorf, G.: Acta Endocrinol. 90, 1964, 35
12. Knoerr, K.: Die Medizin. Welt 51, 1967, 18, 3128

Results of HHG/HCG therapy		no pat	no med cousses	ovulations	pregnancy	overluluner
prim amenorrhoea	hypo	7	21	13	3	7
	normo	8	18	16	3	8
sec amenorrhoea	hypo	8	9	8	2	3
	normo	16	34	25	3	14
anovulat. cycles		8	10	10	1	3
hypophysectomized pat		3	6	5	3	4
total		50	98	77	15	39

Fig. 1

Results of HHG treatment without HCG		no pat	no med cousses	ovulations	ov enlargement
prim amenorrhoea	hypo	3	8	4	0
	normo	6	6	6	2
sec amenorrhoea	hypo	4	5	4	0
	normo	10	15	12	3
anovulat. cycles		2	2	1	0
hypophysectomized pat		4	8	4	0
total		29	44	31	5

Fig. 2

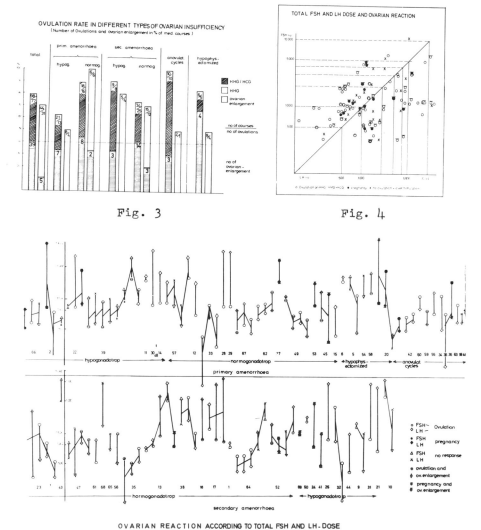

Fig. 3

Fig. 4

OVARIAN REACTION ACCORDING TO TOTAL FSH AND LH-DOSE

Fig. 5

Ovarian Response According to Total FSH-Dose						
	→ 500	1000	Total FSH - Dose i.u 1500	2 000	3 000	5 000	>5 000
no. of patients	13	27	24	13	7	9	4
no. of med courses	15	42	30	13	8	9	5
ovulations	12 (80)	33 (78)	26 (86)	11 (84)	5 (62)	8 (88)	3 (60)
pregnancies	3	3	5	–	–	2	1
ovarian enlargement	7 (46)	13 (31)	12 (40)	4 (30)	2 (25)	4 (44)	1 (20)

Fig. 6

Ovarian Response According to Total LH-Dose						
	→ 500	1000	Total LH - Dose i.u 1500	2000	3000	5 000	>5000
no. of patients	13	20	19	7	10	13	16
no. of med courses	17	26	25	9	12	14	18
no. of ovulations	16 (94)	21 (80)	19 (76)	5 (55)	10 (83)	10 (71)	17 (94)
pregnancies	1	1	4	3	2	1	2
ovarian enlargement	6 (35)	8 (30)	7 (28)	6 (66)	4 (33)	4 (28)	7 (39)

Fig. 7

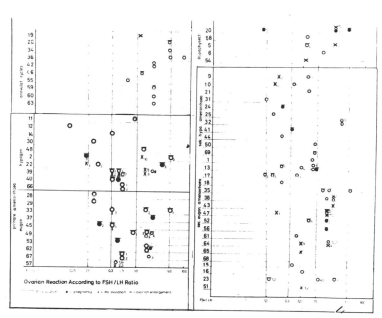

Fig. 8

Response According to FSH / LH Ratio in 63 Patients						
FSH / LH	0,05 -0,1	0,1 - 0,3	0,3 - 1	1 - 5	5 - 10	total
no. of treatments	6	16	45	46	8	121
positive response (%)	5 (83)	13 (75)	36 (80)	35 (76)	8 (100)	97
pregnancies (%)	2 (33)	2 (12)	4 (9)	6 (13)	1 (12)	15 (12)
ovarian enlargement (%)	3 (50)	6 (37)	13 (29)	14 (30)	5 (62)	41 (34)

Fig. 9

		OVARIAN REACTION ACCORDING TO HCG-DOSE															
HCG I.U.	pat	no. of med.courses	ovulation	BBT shift after 1 day of HCG 1	2	3	4	5	6	lenght of luteal ph. 10	11-12	13-14	15	ovarian enlargem. •	••	•••
5 000	5	6	5	3	-	2	-	-	-	2	2	1	-	2	1	-	-
10 000	14	16	13	2	9	-	1	1	-	1	3	2	3	3	5	1	4
15 000	14	16	13	3	6	1	1	1	1	1	4	3	2	2	4	-	3
20 000	15	20	15	4	4	5	2	-	-	-	4	3	4	4	-	-	4
25 000	15	20	13	5	2	2	4	-	-	1	2	3	3	5	4	-	4

Fig. 10

RECENT OBSERVATIONS ON TREATMENT WITH HUMAN GONADOTROPHINS

A. C. CROOKE, MD, FRCP AND P. V. BERTRAND, B.Sc.
THE UNITED BIRMINGHAM HOSPITALS, DEPARTMENT OF CLINICAL
ENDOCRINOLOGY, BIRMINGHAM AND MIDLAND HOSPITAL FOR WOMEN
BIRMINGHAM, 11, ENGLAND

Our approach to therapy with human gonadotrophins has differed from that of many others because our patients receive free treatment. Our human pituitary follicle stimulating hormone (FSH) is the property of the Medical Research Council and cannot be used for routine treatment and our human menopausal gonadotrophin (HMG - Pergonal) has been given by G. D. Searle & Co. Ltd., for research purposes. We have therefore been more concerned with academic problems such as patient variability, dose response relationship (1), sensitivity tests and the response to single injections of FSH (2). Recently two new problems have presented themselves. These are the joint action of FSH and human chorionic gonadotrophin (HCG) and the timing of the peak in excretion of oestrogen following treatment and its relationship to the clinical response.

A   JOINT ACTION OF FSH AND HCG

An experiment was designed in which four patients were given HMG (Pergonal) followed by HCG for four months in succession (3). The total dose of FSH remained the same for each patient but varied between patients according to each individual's sensitivity to the hormone. The clinical data and total dosages are given in Table 1.

The design of the experiment is shown graphically in Figure 1. The total dose of FSH was given as a single injection on day 1 or divided into two, three or four equal doses given on successive days as shown by the upward pointing arrows. The HCG was given as a single injection of 4,000 IU either on day 7 or on day 10 as shown by the downward pointing arrows.

The responses were measured by the rise in excretion of oestriol and pregnanediol in the 24 or 48 hour samples of urine collected on the days shown in the figure. They were expressed as $\mu g/24$ hours for oestriol and mg/24 hours for pregnanediol. The responses were analysed by analyses of variance of the logarithms of the amounts of each steroid excreted and on the day of the peak excretion of each steroid.

The results are summarized in Figure 2 which shows the mean excretion of oestriol for all patients in each group and also the number of peaks in excretion of oestriol which occurred on different days. When HCG was given on day 7 it had a highly significant effect ($P < 0.001$) of increasing the amount of oestriol excreted on days 11 + 12 compared with HCG given on day 10. The figure also shows that HCG had a significant effect ($P < 0.05$) on the time of the peak excretion of oestriol. It occurred on average on days 9 and 10 when HCG was given on day 7 compared with days 7 and 8 when it was given on day 10.

Evidently when HCG was given on day 10 it was too far removed in time from treatment with FSH to affect steroid excretion but when it was given on day 7 it delayed the peak and reduced the subsequent fall in excretion.

We next decided to review our previous results in which we had given single injections of FSH (CP 1) mixed with HCG on day 1, single injections of FSH (CP 1) without added HCG given on day 1 and HMG (Pergonal) without added HCG, given on day 1 or in equally divided doses for up to four days in succession. The results are shown in Figure 3. There were 26 months of treatment in the first, 29 in the second and 17 in the third of these groups. All treatments were followed by HCG usually given on day 10. The excretion patterns for the last two groups were similar and the results were combined for analysis.

The excretion of oestriol reached its peak on day 9 when FSH was mixed with HCG on day 1, and on day 8 when FSH was given alone. This difference is highly significant (P < 0.002). The difference may well have been greater, however, since Figure 3 shows that the pattern of mean excretion of oestriol was still rising in the former and was already falling in the latter.

This interesting effect of HCG given early in treatment reopens the whole question of the optimum ratio of FSH to luteinizing hormone (LH). The results suggest that highly purified preparations of FSH are unsuitable for treatment and it is possible that very insensitive patients, including those with severe Simmonds's disease who are producing little or no endogenous gonadotrophins, require more LH or HCG than sensitive ones.

B   TIME OF PEAK EXCRETION OF OESTRIOL IN RELATION TO RESPONSE

In earlier experiments we gave FSH over eight days, usually in three equally divided doses on days 1, 4, and 8 followed by HCG on day 10. Figure 4 summarizes the results of 51 months of such treatment. The peak in excretion of oestriol occurred most often on day 12 but the mean excretion was still rising on day 15. In four of the treatments the excretion rose to about 250 μg/day. The mean pattern for these four are shown separately. When they were excluded the pattern for the remaining 47 months of treatment was very like the pattern for the normal menstrual cycle and the mean peak occurred on day 11. This is two days later than when FSH was mixed with HCG and given as a single injection on day 1, and the difference is highly significant (P < 0.001).

We then compared the clinical responses obtained with these three different methods of treatment. There were 281 months of treatment for analysis and the results are shown in Table 2. The frequencies of the occurrence of follicular development without luteinization, of ovulation without pregnancy and of pregnancy are recorded for each type of treatment. When FSH was given with added HCG on day 1, 57 per cent of the treatments resulted in follicular development without ovulation compared with only 29 per cent when FSH was given over eight days, a difference which is significant (P < 0.001). However 27 per cent of the treatments in which ovulation occurred resulted in pregnancy with both methods of treatment. When FSH was given without HCG on day 1 only 13 per cent of the treatments in which ovulation occurred resulted in pregnancy, a difference which is significant only at the 10 per cent level.

These figures show that better results are obtained with methods of treatment which produce later peaks in excretion of oestriol. Perhaps the longer time interval is necessary for complete maturation of the follicle or for full development of the endometrium. It is noteworthy however that many pregnancies have occurred with early oestrogen peaks and the difference is only now beginning to reach a level of significance.

REFERENCES

1. Crooke, A. C., W. R. Butt and P. V. Bertrand, Acta endocr., Copenhagen, Suppl. 111, 1966.
2. Crooke, A. C., W. R. Butt, P. V. Bertrand and R. Morris, The Lancet ii: 636, 1967.
3. Idem, The Lancet ii, 180, 1968.

Table 1.

Clinical details and dosages of FSH

Patients:-	S.K.	D.P.	B.E.	R.S.
Age	30	27	28	25
Menarche (age)	11	Primary	13	Primary
Catamenia	$\frac{7}{2-3 \text{ mths}}$	-	$\frac{4}{28}$	-
Cessation	Gradual	-	Gradual	-
Uterus	Small	Sound 1 cm	Small	Sound 2.5 cm
Ovaries	4.5 x 3.8 cm Polycystic	1.5 x 1.0 cm	Not felt	1.5 x 1.0 cm
Tubes	Patent	Patent	Patent	Patent
Endometrium	Atrophic	Atrophic	Atrophic	-
Gonadotrophins	30,5	<5,<5,<5	50,10,<5	5,5,<5
Other conditions	Ovarian resection	-	Occasional lactation	-
Total dose of FSH (IU) per month	4,760	3,920	3,920	2,800

Table 2.

Numbers of different responses to different methods of treatment

Response	FSH over 8 days HCG on day 10*	FSH+HCG on day 1 HCG on day 10*	FSH on day 1 HCG on day 10*
Follicular development	45	29	31
Ovulation	79	16	39
Pregnancy	30	6	6

*HCG was generally given on day 10 and exceptionally on other days, see text.

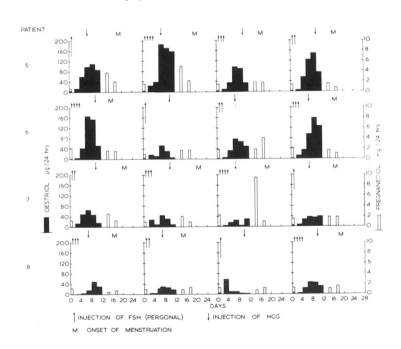

Figure 1. Excretion of oestriol and pregnanediol by patients treated with Pergonal followed by HCG.

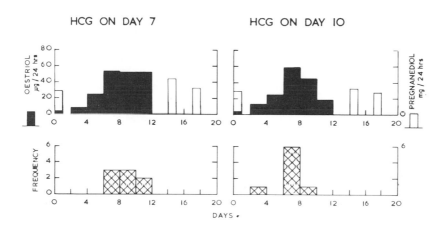

Figure 2.   The mean excretion of oestriol and of pregnanediol after treatment
with FSH followed by HCG on day 7 and day 10 and the distributions
of days of peak oestriol excretion.

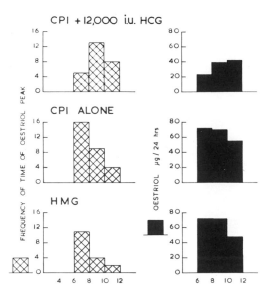

Figure 3.   Days of peak and mean excretion of oestriol with different short treatments with FSH followed by HCG.

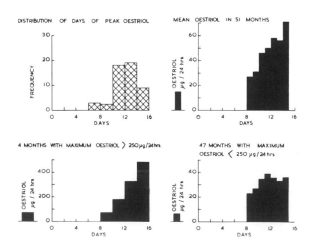

Figure 4.   Days of peak and mean excretion of oestriol with long schedule of treatment with FSH followed by HCG.

DISCUSSION

ROSEMBERG: Dr. Crooke, do you think that the effectiveness of your therapeutic regimen is due to the fact that by the addition of HCG, you increased the amount of LH activity given, hence changing the FSH:LH ratio?

CROOKE: Yes of course this is exactly what we did do in effect.

ASSESSMENT OF THE RESULTS OF GONADOTROPIC THERAPY

B. LUNENFELD, E. RABAU, V. INSLER, S. MASHIAH AND H. MELMED, TEL-HASHOMER GOVERNMENT HOSPITAL.

Pregnancy is the main goal of gonadotropic therapy and the sole unequivocal indicator of its effectiveness insofar as induction of ovulation is concerned. Thus, the results of gonadotropic treatment were assessed using pregnancy as the main parameter of analysis. Two hundred and sixty-four courses of combined HMG-HCG therapy given to 133 women were analyzed. The following parameters were calculated and compared in different groups of patients:
a) The intensity of treatment (the mean number of treatment courses per patient).
b) The efficiency of treatment (the mean number of treatment courses per pregnancy in a given group of patients).
c) The pregnancy rate (the percentage of patients who conceive during therapy).

Table No. 1

Presenting symptom	No. of patients	No. of cycles	Treatment intensity	Treatment efficiency	Preg. rate (%).
Primary amenorr.	33	63	1.9	2.6	61
P/p amenorr. +galact.	10	16	1.6	2.0	80
Sec. amenorr. MAP -*	52	111	2.1	2.6	69
Sec. amenorr. MAP +*	11	20	1.8	3.3	45
Oligomenorrhea	10	15	1.5	2.5	60
Anovulatory cycle	17	39	2.3	9.7	23

* MAP - no evidence of endogenous estrogen activity; MAP + evidence of endogenous estrogen activity.

Table 1 indicates that gonadotropic therapy was satisfactory in all sub-groups of patients, except for those with anovulatory cycles. In this sub-group, efficiency of treatment and pregnancy rate were lower ($P<0.01$), although intensity of treatment was similar. Patients with fairly regular anovulatory cycles seem unsuitable for gonadotropic therapy. Analysis of intensity and efficiency of treatment and of pregnancy rate indicates that in any given group of patients suitable for gonadotropic therapy a satisfactory pregnancy rate of about 75% may be expected whenever the intensity equals or exceeds the efficiency of treatment. This calculation holds true when large enough groups of patients are considered, proper gonadotropic preparations and effective treatment schedules are used and meticulous timing of intercourse is observed.

DISCUSSION

ROSEMBERG: Dr. Lunenfeld, would you please comment on treatment schedules?

LUNENFELD: As mentioned before, we use an individual adjusted treatment schedule, i.e. if the initial amount of HMG does not produce any positive response within a limited period of time, the dose is stepwise increased until a positive response is obtained.   This dose is then continued until the urinary estrogen excretion reaches 60 - 80 μg/24 hours and/or the karyopyknotic index reaches 50 - 80% and/or ferning is strongly positive for 4 days.   HCG is then administered.

ROSEMBERG: Did you test the response to HMG alone prior to giving a full course of medication?   In other words, do you study   patient's threshold?

LUNENFELD: The "sensitivity test" is actually automatically incorporated into the individually adjusted treatment scheme, since the amount of HMG required is determined not only for a particular patient, but also for each specific cycle.

ROSEMBERG: I assume you have available a rapid method for estrogen determination which will allow you to monitor medication. Would you please indicate the dose of HCG which you are presently using.

LUNENFELD: Up to September 1968 we used Brown's method (Lancet, 268, 320, 1955) for urinary estrogen determinations. (One technician can do 3 estimations within 14-15 hours thus, for proper monitoring of treatment the technicians have to work in 2 shifts).   Now we are using the new method developed by Brown et al (1968) which permits the assay of 10 urine samples within 5-6 hours.   The sensitivity of this method in our hands is 8 μg/24 hours and coefficient of variation is about 10% for low and normal levels and 6% for high levels.   The recovery is about 75%.

ROSEMBERG: Do you also follow your patients with serial vaginal smears?

LUNENFELD: A total dose of 2,500 IU HCG is usually given over 3 days; on the 1st day together with HMG and thereafter alone. However, since the treatment is adjusted according to the patient's response in each cycle, the dose and scheme of HCG administration may vary.   Sometimes a lag of one or even two days is allowed after the last HMG and the first HCG injection, and sometimes the dose of HCG is diminished by 30-50%.

ROSEMBERG: Dr. Lunenfeld, you have wonderful laboratory facilities.   However, what would you recommend as a method for monitoring the dose when such facilities are not available?

LUNENFELD: We try not to overload the laboratory with steroid assays and monitor the treatment by cervical mucus examination and vaginal smears. Whenever the slopes of these clinical indices (the time of appearance and magnitude of response) seem to be abnormal we refer to urinary estrogen levels as the reliable parameter. However we try to perform routinely an estrogen assay prior to HCG administration in order to avoid giving HCG to patients with very high estrogen levels.

ROSEMBERG: As a practical consideration, do you think that the determination of estrogens is absolutely necessary? Could the effectiveness of treatment be judged merely by following changes in the cervical mucus or vaginal smears?

LUNENFELD: We feel that estrogen assays are desirable, but in the majority of cases treatment may probably be managed by clinical means only, provided that the patients are examined frequently enough by a physician experienced in HMG treatment. I would like to make a further comment on early HCG administration. Although basal body temperature and urinary steroid patterns may indicate ovulation, it is possible that sometimes this is due to luteinization of follicles without discharge of ova. This effect could be produced by administering HCG early during the treatment course, or by preparations containing very high amounts of LH.

BETTENDORF: I would like to comment on estrogen estimations during treatment. We were not able to carry these out as fast as we can now and therefore, we referred mainly to clinical criteria such as cervical mucus and vaginal smears. I think that for clinical purposes these data are usually sufficient. When the amount of cervical mucus increases, the cervix opens and the fern test is positive for 3-4 days, one should begin HCG injections. If these clinical reactions develop too fast, one should stop treatment to avoid hyperstimulation.

ASSESSMENT OF RESULTS OF GONADOTROPIN THERAPY

Eugenia Rosemberg, M. D. and Than T. Nwe, M. D.

Medical Research Institute of Worcester, Inc.
Worcester City Hospital, Worcester, Massachusetts.

One of the factors involved in the evaluation of the therapeutic effectiveness of HMG preparations is the difference in sensitivity between patients. We have shown (1) that patients respond differently to the administration of similar doses of gonadotropins. The variation in response seen from time to time in the same patient was less marked than that observed between patients. In the present report, the results of gonadotropic treatment were assessed in relation to the therapeutic regimen used and to the total dose of FSH and LH activity given during the entire course of treatment. Ninety-nine courses of combined HMG-HCG* therapy given to 34 women with secondary amenorrhea and anovulatory cycles were analyzed. The FSH and LH activities contained in the HMG preparations used (Pergonal, Cutter Laboratories, Berkeley, California and HMG, Ortho Research Foundation, Raritan, New Jersey) have been reported previously (2). Assessment of clinical and steroid metabolic effect have been described in previous publications (3). The majority of patients received consecutive courses of medication with HMG preparations containing various FSH:LH ratios. During consecutive courses, these patients received varying dosages of "total" FSH and LH activity. Also, several patients in this series received the same amount of FSH activity, via HMG preparations containing similar FSH:LH ratios.

PATIENTS WITH SECONDARY AMENORRHEA
SUMMARY OF RESULTS

A total of forty-eight courses of combined medication were given to 19 patients with secondary amenorrhea. HMG was given according to 2 schedules: 1) uniform daily doses given for periods ranging from 9 to 11 days, combined with 4,000 to 5,000 IU of HCG daily on the last four days of HMG therapy; 2) a single injection of the "total" dose given on day 1 followed by HCG given as a single injection of 10,000 IU on day 10.

---

* Supplied by the Squibb Institute for Medical Research, New Brunswick, New Jersey.

Table 1 shows the overall response to daily and single injection schedules, as well as the comparison of the efficiency of the two schemes of treatment.

Table 1

PATIENTS WITH SECONDARY AMENORRHEA

TOTAL NUMBER: 19 - TOTAL NUMBER OF MEDICATION COURSES: 48

No. Exposed to Pregnancy	Patients not Exposed	No. of Medication Courses		Response					
		Exposed to Pregnancy	Not Exposed	Exposed to Pregnancy			Not Exposed		
				Pregnancy	Ovulation by Indirect Indices	No Response	Ovulation by Indirect Indices	No Response	
11	8	34	14	5 (15%)	17 (50%)	12 (35%)	6 (43%)	8 (57%)	

A: DAILY ADMINISTRATION

11	7	25	11	4 (16%)	13 (52%)	8 (32%)	5 (45%)	6 (55%)	

B: SINGLE INJECTION

4	2	9	3	1 (11%)	4 (44.5%)	4 (44.5%)	1 (33.3%)	2 (66.7%)	

Pregnancy rate as well as ovulatory response (judged by indirect indices of ovulation), was very similar using either the daily or the single injection schedules.

The "total" amount of FSH and LH activity administered, using the daily or single treatment scheme resulting in pregnancy, ovulation, or no response, is indicated in table 2.

Table 2

PATIENTS WITH SECONDARY AMENORRHEA
DOSE IU 2nd IRP

Administration	Pregnancy Dose Range		Ovulatory Dose Range		No Response Dose Range	
	FSH	LH	FSH	LH	FSH	LH
Daily	892-2600	714-1567	888-2400	32-3406	772-2442	15-2612
Single Injection	727	203	452-1871	98-1433	1115-2664	97-1959

The "total" amount of FSH activity used in patients who responded to medication varied from 452 to 2,600 IU. It would appear that the effectiveness of medication was not dependent on the FSH:LH ratio contained in the HMG preparations used. Patients who did not respond to medication (twenty courses) received "total" dosages similar to those given to patients in whom ovulation was induced. Lack of response was observed during six courses of medication given to 3 patients demonstrating high endogenous gonadotropin excretion. Fourteen courses were given to patients with high threshold. Higher doses were not tested in this group.

PATIENTS WITH ANOVULATORY CYCLES
SUMMARY OF RESULTS

A total of fifty-one courses of combined medication were given to 15 patients with fairly regular anovulatory cycles. Various treatment schemes were used as indicated in Table 3.

Table 3

PATIENTS WITH ANOVULATORY CYCLES
TOTAL NUMBER: 15

Administration on Cycle Days		Total Dose (IU)			No. of Courses	Response		
HMG	HCG	FSH* Range	LH* Range	HCG **		Pregnancy	Ovulation by Indirect Indices	No Response
1-5-9 3 to 9 3 to 7 3-5-7-9-11 7-9-11	11-12 13-16 13-17 14-16	378-819	242-1306	8000-20000	7		2 (29%)	5 (71%)
11 to 13	14-16 14-17	384-655	120-929	12000-24000	9		2 (22%)	7 (88%)
11 to 16 10 to 17	14-16 14-17	874-1008	1010-1238	18000-24000	3			3 (100%)
5 to 17 6 to 18	13-17 14-17 14-18	629-1697	23-1238	16000-20000	25	1 (4%)	18 (72%)	6 (24%)
9 (one shot)	14-16	774-819	226-593	12000	7	1 (14%)	4 (57%)	2 (29%)
Total					51	2	26	23

*: IU 2nd IRP; **: IU HCG IS

Although similar amounts of "total" FSH activity were given on each of the treatment schedules used, the ovulatory rate was significantly increased when uniform daily doses of HMG were given from days 5 to 13 or 6 to 14 of the cycle which was combined with HCG from days 13 to 17 or 14 to 18 of the cycle, or when a single injection of the "total" dose was given on day 9 of the cycle followed by HCG which was given daily on days 14 to 16 of the cycle. It would appear that the effectiveness of medication was not dependent on the FSH:LH ratio contained in the preparations used.

Caution should be exercised when administering single "total" doses of HMG as local as well as generalized reactions were observed in 5 patients who received 9 to 36 ampoules (as a single injection) of Ortho HMG (batches 2138, 2225 and 2282).

This work was supported in part by Grant AM-07564, USPHS, National Institutes of Health, Bethesda, Maryland and in part by Grant-In-Aid from the Ortho Research Foundation, Raritan, New Jersey and Cutter Laboratories, Berkeley, California.

REFERENCES

1. Rosemberg, E., and Than T. Nwe. Fertil. and Steril., 19: 197, 1968.

2. Rosemberg, E. In: Gonadotropins 1968. Rosemberg, E. (Ed.) Geron-X, Inc. Los Alto, California, Publishers p.425, 1968.

3. Rosemberg, E. In: Ovulation: Stimulation, Suppression, Detection. Greenblatt, R. B. (Ed.) Lippincott, Philadelphia, Pennsylvania, p. 118, 1966.

GONADOTROPIN THERAPY: EFFECTS OF FIXED DOSAGE
SCHEDULES AND SIGNIFICANCE OF ESTROGEN EXCRETION LEVELS

MELVIN L. TAYMOR, M.D. AND MARVIN A. YUSSMAN, M.D.
FROM THE DEPARTMENT OF OBSTETRICS AND GYNECOLOGY, HARVARD
MEDICAL SCHOOL AND THE DEPARTMENT OF SURGERY (GYNECOLOGY),
PETER BENT BRIGHAM HOSPITAL, BOSTON, MASSACHUSETTS

I would first like to address myself to the possibilities and problems associated with fixed dosage approaches to therapy.

In a number of publications, Crooke and his co-workers (1-3), utilizing gonadotropin derived from human pituitary glands (HPFSH), have reported that a single injection of this material, followed in 9 or 10 days by a single dose of human chorionic gonadotropin (HCG), would in many instances result in ovulation. They theorize that the human follicle once stimulated will continue to develop independently to the point of maturity without the need for further FSH stimulation.

Their observations raise at least two interesting possibilities: in the first place, a more expeditious method of administration of HMG and secondly a more physiologic approach that might result in a decreased incidence of ovarian overstimulation.

Table 1.   Comparison between the ovulatory effects of the standard method of administration of HMG and the administration in a single injection

	Daily divided therapy			Single injection		
	Ampules	*Day of HCG	Ovulation	Ampules	*Day of HCG	Ovulation
D.O.	9	6	+	9	6	0
S.R.	10	6	+	10	7	0
				12	**	0
L.M.	11	7	+	12	7	+
E.K.	12	8	+	14	**	0
				16	10	+
V.B.	14	8	+	14	9	0
M.K.	14	9	+	16	10	0
B.M.	16	9	+	12	10	0
D.P.	20	11	+	24	10	0

*Menotropins (R), 75 IU of FSH and 75IU of LH
**Uterine bleeding before HCG

Table 1 compares the laboratory effects of the straight across or standard method of administration of HMG with the same amount administered in a single injection to the same patient. The plus signs indicate ovulation. The zero's indicate no ovulation. All these patients had previously ovulated with the standard daily divided method of therapy. The same amount of HMG in ampules was then administered to these subjects in a single injection. The HCG was administered on the same day as in the control cycle except that in two instances (S.R. and E.K.) estrogen withdrawal bleeding was reported the day the HCG was due to be given. Only 2 ovulations occurred. In each of these instances slightly more HMG was utilized than in the standard cycle.

Table 2. Comparison of the ovulatory effects of the standard method of administration of HMG with administration of the total dose over a 3 day period

	IU of FSH to achieve Ovulation (Standard)	Total FSH dose in 3 days		
		675 IU	900 IU	1125 IU
D.O.	675	0	+	
H.E.	675	0	0 0	+
S.R.	675	0	0	
B.P.	825		+	0 P**
E.J.	900	0	0	+
J.H.	1200		+	+
P.W.	1500		0	0
J.L.	--*	0	0	+
J.D.	--	0	+	
L.B.	--	0	+	
J.K.	--	0	+	
Y.F.	--	0	+	
D.M.	--	0	+	

*Standard course not carried out
**Pregnancy
0 Indicates no ovulation
+ Indicates ovulation

Ovulation was produced in 13 of 31 cycles when the total dose was given in 3 consecutive days in 13 patients. The 7 patients in the top half of the table also had a control cycle in which the HMG was administered as daily divided therapy.

We next tried giving the total dose over a 3 day period. Table 2 compares the ovulatory effects of the standard method of therapy with the administration of the total dose over a 3 day period. The 7 subjects in the top half of the chart had previously ovulated when HMG was administered in the standard daily dose method. Roughly the same amount of HMG in terms of international units of FSH activity was given over a 3 day period. The dose was repeated and increased when the patient tolerated the repeated visits. Seven of the 18 cycles appeared to be ovulatory. One pregnancy occurred. Ovulation resulted from about the same dosage level as that required for standard therapy.

In the lower half of the table are tabulated 13 additional cycles in 6 patients who had the 3 day therapy without a control standard cycle. Six cycles appeared ovulatory. These subjects were all patients with infrequent ovulation or anovulatory cycles and would be expected to respond to this relatively low dose of HMG. Figure 1 shows that all 13 of the ovulatory cycles that occurred following the administration of the total dose over a 3 day period occurred when treatment was initiated 6 or more days after

The last bleeding episode. No ovulation occurred when therapy
was initiated from the 1st to the 5th day of such a cycle.

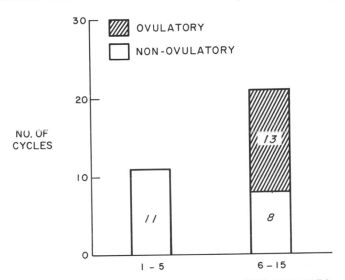

Figure 1. Effect of the day therapy was initiated on
occurrence of ovulation.

Thus we were unable to confirm the effectiveness of a
single shot. Possibly this is due to differences between HPFSH
and HMG. Gonadotropin activity can be found in the urine up to
6 days after a single injection of human pituitary FSH. The
levels of FSH activity in the serum by radioimmunoassay
performed in our laboratory after a single injection of human
menopausal gonadotropin are shown in Figure 2. There was a
rise which was maintained for only 2 to 4 days after the
injection and then a return to baseline levels. It is
theoretically possible that a large single dose of pituitary
material would remain in the circulation long enough to
maintain follicle growth whereas a single injection of
menopausal gonadotropin would be more rapidly excreted.

On the other hand, administration of the dose over a
3 day period appears to have some promise in subjects with a
relatively high degree of follicular activity and particularly
if initiation of treatment is delayed until at least mid-
follicular phase. The 3 days of therapy plus the 2 or 3 days
in which gonadotropin activity is maintained in the serum
before excretion is apparently sufficient to bring follicular
development to the stage where it will respond to the
administration of the HCG. There is no evidence from these
results that the human follicle develops independently
without FSH stimulation.

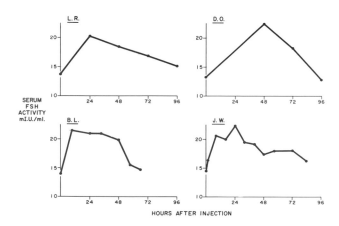

Figure 2.   Effect of single injection of HMG on serum
levels of FSH.

    At the present time subjects requiring prolonged FSH
stimulation seem to respond best to the daily administration
of HMG over a relatively long period of time.   This brings
me to the second portion of this discussion: the relationship
of estrogen excretion levels to the problem of ovarian
overstimulation and the use of daily assessment of estrogen
excretion during the few days prior to HCG administration as
a means of avoiding ovarian overstimulation.

        Table 3.   Relation of total estrogen excretion to
                        ovarian enlargement

Estrogen 24 Hr Prior to HCG μg	No. Cycles	No. Ovulations	No. Pregnancies	Ovarian* Enlargement	With Ascites
Over 200	8	8	4	5	3
100-200	10	10	2	5	1
40-100	15	14	7	1	0
Less than 40	12	7	2	0	0

*Greater than 7 cm.
 (From Taymor, M.L. JAMA 203:362, 1968) (4).

Table 3 demonstrates the relationship of the total estrogen excretion levels to ovarian enlargement (more than 7 cm) in a group of our patients. As you can see, most of the ovarian enlargements with ascites occurred when total estrogen excretion levels in the 24 hours prior to the administration of HCG were over µg/24 hours. If the estrogen levels at this time were between 50 and 100 µg there was still a high incidence of ovulation and pregnancy without significant ovarian enlargement.

We have not had sufficient multiple pregnancies to make a similar comparison but have utilized the data reported by Gemzell (5). In the top half of table 4 are tabulated the mean estrogen excretion levels for groups of single, twin and triplet or more pregnancies. Because of the extreme variability there is overlap of fiducial limits, and Gemzell correctly concluded from this table that there was no statistical evidence of differences in estrogen excretion between the groups.

Table 4.   Relationship of outcome of pregnancy
to estrogen levels

Outcome	No. of Patients	%	Total Estrogen +
Single	20	46	258 ± 74
Twin	14	33	337 ± 43
Triplet or more	9	21	361 ± 82
Total	43		

Estrogen Level	Single	Twin	Triplet or more
Under 100	8	1	0
100-200	5	2	3
Over 200	7	11	6

*Following administration of human pituitary follicle stimulating hormone.
+Mean excretion in µg/24 hr ± standard error of the mean. Data from Gemzell and Roos (5).
(From Taymor, M.L., JAMA 203:362, 1968).

However, if the data is arranged by estrogen excretion, as in the bottom half of the table, it appears that triplet or more pregnancies always occur in association with estrogen excretion levels over 100 µg/24 hours.

Both these studies suggest that if the estrogen levels can be kept at around 100 µg/24 hours just prior to the administration of HCG the incidence of ovarian overstimulation should be markedly reduced. Therefore, we have been utilizing a 6 hour method for total estrogen in order to follow therapy in patients in the manner outlined in table 3.

Table 5.   A plan of therapy with HMG

150 - 225 IU daily until 3+ ferning
Begin daily estrogen determination (6 hour method)

If total estrogens are:

50-100 µg   -   - 1 ampule daily for 2 more days, then HCG
less than 50 µg - 2 ampules for 2 more days, then HCG
over 100 µg -   - give HCG
over 200 µg -   - no HCG this cycle

REFERENCES

1. Crooke, A.L., W.R. Butt, and P.V. Bertrand, Acta Endocrinol Suppl 111, 1966.

2. Crooke, A.C., W. R. Butt, and P.V. Bertrand, Lancet 2:514, 1966.

3. Crooke, A.C., W.R. Butt, P.V. Bertrand, and R. Morris, Lancet 2:630, 1967.

4. Taymor, M.L., JAMA 203:362, 1968.

5. Gemzell, C.A., and P. Roos, Am J Obstet & Gynec 94:490, 1966.

DISCUSSION

VANDE WIELE: Cervical mucus is an excellent index of the
initial response to treatment but in the later stages of treatment I find it to be of limited value as a quantitative index
of follicle stimulation. This has been borne out by a recent
study of Herrmann (Spadoni, L. R., Kitchin, III, J. D., Schindler,
D. E., Ratanasopa, V., and Herrmann, W. L. J. Clin. Endocr. 27:
1738, 1967) who found a poor correlation between the level of
urinary estrogens and the various characteristics of cervical
mucus.

BETTENDORF: I can only answer that we have not had severe
overstimulation in 4 years following these clinical criteria.

McARTHUR: We regard the cervical mucus changes as exceedingly
helpful in guiding treatment. We have, however, found it
essential to follow the vaginal cytology concomitantly. Urinary
estrogen determinations are a further safeguard against overstimulation, particularly in those women whose vaginal smears
reveal extensive cytolysis, a not infrequent finding in patients
with sterility. When such women, whose vaginal smears contain
naked nuclei and intermediate cells to the virtual exclusion of
other types, are treated with gonadotropins their total urinary
estrogens may rise to several hundred micrograms per 24 hours
with almost no increase in superficial cells. Unless one has
concomitant urinary estrogen determinations, one will be seriously
misled. By treating such women with intravaginal estrogen cream
in advance of gonadotropin treatment, we have been able to
reduce or banish cytolysis. The vaginal epithelium then recovers
its responsiveness to estrogen stimulation, and cornification
again becomes a dependable index of estrogen effect.

STEINBERGER: I should like to add a word on the clinical use of
cervical mucus for estimation of ovulation. This is an adequate
clinical technique and when used properly, particularly in
patients with relatively normal ovulatory activity. However,
when one deals with patients with abnormal ovulation or patients
in whom ovulation is being induced with HMG, several problems
arise. First of all, there is tremendous variation between
individuals and in the same individual from cycle to cycle. Thus,
one must make careful judgments concerning the appearance of the
cervical canal and the physical characteristics of cervical
mucus, as far as their being related to actual ovulatory process.
Secondly, as I mentioned before, in patients treated with HMG it
is difficult to find when the cervical mucus and cervical canal
show their "peak" ovulatory signs, since one may find a plateau
during which the actual levels of estrogen may be going up while
no detectable changes in the appearance of the cervical canal
and the quality of the cervical mucus can be observed.

BELL: Mr. Lunn and I (Lunn, S. F. and Bell, E. T. Quart. J. Exp.
Physiol. 53: 129-135, 1968) have studied the effects of PMSG and

HCG on ovulation in the rat and have shown that increasing the
dosage of both hormones results in an increase in the number of
ova shed. However, with high dose levels the number of ova
shed is decreased. This is probably associated with ovum trapping
resulting from the luteinization of unruptured follicles.
Theoretically one can postulate that in the human given high doses
of gonadotropin follicular luteinization may take place without
release of the ovum. This could be associated with normal
progesterone and estrogen production and with clinical evidence
of ovulation. Such a patient would, of course, not become
pregnant. It would be of interest to know whether this concept
has any clinical relevance. Possibly, it may be of importance
in patients such as the one studied by Dr. Bettendorf who in
successive treatment periods showed an increased ovarian response
as judged by the degree of enlargement associated with a decrease
in the dose of gonadotropin administered.

STEINBERGER: I should like to say just one word concerning
pregnancy as a parameter for estimating success in inducing
ovulation. Pregnancy may not occur for a variety of reasons in
individuals who ovulate normally. I think that this point should
be stressed.

LUNENFELD: I fully agree with Dr. Steinberger that one
estimation of the efficiency of treatment is somewhat pessimistic.
We probably had more ovulation than pregnancies. But since
ovulation can "practically" not be diagnosed with certainty we
consider pregnancy as the only unequivocal criterion of ovulation.

MARSHALL: I think that if we are going to talk about pregnancy
rates, and this is really the most appropriate endpoint, we have
to talk in terms of pregnancy rate per ovulatory cycle in patients
who have conceived with the therapy under discussion. There is
no point in talking about pregnancy rates for the total population
or for all ovulatory cycles because there may very well be a
number of women who appear to ovulate, but who are unable to
conceive for reasons unrelated to gonadotropin therapy. Using
simplified life table analysis and treating pregnancy as one
would death in the analysis of cancer survival, we have developed
something we have called a non-pregnancy survival curve and have
examined the cumulative probability of remaining non-pregnant.
When examined in this fashion pregnancy appears to occur as
rapidly following HMG induction of ovulation as it does in either
a normal population or in one conceiving following artificial
insemination with donor semen. We have now 28 pregnancies in
the 60 women that we have treated. We have a pregnancy rate in
those who have ovulated of 50%. We have had 2 sets of twins and
1 set of triplets giving a multiple pregnancy rate of 10%. We
have had no case of ascites. We have never done a single estrogen
determination for clinical purposes. We have used a fixed treatment schedule, have tried to begin with sub-ovulatory doses, and
have relied on cervical mucus to indicate the dosage increase
necessary in the following cycle.

VANDE WIELE: After trying out various schedules, I have come back to the daily injection schedule which I prefer. Injections on alternate days are probably as effective provided that a double dose is injected. I would like to make a plea for the monitoring of treatments with urinary estrogens. The critical decision is the timing of the administration of HCG and I have found information about urinary estrogen to be extremely helpful in making this decision. If HCG is administered at a time when total urinary estrogens are below 20 micrograms per day, only a few patients will ovulate. On the other hand, to induce ovulation in patients whose total urinary estrogens exceed 100 micrograms per day will result in a large percentage of hyperstimulation. Herrmann and Taymor have published evidence confirming these impressions. I am sure that experienced investigators can be quite successful without determinations of urinary estrogens but even so I do not understand the resistance of many to this approach since there are now available several simple and rapid methods for urinary estrogen estimation.

BELL: During the normal menstrual cycle Dr. Loraine and I have shown that the sum of the mean excretion values for estrone, estradiol and estriol is approximately 50 $\mu g/24$ hours at the time of the midcycle peak. (Loraine, J. A. and Bell, E. T. Obstet. Gynecol. Surv. 22: 463, 1967). This observation correlates well with the optimal estrogen level prior to HCG induced ovulation noted by Dr. Vande Wiele.

ROSEMBERG: Dr. Taymor, would you please indicate what dose of HCG you are using?

TAYMOR: HCG has been used at 8,000 IU as a single dose.

CROOKE: I should like to pursue a statement by Dr. Lunenfeld. I rather objected to his calling the one shot technique the "Crooke method". We have more than one method and in fact this is the whole essence of our work. I agree with him that the dosage must be adjusted to the patient and I think that is essentially what one does when using a sensitivity test. I should like to refer to some results using Crooke method 17 B. This was a 34 year-old woman with primary amenorrhea, undetectable urinary gonadotropins and very small white elongated ovaries, who had undergone 11 courses of treatment with all kinds of regimes and who failed to respond satisfactorily. We gave her injections of FSH twice weekly, increasing the dose each time after the first two injections by a factor of 30% until a satisfactory response occurred as judged by her excretion of estriol. She received over the course of a month a total of 16,500 IU of FSH and she had the usual dose of HCG on the last day. She responded satisfactorily for the first time, her pregnanediol rose to 20 mg. per 24 hours and she became pregnant. She is now 3 months pregnant. This demonstrates that patients who are extremely insensitive can sometimes be made to respond with suitable treatment.

LUNENFELD: I am sorry Dr. Crooke that I labeled the single
injection scheme as the "Crooke method". It was meant for
convenience only and, not to imply that you do not use other
methods. I would like to ask people using the single or
triple injection scheme whether the patients who responded to
such treatment respond also to clomiphene. This is because
     in patients responding to the single or triple injection
scheme anovulation is due to lack of endogenous gonadotropin
release. As such they should respond to clomiphene.

MARSHALL: In the last two years, we have treated all of our
patients with clomiphene before treating them with gonadotropins.
You are entirely right. Patients having low thresholds or FODs
of less than 25 ampoules will, in general, respond with ovulation
to clomiphene. The percentage responding to clomiphene tends
to decrease as the gonadotropin threshold rises.

LUNENFELD: Would you then agree that in this group of patients
the single or triple injection scheme affects the production of
ovarian steroids thus triggering off the feedback mechanism?

MARSHALL: This is very possible. It could be tested very well
by eliminating the HCG but we have not yet done this. When
patients with low gonadotropin thresholds are treated with
clomiphene, HCG is usually not necessary to induce ovulation.
Therefore, it might very well be that HMG alone would be enough
to start the cycle which would then continue in a normal manner.

ROSEMBERG: Dr. Marshall, would you please indicate the FSH and
LH activities of the preparations used in your studies?

MARSHALL: This was a Pergonal preparation containing 75 IU of
FSH activity and 75 IU of LH activity per ampoule.

BETTENDORF: I should like to comment on the group of patients
who respond to lower doses of FSH. These patients, who have a
normal gonadotropin excretion, should respond to clomiphene. In
our experience this occurs in 70% of patients and it does not
seem necessary to treat these patients with gonadotropins if
they can ovulate and become pregnant following clomiphene
therapy. The remaining 30% who do not respond to clomiphene
are patients with absent urinary gonadotropins and should be
treated with gonadotropins.

MARSHALL: I completely agree with you. Our work was undertaken
as a study in clinical pharmacology. I am not advocating that
women who will respond to clomiphene should be treated with
gonadotropins.

BETTENDORF: Dr. Crooke, in your last two slides why did you
leave a large time interval between injections? Do you think
that these patients would not respond to daily treatment using
the same dose?

CROOKE: Yes, of course they would respond to daily injections, but it is less trouble to give injections twice a week. Moreover, I believe that it may be sufficient to measure estriol twice weekly only. We use a quick method and have the results ready by mid-day. We assess the dose on these results and treat the patient immediately after they are reported.

BETTENDORF: I have shown that in our patients the sensitivity can change from time to time. What exactly is being measured with a sensitivity test? The results will vary in the same patient at different times. Can the response found once in a patient be representative for all following treatments?

CROOKE: I would only partially agree with this. In our factorial design experiments we have plenty of evidence that the sensitivity does not vary more than, for instance, the sensitivity of a bioassay using rats. Naturally not exactly the same response is produced month by month by month but it is within the same sort of error as with the rat assay. I also agree that patients lose sensitivity. We have seen this loss of sensitivity progress over a period of 12 months associated with a steady increase in excretion of gonadotropins. In other words, the patient appears to be going into an early menopause. Incidentally, we sometimes see the excretion of gonadotropins gradually fall again. This may precede a spontaneous recovery, but it is rare.

TAYMOR: Dr. Crooke, I would like to ask you a question, which is stimulated by the following circumstances. In the U.S. if and when menotropins ® becomes available it is going to be a very expensive medication, and I do not believe that we are going to be in a position to use sensitivity tests and to gradually increase the dosage. We must have an optimum method of administration. Secondly, I doubt if the average infertility patient can tolerate many of these repeat visits, as these patients lose their tolerance from coming back. I should like to ask you one question, considering your experience with single injections. Would you say that the single injection of HMG, this being all we shall have available in the USA for the time being, is effective in the patient who fails to respond to clomiphene? A patient with low gonadotropin is going to require a considerable number of injections. Do you feel it is as effective and as safe as following the patient by daily administration and monitoring the dose by daily estrogen excretion levels?

CROOKE: The answer is no. I have already shown an analysis of 261 months of treatment, in which most of the patients were treated with pituitary FSH, but I agree with Dr. Lunenfeld that there is virtually no difference provided we take into account the ratio of FSH to LH.

VANDE WIELE: I cannot agree with the claim of Dr. Crooke that in one patient only the response to treatment is constant from cycle to cycle. This is not my experience and is contrary to

the evidence recently published by Herrmann. For this reason
I find the test dose approach only of limited value.

CROOKE: You are speaking of the response of single patients,
but it is an analysis that we require.

MARSHALL: I would like to emphasize the consistency of response
to gonadotropins. There is variability, as there is in all
biological responses. However, in examining the human response
to gonadotropin we not infrequently use either a single response
or a small series of single responses rather than the mean of
several determinations common to the laboratory bioassay. What
kind of consistency would we expect in a bioassay using only
one animal per point? It is our feeling that the human response
to gonadotropins is reasonably consistent, and we feel that an
understanding of both the consistency and the variability is
essential to sucessful therapy.

PAULSEN: There is another important issue in relation to
gonadotropin therapy for the induction of ovulation, and that is
the problem of adequate controls. Dr. Pincus Taft working in
collaboration with Dr. Bryan Hudson at the University of Monash
in Melbourne has sent me some data which should be of interest
to you. They studied 197 women (130 with secondary amenorrhea;
67 with oligomenorrhea and anovulation). Each patient was
treated initially with placebo therapy for three consecutive
months. During the period of placebo administration 75 women
ovulated and 28 became pregnant. Then, 122 of the original 197
women received cyclic progestin-estrogen therapy for two months
followed by two months of observation. In this group of patients
40 ovulated and 23 became pregnant. I wonder if anyone here has
similar information.

LUNENFELD: I fully agree with what Dr. Paulsen has said that
even without treatment about 12% of the secondary amenorrheic
patients will eventually become pregnant. In primary amenorrhea
this is extremely rare.

BETTENDORF: I have seen two patients similar to this. The first
was a 36 year old women who had never had a spontaneous menstruation, and who had low gonadotropin levels. She was treated three
times with pituitary material and responded very well. Treatment
was then stopped and four weeks later she was found to be pregnant.
The second patient exhibited secondary amenorrhea of seven years
duration. She became pregnant in the seventh treatment course
with gonadotropins. Following this pregnancy spontaneous
ovulation occurred and the patient became pregnant twice without
further treatment.

ROSEMBERG: It will be of great interest to discuss the use of
human pituitary LH as the ovulation-inducing agent. I shall
therefore ask Dr. Bettendorf to give us some information about
this.

BETTENDORF: Some years ago we started experiments with human
hypophyseal LH (HLH), that is fraction N_4 (Gynaecologia 163,
1967, 134). Follicle stimulation was carried out by administration of HHG and this was followed by injections of HLH instead
of HCG. The dose used was between 5,000 and 10,000 IU of LH
per day on two days or more. Ovulation could be induced in
nearly all of the treatment cycles. At first, we thought that
we could prevent hyperstimulation by this method of treatment.
We saw no severe adverse reactions, although in 2 of 10 courses
of medication the ovaries were somewhat enlarged. I should like
to refer to two patients so treated. The first had primary
amenorrhea and low gonadotropin excretion. After nine days
of daily HHG injections she received 7,000 IU of LH on two
consecutive days. On the day after the second injection the
BBT increased and ten days later menstruation started from a
secretory transformed endometrium. The second patient had
secondary amenorrhea. HHG was administered for nine days
followed by 4,000 IU of HLH on days 10, 11 and 12. The shift
of BBT occurred on day 11. The luteal phase was 12 days. The
pregnanediol excretion increased to 3 mg and the endometrium
showed secretory transformation. The timing of ovulation is not
as easily determined as it is when HCG is used. It can occur
between days 2 and 4 after starting HLH injections. So far we
have not had a pregnancy following HLH treatment.

ROSEMBERG: Dr. Bettendorf, would you please indicate the LH
activity of the HLH preparations used as well as the degree of
FSH contamination present in these preparations?

BETTENDORF: Two different LH preparations were used in our
clinical studies. The specific activity in the first was: LH
415 IU/mg. The FSH contamination was 16.2 IU/mg., and FSH:LH
ratio was 0.039. The specific activity of the second LH preparation was 1160 IU/mg. The FSH contamination was 16.3 IU/mg and
the FSH:LH ratio was 0.014.

ROSEMBERG: How many milligrams of these preparations were
administered?

BETTENDORF: We injected 4 to 5 mg. daily of the HLH depending
on the specific activity of the preparation.

ROSEMBERG: Was the activity of the HLH expressed in terms of
IU of the 2nd IRP?

BETTENDORF: Our biological activities are expressed in terms of
International Units (2nd IRP). Before the 2nd IRP became
available, we tested the activity of our preparation in terms of
the 1st IRP and we have calculated this in International Units
of the 2nd IRP.

ROSEMBERG: Then the amount of LH activity given varied between
4,000 and 8,000 IU of the 2nd IRP. The HCG dose used by most

investigators varies between 5,000 and 10,000 or 20,000 IU of the International Reference Preparation for HCG. Dr. Albert, would you please tell us how to correlate the activity in IU of the 2nd IRP of pituitary or urinary LH preparations with IU of HCG?

DONINI: I think it is not possible to correlate IU's of LH and HCG. Diczfalusy and Robyn seem now to have established that one International Unit of HCG is equivalent to about 3 International Units of LH.

ALBERT: This depends on the assay system. If you get equivalence of IU of HCG and IU of urinary LH or pituitary LH in one assay, it may hold only for that assay system. What is really required is an equivalence in terms of the human ovary, which cannot be inferred from the ventral prostate, ovarian ascorbic acid depletion or ovarian weight methods of bioassay.

SUMMARY OF SESSION

ROSEMBERG: From the wealth of experience presented during this session I am sure we can conclude that, in the hands of careful workers, human urinary menopausal gonadotropin or human pituitary gonadotropins will be of value in the treatment of specific cases of anovulation and infertility with avoidance of ovarian over-stimulation.

Some of the points brought forth during this session are worth summarizing. A) In the design of treatment special attention should be given to the selection of patients. B) Monitoring of dosage schedules should be carried out as patients vary in individual sensitivity to similar doses of gonadotropin preparations. A "standard" dose which will be suitable for the "average" patient may cause an excessive response in a patient with a "low threshold". C) It seems advisable to plan treatment for more than one cycle utilizing the lowest dose of gonadotropin during the first treatment course. In general, a total HMG or HPG dose of about 700 IU (FSH activity) seems to be a suitable starting dose for any given patient, using increments of about one-third of the initial dose in subsequent courses of medication. After stimulation with HMG or HPG, HCG was used to trigger ovulation at doses ranging from 5,000 to 20,000 IU. Various treatment schedules were discussed, such as: daily administration of HMG followed by HCG; three spaced injections of HMG followed by HCG, or single dose administration of HMG followed several days later by the administration of HCG. It was generally agreed that the patient's ovulatory threshold was the significant determinant of response to treatment schedule.

Changes in ovarian size, in the maturation index of the exfoliated cells of the vagina and in cervical mucus arborization as well as measurement of urinary estrogens, were considered extremely useful in the evaluation of the effectiveness of gonadotropin therapy.

CHAPTER 7

GONADOTROPIN THERAPY.
STUDIES IN MALE SUBJECTS

EFFECT OF HUMAN CHORIONIC GONADOTROPHIN AND HUMAN MENOPAUSAL GONADOTROPHIN THERAPY ON TESTICULAR FUNCTION

C. Alvin Paulsen, M.D.
Department of Medicine, University of Washington School of Medicine
Division of Endocrinology, U.S. Public Health Service Hospital
Seattle, Washington

With respect to the action of pituitary gonadotrophins on testicular function, the present concept holds that Follicle-Stimulating-Hormone (FSH) stimulates the germinal epithelium to promote full spermatogenesis and Luteinizing Hormone* (LH) stimulates the Leydig cells to secrete androgens and estrogens (1,2).

For several years we have been interested in the effects of human gonadotrophin administration on human testicular function. As a model for our studies we have selected the pathologic entity, hypogonadotrophic eunuchoidism. Since this disorder assumes a normally responsive immature testis the only variables involved would theoretically be the absence or relative "absence" of endogenous gonadotrophin secretion and the FSH-LH potencies of the various gonadotrophin preparations administered. In this regard human chorionic gonadotrophin (HCG) was used as the LH agent since human LH of clinical grade has not been available. For an FSH effect several human menopausal gonadotrophin (HMG) preparations were used. Unfortunately there is no pure FSH material available. Since all HMG preparations contain small amounts of LH our results must be considered in light of this factor.

Initially, we wanted to ascertain whether or not FSH could stimulate the immature germinal epithelium in the absence of significant amounts of LH. This aspect was studied in two patients with hypogonadotrophic eunuchoidism and one patient with prepuberal onset of hypogonadotrophic hypogonadism secondary to a craniopharyngioma (3,4). Our data suggest that FSH by itself is not able to stimulate the immature germinal epithelium. Figures 1 - 5 document the results obtained in one of the three patients.

HMG was administered in daily doses ranging from 27.3 to 81.9 I.U. FSH and 42.5 to 127.5 I.U. LH. Treatment lasted circa five and one-half weeks (Figure 1). Although this dosage of FSH has been demonstrated to be sufficient for restoration of spermatogenesis in a patient with pituitary insufficiency (5). No effect was noted in the germinal epithelium (Figures 2, 3).

In order to demonstrate that this patient's testis was responsive and to compare the separate effects of FSH and LH on the immature testis, a course

---

* Although the term Interstitial Cell-Stimulating-Hormone (ICSH) is preferred when discussing the male, through common usage LH is used more extensively. Since LH and ICSH are undoubtedly the same hormone, the only importance is in semantics.

of HCG therapy was given next. Predictably, steroidogenesis was stimulated
(Figure 4). In addition to the Leydig cell maturation, seminiferous tubular
growth and Sertoli cell differentiation along with early spermatogonial maturation were noted histologically (Figure 5).

Thus LH in the form of HCG stimulates both aspects of testicular function, i.e., hormonal and germinal. It is postulated that HCG produces its
effect on the seminiferous tubules by indirect means rather than by direct
stimulation. Accordingly the HCG-induced endogenous testosterone secretion
would be the mediator for the observed tubular growth and germinal epithelial
differentiation.

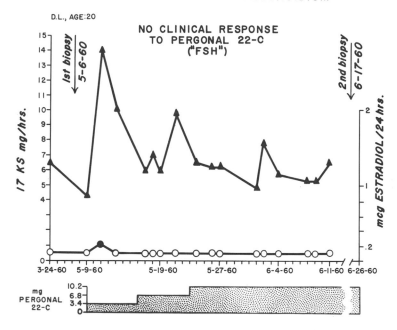

Figure 1. The effect of HMG therapy on urinary 17-ketosteroid and
estrogen excretion titers in patient D.L. Open circles indicate non-detectable
estrogen titers. HMG (Pergonal-22 C) dosage is expressed in mg. material
administered.   3.4 mg. of Pergonal-22C contains 27.3 I.U. FSH and 42.5 I.U.
LH. (From Paulsen, C.A., Estrogen Assays in Clinical Medicine, 1965,
p. 273.)

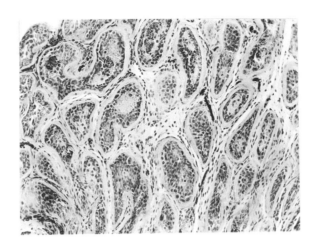

Figure 2. Pretreatment testicular biopsy specimen of D.L. (x 125). Note the immature germinal epithelium and interstitial cells. A moderate amount of seminiferous tubular membrane fibrosis is also present.

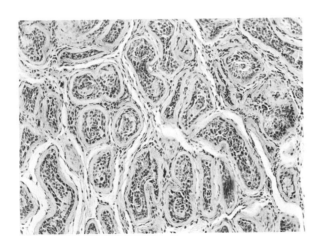

Figure 3. Testicular biopsy specimen of D.L. following HMG administration (x 125). The germinal epithelium and interstitial cells remain undifferentiated. (From Paulsen, C.A., Estrogen Assays in Clinical Medicine, 1965, p. 272.)

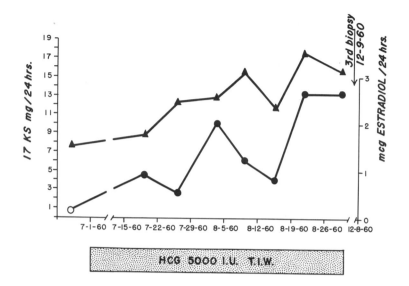

Figure 4. The effect of HCG therapy on urinary 17-ketosteroid and estrogen excretion titers in patient D.L. Note the prompt rise in hormone excretion.
(From Paulsen, C.A., Estrogen Assays in Clinical Medicine, 1965, p. 273.)

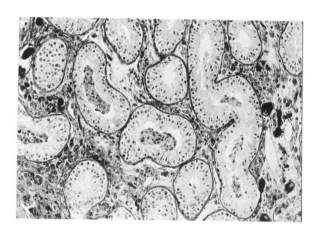

Figure 5. Testicular biopsy specimen, patient D.L. following HCG
therapy (x 125). Leydig cells are now evident in the interstitial spaces. The
seminiferous tubules have enlarged and the Sertoli cells are now differentiated.
Although not seen clearly at this magnification, spermatogonial maturation is
also underway. (From Paulsen, C.A., Estrogen Assays in Clinical Medicine,
1965, p. 275.)

The next portion of our study was designed to extend the observations of Heller and Nelson (6). These workers demonstrated that the administration of purified sheep pituitary FSH could promote full spermatogenesis in patients with hypogonadotrophic eunuchoidism when it was combined with HCG therapy. Some of these data have been reported previously (4).

Four patients with untreated hypogonadotrophic eunuchoidism were studied in detail. Hormonal data obtained prior to treatment are listed in Table 1. Urinary general gonadotrophin assay titers were at undetectable levels in two of three patients while one patient (H.G.) exhibited a low normal titer of 0.9 mg.-eq. UPM-1 per 24 hours on one of two occasions. The fourth patient (M.S.) demonstrated a low normal titer (1.6 I.U./24 hours) for specific urinary FSH excretion on one determination. Each patient was sexually immature. This was substantiated by either undetectable urinary estrogen levels or lower than normal plasma testosterone levels in three patients.

HCG was administered as the initial form of therapy to each patient for a period of 16 to 85 weeks. The dosage ranged from 2000 to 5000 I.U. three times weekly (Table 2). In two patients HCG therapy by itself produced full spermatogenesis within 16 to 85 weeks. Sperm concentration at that time was

HYPOGONADOTROPHIC EUNUCHOIDISM
PRETREATMENT STUDIES

Patient	Age	Urinary Gonadotrophins GGA	FSH	Urinary Estrogens	Plasma Testosterone
J. P.	20	< 0.7	—	< 0.2	—
M. S.*	20	—	< 3.8, 1.6	< 0.3	0.05
H. G.	24	< 0.7, 0.9	—	—	0.02, 0.02, 0.15
G. G.*	19	< 0.7	—	—	—

Table 1. Hormonal data before treatment. GGA refers to a general gonadotrophin assay method which measures the combined effect of FSH and LH. (Normal adult male range 0.7 - 3.8 mg.-eq. per 24 hours.) FSH refers to Steelman-Pohley method. (Normal adult male range 1.6 - 20 I.U. per 24 hours.) Urinary estrogens determined biologically. (Normal adult male range 0.3 - 3.0 μg.-eq. per 24 hours.) Plasma testosterone by double isotope derivative method. (Normal adult male range 0.28 - 1.44 μg. %.)

59 and 42 million per ml., respectively. The seminal fluid of the other two
patients (J.P., G.G.) was still azoospermic, after 59 and 78 weeks of HCG
treatment. At this time a combined HCG-HMG therapeutic regimen was insti-
tuted. In patient J.P., HMG was given daily at first in doses of 64.5 - 74.3
I.U. FSH (Figure 6).

Patient G.G. received HMG three times weekly in doses of 150 I.U.
FSH. Within 5 to 7 weeks of the combined HCG-HMG therapy, motile sperm
were noted in the ejaculate of both patients (Table 2). Testicular changes
induced by HCG and HCG-HMG therapy are documented in Figures 7 - 9 for
patient J.P.

Further data are not available for patient G.G. at this time but extensive
observations have been made in patient J.P. Figures 10 and 11 show these
data. With continued HCG-HMG therapy his seminal fluid sperm concentration
has varied considerably, reaching a high of 40 million/ml. on one occasion.
During the 230 weeks of observation his wife became pregnant twice and delivered two normal male infants.

INDUCED SPERMATOGENESIS HYPOGONADOTROPHIC EUNUCHOIDISM

| | | HCG | | HMG | | |
| | | Sperm Count | | Sperm Count | | Highest |
Patient	Age	Duration of R_x	m/cc	Duration of R_x	m/cc	Sperm Count
J.P.	20	59	Azoo	7	1-2/hpf	39**
M.S.*	20	16	59	—	—	71**
H.G.	22	85	(42)	—	—	(42)
G.G.*	19	78	Azoo	5	1/hpf	

Table 2. Digits under heading "Duration of R_x" indicate weeks. In
patient H.G., the bracket surrounding the sperm count indicates that this was
the only specimen obtained. *Patients with anosmia. **Patients who were
married and achieved a pregnancy.

In order to determine whether or not the gonadotrophin therapy had resulted in independent endogenous pituitary gonadotrophin secretion, treatment was discontinued in patients J.P., M.S. and H.G. (Table 3). In patient J.P., HMG administration was temporarily discontinued at the 96th week (Figure 10). Despite continued HCG treatment, his sperm count decreased to a concentration below 1 million/ml. Reinstitution of HMG therapy resulted in a rise in sperm count to 10 million/ml. within 13 weeks. Later at 216 weeks HMG was again discontinued and his sperm count decreased (Figure 11). HCG was also discontinued (222 weeks), and he manifested androgen withdrawal symptoms within 4 weeks (Table 3). At that time his urinary FSH titer was normal at 4.1 I.U./24 hours and his serum LH by radioimmunoassay (7) was low, i.e., 3.3 m.I.U./ml. (normal male adult range 4 - 19 m.I.U./ml.). Urinary or serum gonadotrophin levels in patients M.S. and H.G. were below normal adult male values at 6 and 16 weeks, respectively, following cessation of therapy (Table 3).

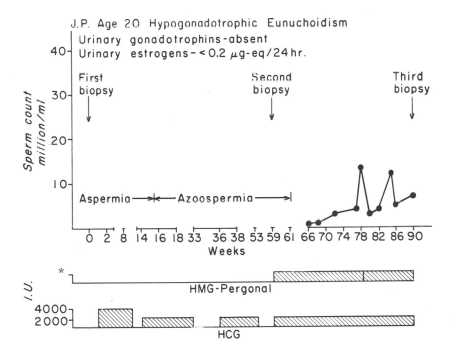

Figure 6. HCG and HMG-HCG therapy in patient J.P. *Patient received one ampule HMG daily. Since two lot numbers of HMG were used, this was a daily dose of 64.5 or 74.3 I.U. FSH. (From Paulsen, C.A., Excerpta Med. Int. Cong. Series 112, 1965, p. 403.)

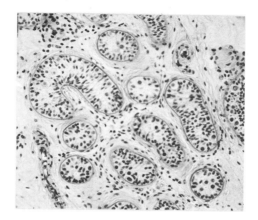

Figure 7

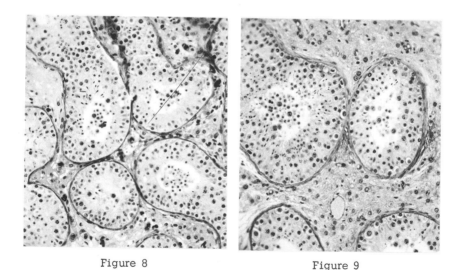

Figure 8   Figure 9

Figures 7, 8, 9. Testicular biopsy specimens from patient J.P. before treatment, following HCG therapy and following combined HCG-HMG therapy respectively. Note that mature spermatids were induced by HCG therapy. Combined HCG-HMG therapy produced greater numbers of germ cells. (From Paulsen, C.A., in Williams, R.H., Textbook of Endocrinology, 1968, p. 436, and Paulsen, C.A., Excerpta Med. Int. Cong. Series 112, 1965, p. 404.)

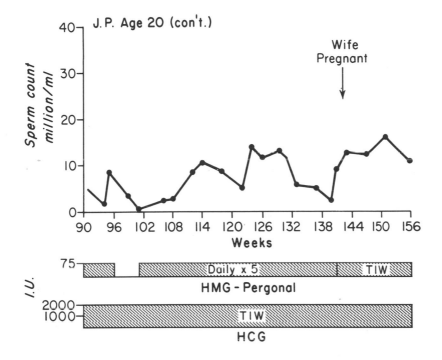

Figure 10

SUMMARY STATUS FOLLOWING CESSATION OF THERAPY

Patient	Age	Last Rx (weeks)	Gonadotrophins Urine FSH (I.U.)	Serum LH (m.I.U.)	Testosterone	Vasomotor Symptoms
J. P.	24	4	4.1	3.3	—	+
M.S.*	23	6	<1.8	1.7	0.03	+++
H. G.	24	16	—	2.7	—	0

Table 3

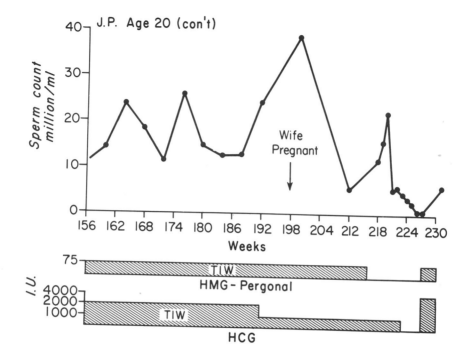

Figure 11

These data indicate that each patient was dependent on exogenous gonadotrophin therapy for maintenance of testicular function.

SUMMARY

It is difficult to make final conclusions from these data but they do provide a guideline for further study. First, HCG can induce full testicular function in some patients but not in others. The results from our study indicate that those patients with some endogenous gonadotrophin secretion (patients M.S. and H.G.) will respond with full spermatogenesis in addition to normal androgen production. While in those patients (J.P., G.G.) who exhibit, for all intents and purposes, absence of clinically effective endogenous gonadotrophin secretion, HCG treatment will not achieve full spermatogenesis. In these patients the addition of HMG therapy may produce full spermatogenesis with eventual fertility.

ACKNOWLEDGEMENTS

Plasma testosterone determinations were performed through the courtesy of Dr. H. Gandy, Cornell University.

Supported in part by grants AM 05161 and AM 05436 from the National Institutes of Health.

REFERENCES

1. Paulsen, C.A., In Williams, R.H. (ed.), Textbook of Endocrinology, ed. 4, W.B. Saunders Co., Philadelphia, 1968, p. 405.

2. Paulsen, C.A., In Astwood, E.B., and C.E. Cassidy (eds.), Clinical Endocrinology II, Grune and Stratton, Inc., New York, 1968, p. 569.

3. Paulsen, C.A., In Paulsen, C.A. (ed.), Estrogen Assays in Clinical Medicine, University of Washington Press, Seattle, 1965, p. 274.

4. Paulsen, C.A., In Proceedings of the Sixth Pan American Congress of Endocrinology, Mexico City 1965, Excerpta Medica Foundation, Amsterdam, 1966, p. 398.

5. MacLeod, J., A. Pagianos, and B. Ray, Fertil Steril 17:7, 1964.

6. Heller, C.G., and W.O. Nelson, Rec Progr Hormone Res 3:229, 1948.

7. Midgley, A.R., Endocrinology 79:10, 1966.

THE EFFECT OF GONADOTROPINS ON THE TESTIS
OF HYPOPHYSECTOMIZED PATIENTS

Mancini, R. E., M. D., Seiguer, A. C., M. D. and
Perez Lloret, A., M. D.

Centro de Investigaciones sobre Reproduccion, Facultad de
Medicina, Paraguay 2155, Buenos Aires, Argentina.

In the past, some reports have dealt with the effects of
HCG, PMS or animal pituitary gonadotropins on the spermatogenesis
of hypogonadal subjects (1, 2, and 3). The expanding therapeutic
use of human pituitary (HPG) or human urinary gonadotropins (HMG),
either alone or, in combination with HCG on cases of eunuchoidal
males (4 to 7), or on hypophysectomized patients (8 and 9), has
renewed the interest in the study of gonadotropin regulation of
spermatogenesis in humans. The unknown role played by these
hormones in the initiation, maintenance and restoration of the
various steps of spermatogenesis, and the lack of evaluation
information concerning the separate and combined effects of PMS,
HCG and HMG on adult hypophysectomized patients, has prompted
us to investigate this problem. A concurrent study was also
made to determine the nature and effect of gonadotropins on the
peritubular hyaline substance which is seen in the tubular wall
of the seminiferous tubules in untreated hypophysectomized subjects.

I. Regression of Spermatogenesis after Hypophysectomy. Effect
    of Gonadotropins. Therapy on Hypophysectomized Subjects.

Material and Methods

The fifteen adult patients selected for this study, ranging
in age from 26 to 53 years, were gathered from 1962 onward at the
Costa Boero Neurosurgical Institute of the School of Medicine in
Buenos Aires. All had been operated for hypophyseal tumors
(cysts or chromophobe adenoma), and had been given x-irradiation;
none had received any previous gonadotropin treatment.

At the time of testicular biopsy, total urinary gonadotropin
levels (10), urinary 17-hydroxy-ketosteroids (11), and 17-
ketosteroids (12), were determined. Before starting hormone
administration and, again, at the end of treatment, each patient
underwent a unilateral testicular biopsy at different intervals
of time, ranging from one month to six years after operation.
For general hystology, the tissues were divided into several
portions and immersed in either Bouin's or Carnoy fixative.
Hematoxylin-eosin and periodic acid-Schiff techniques were also
used. Other samples were processed for histochemistry, chemical
determinations and electron microscopy.

On examination of the control biopsies of the fifteen patients
it was found that the extent of regression of the seminiferous

epithelium, tubular wall, and interstitial cells were of different degrees. It was, therefore, necessary to classify them into three distinct groups. Group I was characterized by seminiferous tubules containing Sertoli cells, an almost complete spermatogenic cell line, slight hyalinization of the tubular wall, and an appreciable number of Leydig cells. In Group II, the tubules contained Sertoli cells, spermatogonial cells and primary spermatocytes up to the pachytene stage, moderate hyalinization of the tubular wall and a low number of Leydig cells. Group III, on the other hand, exhibited seminiferous tubules containing spermatogonial and Sertoli cells only, severe hyalinization of the tubular wall and a few Leydig cells.

Estimation of the variation in the relative number of germinal cells was made by performing cell counts on twenty circular transverse sections of seminiferous tubules (13). Calculations were based on the average number of each cell type per cross-tubular section and verified by a "t" test. The diameter and thickness of the seminiferous tubule wall was also measured and, expressed as the average of all cases. In regard to the inter-tubular spaces, the presence of immature, mature and degenerating forms of Leydig cells and also, fibroblast-like cells as precursors of Leydig cells, were estimated by applying a differential cell count of 200 cells of the intertubular cell population.

All patients in each of the three groups received treatment with one of the following hormones: a) Pregnant Mare Serum Gonadotropin[†] (PMS), 2,000 I.U. per week; b) Human Chorionic Gonadotropin[†] (HCG), 2,000 I.U. per week; c) PMS plus HCG, 2,000 I.U. of each hormone per week; d) Human Menopausal Gonadotropin[††] (HMG), 3 ampoules (each ampoule containing 75 I.U. of FSH and 75 I.U. of LH) per week, or e) 3 ampoules of HMG plus HCG, 1,000 I.U. per week. Since it was estimated that 74 (+4 to 5) days were required for the development of spermatogonia to the level of spermatozoa (15), it was necessary to administer HCG and HMG over a three month period in doses of three ampoules per week. PMS, on the other hand, was administered for a period of only six weeks because of its well known antigenic properties.

In Group I and III the patients who had been given HMG plus HCG were continued on HMG therapy for another three months with the addition of testosterone propionate administered in two weekly doses of 50 mg each. It should also be noted that each patient had been maintained with low doses of Prednisolone, and dessicated thyroid.

---

† PMS and HCG were kindly provided by ELEA Laboratories, Argentina.

††HMG as Pergonal-500 was provided by the Istituto Farmacologico, Serono, Rome, Italy.

RESULTS

CONTROL BIOPSIES

Although complete removal of the pituitary gland was attempted in each case, none proved to be entirely successful. However, all patients experienced loss of libido and potentia. Urinary steroid determinations revealed low levels of 17-keto and hydrozycorticosteroids (16). Urinary gonadotropins were undetectable.

Control biopsies of the three groups revealed no relationship between the regression of the testis and age of the patients. A correlation was found to exist, however, between the time elapsing after operation and the degree of involution of the gland, indicating that the degenerative process took, in general, from few weeks to several years for regression of spermatogenesis from almost complete spermatogenesis found in Group I, back to the spermatocyte level of Group II or, even, to the spermatogonial and Sertoli cell level shown by Group III. In Group I the amount of germinal cells in different phases of spermatogenesis as well as the number of mature Leydig cells present were greatly reduced when compared to the number found in normal adult subjects (13 and 14). Also, the sloughing of the germinal cells was more evident at the spermatid stage than at any other stage. Both Groups I and III, showed that some Sertoli and spermatogonial cells contained extreme vacuolization or abnormal eosinophilic staining of the cytoplasm. Shrinkage of the nuclear membrane was also noted. The latter group displayed more of these changes than the former. The mitotic divisions of metaphase and advanced prophase were occasionally recognized in the spermatogonial cells of both Groups. However, this was more marked in Group I than in Group III.

EFFECT OF GONADOTROPIN THERAPY

GROUP I.   PMS Treatment induced: a) persistence in the sloughing of the germinal epithelium; b) no changes in the number of spermatogonial cells but a significant decrease in the spermatocytes, spermatids and spermatozoa; c) no ostensible modification in the diameter of the seminiferous tubules, and d) a tendency toward the disappearance of mature Leydig cells.

HCG Therapy induced: a) persistence in the sloughing of the germinal epithelium; b) no changes in the number of spermatogonia, spermatocytes or spermatids, but a significant decrease in the number of spermatozoa; c) an increase in tubular diameter, and d) stimulation of the mature types of Leydig cells accompanied by a decrease in the number of degenerating cells. Combined treatment with PMS and HCG showed approximately the effect as HCG alone.

HMG Therapy induced: a) reduction in the sloughing of the
germinal epithelium; b) no changes in the spermatogonial cells,
but a significant increase in the residual germinal cells; c)
an increase in tubular diameter, and d) an increased number of
Leydig cells, especially in the immature type and a decrease in
the number of degenerating cells. Combined treatment of HMG
plus HCG showed: a) disappearance in the sloughing of the germinal epithelium; b) a significant stimulating effect on all
types of cells of the germinal epithelium, especially, from the
spermatocyte stage onward, and c) a marked increase in the number
of mature Leydig cells. HMG plus Testosterone showed: a) significant decrease of all germinal cells, especially, from spermatocytes onward; c) a decrease in the diameter of the seminiferous
tubules, and d) a reduction in both mature and immature Leydig
cells.

GROUP II. PMS Treatment induced: a) significant reduction
in the number of spermatogonial cells and spermatocytes; b)
slight increase in the tubular diameter, and c) changes in the
Leydig cell population. HCG treatment induced: a) no change in
the number of spermatogonial cells, but s significant increase
in primary spermatocytes; b) no ostensible modifications in the
diameter of the tubules, and c) an evident stimulation of both
immature and mature types of Leydig cells. Combined treatment
of PMS and HCG induced: a) significant increase in spermatogonial
cells and spermatocytes; b) stimulation of Leydig cells; c) an
increase in the tubular diameter.

HMG Therapy induced: a) significant increase in the number
of spermatogonial cells and spermatocytes as well as development
of spermatids and even, a few spermatozoa; b) an increase in
Leydig cells, especially of the immature form. Therapy with HMG
and HCG showed: a) a significant increase in spermatogonial cells
and spermatocytes accompanied by the development of spermatids
and spermatozoa; b) an increase in the diameter of the seminiferous tubules, and c) an increase in Leydig cells, especially of
the mature form.

GROUP III. PMS Therapy induced: a) a significant increase
in spermatogonial cells and b) no ostensible changes in the
remaining structures. HCG treatment induced: a) a significant
increase in spermatogonial cells and the appearance of primary
spermatocytes up to the pachytene stage; b) an increase in
immature Leydig cells as well as the development of mature
types. Therapy with PMS and HCG showed: a) a significant
increase in spermatogonial cells, development of spermatocytes
and a high stimulation of mature Leydig cells.

Therapy with HMG induced: a) no change in the spermatogonial
cells, but development of meiotic spermatocytes as well as a few
spermatids; b) an increase in tubular diameter, and c) an increase
in Leydig cells, especially of the immature type. Therapy with
HMG and HCG . The effects were similar except for an increase in
the number of spermatogonial cells and stimulation of both types

of Leydig cells. <u>Therapy with HMG and Testosterone</u> induced: a) a significant increase in spermatogonial cells and the appearance of a few spermatocytes and spermatids; b) no change in the diameter of the seminiferous tubules, and c) decreased number of Leydig cells with a resulting increase in the number of degenerating cells.

In all three groups, a correlation was found to exist between the cytological signs of regression exhibited by both the Sertoli and spermatogonial cells, and the high stimulating effects induced by doses of either PMS given together with HCG or HMG given together with HCG. Also, the mitotic divisions within the spermatogonial cells were more frequent under these treatment schemes. These changes were corroborated by electron-microscopy and will be published elsewhere.

II   Nature and Effect of Gonadotropins on Peritubular Hyalinization.

MATERIAL AND METHODS

Testicular biopsies of the fifteen patients, taken before and after administration of the various gonadotropins, and four biopsies obtained from normal subjects who served as controls, were used for histological, electronmicroscopy and chemical studies. The techniques used were as follows: a) Trichromic Mallory stain and Silver impregnation checked with trypsin digestion; b) pepsin and collagenase digestion for collagen and reticulin fibers, respectively; c) Gammori's stain for elastic fibers, d) Periodic acid-Schiff (PAS), preceded by amylase digestion for glucoproteins and other substances; e) Alcian blue and colloidal iron checked with testicular hyaluronidase digestion for acid mucopolysaccharides; f) Congo Red and fluorescent staining with Tiophlavin T for amyloid; g) Phosphotungstic acid hematoxylin for fibrinoid; h) an indirect immunofluonescent method using rabbit anti-human testicular collagen and antiglycoprotein antibodies.(17) followed by labeled goat, anti-rabbit globulins; i) a direct immuno-fluorescent method using labeled rabbit serum against human globulin fractions; j) electronmicroscopic observations using tissues first fixed in gluteraldehyde and later, fixed in osmic acid, dehydrated, embedded into Epon resin and stained with uranyl acetate and lead citrate.

RESULTS

The seminiferous tubules from the testis of normal subjects showed a thin well defined basement membrane by the trichromic stain and PAS reactions. This structure was found to be clearly separated from the outer tunica propria where a network of fibers were observed with staining characteristics similar to that found in reticulin or elastic fibers. A pale-stained

interfibrillar mucopolysaccharide was also present. In
addition, one or two layers of fibroblast-like cells appeared
to be distributed throughout this boundary structure (18).
Electronmicroscopy showed that this peritubular tissue was
composed of an inner acellular layer and an outer cellular
layer. The acellular layer consisted of two different
structures, the basal lamina and the reticular lamina (basement membranes at the optical level); the former being a
continuous mesh-like band of fibrillar material embedded
into a gel-like amorphous matrix running parallel to the
epithelial cells. There was no evidence to conclude that
any of these fine filaments might have passed through the
cell membrane into the epithelial cells where filaments
similar in appearance were found within the Sertoli cells.
In some sections the basal lamina consisted of stacked
lamellae of alternating layers of low to moderate density.
These structures often followed an undulating course, but
sometimes, remained roughly parallel to the epithelial base.
Some densely staining fibrils were observed immediately
adjacent to the basal lamina at its connective tissue side.
The plasmatic membrane of the nearest fibroblast, extended
the reticular lamina, the latter being composed of typical
collagen fibrils arranged in compact bundles running in
various directions and leaving an interfibrillar space of
very low electron density. Some of these fibrils were also
seen ending at the basal lamina.

The outer structure of the tubular wall, the cellular
layer, consisted of elongated cells, having nuclei running
parallel to their long axis and a numerous number of thin
branching extensions running parallel to the basal lamina.
In a moderately electron-dense hyaloplasm, there appeared to
be a well-developed Golgi apparatus, a few lipid droplets, a
rough endoplasmic reticulum and several mitochondrea containing
dense matrix and irregular cristae. These were especially
common in the perinuclear area. Some smooth vesicles, a few
microtubules and an abundance of filaments were observed in
the cytoplasmic expansions. A fibrillar-banded structure,
sometimes resembling the homogeneous pattern of the basal
lamina, could be seen bordering the plasmatic membrane.
Finally, a stratified arrangement of two or three alternating
cellular and acellular structures with similar characteristics
of both the reticular lamina and the peritubular cells
previously described, completed the peritubular wall.

In comparison with normal testis, the seminiferous tubules
of hypophysectomized patients showed, at the optical level, an
amorphous or hyalin slightly-fibrillar material, which tended
to replace the fibers of the tunica propria. This hyalinization
process was seen in Group I and reached its highest manifesta-
tions in Group III. The process began near the basement membrane and grew eccentrically including the outer-layer fibers
of the tunica propria. A homogeneous aspect of this structure

became evident. The reticulin fibrils appeared to be less
stained and the elastic fibers showed signs of both discontinuity
and fragmentation. A parallel atrophy in the peritubular fibroblasts was seen which could also be traced to similar cells in
the immediate area. The basement membrane, apparently intact
initially, showed some evidence of thinning and discontinuity
in the more advanced stages of hyalinization.

Even though there was a lack of typical fibers, the
hyalin material retained an affinity for both collagen and
reticulin stains, while being negative for PAS reaction and
elastic fibers - amyloid and fibrinoid staining, respectively.
A negative reaction was also seen with fluorescent antisera
used against either human albumin or globulin fractions.
Furthermore, only a highly positive reaction was found to occur
in mucopolysaccharides which became negative by incubation with
hyaluronidase.

In contrast to what is usually seen in the fibrillar tunica
propria of the testis of normal subjects, immunofluorescent
techniques, using antibodies against testicular collagen or
glycoprotein substances, gave a negative response to hyalin
material. Only in the testis of Group I and, to a less extent,
in Group II was fluorescent staining observable in the fibers
at the outer layer of the tunica propria. Of all the enzyme
digestions performed only pepsin and particularly collagenase
demonstrated a lytic action on the hyalin substance.

At the electronmicroscopic level, striking differences were
found to exist between hyalinized tubules and normal ones. The
thickness of the reticular lamina was markedly increased. At
this site, the collagen fibrils exhibited different degrees of
deterioration-like loosenings in the collagen strands and a less-
defined periodicity until, finally, no cross-banding at all could
be distinguished. Transverse sections of the same structure
revealed a central clear core surrounded by a thin ring of dense
material which also tended to fade. The basal lamina did not
change significantly except in areas where the filament networks
appeared to be dissociated. At these points, the interfibrillar
spaces were filled with a moderately dense, homogeneous and, in
some cases, finely-stripped material together with a few scattered
fibrils similar in appearance to those found on the connective
tissue side of the basal lamina. This new material that is,
incipient hyalin substance, was more evident in areas where the
altered collagen fibrils predominated. In the most damaged cases
of Group III, the reticular lamina appeared to be almost completely
replaced by a homogeneous and low electron dense material (true
hyalin substance). The peritubular cells showed regressive
changes in the nuclei and, to a greater extent, in the cytoplasm.
They displayed a lesser electron density and swollen hyaloplasm
apparently caused by loosenings in a major portion of the
organelles. This condition gave rise to an oval or sometimes
round-shaped cell having very few cytoplasmic extensions.

The effect of the administration of various gonadotropins on the hyalinization process occurring in the testis of the three groups were as follows: a) PMS did not induce any ostensible changes on the extent of peritubular hyalinization; b) HCG produced a marked reduction in the thickness of the hyalin deposition, a response which was also observable after the administration of HMG. Furthermore, this effect reached its maximum effect with combined treatment with HMG and HCG; c) a simultaneous reappearance in the tunica propria of reticulin and elastic fibers along with normal fibroblasts, paralleled with a disappearance of mucopolysaccharides, and d) the beneficial effects of HMG were not readily apparent when testosterone was added, for, hyalinization not only persisted but was probably increased.

CONCLUSIONS

Despite the fact that no strict correlation could be established, our data suggests that, involution of germinal epithelium at the level of spermiogenesis will occur a few weeks or months after hypophysectomy, whereas several months to years are necessary to regress back to the spermatocyte or spermatogonial phase, respectively. Furthermore, it is important to note that the quality of the post-surgical regression of the gland may have been influenced by either the nature of the hypophyseal lesion, time elapsed from initiation of lesion to operation or, the different degrees of completeness of hypophysectomy.

The classification of the fifteen patients into three distinct groups according to the various cytological levels at which the regression of the germinal epithelium had stopped, allowed us to evaluate, on a uniform ground, the action of gonadotropins in the restoration of the different phases of spermatogenesis. Both PMS and HCG seemed to have a predominant action on only one particular phase of the process. PMS acted upon the spermatogonial cells whereas HCG influenced a more advanced type of spermatogonial cells, thus giving rise to primary spermatocytes. Whether or not HCG and PMS were influential in promoting the complete development of germinal cells remains in doubt. The more potent action of HCG may be explained by its homologous origin and, also, because of the simultaneous stimulation of both Sertoli and Leydig cells. The failure to restore all phases of spermatogenesis, even with the combined use of PMS and HCG, points to the necessity of having hormones of human origin containing both FSH and LH activity. This fact was corroborated by the use of HMG. The administration of HCG, however, resulted in a more complete recovery of the germinal cell line accompanied by the development of Leydig cells and repair of Sertoli cells. This cellular response was better seen in those patients having pre-existent spermatocytes or advanced spermiogenic phases rather than in those who showed only spermatogonial cells. With the completion of the induction of spermatogenesis, we deduced that both gonadotropins, HCG and PMS, act simultaneously in all phases of the process.

In regard to the second study dealing with the effect of gonadotropins on the peritubular hyalin substance, we found that the extensiveness of the hyalinization process was directly related to the degree of regression which was observed in both the germinative epithelium and the Leydig cells. Adjacent fibroblast-like cells were also found to have been influenced by the amount of hyalin substance present. The hyalin substance developed among the collagen fibrils as an amorphous collagenous material mixed with mucopolysaccharides. Breakdown of the collagen fibrils took place at these sites at precisely the same time. PMS did not induce ostensible changes in the extent of peritubular hyalinization. HCG, however, produced a marked reduction in the thickness of the hyalin deposition which was also observed after the administration of HMG. Furthermore, this effect reached its maximum with the combined administration of HMG and HCG.

REFERENCES

1. Maddock, O. W. J. Clin. Endocr. 9: 213, 1949.

2. Bartter, F. C., R. C. Sniffen, F. A. Simmons, F. Albright and R. P. Howard. J. Clin. Endocr. 12: 1532, 1952.

3. Heller, C. G. and W. O. Nelson. J. Clin. Endocr. 8: 345, 1948.

4. Paulsen, C. A. In Paulsen, C. A. (ed.). Estrogen Assays in Clinical Medicine, Univ. of Washington Press. Seattle, 1965, p. 274.

5. Lytton, B. and N. Kase. New Eng. J. Med. 274: 1061, 1966.

6. Johnsen, S. G. Acta Endocr. 53: 315, 1966.

7. Lunenfeld, B., A. Mor and M. Mani. Fertil. and Steril. 18: 581, 1967.

8. Gemzell, C. A. and B. Kjessler. Lancet, 1: 644, 1964.

9. MacLeod, J., A. Pazianos, and R. Bronson. Fertil. and Steril. 17: 7, 1966.

10. Klinefelter, H. F., F. Albright and G. C. Griswald. J. Clin. Endocr. 3: 529, 1943.

11. Appleby, J. L., G. Gibson, J. Norymberski and R. D. Stubbs Bioch. J. 60: 143, 1955.

12. Ricca, A. Rev. Bioq. Argen. <u>22</u>: 11, 1957.

13. Mancini, R. E., R. Narbaitz and J. C. Lavieri. Anat. Record. <u>136</u>: 477, 1960.

14. Mancini, R. E., O. Vilar, J. C. Lavieri, J. A. Andrada, and J. Heinrich. Am. J. Anat. <u>112</u>: 2, 1963.

15. Heller, C. H. and Y. Clermont. Recent Prog. Horm. Res. <u>20</u>: 545, 1964.

16. Irigoyen, M., M. Molosnik, J. Varela, C. Pardal and G. Dickman. Actas Congr. Intern. de Invest. Neurol., Lima, Peru, 1967.

17. Denduchis, B., L. Lustig, N. Gonzalez and R. E. Mancini Labor. Invest. 1968 (In Press).

18. Mancini, R. E., O. Vilar, M. Perez del Cerro. Acta Physiol. Latinoam. <u>14</u>: 382, 1964.

This work was supported by a Grant-In-Aid from the Population Council, Inc., New York, New York

ASSESSMENT OF RESULTS WITH GONADOTROPIC THERAPY

B. LUNENFELD, B. GOLDMAN AND B. ISMAJOVICH, INSTITUTE OF ENDO-
CRINOLOGY, TEL-HASHOMER GOVERNMENT HOSPITAL, ISRAEL.

Forty-six genetically normal azoospermic men with no evidence of any uro-
genital abnormality or disease were treated with 75 IU FSH + 75 IU LH + 2500 IU
HCG; three times weekly.

In all six cases of hypogonadotropic azoospermic males whose pre-treatment
testicular biopsies revealed infantile testes with mean tubular diameter of 50-70 μ
containing Sertoli cells and cell elements up to various forms of spermatogonia,
complete gonadal maturation could be obtained within 80-190 days.

Five out of 15 hypogonadotropic patients who had tubules of normal or near-
normal size (170-250 μ) with normal, moderate, or thickened walls, containing
spermatogonia, Sertoli cells and, in some tubules, occasional spermatocytes, had
normal sperm counts 80-144 days after HMG-HCG treatment.

Eight normo-gonadotropic-azoospermic patients were treated with 75 IU FSH
+ 75 IU LH + 2500 IU HCG; three times per week, without fixing a definite time
limit in the treatment course. One patient responded after 17 months with occasional spermatozoa in the ejaculate; a month later a normal sperm count was obtained and his wife became pregnant. Three other patients responded (significant
increase in sperm count) after 12-15 months of treatment, and the 4 remaining
patients are still under therapy.

The unresponsiveness of 16 out of the 17 patients who had tubules of normal
or near-normal size, most of which contained only Sertoli cells, might be explained by the fact that in the absence of cellular elements pertaining to the germinal
line, no spermatogenic response can be expected. Since biopsy material might
not represent the status of all the tubules, patients diagnosed as having a "Sertoli-
only cells" syndrome might actually have mixed forms. In such cases gonadotropic therapy may be beneficial as it may at least serve as a diagnostic tool.

It can be concluded that HMG-HCG therapy can activate spermatogenesis and
spermiogenesis in patients with pituitary gonadotropic insufficiency whose testicular biopsies reveal tubules containing cells of the germinal line. The relatively
low success rate might be due to the fixed dosage scheme, which does not allow
for variation in target cell sensitivity within patients.

SPERMATOGENESIS AND CONCEPTION DURING HMG TREATMENT OF HYPOGONADOTROPIC HYPOGONADISM

Svend G. Johnsen and Peter Christiansen

(From The Male Hypogonadism Study Section, Medical Dept. P, University Hospital of Copenhagen, and The Hormone Dept., Statens Seruminstitut, Copenhagen)

INTRODUCTION

In recent years, few papers have been written describing the treatment of male infertility with preparations of human follicle stimulating hormone (FSH). Some of them report discouraging results (1, 2, 3, 4), while others (5, 6, 13) describe improvement of fertility with this mode of therapy. Unfortunately, however, it is difficult to adequately evaluate the data as hormone assays were frequently omitted, testicular biopsies were lacking or insufficient, and in general, no attempts were made to investigate the etiology and pathogenesis of the infertility in each of the cases treated.

The present report describes the effect of human FSH, obtained from menopausal urine (HMG), in 4 cases with panhypopituitarism, 1 with isolated FSH insufficiency, 1 case of primary infantilism and 1 with hypogonadotropic eunuchoidism. The last two studies are extensions of previous cases treated with HMG described in 1966 (7). The results obtained in this study were recently confirmed elsewhere (8).

The methodology used in this study has been described in the previous report (7). Urinary FSH was assayed by a modification of the rat ovarian augmentation assay (9) and LH by the ventral prostate weight method in hypophysectomized rats (9). Normal limits for FSH and LH in adult men have been established in our laboratory (9)

The HMG preparations used were HMG Leo† batch 64021 and 65101 [the FSH:LH ratios contained in these preparations have been described elsewhere (7)].

---

†We are indebted to Leo Pharmaceutical Products, Copenhagen, for the generous gift of HMG.

RESULTS AND DISCUSSION

Case 1.   (Patient P.E.N.)

A previously normal virile man, who at the age of 23 years underwent operation for a hypophyseal tumor (craniopharyngioma).
During the following 9 years, he lost sexual potency; pubic and
axillary hair disappeared whereas a faint growth of beard persisted. His general health was fair and he remained untreated for 9
years. Our first examination performed at 32 years of age showed
(cf. Fig 1) that the external genitals were small and the testes
very soft. There was a small amount of pubic hair around radix
penis, no axillary hair and a small amount of facial hair around
the mouth. Gonadotropins were repeatedly undetectable (< 3 MUU
at 3 assays during 10 months) and androgen output was very low
(androsterone 0.5 mg); the metopirone test induced no adrenal
response and the BMR was 82%. The testicular biopsy (cf. Fig 2)
showed small tubules (mean diam. 113 μ) with pronounced peritubular fibrosis and very marked hyalinization (hyaline layer
4-10 μ). The germinal epithelium contained a reduced number of
spermatogonia and few tubules showed very small numbers of spermatocytes. 2-4 spermatids were seen in a single tubule. No spermatozoa were present. No Leydig cells were found.
       The findings indicated complete loss of hypophyseal function.
During the next 15 months, the patient was maintained on cortisone
(25 mg. daily), thyroidine (200 U daily) and testosterone supposi-
tories (20 mg. daily).
       The courses of treatment are shown in Fig. 3. Testosterone
was discontinued and substituted by HCG 3,000 IU twice a week for
2 months. A substantial increase (up to normal) of androsterone
and etiocholanolone occurred, but 2 sperm samples at the end of
this period showed aspermia. 1 month later HMG treatment was
begun with 60 IU FSH plus 350 IU HCG 3 times a week. Aspermia
persisted for 6 weeks, but after 9 weeks of treatment, a very
small number of spermatozoa (0.07 mill.) appeared in the ejaculate.
During the course of continuous treatment,the number of spermatozoa
rose gradually from 0.2 and 2.1 million up to 16 million which was
achieved after 17 weeks of treatment. Apart from the number, the
quality of the sperm was excellent, the motility was good, and the
number of abnormal head forms was 25 percent. 1 week after the
collection of this sperm sample, conception occurred. Pregnancy
was normal and resulted in the delivery of a normal baby boy
(weight 3900 g).
       HMG treatment which was interrupted because of pregnancy,
was continued with HCG alone (3,000 IU once a week), and it was
found that this treatment was able to maintain spermatogenesis
at a level of 15 and 11 million sperm. However, in contrast to
the sperm samples during HMG treatment, the motility was poor.

       Comments : The loss of hair, lack of gonadotropins, androgens and
Metopirone response, and the appearance of the testicular tissue give ample
evidence of a total loss of hypophyseal function in this patient. Several

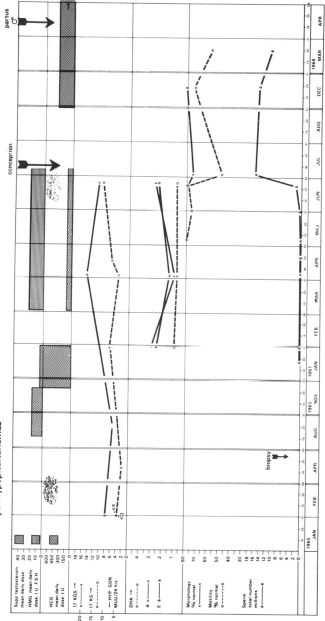

Fig. 3. Case 1 (P.E.N.). Treatment courses, hormone assays and sperm counts. Gonadotropin doses are given in mean daily dose calculated from injections given 2 - 3 times weekly. HMG dose is stated in IU FSH, steroid excretion in mg. per 24 hours, total gonadotropin excretion in MUU per 24 hours, and sperm count in million per ejaculate.

points are remarkable. First, it has been shown that a rather small dose of
HMG (26 IU FSH per day) together with HCG is capable of re-creating spermatogenesis in a man who has been deprived of gonadotropin stimulation for 11 years.
Secondly, since it is highly unlikely that good spermatogenesis can take place
in tubules with advanced hyalinization (cf. 10) it would appear that HMG-HCG
treatment has also been able to reverse the hyalinization processes (cf. also
Case 4). Thirdly, it is remarkable that sperm morphology and motility became
excellent (indicating that optimal conditions for spermatogenesis were created)
and that conception occurred with a sperm number far lower than usually is
considered necessary. Finally, it is interesting that HCG, which was unable to
produce spermatogenesis, was capable of maintaining it in this patient.

Case 2. (Patient B.E.)

40 year-old-man examined because of sterility of 8 years duration.
At examination, the patient was in perfect general health.   No
signs of hypothyroidism or hypocorticism.   Normal virility.
Testis size was for both 25 ml., consistency normal.   The level
of excretion of androgens was normal (androsterone (A) 3.1 mg.,
etiocholanolone (E) 6.2 mg.) but the A/E ratio (cf. (11)) was
low.   Total urinary gonadotropins were within the limits of
detection (< 4 MUU); the FSH-excretion was 4 IU per 24 hours and
LH 7 IU.   2 sperm examinations indicated a total count of 90 and
118 million with 44 and 40 percent abnormal head forms.   Motility
was good in the first, poor in the second, and fertility was
reduced considerably.
      Testicular biopsy showed (cf. Fig 4) that the tubular size
was within the lower normal limit (mean diameter 164 μ). Tubular
walls were thin and delicate.   Spermatogenesis was normal up to
spermatid stage, but the number of spermatozoa was reduced, and
in the majority of tubules only few spermatozoa were seen.   The
Leydig cells were normal.
      The course of treatment is shown in Fig 5.   HMG was given
at a dose of 60 IU FSH along with 450 IU HCG 3 times a week for
7 weeks.   The sperm count dropped from about 100 to about 40
million while morphology and motility remained unchanged.   Nevertheless, conception occurred after 19 days of treatment.   The
pregnancy terminated with abortion 3 months later.
      After cessation of treatment, the sperm count rose to the
pretreatment level, but in other respects the sperm count remained unaltered.   In order to study the effect of HMG on testicular
histology, a new course of HMG-HCG treatment was constituted for
4 weeks, and at the end of this period a second biopsy was taken.
The second biopsy was (cf. Fig.4), in every respect, identical
with the first.   Mean tubular diameter was 170 μ.   Membranes were
normal.   Spermatogenesis up to spermatid stage was normal, but
the number of spermatozoa considerably reduced as seen in the
first biopsy.   The number of Leydig cells was increased somewhat.
Cell count, according to a new procedure developed in this
laboratory (12), was also performed but the two biopsies
achieved practically the same mean score.

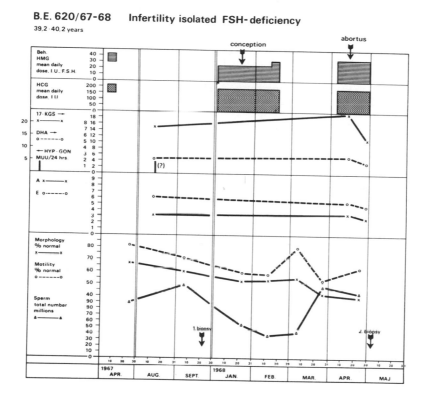

B.E. 620/67-68   Infertility isolated FSH-deficiency

39.2-40.2 years

Fig. 5.   Case 2 (B.E.). Courses of treatment,
cf. legend to Fig. 3.

Comments: Unexpected conception is sometimes met in hypofertility and the
interpretation of this case is open for discussion. However, conception in
this case might be attributed to HMG treatment. The patient had been infertile
for 8 years, through 2 marriages, and the first conception occurred after 3
weeks of treatment, i.e. at the time where an influence on spermatid maturation would show up in the ejaculate. The data suggest that the cause of
infertility in this case was FSH-insufficiency. Complete lack of hyaline
degeneration in hypospermatogenesis is in itself an indication of gonadotropin
insufficiency and so is impairment of spermatid maturation. Urinary FSH was
at the lowest level found in normal individuals, total gonadotropins were
decreased, and the low A/E-ratio is presumably one more indication of partial
hypopituitarism (cf. (11)). No parameter in sperm examination gives a direct

clue to the fertilizing capacity of the spermatozoa. Conception, in this case, points to the occurrence of a change in sperm quality which does not show up by conventional methods of examination.

Case 3. (Patient A. R.)

This is an extension of the observations during long-term treatment of a patient reported previously (7). At the age of 17, the patient had severe primary infantilism. During 4 years of treatment with HCG and HMG, the patient displayed testicular growth and finally achieved spermatogenesis with 21 mill. sperms in the ejaculate. During subsequent periods during which therapy was withdrawn, the testes regressed rapidly in size. The HMG doses employed had varied between 80 and 160 IU FSH 3 times a week. The question was raised if smaller doses would have been capable of maintaining spermatogenesis.

The extension of the study deals with this question. The course of treatment is shown in Fig. 6 which begins with the end of the observation made previously. For 14 months, the patient received testosterone (in suppository form) in increasing doses from 20-80 mg. daily. Before and during this period, gonadotropin excretion was low (March 1966 <3 MUU, July 1966 4 MUU and May 1967 3 MUU). Similar levels were observed at 16-17 years of age. After testosterone therapy for 13 months,   2 sperm examinations showed 0.8 and 10 mill. of spermatozoa in the ejaculate which indicated that a limited spermatogenesis had been maintained either by the testosterone or by endogenous gonadotropin production.

Low-dose HMG treatment was started with 24 IU FSH twice a week for 2 months and continued with 60 IU twice a week for 3 weeks. HMG was given with 450 IU of HCG and testosterone. During this treatment, the sperm count rose to 42 million and 3 weeks later the sperm count was 13 million. 6 months later the patient, still under testosterone medication, had 70 mill. of spermatozoa in the ejaculate. In all the sperm samples, between 40 and 58 percent of spermatozoa showed normal head form and motility was fair or moderately decreased. At the end of the observation, gonadotropin excretion had increased to 17 MUU.

Comments: Testicular regression, after termination of the previous long-term HMG-HCG treatment, was marked. Urinary gonadotropins were barely detectable and spermatogenesis practically ceased. It may, therefore, be concluded that a HMG dose as low as 7 IU FSH per day is capable of stimulating spermatogenesis. It is seen, however, that in contrast to previous findings, the treatment did, this time, induce endogenous puberty (at the age of 23 years). The sperm count continued to rise after discontinuation of HMG and a very large rise in gonadotropin output was found. Presumably, the treatment has triggered the gonadotropin releasing hypothalamic centers after 7 years of continuous therapeutic efforts.

Plate 1

Figure 1.   Case 1 (P.E.N.) 32 years. Untreated.
Figure 2.   Control testicular biopsy, Case 1. No tubular fibrosis or
               hyalinization of tubular wall. Few spermatogonial cells.

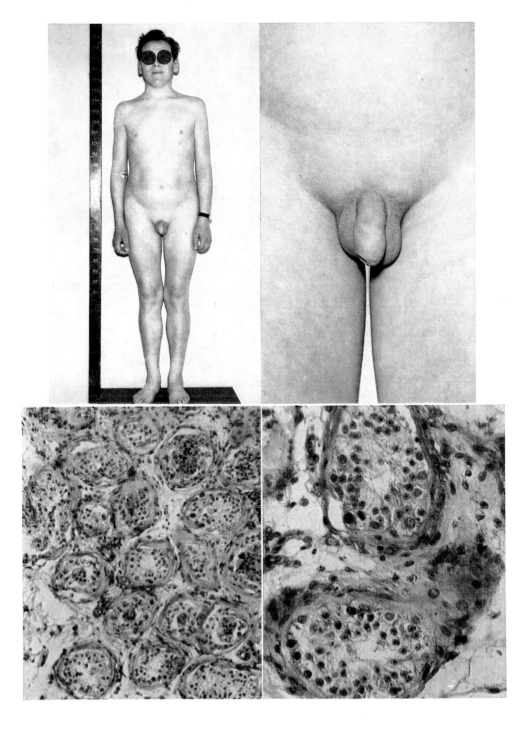

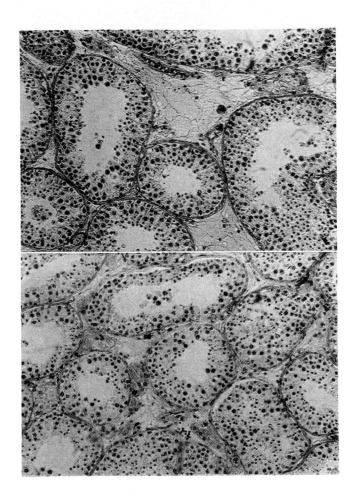

Plate II, Fig. 4 (Above)

Case 2 (B.E.). Upper: Biopsy before treatment. No degenerations. Normal stages up to spermatids but reduced number of spermatozoa (60 per cent of tubuli have no or very few spermatozoa). Lower: After treatment with HMG and HCG for 3 months. No change.

Plate III, Fig. 8 (Right)

Testicular biopsies in case 4 (E.M.). Upper: 1963. Before treatment. Note the wall hyalinization. Middle: 1965. After treatment with HMG alone for 11 months. Hyalinization unchanged. Few spermatogonia. Large Sertoli cell hyperplasia. Lower: 1968. After several courses of HMG plus HCG. Hyaline and Sertoli cell hyperplasia gone. Normal Leydig cells but germ cells little changed. All in same magnification.

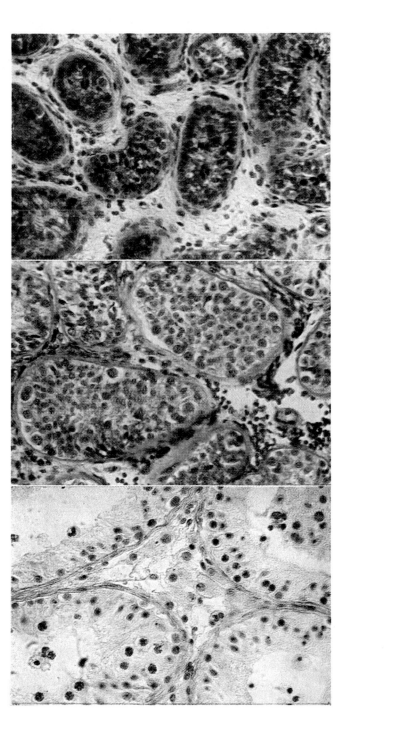

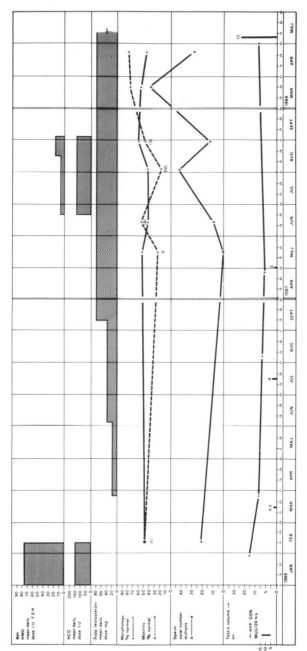

Fig. 6. Case 3 (A.R.). Courses of treatment, cf. legend to Fig. 3.

Case 4. (Patient E.M.)

This is an extension of the observations made during long-term
HMG treatment on the second patient in our previous report (7).
This patient displayed, at the age of 22 years, the classical
picture of hypogonadotropin eunuchoidism. During HMG and HCG
treatment for 3 years, the patient showed great increase in
androgen output and became virilized. His testicular size
increased from 2 to 8 ml.; and it was believed that this increase
reflected a good tubular development, although the sperm could
not be examined.

During subsequent withdrawal of the HMG and HCG therapy, the
testes regressed markedly in size and no gonadotropin was found
in the urine.

The following developments are shown in Fig. 7. The patient
was maintained for 9 months on testosterone. At the end of this
period, a semen examination showed aspermia which was indicative
of further testicular regression.

A low dose of HMG (24 IU FSH 3 times a week), combined with
350 IU HCG was then started and maintained for 5 months, but
repeated semen examinations continued to show aspermia, although,
androgen assays showed a very good effect on the Leydig cells.
The testis size increased from 3½ to 5 ml.

Subsequently, a higher HMG dose (60 IU FSH 3 times a week)
with 450 IU HCG with addition of 40 mg. testosterone per day,
was attempted for 4 months, but aspermia persisted through 3
examinations. After further treatment with 75 IU HMG + 450 IU
HCG and 40 mg. testosterone, the patient agreed to have one
more testicular biopsy (his third) performed.

Reference is given to the previous report regarding the
first biopsy in 1963 before treatment and the second in 1965
after treatment with HMG alone. Fig. 8 shows the three biopsies
and data from them are given in table 1. The third biopsy was,
in several respects, different from previous biopsies. Leydig
cells were present in perfectly normal number and distribution
and had normal appearance. Secondly, the previously thickening
and moderate hyalinization of the tubular wall had completely
disappeared. As shown in table 1, a significant tubular growth
had occurred and the clear-cut Sertoli-cell hyperplasia induced
by HMG given alone had disappeared. However, despite all these
improvements, the germinal epithelium was largely unchanged.
The number of spermatocytes had increased but remained very
low and only a small number of spermatids were found.

Comments : Evaluating this surprising lack of effect on the germinal
epithelium, one should consider: 1) that the HMG doses employed have
been found fully effective in the other cases; 2) that the patient
previously showed a urinary excretion of the exogenously administered

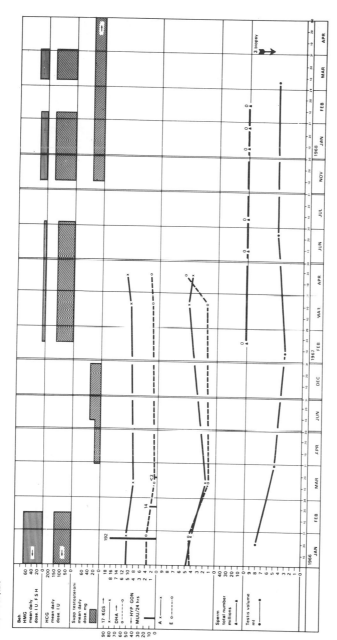

Fig. 7. Case 4 (E.M.). Courses of treatment, cf. legend to Fig. 3.

Table 1

Case 4. (E.M.). Testicular biopsies before treatment, after
HMG given alone for 11 months, and after HMG + HCG given for
19 months. Mean values (± standard deviation) per 25-cross-
sections of tubules.

	Before treatment	After HMG alone	After HMG plus HCG
Tubular diam. m μ	51.9(±7.7)	81.8(±13.6)	144.5(±15.5)
Number per tubule:			
Sertoli cells	38.9(±10.9)	51.8(±20.8)	29.0(±8.2)
Spermatogonia	2.8(± 2.4)	8.0(± 2.8)	12.1)±3.6)
Spermatocytes	0	0.9(± 2.0)	8.8(±7.8)
Spermatids	0	0	0.4(±0.9)
Spermatozoa	0	0	0

HMG of 12% indicating a normal metabolism of HMG; 3) that the patient after
22 months of continuous HMG treatment had developed no antibodies against
HMG; 4) that the combined HMG-HCG treatment induced development of normal
Leydig cells as judged histologically and by urinary androgen assays; and
5) that the treatment had reversed hyalinization of the tubular wall, thus
bringing about what appears to be an optimal milieu for development of
spermatogenesis.

The lack of ability to stimulate spermatogenesis beyond the spermatocyte stage is interesting and open for speculation. One possibility is
that the patient, for unknown reasons, requires much higher HMG doses than
others; another, that some other unknown factor which is lacking in hypogonadotropic eunuchoidism plays a role in testicular maturation.

CONCLUSION

The study shows that HMG at a dose of 7-26 IU FSH per day
supplemented with HCG is capable of restoring spermatogenesis
and fertility in hypogonadotropic hypogonadism. HMG can also
reverse hyalinization of the tubular wall. Other effects noted
are discussed in the comments on each case. Therapy did not
produce any side effects.

ACKNOWLEDGMENTS

Supported by the Ford Foundation.

REFERENCES

1. Kremer Door J.: Ned. T. Geneesk. 109: 888, 1965.

2. Calise M.: Excerpta med. (Amst.) Int. Congr. Ser. 109: 86, 1966.

3. Polishuk, W. Z., Palti, Z. & Laufer, A.: Fertil. and Steril. 18: 127, 1967.

4. Mroueh, A., Lytton, B. & Kase, N.: J. Clin. Endocr. 27: 53, 1967.

5. Lunenfeld, B., Mor, A., & Mani, M.: Fertil. and Steril. 18: 581, 1967.

6. Danezis, J. M., & Batrinos, M. L.: Fertil. and Steril. 18: 788, 1967.

7. Johnsen, S. G.: Acta Endocr. (Kbh.) 53: 315, 1966.

8. Martin, F. I. R.: J. Endocr. 38: 431, 1967.

9. Christiansen, P.: To be published.

10. Johnsen, S. G.: Acta Endocr. (Kbh.) suppl. 124: 17, 1967.

11. Johnsen, S. G.: Acta Endocr. (Kbh.) 57: 595, 1968.

12. Johnsen, S. G.: To be published.

13. Staland, B.: Int. J. Fertil. 13: 1, 1968.

EFFECT OF HUMAN MENOPAUSAL GONADOTROPIN ON PREPUBERAL TESTES

Eugenia Rosemberg[1], Roberto E. Mancini[2],
John F. Crigler[3] and Cesar Bergada[4]

Medical Research Institute of Worcester, Worcester City Hospital,
Worcester, Massachusetts; Departamento de Histologia Facultad de
Medicina, Buenos Aires, Argentina; The Children's Hospital,
Boston, Massachusetts, and the Departamento de Endocrinologia,
Buenos Aires, Argentina.

The role played by pituitary gonadotropins in the initiation and
maintenance of spermatogenesis and spermiogenesis awaits clarification. It seemed,therefore,pertinent to investigate the
effect of human menopausal gonadotropin (HMG) on prepuberal testes,
for in this situation, the testes would not have been exposed to
endogenous gonadotropin stimulation and the only variable involved
would be the follicle-stimulating (FSH) and luteinizing (LH)
potency of the HMG preparations administered.

1. In order to ascertain the effect of HMG on the immature
testis, four patients with unilateral cryptorchidism aged 6 to
7 years were given HMG (Pergonal, Cutter Laboratories, Berkeley,
California) for periods ranging from 16 to 75 days. The potency
of the various batches of Pergonal used is presented in Table
1.

Table 1

POTENCY OF PERGONAL IN TERMS OF THE 2nd IRP

Pergonal Batch	IU 2nd IRP/ampoule		Ratio FSH:LH
	FSH	LH	
25-EX-1899	108.8	73.8	1.47
25-EX-1938	118.5	63.8	1.86
25- E - 35⁾ (500)	71.0	80.0	0.86

⁾ Information supplied by Dr. P. Donini, Istituto
Farmacologico, Serono, Rome, Italy.

[1] Supported in part by Grant AM-07564, USPHS; National Institutes of Health,
Bethesda, Maryland, and in part by a Grant from Cutter Laboratories, Berkeley,
California.
[2] Supported by a Grant from The Population Council, Inc., New York, New York.
[3] Supported by Grants AM-08365 and FR 00128, USPHS, National Institutes of
Health, Bethesda, Maryland.
[4] Supported by a Grant from Fundacion de Endocrinologia Infantil, Buenos Aires,
Argentina.

The "total" amount of FSH and LH activity given to each subject throughout the entire course of medication is indicated in Table 2.

Table 2

TOTAL FSH AND LH ACTIVITY ADMINISTERED
THROUGHOUT EACH MEDICATION COURSE

Subject	Total Dose Administered IU 2nd IRP		Length of Medication Days
	FSH	LH	
1	5,184	2,678	16 *
2	3,927	2,234	32 *
3	2,400	1,875	60 †
4	3,552	2,775	75 †

* 3 ampoules daily; ** 2 ampoules every other day; † ampoule every third day.

At the end of the medication period, testicular descent did not occur. Orchiopexy of the cryptorchid testis was performed one day after medication and biopsies* obtained from the scrotal and cryptorchid testis were then obtained. These specimens were compared with testicular biopsies obtained from the scrotal and cryptorchid testis of three subjects of the same age who did not receive medication.

Tables 3 and 4 show the testicular cell types of the germinal epithelium, Sertoli cell line and of the intertubular spaces in both the scrotal and cryptorchid testis of control and treated subjects.

Table 3

SPERMATOGONIAL AND SERTOLI CELL LINE
TOTAL NUMBER OF EACH CELL TYPE PER 50 CIRCULAR TRANSVERSE SECTIONS OF TUBULES

Cell Type	Control Subjects *		Treated Subjects **							
	Cryptorchid	Scrotal	Cryptorchid				Scrotal			
			1	2	3	4	1	2	3	4
Spermatogonial Cells	68(±15)	239 (±34)	149	118	174	140	360	344	520	458
Mitosis			5	2	8	3	16	26	48	33
Primary Spermatocytes							3		122	55
Precursor Sertoli Cells	755 (±38)	900 (±21)	794	932	598	591	697	906	584	601
Immature Sertoli Cells			142		46	41	261	263	287	132
Mature Sertoli Cells									27	21
Tubular Diameter	45.2μ (±2)	59.9μ (±2)	31.1μ	67.8μ	62.3μ	53.2μ	91.9μ	89.5μ	81.6μ	78.6μ

*Average, three subjects (±SE). **Total number of each cell type.

* Histological technics used as well as microscopic measurements and methods used for cell count have been described previously (1).

Table 4

CELL POPULATION OF THE INTERTUBULAR SPACES
DATA REPRESENT DIFFERENTIAL COUNT OF 200 CELLS

Cell Type	Control Subjects *		Treated Subjects **							
	Cryptorchid	Scrotal	Cryptorchid				Scrotal			
			1	2	3	4	1	2	3	4
Fibroblast Precursor Leydig Cells	200	200	173	187	143	162	149	181	162	190
Immature Leydig Cells			27	13	35	30	37	19	31	8
Mature Leydig Cells					19	8	12		7	2
Degenerating Cells					3		2			
Thickness of Albuginea †	291.2 μ	249.3 μ	332.4 μ				522.3 μ			

*, **: Same as preceding Table. †: Average.

The scrotal testis showed histological changes similar to those observed at approximately the second phase of normal puberty (1). Spermatogonial cells in mitosis and meiotic spermatocytes reaching the pachytene stage were seen. These changes were accompanied by maturation of Sertoli cells. The presence of immature and mature type of Leydig cells indicated differentiation of fibroblasts into Leydig cells. The development of the connective tissue structures in the tubules and albuginea coincided with the stimulation observed in the germinal, Sertoli and Leydig cells.

The cryptorchid testis*, however, showed an apparent dissociation in the developmental process seen in the scrotal gland in that the tubular content did not show presence of primary spermatocytes; mature Sertoli cells were also absent. In contrast, the cellular content of the intertubular spaces showed the same degree of stimulation as that seen in the scrotal gland.

Considering only the scrotal gland, it would appear that in a totally immature testis, both FSH and LH are necessary to initiate spermatogenesis including development of the Sertoli cells. These changes were observed when treatment was given for only 16 days, although, these were more pronounced when approximately equal "total" amounts of FSH and LH activity were given for periods ranging from 60 to 75 days. As the longest period of treatment was two and one-half months, the question arises as to whether the dose or duration of treatment was not sufficient to bring about full spermatogenesis as well as full development of Leydig cells.

2. The effect of the administration of HMG, HMG combined with testosterone and of HCG in the immature testis was studied in

---

* Changes observed in the scrotal gland will be considered in this report. Considerations of the effect of HMG on the cryptorchid testis will appear elsewhere.

two patients with prepuberal onset of hypogonadotropic hypogonadism.* The potency of the various batches of Pergonal
used are listed in Table 5. HMG was kindly supplied by the
Squibb Institute for Medical Research, New Brunswick, New
Jersey.

Table 5

POTENCY OF PERGONAL IN TERMS OF 2nd IRP

Pergonal Batch	IU 2nd IRP/ampoule		Ratio FSH:LH
	FSH	LH	
25-EX-1958	110.0	34.4	3.20
25-EX-1990	84.5	93.8	0.90
25-EX-2015	63.0	63.1	1.00
25-EX-2040	74.3	130.6	0.57
25-EX-2127	75.0	84.0	0.89

Patient SA: Demonstrated onset of intracranial symptoms at
age 10; the tumor was removed at age 12; a control testicular
biopsy was performed at age 17. HMG was then administered
daily for 155 consectuve days. On the last 29 days of its
administration,200 mg./week of testosterone cyclopentylpropionate
were added to the therapeutic regimen. Testicular biopsies
were obtained 57 and 99 days after initiation of HMG administration, and after withdrawal of combined (HMG + testosterone)
therapy.

Tables 6 and 7 depict the testicular cell types of the germinal
epithelium, Sertoli cell line, and of the intertubular spaces
seen on each of the four biopsies. The amount of FSH and LH
activity administered prior to each biopsy is also indicated.
The "total" amount of FSH and LH activity given during the
entire course of medication (155 days) was 33,796 IU FSH and
24,224 IU LH, respectively.

---

* In both patients the condition was due to the presence of a craniopharyngioma.

Table 6

SPERMATOGONIAL AND SERTOLI CELL LINE
TOTAL NUMBER OF EACH CELL TYPE PER 50 CIRCULAR TRANSVERSE SECTIONS OF TUBULES

Cell Type	BIOPSIES			
	Control	1*	2**	3***
Spermatogonial Cells	151	213	304	336
Mitosis		11	23	13
Primary Spermatocytes			11	33
Precursors Sertoli Cells	471	446	177	105
Immature Sertoli Cells		123	458	116
Mature Sertoli Cells			51	74
Tubular Diameter	49.6 μ	66.1 μ	86.9 μ	83.4 μ
Tubular Wall	1.8 μ Moderate fibrosis	2.2 μ diminished fibrosis	2.5 μ normal	3.3 μ normal

* : Pergonal given for 57 days. Total dose administered: 6,140 IU equiv/2nd IRP (FSH
  activity); 3,290 IU equiv./2nd IRP (LH activity).

** : Pergonal continued for 42 days. Total dose administered: 11,616 IU equiv./2nd IRP
  (FSH activity); 8,384 IU equiv./2nd IRP (LH activity).

*** : Pergonal continued for 56 days plus depotestosterone 200 mg./weekly. Total dose
  administered: Pergonal 16,040 IU equiv./2nd IRP (FSH activity); 12,550 IU equiv./
  2nd IRP (LH activity). Depotestosterone: 600 mg.

Table 7

CELL POPULATION OF INTERTUBULAR SPACES
DATA REPRESENT DIFFERENTIAL COUNT OF 200 CELLS

Cell Type	BIOPSIES			
	Control	1 *	2 **	3 ***
Fibroblasts Precursors Leydig Cells	200	200	184	170
Immature Leydig Cells			9	19
Mature Leydig Cells				
Degenerating Cells			7	11

*, **, ***: Same as preceding Table.

After 57 days of HMG administration slight stimulation of the germinal epithelium and the Sertoli cell line was seen (Biopsy 2). However, the tubular diameter was increased; regression of seminiferous tubular membrane fibrosis seen in the control biopsy was also observed. There was no stimulation of the cell population of the intertubular spaces. After 99 days of treatment (Biopsy 2), proliferation and differentiation of the germinal epithelium to spermatocyte stage, maturation of Sertoli cells, increase in tubular diameter and normal appearance of the tubular wall was noted. There was slight stimulation of cell population of the intertubular spaces which showed the presence of immature Leydig cells. The combined administration of HMG and testosterone (Biopsy 3) did not induce any further changes.

HMG induced changes similar to those seen in the scrotal gland after 60 to 75 days of HMG administration. However, in this case, this effect was attained after 99 days of continuous therapy during which the "total" amount of FSH and LH activity given was four times higher than that administered to the previous subjects. The addition of testosterone for a period of about three weeks to HMG therapy did not reverse the changes observed after 99 days of continuous HMG administration.

Patient WH: Demonstrated onset of intracranial symptoms at age 5; the tumor was removed at age 11 years and 6 months; at age 11 years and 10 months, the patient received HCG for a period of six months. The dosage used was 4.000 IU three times weekly. The first testicular biopsy was obtained (under no medication) sixteen months after withdrawal of HCG. HCG therapy was reinstituted at doses of 4.000 to 5.000 IU three times weekly and was given for a period of three months; a second testicular biopsy was obtained at the medication period. The third testicular biopsy was obtained fourteen months after withdrawal of the second course of HCG. The patient was then given HMG* (Pergonal) for 20 days; the fourth testicular biopsy was obtained at the end of the medication period. Therapy with testosterone enanthate was then initiated and continued for one year at a dose of 200 mg. given every four weeks. The fifth testicular biopsy was obtained at the end of the medication period. Therapy with testosterone enanthate was continued for twenty additional days in combination with HMG*. The sixth testicular biopsy was obtained after withdrawal of combined medication.

---

* Total FSH and LH activity administered is indicated in Table 8.

The histological changes observed on each of the testicular biopsies obtained are depicted in Tables 8 and 9.

Table 8

SPERMATOGONIAL AND SERTOLI CELL LINE
TOTAL NUMBER OF EACH CELL TYPE PER 50 CIRCULAR TRANSVERSE SECTIONS OF TUBULES

Cell Type	BIOPSIES *					
	Control 1	After HCG 2	Control 3	After Pergonal 4	Under Testosterone 5	After Pergonal and Testosterone 6
Spermatogonial Cells	221	304	232	319	247	412
Mitosis	7	13	19	26	4	11
Primary Spermatocytes		102		88		61
Pre-Sertoli Cells	586				433	197
Immature Sertoli Cells	37		610	451	191	405
Mature Sertoli Cells		488	34	257		32
Tubular Diameter	45.6 μ	81.2 μ	47.5 μ	83.7 μ	56.3 μ	89.3 μ
Tubular Wall	2.9 μ hyalinized	2.6μ normal	3.4 μ hyalinized	2.0 μ normal	3.1 μ hyalinized	2.1 μ normal

* 1. 16 months after 1st HCG course: 4,000 IU [3 times/week (9/24/60 to 4/7/61)].

  2. Day after withdrawal of HCG (2nd course): 4,000 to 5,000 IU [3 times/week (8/15/62 to 11/22/62)].

  3. 14 months after 2nd course HCG (3/26/64).

  4. Day after withdrawal of Pergonal (2 amp/day/20 days, 7/15/65 to 8/3/65). Total Dose: 2972 IU FSH and 5224 IU LH activity.

  5. One year on testosterone enanthate 200 mg. every 4 weeks (7/7/66).

  6. Day after withdrawal of Pergonal (2 amp/day/20 days). Total Dose 3,000 IU FSH and 3,000 IU LH activity plus testosterone enanthate 200 mg. (every 4 weeks).

Table 9

CELL POPULATION OF INTERTUBULAR SPACES
AVERAGE PER 200 CELLS OF EACH CELL TYPE

Cell Type	BIOPSIES *					
	Control 1	After HCG 2	Control 3	After Pergonal 4	Under Testosterone 5	After Pergonal and Testosterone 6
Fibroblasts Precursors Leydig Cells	200	44	200	121	200	180
Immature Leydig Cells		37		46		10
Mature Leydig Cells		109		17		8
Degenerating Cells		10		16		2

* Same as preceding Table.

The effects of HCG, HMG, testosterone and testosterone in combination with HMG can thus be compared. HCG administration (Biopsy 2) induced maturation of the spermatogonial cell line to primary spermatocyte stage, maturation of the Sertoli cell line, increase in tubular diameter, and disappearance of hyalinization of the tubular wall. In addition, to the changes observed in the tubular cell content, Leydig cell maturation was also seen.   HMG administration (Biopsy 4) induced histological changes similar to those seen after HCG administration but, to a lesser degree. Testosterone administration (Biopsy 5) induced regressive changes in the tubular cell content, the tubular wall and the cell content of the intertubular spaces. These changes were similar to those observed in the first biopsy. Combined testosterone - HMG therapy (Biopsy 6) reversed the changes observed under testosterone administration, However, the effect was not as marked as that induced by HMG alone.

SUMMARY

HMG which contains both FSH and LH activity, induced stimulation of the germinal cell epithelium to spermatocyte stage, Sertoli cell differentiation, and development of Leydig cells. The effect of HCG on the germinal and Sertoli cells was similar. However, Leydig cell maturation was more marked. Whether HMG or HCG would be influential in promoting complete development of the germinal cells remains to be established. HMG prevented the deleterious effect exerted by testosterone on the seminiferous tubules and the Leydig cells.

REFERENCES

1. Mancini, R. E., E. Rosemberg, M. Cullen, J. C. Lavieri, O. Vilar, C. Bergada, and J. A. Andrada. J. Clin. Endocrinol., 25: 927, 1965.

DISCUSSION

BURGOS: My first question concerns the first biopsy presented by
Dr. Paulsen. As far as I can see, there was no evidence of
germinal cells but there was strong hyalinization of the tubules
which contained only immature Sertoli cells. After treatment,
hyalinization disappeared and the Sertoli cells matured, but
there was no evidence of spermatogenesis because the base line
of spermatogenesis did not exist. The second point which I would
like to raise is merely academic. Dr. Paulsen used the word,
syncytium,for the arrangement of Sertoli cells in the tubule. It
has been demonstrated that Sertoli cells do not form a **syncytium**
They are independent cells which have well-defined boundaries.

PAULSEN: Although it was not clear in the projection, careful
inspection of the control biopsy specimen revealed cells that
appeared to me to be immature gonocytes. Following HCG therapy,
spermatogonia were seen. They may have been present in reduced
numbers, but quantitation was not carried out.

DONINI: Does anyone know what would be the best FSH-LH ratio for
a gonadotropic preparation to be used for therapy of male infertility?

PAULSEN: If we confine your question to patients with hypogonadotropic eunuchoidism, the available preparations with varying ratios of FSH/LH appear to be equally effective in our
experience. Although we did not present our results in males
who exhibit adult seminiferous tubule failure, the results obtained by us have been uniformly unsuccessful. Therefore, we
cannot suggest a specific FSH/LH ratio for these patients.

ALBERT: The normal testis at a comparable stage of development
to that of your first patients does not show a thickened tubular
wall,while that of your patient did. Under therapy with HCG, the
thickening disappeared. Would you care to speculate?

PAULSEN: I do not have any explanation for the disappearance of
tubular hyalinization following HCG therapy in these patients. It
should be pointed out that we have had only one patient with hypogonadotropic eunuchoidism who demonstrated seminiferous tubule
hyalinization prior to any therapy. Dr. Bartter, when working
with Fuller Albright, also showed disappearance of hyalinization
following HCG in such patients. (F.C. Bartter, R.C. Sniffen, F.A.
Simmons; F. Albright, and R.P.Howard, J. Clin. Endocr. 12:1532,
1952)

MANCINI: I think that Dr. Albert has raised a very critical point
concerning the effect of HCG which needs to be clarified. First
of all, when we speak about thickening of the seminiferous tubule
wall in the human testis, two different types of material may be
present. One would correspond to a true fibrosis, i.e. an apparent

increase in the stratified layers of pre-existent collagen fibers
and fibroblasts (as it occurs in the post-inflammatory condition
of the testis and in some cases of spermatogenic arrest), and the
other to so-called hyalinosis. In this process, as we demonstrated with electronmicroscopy and histochemistry, a breakdown of
collagen and elastic fibers, some loss of basement membrane material and involuting peritubular fibroblasts accompany the appearance of an interfibrillar amorphous material which seems to be
composed of non-structured collagenous and mucopolysaccharide
substances. Hyalinosis may appear in many different pathologic
conditions of the testis, so that a hypothetical unitary pathogenic
criterion is hard to make. It develops under circumstances in
which germinal and Leydig cells are not stimulated by gonadotropins
when puberty is approached (eunuchs), or when both cell populations
have regressed in the adult subject (hypogonadism) or when germinal
cells are not able to proliferate and differentiate to spermatozoa
at pubertal ages (Klinefelter syndrome, cryptorchid testis). In
prepuberal hypogonadism HCG or HMG alone or , better still, a combination of both, may induce development of peritubular collagen
fibers and fibroblasts, in cases showing the pre-existent infantile
type of tubules. In some others having hyalinized tubular walls,
disappearance of this degenerative process takes place and a normal peritubular structure reappears, as seen in some hypophysectomized patients.

It seems to me that in no case was there an isolated effect on the
tubular wall, independent of a parallel stimulation of Sertoli,
germinal and Leydig cells which suggests that the three main
structures of the testis react as a unit. If one recognizes that
peritubular fibroblasts are responsible for the production and
maintenance of tubular wall structures as we have postulated (Acta
Physiol. Latinoamer. 14: 382, 1964) then the beneficial effects of
large doses of HCG may be due to increased androgen production by
the Leydig cells occuring under HCG stimulation.

VILAR: Dr. Paulsen, did any of your patients develop puberal
changes before hypogonadism?

PAULSEN: Only one of the four patients listed in the summary
slide experienced slight puberal changes before treatment. This
patient was 22 years old at the time of initiation of treatment.
The puberal changes consisted of slight pubic hair growth and
minimal scrotal rugal development.

VILAR: Did the biopsy that showed remarkable hyalinization and
fibrosis belong to one of those who showed some puberal development
before development of hypogonadism? In our experience, hypogonadism which develops during or after puberty, usually shows fibrosis
hyalinization of the seminiferous tubules, and in your cases, these
changes could be already present when treatment is initiated.

PAULSEN: Unfortunately, we could not obtain a control testicular
biopsy, thus, I do not know whether or not his testes were com-

pletely immature.

ROSEMBERG: Dr. Johnsen was very anxious to hear some answers to specific questions. As we are participating in a Workshop Conference, we should allow this. Dr. Johnsen, could you repeat your questions?

JOHNSEN: I should like to refer to the patient with no pituitary function. The patient was given HCG alone, but no spermatogenesis was seen. He was then given HMG plus HCG which induced spermatogenesis and spermatogenesis could then be maintained with HCG alone. I would like to know whether HCG has the capacity to maintain spermatogenesis - once initiated - or whether we must believe that the patient's pituitary produced after all, small amounts of FSH.

ALBERT: This could be the counterpart of the Nelson rat. Having produced spermatogenesis, you can now maintain it with the androgen produced by HCG.

PAULSEN: This could be true for some of these patients, but not in all. For example, in one patient, we discontinued HMG therapy and continued with HCG administration. Despite HCG maintenance therapy, his sperm count decreased. It may be that subcategories exist within this disease entity of hypogonadotropic eunuchoidism. But so far, apart from the so-called fertile eunuchs, I would not know by what criteria to subclassify them.

LUNENFELD: In 3 of the 5 azoospermic patients whose pretreatment testicular biopsy revealed small tubules, spermotogenesis was maintained also without HMG. In one of them it was maintained for at least 5 years, in the others for 3 - 4 years. Urinary gonadotropins were still undetectable.

PAULSEN: This was by continuing HMG therapy?

LUNENFELD: No, without any therapy.

PAULSEN: I have not observed such a sequence of events in these patients i.e. hypogonadotropic eunuchoidism.

ROSEMBERG: Dr. Lunenfeld, you have referred to patients in whom spermatogenesis was maintained when given HMG and HCG therapy. Could you tell us the testosterone excretion values obtained under medication?

LUNENFELD: We are still unable to measure testosterone. Therefore, I can not report any values.

MANCINI: In relation to the differences in the response to gonadotropin therapy, I should like to stress the fact that the status of the germinal cells in the seminiferous tubules seen in

the control biopsy should be taken into consideration. More than
fifteen years ago W. Nelson (J. Urol. 69:325, 1953) showed that
almost complete progression of spermatogenesis could be achieved
with HCG in eunuchs having a preferentially preexistent germinal
cell line up to the primary spermatocyte stage. Results were not
so successful in some other cases showing infantile tubules with
only spermatogonial types of cells. Admitting that both FSH and
LH acting together (HMG) are basically the more potent activating
factors on spermatogenesis, is it possible that cases who have
responded to HCG may have had some endogenous FSH.

PAULSEN: I wish that it was as simple as that, Dr. Mancini.
Throughout some 15 years of experience with these patients, we
have found considerable variation so far as the characteristics
of the pretreatment testicular biopsy specimens are concerned.
In some patients whose spermatogenesis has progressed to an
occasional pachytene spermatocyte, the administration of HCG alone
will result in complete spermatogenesis. In other patients with
similar testicular findings, HCG therapy will not be sufficient.
Then HMG treatment will be necessary to produce sperm in the
ejaculate. Perhaps we will be able to catalog these patients
properly when we have had an opportunity to study their serum FSH
and LH levels by radioimmunoassay.

MANCINI: This again raises another very basic point with regard
to some definitions of human testicular function. One problem is
how spermatogenesis may be induced from the primary spermatogonia
or other more advanced cellular types as seen in prepuberal boys
or eunuchs and another is how to recover an atrophied germinal
cell line in adult hypogonadism. This consideration includes the
more complex problem of how to maintain spermatogenesis which
has already developed after the impact of gonadotropin stimulation
or how to preserve it after cessation of pituitary function. The
qualitative progression and the quantitative completion from one
phase to another in the spermatogenic cycle should also be considered in this discussion as fundamental parameters of the dynamics
of spermatogenesis in terms of gonadotropin control of this process.

PAULSEN: With respect to the issue of restoring previously normal
spermatogenesis following the development of panhypopituitarism,
I would like to obtain an opinion from anyone in the audience as
to the longest duration of time observed from the onset of pituitary insufficiency to the onset of treatment in which gonadotropin
therapy would be successful. In our experience, we were unable
to restore testicular function in a previously normal male who
developed acute panhypopituitarism consequent to a basal spine
fracture five years prior to our therapeutic attempt. Dr.
Johnsen, in your cases what was the longest time?

JOHNSEN: In my patient, 9 years.

PAULSEN: Did he have complete panhypopituitarism?

JOHNSEN: Yes, the total loss of pituitary function was well demonstrated and he was untreated for 9 years. Just one word about my case no. 3 because it answers one question in Dr. Mancini's paper. In this patient, we induced spermatogenesis by gonadotropins while he was on continuous testosterone medication, so that testosterone obviously had no inhibitory effect. We found that long-term HMG and HCG treatment finally induced endogenous puberty at the age of 23 years. I would like to know whether this is a unique finding or whether HMG-HCG treatment can stimulate the hypothalamic centres and thus open up new therapeutic possibilities in puberal failure?

MANCINI: Results from our patients indicate that the different degree of involution of the testis is independent of the age of the patient. Although there was in general some relationship between the time which had elapsed after operation and the progressive deterioration of the gland, no close correlation could be established. Differences in the completeness of hypophysectomy, some persistence of thyroid and adrenal function and the presence of a hypophyseal lesion before operation may have had some influence on the quality of post-surgical involution of the gonad. This assumption is backed by the fact that in our cases, a few weeks or months after operation, the involution of germinal epithelium sometimes stopped at the level of spermiogenesis, whereas several months or years were needed for the germinal cells to regress to the spermatocyte or spermatogonial level. In our series, in one case which had preexistent germinal cells up to the spermatocyte stage 5 months after operation, complete spermatogenesis was obtained after HMG plus HCG. In another case having only spermatogonial cells recovery up to the spermatid stage was achieved 10 years after operation with the same treatment.

DONINI: Yesterday Dr. Cargille reported the effects of clomiphene in the male; it seems that FSH and LH levels in the plasma are increased following clomiphene treatment. May I ask for any comments on the effect of clomiphene on spermatogenesis?

PAULSEN: We administered clomiphene citrate to two patients with hypogonadotropic eunuchoidism without success. The group at Bethesda have studied changes in serum gonadotropins following clomiphene administration in normal patients and in individuals with hypogonadotropic eunuchoidism. Clomiphene did not produce any rise in gonadotropins in the latter group. Perhaps, Dr. Cargille, you would like to extend these comments?

CARGILLE: Dr. Bardin and others from our laboratory reported a group of 7 chromatin negative men characterized by the findings of retarded sexual development, hyposmia, skeletal anomalies, cryptorchidism, "prepubertal testes", and relative gonadotropin (HCG) insensitivity. Urinary FSH and LH measurements performed by bioassay and radioimmunoassay revealed levels of both hormones to be less than those found in normal men. However, they were similar to levels observed in hypopituitary men and prepubertal **boys.**

Plasma FSH and LH levels measured by radioimmunoassay were in the low normal range but did not increase significantly in response to clomiphene. Thus, it appeared that these 7 hypogonadal men had demonstrable defects in both pituitary and Leydig cell function.

ALBERT: This morning a problem was raised about the comparative efficiency of human LH and HCG on the maintenance of function of the human corpus luteum and also for the induction of human ovulation. The relative potencies of PMSG, LH and HCG are well-known in standard rodent assay systems. I think that we all agree to the principle that these ratios may not be helpful in the human. We have heard several papers dealing with the human interstitial cell receptor and human LH and HCG. I wonder if someone can give the relative potency of human LH and HCG for the maintenance of the Leydig cell after hypophysectomy, for the induction of Leydig cell maturity or for their steroidogenic effect (testosterone or estrogen production).

ROSEMBERG: We are presently conducting a study which may provide an answer to Dr. Albert's question. This study is being conducted in collaboration with Dr. J. F. Crigler, Children's Hospital, Boston. Eight patients of ages ranging from 18 to 20 years with delayed adolescence or hypopituitarism due to removal of craniopharyngioma are being treated with HCG for periods ranging from one to one-and-a-half years or longer. Testicular biopsies are being performed prior to initiation of treatment and at various intervals during the treatment period. Urinary testosterone and estrogen levels are also being obtained. The level of response will be correlated to the dose of HCG administered and the length of treatment.

JOHNSEN: This is a very complex question because it would appear that FSH also has an influence on the Leydig cells. We were able to induce a fully normal Leydig cell function in hypopituitarism by means of a dose of 350 I.U. HCG 3 times a week when given together with HMG. With HCG alone, much higher doses, up to 10 times as much, would have been necessary. An effect of FSH on Leydig cells has also been shown by others.

PAULSEN: Do you know what the minimal effective dose of PMS is with respect to Leydig cell stimulation?

JOHNSEN: No.

BURGOS: I consider that hypogonadotropic eunuchoids are ideal subjects for the study of the action of the different gonadotropin hormones. I did not understand clearly from Dr. Mancini's presentation which is the gonadotropic hormone which has the ability to promote the entire spermatogenic wave.

MANCINI: As far as I understand, Dr. Burgos is referring to the effect of different gonadotropins on the testes of our series of hypophysectomized patients. PMS or HCG **have** a predominant action on a particular spermatogenic phase, i.e., PMS acts on spermatogonial cells and HCG has a strong action on this line of cells thus giving rise to primary spermatocytes, but both have a doubtful influence on the development of later phases of germinal cell development. The more potent action of HCG might be explained by its homologous origin and the simultaneous stimulation of Sertoli and of Leydig cells, the latter being able to secrete steroid hormones, supposedly necessary for seminiferous tubule maintenance. On the other hand, the restricted effect of PMS could be due either to the induction of antihormone, to the short length of time of administration or to the absence of an adequate Leydig cell stimulation. The failure to restore all phases of spermatogenesis even by the combined use of both PMS and HCG, points to the need for hormones of human origin with both FSH and LH activity. This was corroborated by the use of HMG. However, only the addition of HCG resulted in the complete recovery of the germinal cell line together with development of Leydig cells and repair of Sertoli cells. This cellular response was seen better in cases having a preexistent spermatocyte or spermiogenic phase than in those showing only spermatogonial cells.

PAULSEN: From the results obtained in one of our patients, I would estimate that for human LH, the minimal effect Leydig cell stimulating dose would be in the neighborhood of 200 I.U. per day. It is going to be extremely interesting, now that we have human LH available for clinical studies, to see whether or not a qualitative difference exists between LH and HCG administration.

DONINI: Dr. Mancini, would you comment briefly on the effect of pure FSH on the testes?

MANCINI: Our group has had the opportunity to use pure FSH preparations (of urinary origin) provided by Dr. Donini. We administered such a preparation to a boy who had undergone an operation for a craniopharyngioma. A control biopsy showed that he had an infantile testis, and after 3 months of treatment with 3700 units of this FSH preparation (in terms of the 2nd IRP) only some enlargement of tubules and slight stimulation of spermatogonial cells was seen.

PAULSEN: What was the status of his spermatogenesis prior to the loss of pituitary function? Was it known?

MANCINI: The patient had been operated on at the age of 15. Puberty had not been reached at that time and the testis was of an infantile type.

PAULSEN: McLeod's experience with a 38-year-old diabetic male who underwent pituitary stalk section is of interest. Following surgery, his spermatogenesis ceased. McLeod treated this patient with an HMG preparation containing 75 I.U. FSH and 75 I.U. LH per ampule. HMG therapy restored his germinal epithelium so that mature spermatids were present. However, he did not have an ejaculate until HCG was also administered.

LUNENFELD: The preparation used by McLeod contained both FSH and LH activity. It was, therefore, not "relatively" pure FSH.

RYAN: I have several questions that are only indirectly related, but I think they are pertinent. In the course of normal puberty, does the pituitary increase its rate of secretion of FSH or LH first, or do they both increase simultaneously? What is the time interval between this rate of change in secretion of gonadotropin by the pituitary, the appearance of sperm in the epididymis and the appearance of sperm in the ejaculate? Does the sperm concentration in the ejaculate, during puberty, abruptly increase to adult concentrations or does it do so gradually?

PAULSEN: Dr. Ryan's question is very important. One piece of data that comes to mind was published by Dr. Bryan Hudson. (B. Hudson, J. P. Coghlan, and A. Dulmanis, Ciba Found. Colloquia, Vol. 16, p. 140, 1967). He demonstrated that there was a significant rise in plasma testosterone levels about six months to one year prior to beginning sexual maturation. In his studies, gonadotropin titers were not measured in serum or urine. Perhaps someone can comment on other data which may be available?

McARTHUR: A recent study which seems relevant to this discussion is that of Rifkind, Kulin and Ross (J. Clin. Investig. 96: 1925, 1967). Using biological methods, they assayed the FSH and LH content of the pooled urine of male and female children attending nursery school. The FSH level was surprisingly similar to that of adults. However, the LH level was exceedingly low. Puberty was characterized by a marked rise in LH, but, at most, a doubling of FSH excretion. Thus, throughout childhood, the testis is exposed to endogenous FSH stimulation, and at puberty it is subjected to a further increase in stimulation by both gonadotropins.

JOHNSEN: In answer to Dr. Ryan's questions, we have found that there is a time difference of 2½ years between the first appearance of gonadotropins in the urine and the breaking of the voice in boys. We have carried out work on the sequence of events in puberty. Growth of the testis comes first, followed by signs of androgenic function. At the time when pubic hair appears, the testis is almost adult size. This indicates that tubular development precedes the appearance of Leydig cells in man.

RYAN: What is the interval between the appearance of gonadotropin and enlargement of the testis?

JOHNSEN: This we have not followed, but I am very pleased to hear what Dr. McArthur said because it is very relevant to this work.

ROSEMBERG: Two people in this audience, Dr. Albert and Dr. Mancini, are the experts in the histological development of human testis. As you may recall, Dr. Albert published his first studies in 1953

(Mayo Clinic Proceedings 28:409, 557 and 698, 1953; 29:131; 317 and 368, 1954; 30:31, 1955). We should hear his views. I had the pleasure to collaborate with Dr. Mancini in some aspects of his work. From these studies, it was concluded that the spermatogenesis seen at puberty was preceded by full development of mature Leydig cells. (Mancini, R.E. Cullen, M., Rosemberg, E., Lavieri, J., Vilar, D., and Bergada, C.: J. Clin. Endocr. 25: 927, 1965).

ALBERT: Scanning various types of testes obtained at postmortem from boys who apparently did not have any endocrine disease gives the impression that the tubule as a whole develops before the Leydig cells mature. The end point here is simply tubular enlargement versus maturity of the Leydig cells as determined histologically. If you assume that tubular enlargement is related to FSH and maturity of Leydig cells to LH, then it would seem that FSH appears first. But, there must be a beginning of development. Dr. Mancini has more information on the early signs of Leydig cell function.

PAULSEN: With respect to your observations, would you not agree that it might be possible for androgen production to occur before mature Leydig cells are evident? Dr. Hooker's studies in young bulls suggested this. (Rec. Progr. Hormone Res. Vol. 3, p. 172, 1948).

MANCINI: I fully agree with Dr. Albert that it is difficult to determine which of the testicular structures develops first. Do the seminiferous tubules or the Leydig cells appear first in pubertal boys? In our histological studies, where we obtained biopsies of boys of different ages from 11 to 16 years, we have had the opportunity to see that an active proliferation of fibroblast-like cells, which are considered precursors of Leydig cells, developed first. The seminiferous tubules then showed some enlargement with proliferation of spermatogonial cells and, at the same time, the immature and mature type of Leydig cells began to develop. Full maturation of Leydig cells coincided with the development of Sertoli cells and the completion of meiosis from spermatocytes onward. We do not know yet if the so-called precursors of Leydig cells function in terms of steroidogenesis, and if so, whether local action on seminiferous tubules may be exerted by these cells.

CARGILLE: We have measured plasma levels of FSH in the prepubertal children studied by Rifkind, Kulin, and Ross who reported levels of FSH and LH obtained by bioassay of urinary concentrates. The mean level of plasma FSH in 16 boys aged 4 - 5 years was 5.9 mIU/ml. which is significantly less than the mean level of 9.6 mIU/ml. observed in 30 adult men (p = $<.05$). This is consistent with the observation by bioassay that the urinary excretion of FSH in prepubertal children is approximately one-half that of adult men. The mean plasma FSH level in 45 samples taken from 6 hypopituitary men was 6.6 mIU/ml. with a range of 3.1 to 11.7 mIU/ml. Thus, considerable overlap of the hypopituitary men and normal men was evident.

PAULSEN: Dr. Cargille, does it not seem curious that the mean gonadotropin levels in your prepuberal boys are lower than the mean levels in patients with hypopituitarism? Thus, one wonders about the biologic significance of your gonadotropin levels at low titers.

CARGILLE: Although these six patients were hypogonadal and had documented deficiencies of two or more anterior pituitary hormones, our findings of some normal levels for plasma FSH and LH indicate that not all were hypogonadotropic. This observation was consistent with the finding of measurable total urinary gonadotropin by the mouse uterine weight assay.

PAULSEN: Including patients with panhypopituitarism?

ROBYN: Dr. Cargille, I wonder why so many points are beyond the 95% fiducial limits presented in your figures. What is the meaning of these 95% fiducial limits?

NAFTOLIN: In the figures that Dr. Cargille showed for both the children, more than half of the values fall outside the 95% limits. In the first figure, at lease ¼ of the values in the lower limits of the adult range fall in the range of prepubertal children. Applying means and standard errors to this group of figures without seeing the actual spread is misleading.

GANDY: In view of some of the evidence presented earlier in support of diurnal variation of FSH and LH levels in plasma as determined by radioimmunoassay, I would like to know whether the plasma samples from the normal and hypogonadal men, children and hypopituitary patients were obtained at approximately the same time of day.

CARGILLE: Our samples from children, hypopituitary men and normal men were not necessarily drawn at the same time of day. We do not have definitive results as yet pertaining to the existence of a diurnal variation for FSH and LH.

GANDY: I think it is difficult to compare values in normal men with one another or even with values in prepubertal children when the plasma samples were obtained at random times of the day. In addition to the data we presented here suggesting that there is diurnal variation in plasma FSH and LH, we have also reported results of FSH and LH as well as testosterone levels in plasma obtained from 8 men on 5 or more days at 8 a.m. and 8 p.m. The values for gonadotropin levels in evening plasmas were significantly lower than the a.m. values.

PAULSEN: Dr. Lunenfeld, you stated that all that is required to treat male infertility is long term HMG therapy in appropriate doses. Would you care to clarify this point?

LUNENFELD: No, I was speaking of treatment of azoospermic patients with undetectable endogenous gonadotropins. I mentioned 3 groups of azoospermic patients. One group had small tubules (less than 50 microns in diameter). This was the group which responded best. The second group had almost normal tubular diameter and only 5 of 15 patients responded to medication. The third group was unresponsive, the tubules being of normal or near normal size containing Sertoli cells only.

PAULSEN: I am sorry. Then what is the position regarding treatment of individuals who have normal or high endogenous gonadotropins?

LUNENFELD: It is very difficult to assess the responsiveness of oligospermic patients since significant variations in sperm counts can be encountered at different intervals.

SUMMARY OF SESSION

ROSEMBERG: The dependence of testicular function in man on the tropic hormones has been extensively discussed during this session. It should be remembered that the study of the action of the pituitary gonadotropins FSH and LH (ICSH) on the human testes is dependent upon a number of factors. The state of purification of the tropic hormones utilized and the status of the target organ need to be clearly defined if meaningful conclusions regarding the effect of gonadotropins on the testes are to be reached.

The discussants clearly demonstrated the complexities involved in such studies. Spermatogenesis is a complex phenomenon, which involves transformation of the germ cells of the seminiferous tubules leading to formation of spermatozoa. The duration of this process has been estimated by Heller and Clermont (Rec. Progr. Hormone Res.; $\underline{20}$:545, 1964) to be about $74 + 4$ or 5 days. Moreover, normal germinal cell differentiation may be dependent upon Sertoli cell function and steroid production i.e., testosterone, by the Leydig cells. It was pointed out that the gonadotropins of human origin which have been available to investigators conducting physiological studies or testing the therapeutic effectiveness of these hormones contained both FSH and LH activity. Their value, or lack thereof, in the treatment of oligospermia, azoospermia and hypogonadotropic eunuchoidism with or without the addition of HCG to the therapeutic regimen was discussed.

The role of gonadotropins in the initiation and maintenance of spermatogenesis and spermiogenesis was not clarified. The question of what type of gonadotropic hormone or hormones is responsible for initiation and maintenance of spermatogenesis and spermiogenesis awaits the availability of pure FSH and LH preparations. The pathogenesis of altered spermatogenesis is more or less obscure. It was pointed out that considerable effort should be spent in this area in order to delineate properly the use of gonadotropin in the treatment of male infertility.

CONCLUDING REMARKS

I shall not attempt to summarize what has been discussed during the last three days. I am sure you all agree that this meeting has generated a great deal of illuminating discussions on many topics. It has been extremely helpful, informative, and above all, very enjoyable. In the light of our own personal experiences, through exchange of opinion, and reasoning together, we have sought to provide concise compilation of current views in certain areas of gonadotropin research.

I only wish to make two final comments. It is comforting to note that newer techniques such as the radioimmunoassays for FSH and LH are, for the moment, confirming what the literature has recorded using bioassay methods. Secondly, we are now overwhelmed by the number of available standards and reference preparations and by the numerical values which relate the activity of one reference preparation to that of another. However, I am quite confident that the future holds the answer for the establishment of proper standards. We are passing through an intermediary period, and should be as precise as possible in reporting results when employing either biological or immunological methods in the measurement of gonadotropic hormones.

It is hoped that conferences such as this, when the participants enjoy the opportunity of discussing matters with each other across the room would keep the flame of unselfish scientific interest burning. I wish to thank you all for participating in this meeting and for having worked with great intensity, frankness of expression and amiable firmness.

EUGENIA ROSEMBERG

INDEX OF PARTICIPANTS

(Major contributions are listed in bold-face type:
other contributions follow)

INDEX OF SUBJECTS